PRINCIPLES OF
INDUSTRIAL WELDING

A Text for Students
and Others Interested in
Welding

THE JAMES F. LINCOLN ARC WELDING FOUNDATION

P.O. Box 17035
Cleveland, Ohio 44117

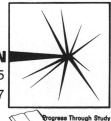

Progress Through Study

PRINCIPLES OF INDUSTRIAL WELDING

A Text for Students and Others Interested in Welding

TABLE OF CONTENTS

Preface

This book is intended as a background and reference text for students intending to prepare themselves for careers in welding technology. The contents follow to some extent the course work in welding technology offered by the Welding Department, California Polytechnic State University, San Luis Obispo, California. The intent is to give the student a broad perspective on the fusion processes by which metals are joined, without overelaboration on specific subjects.

The text has been intentionally simplified to give it widespread application to any career associated with welding as a production process.

In some areas, the simplification may be considered overdone; in others, in contrast, the text may appear to be out of balance by being quite comprehensive. These variations are recognized and result from the authors' judgements as to what best fit the needs of student readers. Thus, plasma-arc welding is treated briefly, while shielded metal-arc and various semiautomatic arc-welding processes are discussed in considerable detail. Obviously, this treatment is in agreement with the preponderance of usage of the welding processes in industry — and thus with the preponderance of career opportunities for the student.

Some readers of this text may note that it draws heavily on a prior work *The Procedure Handbook of Arc Welding, Twelfth Edition,* published by The Lincoln Electric Company. This is with the permission of the publisher and is a testimony to the practicality of that prior volume — both as source material for the professional and for the pupil. The text also draws from the descriptive, standardizing and code literature of such organizations as the American Welding Society, American Society for Metals, American Institute for Steel Construction, American Society for Testing Materials, American Petroleum Institute, American Iron and Steel Institute, American Society of Mechanical Engineers and others, including various manufacturing companies. To all, the authors and publisher express their thanks.

The contributing authors are teachers at the California Polytechnic State University, assisted by members of the staff and associates of the James F. Lincoln Arc Welding Foundation. Authors include Harry Honegger, Thomas Kay, William Oliver and Glenn Seeber. Enrico P. Bongio, of California Polytechnic State University, served as editor, assisted by Emmett A. Smith and Richard Sabo, of the James F. Lincoln Arc Welding Foundation.

Introduction

In recent decades, welding has become a dominant process in the fabrication of industrial products and in the building of structures from steel. It is used in all phases of production from the manufacture of microelectronics to the construction of skyscraper framing and the building of bridges and ships. Weld-assembly has been outmoding other methods of joining, especially the riveting and bolting of steel structures, and weld-fabrication has been rapidly taking over areas of manufacture that once were served exclusively by cast iron and steel foundries. Almost day-by-day older methods of manufacturing metal products — especially steel products — are being abandoned in favor of methods of welding or new ideas in welded design.

The rapid and continuing growth of welding results not from promotional effort, but from advantages inherent in this joining technique. Welding, unlike riveting or any form of mechanical fastening, often permits the utilization of the full strength of the material at the joint. This enables the reduction of over-all costs, since structural units do not have to be made oversize to make allowance for weakening by bolt or rivet holes. The savings in material is frequently dramatic. Almost invariably while reducing costs of a structure, welding improves the strength and appearance, reduces the mass, and enables greater flexibility in designing other components, such as the mechanical systems in a large building.

When a weld design replaces the design in cast steel, the cost savings are usually substantial — frequently as much as 50 per cent. The savings result from the reduction in material, pattern costs, decreased shipping weight, decreased rejects, and various other factors. By in-plant weldfabrication rather than purchasing the part from a foundry, companies are able to control delivery schedules, use their manpower more fully, and realize a contribution to overhead costs.

Weld design fits into any scheme for putting parts together. If a cast part is advantageous, it can be joined to welded parts — actually weld-attached. If usage or service requires the breakdown of assembly units, bolted attachments can be used in connection with a basic welded structure.

Welded design, although highly sophisticated at this writing, is continually advancing — constantly showing improved ways of getting the most out of materials. In industry, weldments are frequently spoken of as 'second-generation' or 'third-generation' designs — meaning, that through the application of new design knowledge and engineering ingenuity, a product is in the second or third evolutionary phase of weld design. With new materials becoming available periodically and with engineers constantly finding new and better ways to create weldments, this evolution can be expected to continue.

A factor that additionally presages the growth of welding is the application of mechanization to welding processes. Hand welding is giving ground to semiautomatic welding and full-automatic welding, with further reduction in production costs. The nature of welding is such that it is more adaptable to automation than most other metals-joining processes.

The fact that welding is in a strong growth trend accounts for the mounting interest in it as a career. The students who complete trade courses in welding can be virtually assured of gainful employment and opportunities for advancement during their working years. Similarly, those who become professional welding engineers or designers can look forward to fruitful careers.

THE BASIC PRINCIPLE IN METAL BONDING

It is desirable that beginners in welding technology have a broad perspective on fastening or joining methods. Such a perspective will give greater appreciation of why welding has an unchallengeable role in metal fabrication.

Basically, there are two broad methods by which metals are joined. One method is mechanical; it achieves joining by rivets, bolts, screws, pinning, crimping, shrink-fitting, and so forth. The other method achieves joining by imposing a liquid between the metal parts and then allowing that liquid to solidify. In this latter method, joining results from molecular bonding, or from molecular bonding plus commingling of the base materials.

Brazing, soldering, and adhesive bonding are

examples of "solid-liquid-solid" molecular bonding. With brazing and soldering, the brazing and soldering metals are liquified by heat and the fluxes clean the base metal surfaces to enable molecular contact. When the liquid metals solidify, they provide a solid bond between the parts joined. The strength of the bond depends on the intimacy of the contact at the interfaces and on the strength of the bonding material. To a degree, any liquid that solidifies at reasonable temperatures is a 'solder'. Two pieces of flat steel can readily be joined together with water, by reducing the temperature below the freezing point of water. The "solder" in this case would not be very durable — but the water analogy illustrates well the principle of solid-liquid-solid molecular bonding.

In the adhesive bonding of metals, the starting point is a liquid or semiliquid adhesive and clean metal surfaces. Under heat and pressure, the adhesive becomes a solid — either by evaporation of a solvent or solidification by chemical change. The end result in any event is a "solid-solid-solid" joint, with molecular bonding at the interfaces.

Welding employs the solid-liquid-solid principle, but with a significant difference. The liquid phase in the case of welding results either from the melting and commingling of the base metals or from the liquefaction of base metals plus the liquefaction of filler metal from the welding electrode, wire, or rod. At welding temperatures, liquid base and filler metals coalesce. On cooling there are no defined interfaces where molecular attraction alone effects joining. Admixture and coalescence have made the two base parts plus any filler metal essentially one. If through proper welding procedures and selection of filler material, the properties of the base metals are retained at the joint, the welded area will be as strong as the base metals.

Before the development of high-strength steels, it could be said that a properly made welded joint was always stronger than the steels it joined. That was true when the weld filler metal used had a higher yield strength than the steel, as an example, when 60,000-psi weld metal was used to join 35,000-psi steel. Now, that some steels have yield strengths well over 100,000 psi, the weld metal in the joint is likely to be weaker than the steel. But no mechanical device for joining such steels can approach the strength of a properly designed and executed weld.

TYPES OF WELDING

There are various types of welding based on fusion and the creation of coalescence between parts. The most widely used are arc welding and gas-oxygen (usually oxyacetylene) welding.

In the first, an electric arc generates the heat needed to melt the edges of the joint and any filler metal that may be used. In the second, the combustion of a fuel gas mixed with oxygen provides the high temperatures required to melt metals. Other types of welding, used in special applications, include electroslag, electrogas, plasma-arc, atomic-hydrogen, electron-beam, forge, friction, ultrasonic, induction, resistance. thermit, explosion, and laser-beam. This text will be concerned primarily with arc and gas-oxygen welding, with most attention given to arc welding.

Most of the welding in metal fabrication and manufacture and the erection of structures is done by arc welding. Gas welding — usually oxyacetylene — is widley used also, but for maintenance and repairs, rather than for manufacture.

Brazing and soldering are not liquid fusion welding, but are included in this book because they are metals-joining processes requiring heat, and the shop worker will likely have occasion to employ these processes. Flame-cutting and arc-cutting are closely allied to welding, being methods of sizing materials and preparing weld joints. They are also included in this text.

There are many variations of arc welding — variations in process, equipment, materials used, degree of mechanization, and the special requirements for different metals. Trying to cover these in one text, to which is added discussion of gas-oxygen welding, brazing, soldering, metal cutting, and other subjects prohibits simple and straightforward progression. The reader will find that subjects are mentioned before they are defined, which is rhetorically unfortunate but required because of the overlapping of subjects and the need to keep the text within reasonable size. A glossary of terms, such as the one published by the American Welding Society, might be helpful to the reader. This glossary, *Terms and Definitions, AWS A3.0-76,* is available by contacting: The American Welding Society, 2501 N.W. 7th Street, Miami, Florida 33125.

Safety Precautions In Welding

It is appropriate that a text on welding and associated metal-fabrication processes should begin with a discussion of safety precautions. The types of welding that the student will likely use once employed in industry are electric-arc welding and oxygen-gas welding. Although these metals-joining techniques are no more dangerous than most industrial practices, strict rules of safety must be observed to prevent potential hazards to life, limb and property. The idea is to use the intense heat of the electric arc or the oxygen-acetylene torch beneficially — and, through strict safety procedures, never permit the harnessing of a useful phenomenon to stray from personal control.

The student at first may experience some apprehension in handling a fiery, sputtering electric arc or a torch in which explosive gases are mixed. This is desirable — and all through his career the weldor should hold *justifiable fear* of the equipment with which he works. In everyday life, highly dangerous equipment and substances are handled with immunity because the user has justifiable fear, and safety precautions become automatic. Thus, millions of people drive automobiles every day, observing safety precautions that prevent hazards to life, limb, and property. And thousands of people work with a high explosive — gasoline — every day without disastrous results. Just as the auto driver handles his equipment observing safety precautions automatically — and as the gas station attendant pumps gasoline observing safety precautions automatically — so the experienced weldor or flame-cutter becomes so conditioned to his operation that safety precautions are 'second nature' to him.

The inherent hazards to personnel in welding or flame-cutting are:

- Fires and explosions
- Burns
- Electric Shock
- Noxious fumes
- Eye-damaging radiation

The hazards to property are fires and explosions.

Standards have been developed covering the installation and use of welding and cutting equipment by such organizations as the American Welding Society (AWS), the American National Standards Institute (ANSI), and the National Electrical Manufacturers Association (NEMA). These standards are, for the most part, incorporated in the Occupational Safety and Health Standards of the Occupational Safety and Health Administration (OSHA), U. S. Department of Labor, giving them the force of law under the Williams-Steiger Occupational Safety and Health Act of 1970. It is, thus, mandatory that employers provide working conditions that meet established safety standards.

Seven of the most widely used safety standards applying to welding and cutting are:

1. *Safety in Welding and Cutting,* American National Standards Institute, Z49.1 — 1973.
2. *Recommended Safe Practices for Gas-Shielded Arc Welding,* American Welding Society, A6.1 — 1966.
3. *Safe Practices in the Installation and Operation of Oxyacetylene Welding and Cutting Equipment,* International Acetylene Association.
4. *Safe Practices for Welding and Cutting Containers That Have Held Combustibles,* American Welding Society, A6.0 — 1965.
5. *Handbook on Health and Safety in Welding and Allied Processes,* International Institute of Welding, Document 11S-11W-58-60.
6. *Recommended Safe Practices for Plasma-Arc Cutting,* American Welding Society, A6.3 — 1969.
7. *Recommended Safe Practices for Thermal Spraying,* American Welding Society, C2.1 — 1973.

FIRES AND EXPLOSIONS

The employer will be largely responsible for providing the conditions that minimize the possibility of fires and explosions. It is up to him to see that welding or cutting operations are not carried on in hazardous areas. It is also his responsibility to see that equipment meets safety standards; for instance, that gas lines be protected by suitable flashback and other fire-protection devices. The worker, however, must exercise precautions to protect himself and others in his working environment, and he should be aware of environmental conditions conducive to fires and explosions.

Welding or cutting should never be done in an area where an arc or flame could come in contact with flammable vapors, dusts, lints or other combustible materials. Also, these operations should never be conducted near rooms, containing flammable vapors, dusts, or liquids, to avoid a minor fire from being propagated into a major fire or disastrous explosion.

Areas in which welding or cutting are done should be floored with noncombustible materials, such as concrete. Wooden floors should be covered with metal or other noncombustibles. Floors should be kept clean of oil, grease, or other combustibles that might be ignited by sparks or fallen hot metal. Floors, in addition to being noncombustible, must be tight and free from cracks or holes that would allow sparks or hot metal to fall into areas below.

The walls or working areas must likewise be either noncombustible or protected by metal or asbestos screens or curtains. When relocation of combustible materials is impractical, they should be protected with flameproof covers or shielded with noncombustible screens. When it is necessary to do welding or cutting in an area not fireproofed, or from which certain combustibles cannot be removed, it is accepted practice to dampen the area before beginning work, to have fire-extinguishing equipment ready, to provide a fire watch while the work is in progress, and to follow the work with a careful wetting operation. Under no circumstance, however, should such a procedure be followed in areas where flammable vapors or dusts could be present or where flammable liquids or solids are stored.

Disastrous explosions can occur when the worker tries to weld or flame-cut a tank that has held combustible materials. Tanks, vessels, or other closed containers that have held combustible materials or gases should not be welded or cut unless they have been properly cleaned and marked as safe. Combustible materials include not only the common volatile petroleum products, but also:

1. Acids that react with metals to produce hydrogen.
2. Normally nonvolatile oils or solids that can release hazardous vapors when heated.
3. Fine, dust-like particles of a combustible solid that are potentially explosive.

Acceptable cleaning methods for such containers include water cleaning, hot chemical-solution cleaning, and steam cleaning. The method used depends on the type of material that must be removed from the vessel. Details of approved cleaning procedures are given in *Safe Practices for Welding and Cutting Containers That Have Held Combustibles,* American Welding Society, A6.0 — 1965.

BURNS

Burns are prevented by following ordinary precautions to avoid body contact with sparks, hot metal, or flames. Weldors and cutters (Fig. 2-1) should wear clothing and head gear to protect all skin areas. Woolen clothes are preferable to cotton or synthetic-fiber, since wool is less easily ignited. Leather welding gloves, aprons, and jackets, worn in conjunction with the welding head shield, goggles, and high-top safety shoes, reduce the possibility of burns. Outer clothing, such as overalls, should be free from grease or oil, front pockets should be removed, and cuffs should be nonexistent or turned up inside the garment. Collars should be kept buttoned to prevent sparks from going down the neck. For overhead operations where the worker may be showered with sparks, special leather capes and caps and wire-screen ear protectors are available. Excessively long hair is a potential hazard in the welding or cutting shop.

Fig. 2-1. What the well dressed weldor should wear; a cap or hard hat depending on the job, safety glasses (not shown), head shield with the proper lens shade, leather jacket with long sleeves, leather gauntlet gloves, heavy trousers with no cuffs, and safety shoes.

ELECTRIC SHOCK

Anyone who works with electrical equipment is subject to the possibility of electric shock. Most of the shocks likely to occur in arc welding are mere stings or mild jolts — nuisances rather than threats. For this reason, as the American National Standards Institute warns in its publication Z49.1, arc weldors may tend to become careless in handling their equipment. The danger is not so much from the electrical shock as from the involuntary muscular reactions resulting from it. Thus, as ANSI states: "These voltages are ... sufficiently high that, under some circumstances, they may be dangerous to life. Even mild shocks from normal working voltages or high-frequency (arc) stabilizers, not dangerous in themselves, can cause involuntary muscular contraction, leading to injurious falls from high places. Severity of shock is determined largely by the path and amount of current flowing through the body, and this is determined by voltage and contact resistance of the area of skin involved. Clothing damp from perspiration or wet working conditions may ... increase the imperceptible current to a value high enough to cause such violent muscular contraction as to prevent the weldor from letting go of the live part."

The voltage that exists between the arc-welding electrode holder and the ground during the "off-arc" or "no-load" period is known as the open-circuit voltage. This voltage is not as high as lighting circuits in the home and, thus, not as high as that used with many portable electric tools. For safety reasons, the maximum open-circuit voltage allowed on manual arc-welding power sources is 80 volts for AC machines and 100 volts for DC machines. A typical transformer welder capable of a 225-ampere output has an output voltage of only 25, even though its open-circuit voltage ranges from 55 to 79 volts. The weldor who follows standard safety practices rarely makes body contact with dangerous voltages since he works on the secondary side of the machine's circuitry.

There are two circuits in a welder — the primary and the secondary. The transformer-type welder is a voltage step-down transformer that changes the high-voltage, low-current power applied to the primary circuit to low-voltage, high-current AC power in the secondary. The secondary current is the welding current. The addition of rectifiers in the secondary circuit converts the machine to a DC welder. In DC motor-generator welders, the motor is connected to the power line (primary circuit) and a generator (secondary circuit) generates the welding current. The higher-voltage primary circuit is the one that is dangerous, but the weldor, in the execution of his work, has no reason for coming into contact with it. Only a qualified electrician should do work on the primary side of the circuitry.

The frame or case of welding machine must always be well grounded. A positive ground with an AC welder is made through the ground wire in the power-supply cable, which connects to the ground of the AC power circuitry. This, in turn, makes positive contact with the earth by its connection to a water pipe or to a driven ground rod. Grounding is necessary to protect the weldor against incoming primary voltage in the event of breakdown of insulation in the machine.

NOXIOUS FUMES

The respiratory health hazards associated with welding and cutting are caused principally by inhalation of gases, dusts, and metal fumes. The type and quantity of toxic fumes in a welding area depend on the type of welding being done, the filler and base metals used, contaminants on the base metal, solvents in the air, and the amount of air movement or ventilation in the area. Good ventilation is a primary key to avoiding or minimizing respiratory hazards.

Ventilation requirements in respect to exhaust systems, air flow, hoods, booths, and other equipment are detailed in the various standards and in OSHA Regulations. The employer has the responsibility in ascertaining that proper condition of ventilation exist. The worker, however, should be able to recognize when a potentially dangerous situation exists and when extraordinary precautionary measures — such as the wearing of hose masks, hose masks with blowers, or self-contained breathing equipment — should be taken.

The fumes and dusts that result from the welding or cutting of carbon steels are not toxic. With proper ventilation, no respiratory distress is likely. When welding or heating to high temperatures materials containing zinc, lead, beryllium, mercury, or cadmium, special precautions must be taken to avoid the breathing of toxic fumes. Metal-fume fever (weldor's fever) can result from breathing zinc fumes generated during the welding or cutting of galvanized steel, brass, or bronze, or by the use of bronze as a weld filler metal. Beryllium, lead, and cadmium fumes are especially toxic. Toxic fluorine gas may be released when welding with fluxes containing fluorine compounds. Welding materials that have just been removed from vapor-degreasing units should be avoided, since the degreasing compounds remaining on the materials decompose under heat and the ultraviolet radiation of the arc, giving rise to products irritating to the eyes and respiratory system; delay welding until all degreasing substances and their vapors have disappeared.

EYE PROTECTION

Eye damage from radiation is the most insidious hazard in welding and cutting. The electric arc and the incandescence generated by the gas welding or cutting torch emit rays that can be damaging to the eyes. Protection is mandatory. OSHA regulations state:

"Helmets or hand shields shall be used during all arc-welding or arc-cutting operations, excluding submerged-arc welding. Goggles should also be worn during arc welding or cutting operations to provide protection from injurious rays . . . and from flying objects . . . Helpers or attendants shall be provided with eye protection.

"Goggles or other suitable eye protection shall be used during all gas-welding or oxygen-cutting operations . . . All operators and attendants of resistance-welding or brazing equipment shall use transparent face shields or goggles. . ."

The electric arc is especially productive of radiation harmful to the unprotected eyes. The arc gives rise to two types of invisible radiation — infrared and ultraviolet — and to high-intensity visible light. The welding arc should never be observed at close quarters with unprotected eyes. Failure to observe this rule can result in various degrees of eye burn. These burns do not usually cause permanent injury, but they can be very painful for several days.

A helmet-type head shield (Fig. 2-2), equipped with a lens of proper shade number, is standard equipment for protecting the eyes and face from harmful rays. A hand-held shield is useful for onlookers. Goggles with side shields should also be worn during arc-welding or cutting operations.

The type of welding, cutting, or brazing operations dictates the lens shade number — or degree of radiation protection — that should be used. The following chart from ANSI Z49.1 — 1973 gives recommended shade numbers for various operations.

Welding Operation	Suggested Shade Number*
Shielded Metal-Arc Welding, up to 5/32 in. (4 mm) electrodes	10
Shielded Metal-Arc Welding, 3/16 to 1/4 in. (4.8 to 6.4 mm) electrodes	12
Shielded Metal-Arc Welding, over 1/4 in. (6.4 mm) electrodes	14
Gas Metal-Arc Welding (Nonferrous)	11
Gas Metal-Arc Welding (Ferrous)	12
Gas Tungsten-Arc Welding	12
Atomic Hydrogen Welding	12
Carbon Arc Welding	14
Torch Soldering	2
Torch Brazing	3 or 4
Light Cutting, up to 1 in. (25 mm)	3 or 4
Medium Cutting, 1 to 6 in. (25 to 150 mm)	4 or 5
Heavy Cutting, over 6 in. (150 mm)	5 or 6
Gas Welding (Light), up to 1/8 in. (3.2 mm)	4 or 5
Gas Welding (Medium), 1/8 to 1/2 in. (3.2 to 12.7 mm)	5 or 6
Gas Welding (Heavy), over 1/2 in. (12.7 mm)	6 or 8

*The choice of a filter shade may be made on the basis of visual acuity and may therefore vary widely from one individual to another, particularly under different current densities, materials, and welding processes. However, the degree of protection from radiant energy afforded by the filter plate or lens when chosen to allow visual acuity will still remain in excess of the needs of eye filter protection. Filter plate shades as low as shade 8 have proven suitably radiation-absorbent for protection from the arc welding processes.

Note: In gas welding or oxygen cutting where the torch produces a high yellow light, it is desirable to use a filter lens that absorbs the yellow or sodium line in the visible light of the spectrum.

SOME SAFETY RULES WHEN WORKING WITH COMPRESSED GASES

1. Never use a gas-piping system as a ground for electrical equipment.

2. Never use compressed oxygen to power pneumatic tools, to blow out pipe lines, to dust clothing or work, or for any purpose other than welding or cutting.

3. Never convert a fuel-gas regulator into one for oxygen use.

4. Never use a grinding compound to seat gas-line connections.

5. Never use oversize wrenches when repairing gas welding and cutting apparatus.

6. Never utilize cylinder gas without a suitable pressure-reducing regulator.

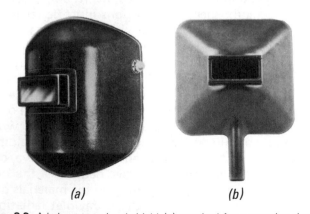

(a)   *(b)*

Fig. 2-2. A helmet-type head shield (a) required for protecting the weldor's eyes and face and (b) a hand-held face shield that is convenient for the use of foremen, inspectors, and other spectators.

7. Never stand directly in front of or behind an oxygen regulator when opening an oxygen-cylinder valve.

8. Don't attach new or stored hose lengths on a torch without first blowing out the hose to eliminate any accumulated foreign matter that might enter and clog the torch orifices.

9. Always protect oxygen and acetylene hoses from flying sparks or hot metal.

10. Examine hoses frequently for worn places and loose connections.

11. Do not repair worn hoses with tape. Use hose splicers and connectors made for the purpose.

12. Never test for leaks with a flame. Use soap suds and check for bubbles.

13. If you cannot stop a cylinder-valve leak by closing it, notify the manufacturer or supplier. Place the cylinder outdoors and beyond the range of any open flames.

14. Never fill a small gas cylinder from a larger one or attempt to mix fuel gas with oxygen except with equipment designed for that purpose.

15. Never carry or lift cylinders by their protective valve cap.

16. Never use acetylene at over 15 psi pressure.

OSHA RULES AND REGULATIONS

Strict regulations of worker safety in industry became mandatory with the passage of the Occupation Safety and Health Act (OSHA) by the U. S. Congress. The Act gives the Secretary of Labor the responsibility for setting and enforcing job safety and health standards. Under the Act, employers must provide working conditions free from recognized hazards, and employees must obey the safety rules that apply to their jobs. OSHA inspectors visit plants to assure compliance with the prescribed rules and regulations.

In general, OSHA safety and health regulations embody those previously established by technical societies, trade associations, and various regulator bodies. As a consequence, they impose no hardship on companies that were previously meeting established standards, but they add the force of law to industrial safety. Details regarding OSHA standards are available from the following regional offices of the Occupational Safety and Health Administration:

OSHA Regional Offices

Region I. John F. Kennedy Federal Bldg., Government Center, 1700 C., Boston, MA 02203. (Connecticut, Maine, Massachusetts, New Hampshire, Rhode Island, Vermont)

Region II. 341 Ninth Ave., N.Y., NY 10001. (New York, New Jersey, Puerto Rico, Virgin Islands)

Region III. Penn Square, Juniper & Filbert Sts., Philadelphia, PA 19107. (Delaware, District of Columbia, Maryland, Pennsylvania, Virginia, West Virginia)

Region IV. 1371 Peachtree St. N.E., Atlanta, GA 30309. (Alabama, Florida, Georgia, Kentucky, Mississippi, North Carolina, South Carolina, Tennessee)

Region V. 848 Federal Office Bldg., 219 S. Dearborn St., Chicago, IL 60604. (Illinois, Indiana, Michigan, Minnesota, Ohio, Wisconsin)

Region VI. Mayflower Bldg., 411 N. Akard St., Dallas, TX 75201. (Arkansas, Louisiana, New Mexico, Oklahoma, Texas)

Region VII. 1906 Federal Office Bldg., 911 Walnut St., Kansas City, MO 64106. (Iowa, Kansas, Missouri, Nebraska)

Region VIII. Denver Federal Center, Bldg. 53, Kipling & 6th Ave., Denver, CO 80225. (Colorado, Montana, North Dakota, South Dakota, Utah, Wyoming)

Region IX. 10353 Federal Bldg., 450 Golden Gate Ave., San Francisco, CA 94102. (Arizona, California, Hawaii, Nevada)

Region X. 1904 Smith Tower Bldg., 506 Second Ave., Seattle, WA 98104. (Alaska, Idaho, Oregon, Washington)

BIBLIGRAPHY

WELDING SAFETY PRACTICES

1. *Safety in Welding and Cutting,* ANSI Standard Z49.1, American Welding Society Inc., Miami, Florida.

2. *Standard for Fire Protection in Use of Cutting and Welding Processes,* NFPA 51B, National Fire Protection Association, Boston, Mass.

3. *Recommended Safe Practices for Gas-Shielded Arc Welding,* AWS A6.1, American Welding Society Inc., Miami, Florida.

4. *Safe Practices for Welding and Cutting Containers That Have Held Combustibles,* AWS A6.0, American Welding Society Inc., Miami, Florida.

5. *Procedures for Cleaning Small Tanks and Containers,* NFPA 327, National Fire Protection Association, Boston, Mass.

6. *Standard for the Control of Gas Hazards on Vessels to be Repaired,* NFPA 306, National Fire Protection Association, Boston, Mass.

7. *Cleaning Tanks Used for Gasoline or Similar Low-Flash Products,* API Bulletin 2016, American Petroleum Institute, New York, N.Y.
8. *Purging Principles and Practices,* American Gas Association, New York, N.Y.
9. *Safety Code for Head, Eye, and Respiratory Protection,* ANSI Standard Z2.1, American National Standards Institute, New York, N.Y.
10. *Effects of Arc Radiation and Heat on Weldors,* Welding Journal, May, 1973.
11. *The Effects of Ultraviolet on the Eye,* American Industrial Hygiene Association Journal, Vol. 32, 1971.
12. *Rules and Regulations of the Occupational Safety and Health Administration,* Federal Register, Vol. 37, Number 202, October, 1972.

Fundamentals Of Arc Welding

As noted in Chapter 1, arc welding is one of several fusion processes for joining metals. By the application of intense heat, metal at the joint between two parts is melted and caused to inter-mix — directly or, more commonly, with an intermediate molten filler metal. Upon cooling and solidification, a metallurgical bond results. Since the joining is by intermixture of the substance of one part with the substance of the other part, with or without an intermediate of like substance, the final weldment has the potential for exhibiting at the joint the same strength properties as the metal of the parts. This is in sharp contrast to nonfusion processes of joining — such as soldering, brazing, or adhesive bonding — in which the mechanical and physical properties of the base materials cannot be duplicated at the joint.

In arc welding, the intense heat needed to melt metal is produced by an electric arc. The arc is formed between the work to be welded and an electrode that is manually or mechanically moved along the joint (or the work may be moved under a stationary electrode). The electrode may be a carbon or tungsten rod, the sole purpose of which is to carry the current and sustain the electric arc between its tip and the workpiece. Or, it may be a specially prepared rod or wire that not only conducts the current and sustains the arc but also melts and supplies filler metal to the joint. If the electrode is a carbon or tungsten rod and the joint requires added metal for fill, that metal is supplied by a separately applied filler-metal rod or wire. Most welding in the manufacture of steel products where filler metal is required, however, is accomplished with the second type of electrodes — those that supply filler metal as well as providing the conductor for carrying electric current.

BASIC ARC-WELDING CIRCUIT

The basic arc-welding circuit is illustrated in Fig. 3-1. An AC or DC power source, fitted with whatever controls may be needed, is connected by a ground cable to the workpiece and by a "hot" cable to an electrode holder of some type, which makes electrical contact with the welding electrode. When the circuit is energized and the electrode tip touched to the grounded workpiece, and then withdrawn and held close to the spot of contact, an arc is created across the gap. The arc produces a temperature of about 6500°F at the tip of the electrode, a temperature more than adequate for melting most metals. The heat produced melts the base metal in the vicinity of the arc and any filler metal supplied by the electrode or by a separately introduced rod or wire. A common pool of molten metal is produced, called a "crater." This crater solidifies behind the electrode as it is moved along the joint being welded. The result is a fusion bond and the metallurgical unification of the work-pieces.

NATURE OF THE ARC

An arc is produced when an electric current flows between two electrodes through an ionized column of gas, called a "plasma" (Fig. 3-2). The electrodes are designated "anode", which is positive, and "cathode", which is negative. The anode is deficient in electrons — the negative particles of the atom — while the cathode has an excess of electrons. An electric current results when electrons move from the cathode to the anode in an attempt to correct the imbalance. The ionized particles in the plasma provide the path. The ions in the plasma are produced by what might be termed the "pull" of the electrodes. In an

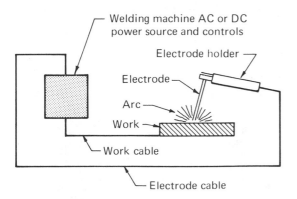

Fig. 3-1. The basic arc-welding circuit.

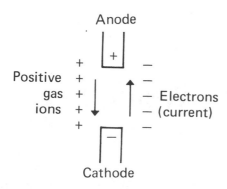

Fig. 3-2. Representation of the mechanics of the arc.

overly simplified sense, the anode needs electrodes to satisfy its deficiency, and it pulls electrons from the intermediate gas atoms in the gap while "reaching to get the excess electrons from the cathode." This creates gas atoms with a positive charge that are pulled toward the cathode.

Heat is generated in the cathode area mostly by the positive ions striking the surface of the cathode. Heat at the anode is generated mostly by the electrons. These have been accelerated as they pass through the plasma by the arc voltage, and they give up their energy as heat when striking the anode.

The plasma, or arc column, is a mixture of neutral and excited gas atoms. In the central column of the plasma, electrons, atoms, and ions are in accelerated motion and constantly colliding. The hottest part of the plasma is the central column, where the motion is most intense. The outer portion or the arc flame is somewhat cooler and consists of recombining gas molecules that were disassociated in the central column.

The distribution of heat in the three heat zones can be changed. Changing the arc length has the greatest effect on the arc plasma. Changing the plasma gas can change the heat balance between the anode and cathode. The addition of potassium salts to the plasma reduces the arc voltage because of increased ionization.

The difference in the heat generated between the anode and cathode can determine how certain types of arcs are used. For example, when welding aluminum with TIG and argon gas, for a given electrode size, about ten times more current can be used without melting the electrode when the electrode is negative than positive. This indicates the anode generates more heat than the cathode. The submerged-arc welding process generates more heat at the cathode rather than the anode, as evidenced by the higher melt-off rate when the electrode is

negative. The same is also true for EXX10 stick-electrode welding.

In welding, the arc not only provides the heat needed to melt the electrode and the base metal but under certain conditions must also supply the means to transport the molten metal from the tip of the electrode to the work. Whereas gravity can account for molten metal transfer when the welding is done in a flat or slightly inclined position, it is obvious that other transfer forces are involved when welding is done overhead. The defiance of gravity in overhead welding is explained by three phenomena: (1) surface tension when the molten drop of metal before leaving the electrode touches the molten metal in the crater; (2) a propelling force caused by the expansion of gas at the tip of the electrode; and (3) a magnetic pinch effect that aids in separating the molten globule and accelerating it in the directed path.

If the electrode is consumable, the tip melts under the heat of the arc and molten droplets are detached and transported to the work through the arc column. Any arc-welding system in which the electrode is melted off to become part of the weld is described as "metal-arc." If the electrode is refractory — carbon or tungsten — there are no molten droplets to be forced across the gap and onto the work. Filler metal is melted into the joint from a separate rod or wire.

More of the heat developed by the arc ends up in the weld pool with consumable electrodes than with nonconsumable electrodes, with the result that higher thermal efficiencies and narrower heat-affected zones are obtained. Typical thermal efficiencies for metal-arc welding are in the range from 75 to 80 percent; for welding with nonconsumable electrodes, 50 to 60 percent.

Since there must be an ionized path to conduct electricity across a gap, the mere switching on of the welding current with a cold electrode posed over the work will not start the arc. The arc must first be "ignited." This is accomplished either by supplying an initial voltage high enough to cause a discharge or by touching the electrode to the work and then withdrawing it as the contact area becomes heated. High-frequency spark discharges

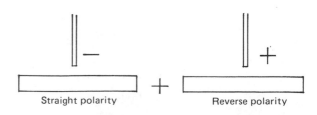

Straight polarity   Reverse polarity

Fig. 3-3. Polarity of a DC welding arc.

are frequently used for igniting gas-shielded arcs, but the most common method of striking an arc is the touch-and-withdraw method.

Arc welding may be done with either AC or DC current and with the electrode either positive or negative. Electrode negative is termed "straight" polarity in the welding industry, and electrode positive, "reverse" polarity. (See Fig. 3-3.) The choice of current and polarity depends on the process, the type of electrode, the arc atmosphere, and metal being welded. Whatever the current, it must be controlled to satisfy the variables — amperage and voltage — which are specified by the welding procedures.

ARC SHIELDING

Metals at high temperatures are reactive chemically with the main constituents of air — oxygen and nitrogen. Should the metal in the molten pool come in contact with air, oxides and nitrides would be formed, which upon solidification of the molten pool would destroy the strength properties of the weld joint. For this reason, the various arc-welding processes provide some means for covering the arc and the molten pool with a protective shield of gas, vapor, or slag. This is referred to as arc shielding, and such shielding may be accomplished by various techniques, such as the use of a vapor-generating covering on filler-metal-type electrodes, the covering of the arc and molten pool with a separately applied inert gas or a granular flux, or the use of materials within the core of tubular electrodes that generate shielding vapors.

Whatever the shielding method, the intent is to provide a blanket of gas, vapor, or slag that prevents or minimizes contact of the molten metal with air. The shielding method also affects the stability and other characteristics of the arc. Covered and tubular electrodes also provide materials for fluxing the molten pool and often for deoxiding the metal. The granular flux used with submerged-arc welding may add alloying elements to the molten pool as well as shielding the pool and the arc.

Fig. 3-4 illustrates the shielding of the welding arc and molten pool with a covered "stick" electrode — the type of electrode used in most manual arc welding. The extruded covering on the filler metal rod, under the heat of the arc, generates a gaseous shield that prevents air from contacting the molten metal. It also supplies ingredients that react with deleterious substances on the metals, such as oxides and salts, and ties these substances up chemically in a slag that, being lighter than the weld metal, rises to the top of the pool and crusts over the newly solidified metal. This slag, even after

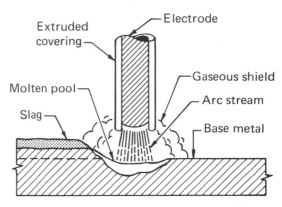

Fig. 3-4. How the arc and molten pool are shielded by a gaseous blanket developed by the vaporization and chemical breakdown of the extruded covering on the electrode when stick-electrode welding. Fluxing material in the electrode covering reacts with unwanted substances in the molten pool, tying them up chemically and forming a slag that crusts over the hot solidified metal. The slag, in turn, protects the hot metal from reaction with the air while it is cooling.

solidification, has a protective function; it minimizes contact of the very hot solidified metal with air until the temperature lowers to a point where reaction of the metal with air is lessened.

OVERCOMING CURRENT LIMITATION

The objective in commercial welding is to get the job done as fast as possible so as to lessen the time costs of skilled workers. One way to speed the welding process would be to raise the current — use a higher amperage — since the faster electrical energy can be induced in the weld joint, the faster will be the welding rate.

With manual stick-electrode welding, however, there is a practical limit to the current. The covered electrodes are from 9 to 18-in. long, and, if the current is raised too high, electrical resistance heating within the unused length of electrode will become so great that the covering overheats and "breaks down" — the covering ingredients react with each other or oxidize and do not function properly at the arc. Also, the hot core wire increases the melt-off rate and the arc characteristics change. The mechanics of stick-electrode welding is such that electrical contact with the electrode cannot be made immediately above the arc — a technique that would circumvent much of the resistance heating.

Not until semiautomatic guns and automatic welding heads, which are fed by continuous electrode wires, were developed was there a way of solving the resistance-heating problem and, thus, making feasible the use of high currents to speed the welding process. In such guns and heads, electrical contact with the electrode is made close to the arc. The length between the tip of the electrode and the point of electrical contact is, then, inadequate for enough resistance heating to take place to overheat the electrode in advance of the arc, even with currents two or three times those usable with stick-electrode welding.

This solving of the "point-of-contact" problem and circumventing the effects of resistance heating in the electrode was a breakthrough that substantially lowered welding costs and increased the use of arc welding in industrial metals joining. In fact, through the ingenuity of welding equipment man-ufacturers, the resistance-heating effect has been put to work constructively in a technique known as long-stickout welding. Here, the length of elec-trode between the point of electrical contact in the welding gun or head and the arc is adjusted so that resistance heating almost — but not quite — over-heats the protruding electrode. Thus, when a point on the electrode reaches the arc, the metal at that point is about ready to melt. Thus, less arc heat is required to melt it — and, because of this, still higher welding speeds are possible.

Power Sources And Equipment For Arc Welding

All arc-welding processes require a continuous supply of electrical current in sufficient amount (amperage) and of proper voltage to maintain an arc. This current may be either alternating (AC) or direct (DC), but it must be supplied to the welding electrode through a device that enables its precise control. Only when the welding current is carefully controlled can the desired welding arc characteristics — and thus maximum welding efficiency — be obtained. The controlling device is called a power source or welder. Current may be supplied to it from utility power lines, or developed within it by generators or alternators driven by close-coupled gasoline or diesel engines.

Various types of power sources provide a range of voltage across the welding arc from 17 — the minimum voltage for starting an arc — to approximately 45 volts. The currents supplied through the power source may range from less than 10 amperes to 1500 amperes or more, the higher currents for automatic welding.

For efficient welding, the power source must permit control of the arc characteristics needed for a specific job. In one job, a forceful, deeply penetrating arc may be required, while, in another, a soft, less-penetrating arc may be necessary to avoid burnthrough. Electrodes are designed for various welding positions, and they help compensate for power sources that have no arc characteristic adjustment. The welding process also dictates the type of power source needed. Table 4-1 shows the power source requirements for various processes.

TABLE 4-1. Power Requirements for Arc-Welding Processes

Process	Output Characteristic	Type of Current	Polarity
Shielded metal-arc, gas tungsten-arc, submerged-arc	Variable-voltage*	AC or DC	DCSP, DCRP, or AC
Flux-cored	Constant-voltage	DC	DCSP, DCRP
Gas metal-arc	Constant-voltage	DC	DCRP

*In some applications, the submerged-arc process can use constant-voltage DC.

CLASSIFICATION OF POWER SOURCES

Power sources are classified according to the type of current — AC or DC — and according to their voltage output, which may be either variable or constant. A further classification designates the method by which energy is supplied to the power source — from a power line directly or through an electric motor, or from a gasoline or diesel engine.

Whatever the type of power source, its main function is to supply the type of current needed for welding. Alternating current direct from the power line goes through a transformer in AC welders that allows control of the current. Thus, a simple AC welder is fed 230-volt single-phase current the same as a kitchen stove, and a selector switch enables the operator to use what AC current he needs for the job — say, a 225-amp output for 3/16-in. electrodes or 180-amp for 5/32 in. electrodes. A DC welder also gives similar control of the current. Direct current is produced from AC line power by either using the line power to run an electric motor that turns a DC generator (an electric motor-generator set) or running the line power through a transformer and then a rectifier (a rectifier set). Direct current may also be produced by driving a DC generator with any type of fuel-burning engine, such as gasoline or diesel engine (engine-driven generator set). A fuel-burning engine may also be used to produce AC current for welding by using it to drive an alternator instead of a generator. Combination welders, producing both AC and DC, are basically transformer-rectifier sets.

Welding machines of all types are rated according to their current output at a specified voltage and duty cycle. This rating is generally set by manufacturers in accordance with standards established by the National Electrical Manufacturers Association (NEMA). These standards are established on a conservative basis, requiring a rating well below the maximum overload capacity of the machine so that it will provide safe operation efficiently over a long period of time.

Ratings are given with a percentage "duty cycle." The duty cycle of a welder is the percentage of a ten-minute period that a welder can operate at a given output current setting. For example, if a welder is rated 300 amperes at a 60% duty

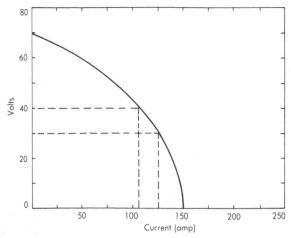

Fig. 4-1. Typical output curve for a variable-voltage power source, adjusted for minimum current variation.

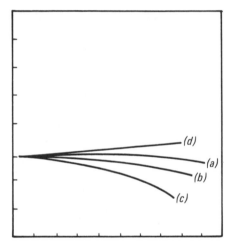

Fig. 4-2. Typical output curves for a constant-voltage power source.

cycle, it means that the machine can be operated safely at 300-amp welding current for 6 out of every 10 minutes. If this duty cycle is reduced in actual operation, the maximum permissible current is increased. Thus, at 35% duty cycle, this same 300-amp machine could be operated at 375 amperes.

Welders are classified as "variable-voltage" (also called constant-current) or "constant-voltage." A variable-voltage machine is one that delivers a current that changes only slightly with changes in voltage. A constant-voltage machine is one that delivers current with the voltage rising or dropping only slightly with changes in current output.

Fig. 4-1 shows a typical output curve for a variable-voltage welder. This type of output is used for submerged-arc, gas tungsten-arc, and shielded metal-arc applications. Fig. 4-2 shows typical output characteristics of a constant-voltage welder. Here, the voltage in the constant-voltage curve (a) rises slightly at the low currents and drops at the

high currents. Most constant-voltage welders are designed with a small downward slope, as in curve (b), and have adjustments to increase the downward slope, as in curve (c). Some welders have a rising slope, as in (d), but this type is becoming less common.

AC WELDERS

Transformer Welders: The transformer welder is a voltage step-down transformer that changes high-voltage, low-amperage AC input current to low-voltage, high-amperage AC welding current. Transformer welders usually operate on single-phase power. Most AC power produced in the United States is 60-hertz, and each time the polarity changes the voltage goes through zero, which tends to create an unstable condition in the arc. This problem, however, has been solved by designing better transient characteristics in the welder and better AC electrodes.

Transformer welders have controls to stabilize and adjust the welding current. A system for controlling the output current is provided either through a series of taps into the secondary windings or by a movable or saturable reactor in the output circuit. The taps provide step control. A reactor provides a continuous stepless control. Various types of starters are used and some are equipped with low-voltage contactors to reduce open-circuit voltage when the machine is not operating. Some machines have an "arc booster" that gives an extra surge of current for a few seconds at the start of the arc in order to get deeper penetration at the beginning of the weld. Most welding transformers can be equipped with condensers to improve power factor and reduce the amount of input current used.

Fig. 4-3. A typical small AC transformer welder for light-duty and limited-service welding.

Fig. 4-4. A typical engine-driven power source that supplies AC current for welding or power for lights and tools.

For the inert-gas-shielded arc-welding processes, transformer welders are equipped with necessary auxiliary controls. A device is required with TIG welding to help establish and maintain the arc.

Small, inexpensive transformer welders are widely used in light industry, maintenance work, and by farmers. Fig. 4-3 illustrates a typical small (225-amp) AC welder. Rotating the switch at the center of the machine changes taps on the secondary coil, which, in turn, changes the welding current.

Transformer welders rated at 600 amperes or more are used primarily for automatic welding. Available with these machines are optional accessories required for automatic welding, such as line contactors, remote current control, and DC for control power.

Table 4-2 shows typical AC welder ratings and output currents. A disadvantage of many transformer welders is that the output current changes with a change in line voltage. In most shops this is not a serious problem, but if the power-line voltage regulation is poor, the welding may not be satisfactory.

Alternators: AC welding current can also be obtained from an engine-driven alternator. A gasoline engine is usually used, and the engine-alternator set serves both as a portable welder and as an auxiliary power supply. Power output — 115 to 230 volts AC — can be used for lights, small tools, or as a standby energy source. A typical machine is illustrated in Fig. 4-4. Table 4-3 shows typical alternator ratings and output currents.

DC AND AC-DC WELDERS

Transformer-Rectifier Welders: Rectifiers for converting AC current to DC have been developed to a stage of efficiency and reliability. A result of this development has been the combination of a rectifier with a transformer to form a DC welder. Various semiconducting materials have been used in current rectifiers, but, at the time of publication, the silicon rectifier had replaced most other types in welding machines.

In principle, the single-phase rectifier welder is a transformer welder with a rectifier added to obtain a DC output. Adjustment of the welding current is through the AC section, as described for transformer welders. The output characteristic can be either constant or variable-voltage. Welders built especially for gas metal-arc welding have adjust-

TABLE 4-2. Typical Ratings and Outputs for AC Variable-Voltage Welders

NEMA Rating			Output Current Range (amp)
Rated Current (amp)	Arc Voltage	Duty Cycle (%)	
180	25	20	30-180
225	25	20	40-225
250	30	30	30-300
300	32	60	30-450
400	36	60	40-600
500	40	60	50-750
600	44	60	50-850
1000	44	60	200-1250

Note: Input power is single-phase.

TABLE 4-3. Typical Ratings and Outputs for Alternator Welders and Auxiliary Power Sources

NEMA Rating			Output		Engine	
Rated Current (amp)	Arc Voltage	Duty Cycle (%)	Current (amp)	Type	Number of Cylinders	HP and Speed (rpm)
150 AC	25	100* 100	60-150* 4500 †	Variable-voltage	1	10.0 3700
225 AC	25	50* 100	20-225* 5000 †	Variable-voltage	2	14.2 2200

* Welding output.   † Watts output when used as auxiliary power source.

ments for changing both the slope of the output curve and the reactance in the circuit for better performance when welding with short-circuiting transfer.

Transformer-rectifier welders are often designed with provisions for both AC and DC welding. These power sources, called combination welders, are especially convenient for structural work where vertical welding is done by DC with E7018 electrodes, and flat welding is done by AC with E7028 electrodes. Combination welders are also convenient for gas tungsten-arc welding; AC is available for welding aluminum, and DC is available for welding stainless and carbon steel, Table 4-4 shows typical ratings and outputs for combination AC-DC transformer-rectifier welders.

Another type of transformer-rectifier welder is the step-down transformer, in which three-phase AC is fed to rectifier units which, in turn, feed DC to a single-output circuit. The output can be either variable or constant-voltage, but only DC is available since the AC is three-phase and cannot be used for welding. Table 4-5 shows typical ratings and out-puts for three-phase transformer-rectifier welders. See Fig. 4-5

Making optimum use of some welding processes may require that accessory equipment be added to the power source. This is especially true if the process is automated. A good example is the AC-DC transformer-rectifier welder built for the gas tungsten-arc process, sometimes called a TIG welder. A typical machine is shown in Fig. 4-6.

This welder can be used for any process using AC or DC variable voltage, but the accessories are designed primarily for gas tungsten-arc. A high-frequency voltage is superimposed on the output voltage so that the arc is established without touching the electrode to the work. The high frequency also stabilizes the arc by igniting the 60-cycle current each time it goes through zero. The intensity of the high-frequency voltage can be adjusted. The

Fig. 4-5. A typical industrial-type AC three-phase input, DC output variable-voltage welder. The heavy duty welders are available in a wide range of sizes (see Table 4-5).

welding current is adjusted electrically by a small rheostat, and a provision is made to connect a remote current control, which can be used to compensate for poor fitup or for crater filling in critical welds. The current can be adjusted to a very low value — some welding is done at less than 10 amperes. Solenoid valves start and stop the flow of cooling water and gas. The gas valve has an electronic delay so that gas continues to flow after the arc is extinquished — to protect the crater and electrode from oxidation.

The transformer-rectifier welder has the same disadvantage as the transformer welder. A change

TABLE 4-4. Typical Ratings and Outputs for Transformer-Rectifier Welders with Both AC and DC Variable-Voltage Outputs

NEMA Rating			Output Current	
Current (amp)	Voltage	Duty Cycle (%)	AC (amp)	DC (amp)
250	30	30	30-300	30-250
300	32	60	30-450	45-375
400	36	60	40-600	60-500
500	40	60	50-750	75-625
600	44	60	50-850	75-750

TABLE 4-5. Typical Ratings and Outputs for Three-Phase Transformer-Rectifier Welders

NEMA Rating			Output Current	
Current (amp)	Voltage	Duty Cycle (%)	DC Current (amp)	Type
300	32	60	45- 375	Variable-voltage
300	32	100	50- 375	Constant-voltage
400	36	60	60- 500	Variable-voltage
400	36	80	50- 500	Constant-voltage
500	40	60	75- 650	Variable-voltage
600	44	100	70- 750	Constant-voltage
600	44	60	75- 750	Variable-voltage
800	44	100	100-1000	Constant-voltage

Fig. 4-6. An AC-DC transformer-rectifier welder designed for gas tungsten-arc welding.

in voltage on the transformer primary changes the welding current. The transformer-rectifier shown in Fig. 4-6 has line voltage compensation to eliminate the problem.

DC Generators: In the direct-current generator, an armature rotates in an electrical field. Current is generated in the armature and is taken off for use through a commutator. The armature is rotated either by an electric motor or an internal-combustion engine. The speed of rotation of the armature and the electrical design of the generator change the output characteristics. The arc characteristics of a generator can be precisely controlled. Polarity

of the electrode can be changed with a flip of a switch.

The DC motor-generator welder is driven by AC utility power. It can provide either variable or constant voltage, or a single unit may provide both types of output. The motor is usually a three-phase induction motor.

The variable-voltage type is a compound generator with a series field that causes the voltage to decrease as the current is increased. Two adjustments can be made to change the welding current:

1. For a given voltage, the output current can be changed by adjusting the series field. This produces an output change as shown in Fig. 4-7(a), and is sometimes called the "current" control. trol.

2. For a given current-control setting, the output can be changed by adjusting the shunt field. This produces an output change as shown in Fig. 4-7 (b).

Combining both adjustments can produce output characteristics similar to those shown in Fig. 4-1 or 4-9. A typical motor-generator welder is shown in Fig. 4-8.

DC-generator power sources, in general, have an adjustment that can provide an output of the type shown in Fig. 4-9. This output is highly suitable for vertical and overhead welding, where the operator uses a whipping motion that alternately raises and lowers the arc voltage. With the flatter characteristic shown in Fig. 4-9, there is greater change in current for a given change in voltage than with the output in Fig. 4-1. Since deposition varies with current, the weldor can vary deposition and thereby exercise more control of the molten puddle with the flatter output characteristic.

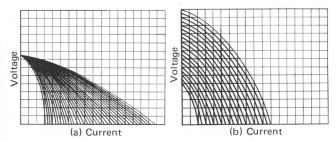

Fig. 4-7. Output for a DC generator welder having adjustments in both the series and shunt fields. Output curves produced by adjusting the series field are shown in (a); curves produced by adjusting the shunt field are shown in (b).

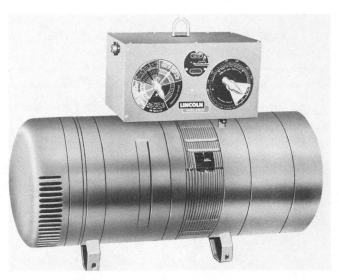

Fig. 4-8. A typical motor-generator welder.

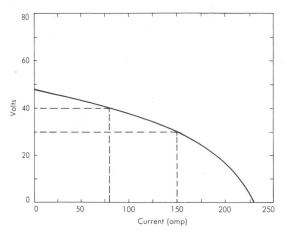

Fig. 4-9. Typical output curve preferred for vertical and overhead shielded metal-arc welding.

The constant-voltage motor-generator welder is a compound generator with a series field designed to keep the voltage nearly constant within the current capacity of the machine, as in Fig. 4-2 (a). The slope of the output curve can be changed by an adjustment in the series field, as in curves (b) and (c). In some welders, an output shown by curve (d) can be obtained. These welders are always used with automatic or semiautomatic wire-feeding equipment, and the current is changed by changing the speed of the wire feed. The arc voltage is changed by adjusting the shunt field in the generator.

Motor-generator welders that provide both variable-voltage and constant-voltage are gaining wider application, because they can meet a wide range of process requirements. Variable voltage is used to manually tack-weld an assembly, and the welding is then completed with an automatic or semiautomatic process using constant voltage. Table 4-6

shows typical ratings and outputs for these motor-generator welders.

Every type of DC welder driven by an electric motor can be duplicated with a gasoline or diesel engine drive. On heavy-duty machines 200 amperes and larger, the engines are liquid cooled. Gas engines are equipped with governors to maintain constant engine speed and with idling devices to reduce the engine speed when welding is not being done. Machines with air-cooled engines are available for light-duty work.

Diesel engines cost more than gasoline engines, but the diesel has several advantages. Diesel fuel costs less than gasoline, is less hazardous to handle, and is consumed less rapidly. Less maintenance is required with diesels, and engine life is longer.

Multiple-Output Power Source: A multiple-output power source is a single welding machine capable of providing welding current to several operators simultaneously. The use of such machines is limited to manual welding where several operators are working in a relatively small area. Many factors limit the economic use of these units; when an application appears feasible, the equipment manufacturers should be consulted.

SELECTING A POWER SOURCE

In selecting a power source, two important considerations are its output capacity and its suitability for the particular job.

The size or rated output of a machine required for a given job depends on the thickness of the metal to be welded and the amount of welding to be done. If a conservatively rated machine, made by a reputable manufacturer, is purchased, the selection can be made with confidence on that rating. There is no need to buy more capacity than will be required by the job. Be sure, however, to check the duty cycle. Machines with a low duty cycle should be used only for maintenance or intermittent welding. Continued operation of a machine beyond its rated capacity will shorten its service life. Of course, properly made and rated machines have large overload capacity, which means that higher than rated amperages can be used for shorter periods than the rated duty cycle allows.

In selecting the type of welder, an essential consideration is the energy source available. Motor-generator sets are generally available for only three-phase utility AC power, but can be ordered to different cycles and voltages. They are also available for DC power. AC machines are generally available for only single-phase power in various cycles, with or without power factor correction in the machine. Fortunately, in most manu-

TABLE 4-6. Typical Ratings and Outputs for Motor-Generator DC Welders

Rating			Output	
Current (amp)	Voltage	Duty Cycle (%)	Variable-Voltage (amp)	Constant-Voltage (amp)
200	28	60	30-300	. . .
250	30	30	40-250	. . .
300	32	60	45-450	. . .
300	32	60	60-375	60-375
400	36	60	60-600	. . .
400	36	60	60-600	60-600
600	44	80	. . .	875 max
800	44	80	100-900	1000 max
1000	44	80	. . .	1250 max

facturing, the source of power does not present a limiting factor on the selection of a welder. The decision can be made on the basis of which is the most efficient and economical machine for a given job.

The most important factor to be considered in selecting a power source is performance — what type machine will do the job easiest and enable better welding to be done at lower costs.

There is one best way for every welding job. Sometimes it is AC; sometimes it is DC. For one job, sensitive control may be required for maximum efficiency. For another, certain types of controls may be unnecessary. A welder should be selected, therefore, according to the job to be done.

The following may be used as a guide to select the proper power source based on the type of current.

DC only:
Gas metal-arc welding
Flux-cored arc-welding
Exx10-type electrodes
Exx15-type electrodes

DC preferred:
Fast-freeze applications
Fast-follow applications
Welding stainless steel
Nonferrous electrodes
Surfacing with high-alloy electrodes

AC preferred:
Fast-fill applications
Iron-powder electrodes, except out-of-position welding
Where arc blow is a problem

AC or DC depending on the application:
Gas tungsten-arc welding
Submerged-arc welding.

The small transformer-welder shown in Fig. 4-3 is widely used on farms, in garages and small machine shops, and by hobbyists. Obviously AC is not always the best type of welding current for such a wide variety of applications. However, the special electrodes and accessories developed for this type of welder make it very versatile even though limited to AC welding current. In this case, the selection of the power source is based on low-cost, low-power input requirements, and versatility rather than AC or DC.

If a job is entirely downhand in heavy plate, an AC machine will be most efficient. If the job is exclusively sheet-metal welding, a DC machine will be most efficient. If the work is a combination of jobs, involving out-of-position welding, as well as straight downhand work, a combination AC-DC machine is the logical choice. These machines can be adapted to individual job requirements, combining larger AC capacity with smaller DC capacity, or in any way that is required. For most manufacturing situations, both AC and DC are needed for maximum efficiency. The combination machine, therefore, is most efficient for general purpose welding. It gives the weldor the opportunity to select for himself the type of arc and current he can use most efficiently for the job at hand.

WELDING EQUIPMENT

Since there are several major arc-welding processes and various stages of mechanization in each, the welding equipment, in addition to the power source, involves numerous mechanisms and devices to facilitate laying a weld bead. It is beyond the scope of this text to catalog the many hundreds of items that are available. However, by observing the items of equipment required for the simplest form of arc welding — stick-electrode welding — and, then selectively replacing elements of this simple process with the counterparts that give increasing mechanization, it is believed that the reader can be given an understanding of the relation of any item of welding equipment to the basic scheme of fusion-joining by arc heating. In essence, all items of welding equipment other than the protective shields and clothing worn by workers are devices introduced in the basic welding circuit, discussed in Chapter 3. Also, the differences between processes at the basic level amount to no more than different ways for accomplishing the same end.

In Fig. 3-1, the basic welding circuit is illustrated. In this circuit is the power source, with cables running from it in one direction to the work and in the other direction to the electrode, from the tip of which the arc is struck. On each side of the power source — extending to the work or the arc-delivering electrode — are other items of equipment needed to accomplish welding. This equipment will vary according to the welding process and its degree of mechanization.

THE WELDING CABLE

Whatever the process, the first item of equipment on both sides of the power source is a cable for carrying electrical current. The cable from the power source to the electrode carries current to the electrode and via the arc to the workpiece. The cable from the power source to the workpiece is the ground cable; it completes the circuit from the workpiece back to the power source.

These conductors are extremely important to the efficiency and success of welding. They must be properly sized to deliver the required current to the welding arc. The size must be adjusted to the length of cable, and the cable assembly must be so designed and built that it performs its current-conducting function efficiently while giving wear resistance where wear is needed and flexibility where flexibility is advantageous.

The conductors in a welding cable are made from strands of fine copper or aluminum wire — preferably copper. The fine wires may be bunched in bundles, with a twisted assembly of bundles enclosed by a paper wrapping. A high-grade insulating material — usually natural or synthetic rubber — over the paper wrapping provides positive insulation. The paper wrapping allows the copper wire to slip within the rubber cover, enhancing the cable's flexibility. A special cable design adds cotton or rayon braiding, followed by a second "outside" covering of rubber. This outside covering is often fluted to increase the cooling area and enhance flexibility.

Fig. 4-10 shows the construction of a premium-type cable, designed to give good flexibility and long service life. Often a "whip" cable of this flexibility grade would be used within 10 to 12 feet of the electrode holder in manual metal-arc welding, where its flexibility would allow ease in maneuvering the electrode. Such a whip section would use the smallest size permissible for its length and the current to be carried, in order to assure maximum flexibility. A whip section of highly flexible cable is usually connected to a stiffer length of cable that runs to the output terminal of the power source. This section of cable is similar in construction, except that often synthetic rubber is used for insulating coverings to provide toughness and impact and abrasion resistance. The

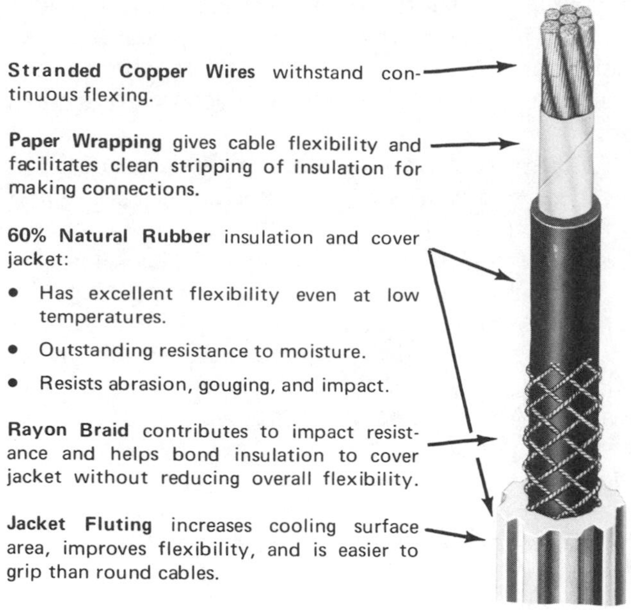

Stranded Copper Wires withstand continuous flexing.

Paper Wrapping gives cable flexibility and facilitates clean stripping of insulation for making connections.

60% Natural Rubber insulation and cover jacket:

- Has excellent flexibility even at low temperatures.
- Outstanding resistance to moisture.
- Resists abrasion, gouging, and impact.

Rayon Braid contributes to impact resistance and helps bond insulation to cover jacket without reducing overall flexibility.

Jacket Fluting increases cooling surface area, improves flexibility, and is easier to grip than round cables.

Fig. 4-10. Construction of a typical welding cable designed for good flexibility. A cable of this type would be used as the "whip" section of a cable assembly in manual metal-arc welding.

ground cable extending from the power source to the workpiece is also usually made from the stiffer, highly wear-resistant type of cable.

The size of cable used depends on the amperage to be carried and the total length of the electrical circuit. The longer the circuit, the larger the size wire needed to prevent voltage drop and the dissipation of current by resistance heating within the conductor.

Table 4-7 shows recommended copper cable sizes for manual welding. Using this table, one can

TABLE 4-7. RECOMMENDED CABLE SIZES FOR MANUAL WELDING*

Machine Size in Amperes	Duty Cycle (%)	Copper Cable Sizes for Combined Lengths of Electrode plus Ground Cable				
		Up to 50 feet	50-100 feet	100-150 feet	150-200 feet	200-250 feet
100	20	#8	#4	#3	#2	#1
180	20	#5	#4	#3	#2	#1
180	30	#4	#4	#3	#2	#1
200	50	#3	#3	#2	#1	#1/0
200	60	#2	#2	#2	#1	#1/0
225	20	#4	#3	#2	#1	#1/0
250 +	30	#3	#3	#2	#1	#1/0
300	60	#1/0	#1/0	#1/0	#2/0	#3/0
400	60	#2/0	#2/0	#2/0	#3/0	#4/0
500	60	#2/0	#2/0	#3/0	#3/0	#4/0
600	60	#3/0	#3/0	#3/0	#4/0	* * *
650	60	#3/0	#3/0	#4/0	* *	* * *

* For fully automatic welding, use two 4/0 cables for less than 1200 amperes or three 4/0 cables for up to 1500 amperes.
* * Use double strand of #2/0.
* * * Use double strand of #3/0.
+ For 225-amp 40% duty-cycle machines, use same cable size as 250-amp 30% duty-cycle machines.

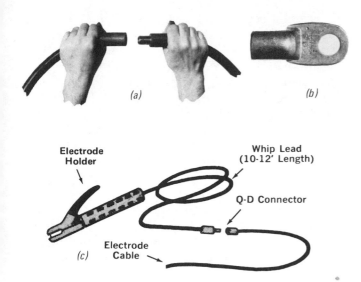

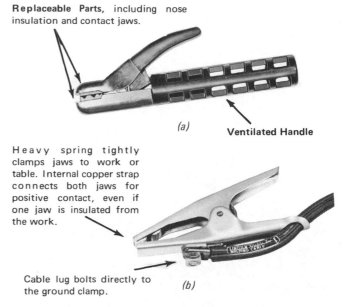

Fig. 4-11. All connections in a cable are important to efficient welding. (a) A quick-detachable connector, used for splicing or to connect (c) the whip section to the main cable. (b) The type of lug used at terminals.

determine the size needed for the particular welding station. Thus, if the maximum machine current is 200 amperes and the station is 250 feet from the power source, 1/0 cable would be required. This size would allow up to a 60% duty cycle — or welding 6 out of every 10 minutes — without excessive heating of the cable or excessive voltage drop.

Just as the proper construction and size of the cable are important to efficient welding, so are all connections within it or at its terminals. Quick-detachable (Q-D) connectors, Fig. 4-11 (a), are provided for splicing cable lengths or for attaching the whip length to the main cable, Fig. 4-11 (c). These connectors are designed to lock so they cannot accidentally be pulled apart or work loose. They also are insulated. Cable lugs, Fig. 4-11 (b), are needed for connecting welding cables to power sources, panels, switchboards, and some types of ground clamps or electrode holders and are provided in sizes to fit the cables. Lugs and Q-D connectors should be soldered to the cable.

THE ELECTRODE HOLDER

Following the basic welding circuit, there is one more item of welding equipment between the power source and the electrode in manual metal-arc welding — namely, the electrode holder. This is basically no more than a clamping device for grasping and making firm electrical contact with the electrode, with an insulated handle for the operator's hand. It can be designed, however, with a number of refinements, such as replaceable jaws, a ventilated handle, and a hand shield. Fig. 4-12 (a)

shows a type of holder with replaceable jaws, ventilated handle, and nose and arm insulation. The cable conductor may be connected to the holder by a nut-and-bolt arrangement, or the holder may come from the supplier with a whip section of cable permanently attached by some type of fused joint. Solder connections are provided in some designs.

Electrode holders are rated according to their current capacities, which are usually in the range of 300 to 600 amperes, and are produced in sizes to accommodate the sizes of electrodes required. Since operator comfort is desired, the smallest holder that will do the job is usually chosen. If a holder becomes hot while welding, the operator knows that it is too light for the welding current being used. There should be a margin between the current rating for the holder and the amperage used on the job. Thus, if the welding is done at 275 amp, the holder should be rated at least 300 amp.

GROUND CONNECTIONS

On the ground side of the power source, there must be a means of connecting the ground cable to the workpiece. A ground clamp, bolted to the lug at the end of the ground cable, is a simple and versatile connector. A ground clamp is shown in Fig. 4-12 (b). The ground clamp may be attached to the workpiece directly or to a fixture that holds the workpiece and makes good electrical contact with it.

Fig. 4-12. (a) An electrode holder with replaceable jaws, ventilated handle, and nose and arm insulation. (b) A ground clamp for attaching the ground cable to the workpiece or fixture.

The ground connection varies with the process, and, in highly automatic welding installations, may be a permanent stationary connection or a connection made through brushes or rotating or sliding shoes. The ground must make a firm, positive connection, and its placement in respect to the layout of the assembly and direction of welding is important for good arc characteristics and the prevention or minimization of arc blow. The experienced weldor knows that good grounding is essential to good work and that attention to this factor cannot be overemphasized.

In some welding installations, it is the practice of using a steel bar or a reinforcing rod as a common grounding connection between two or more workholding fixtures. When this is done, care must be taken to assure that the steel grounding bar has adequate cross-sectional area to match the copper welding cable in electrical conductivity. Since the conductivity of copper is almost 7 times that of mild steel, the cross-sectional area of any common steel grounding bar should be at least 7 times the cross section of the welding cable conductor. If the grounding bar is inadequate in cross section, high resistance will develop in the circuit, the voltage will drop, and poor performance will result.

Grounding is discussed in subsequent chapters, emphasizing its importance to efficient welding. A point to bear in mind is that the ground connection should occupy the total surface of contact and the area of that surface must be at least equal to the cross-sectional area of the conductor. This means that the area of contact must be free from any scale, rust, oil, grease, oxides, or dirt that would act as points of insulation. Brightening the area of contact with sandpaper or a wire brush before making the connection is good practice.

There is a simple way to test the soundness of the circuit during welding — namely, any time the circuit is off, run the hand over the length of the cable from power source to the electrode. If a "hot" section or a section warmer than the rest of the cable is felt, one knows that undue resistance heating is occurring in that section. If the hot section is near a terminal, the connection at the terminal is suspect; if any place along the cable, the cause is probably broken strands within the cable. If the entire cable is hot to touch, it is probably undersized for the welding current being used.

With mechanized welding equipment, conductors other than those carrying the welding current may also be required between the power source and the welding gun or head. These conductors are small wires that carry just enough current to operate controlling devices. They are usually in a cable separate from the welding current cable, but, in some instances, may be incorporated in the welding-cable construction.

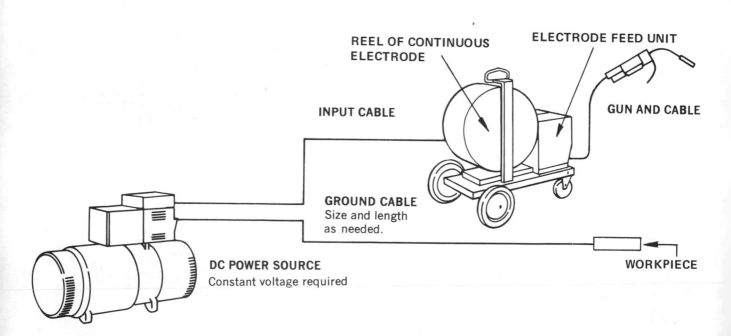

Fig. 4-13. A schematic of the semiautomatic open-arc self-shielded flux cored electrode process — one of the simplest semiautomatic processes in terms of equipment and the most versatile for steel welding.

THE SEMIAUTOMATIC GUN AND WIRE FEEDER

Once any degree of welding mechanization is attempted, the equipment becomes complicated — but still it is merely a modification of the primary elements in the basic welding circuit. Thus, when one moves from stick electrode to semiautomatic welding with continuous electrode, a semiautomatic gun and an electrode wire-feeding mechanism take over the function of the simple electrode holder. A passageway, or conduit, made from plastic tubing or spirally-wound steel wire, is provided for movement of the continuous electrode. This conduit is usually incorporated into the cable carrying the welding current, which may also contain wires for the control circuit that initiates electrode feeding. Additionally, tubing or another arrangement may be required to supply granular flux or shielding gas to the arc, depending on the process.

If the mechanization is carried a step further — to full automation — a welding head with all the auxiliary equipment required is substituted for the simple electrode holder in the basic welding circuit.

One of the simplest semiautomatic processes in terms of equipment is the self-shielded flux-cored electrode process, a schematic of which is shown in Fig. 4-13. Here, a wire-feeding mechanism with its controls and a reel of electrode wire has been interposed in that part of the basic welding circuit between the power source and the arc, and the electrode holder used in stick-electrode welding has been replaced with a welding gun.

Fig. 4-14 (a) depicts a typical wire feeder with the wire drive-roll and control unit built integrally with the wire reel. Note that two cables exit from the mechanism. The large one contains both the welding current cable and the conduit passage for the electrode wire. The small cable contains the wires for the circuit that activates wire feed and also activates contactor circuit so the electrode is

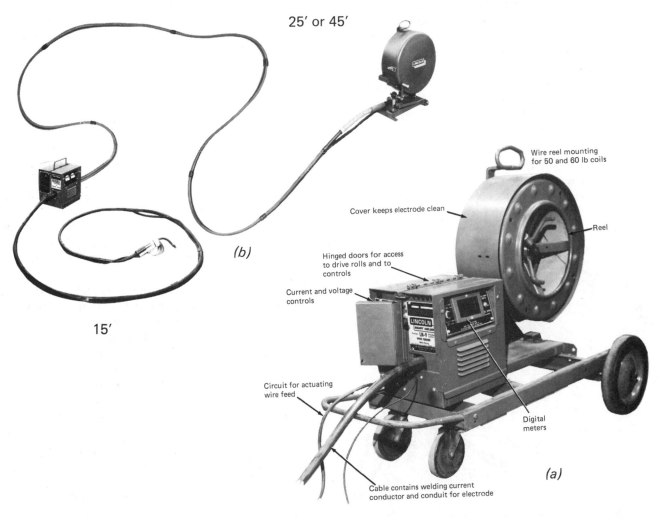

25' or 45'

(b)

15'

Wire reel mounting
for 50 and 60 lb coils

Cover keeps electrode clean

Reel

Hinged doors for access
to drive rolls and to
controls

Current and voltage
controls

Digital
meters

Circuit for actuating
wire feed

Cable contains welding current
conductor and conduit for electrode

(a)

Fig. 4-14. (a) A typical wire-feeding mechanism, as used with semiautomatic self-shielded flux-cored or submerged-arc welding. (b) How the drive-roll and control unit may be separated from the coil of electrode to give even greater flexibility to semiautomatic welding.

cold when not welding. The electrode feed rate is set by the controls on the control box, and this rate, in turn, regulates the amperage supplied by the constant-voltage power source.

In Fig. 4-14 (b) the drive-roll and control unit are seen detached from the reel housing — a modification that permits working farther from the electrode supply and moving the control mechanism into tighter working quarters. Here, the drive mechanism pulls wire from the reel and then pushes it the remaining distance to the welding gun. Wire feeding is initiated and the welding circuit energized when the operator presses a trigger on the welding gun.

Flux-cored electrodes require drive-rolls that will not flatten or otherwise distort the electrode. Various grooved and knurled surfaces are used to advance the wire. Some wire feeders have a single pair of drive-rolls; others, two pairs with at least one roll of each pair powered.

Good, trouble-free wire feeding depends on the size of the drive motor, the diameter of the electrode, the length of cable between feeder and gun, the type of gun — straight-through or curved nozzle — and the surface condition of the electrode. Thus, a system that is satisfactory for driving a 3/32-in. electrode through a 10-ft. conduit and a straight-through gun may be unsatisfactory for driving a 7/64-in. electrode 15 feet through a cable and through a 60° curved-nozzle gun.

The semiautomatic welding gun (Fig. 4-15) is designed for comfortable holding and ease in manipulation. The gun provides internal contacts that initiate wire feed and complete the welding circuit at the press of the trigger switch. Most semiautomatic guns for the self-shielded, gas-shielded, and

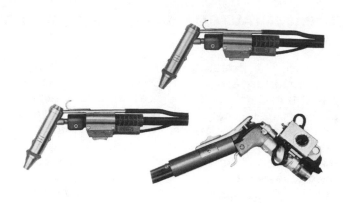

Fig. 4-16. Semiautomatic guns for submerged-arc welding. The concentric nozzle supplies flux as well as electrode wire. The gun at the top is rated at 350 amp; the others at 600 amp. Note the mechanized hand travel unit attached to the bottom gun; this small motorized unit paces the welding travel (see Fig. 4-17).

submerged-arc processes are designed for air cooling, which permits them to be small, light, and highly maneuverable. Water-cooled guns are also available, but this requires separate tubing for supply and return of water and a bulkier construction to provide water passages; thus, ease of handling and maneuverability are lessened.

Guns may have either straight or curved nozzles. The curved nozzle may vary from 45° to 80°. Straight-through nozzles are favored for fillet welds and when the work flows under the gun. Curved nozzles are preferred for depositing butt welds in heavy sections. The curved nozzle enhances flexibility and ease in manipulation, but requires heavier-duty wire-drive units. Curved nozzles are generally favored with the self-shielded process.

Semiautomatic guns should be of simple construction for minimum maintenance, but must be rugged to withstand physical abuse. Nozzles, contact tips, and switches should be designed for long life and ease of replacement. Nozzles should be rugged, insulated to prevent shorting to the workpiece and resist adherence of spatter. Contact tips should be made of suitable alloy and should have sufficient cross-sectional area to provide optimum life for the size of electrode and current used.

The equipment for gas-shielded or submerged-arc semiautomatic welding requires additional features — such as equipment for containing, metering, and conducting shielding gas to the welding gun; tanks, and hoses for submerged-arc flux; and modifications at the gun for dispensing the shielding material. The chapters treating the individual processes discuss some of the specific items of equipment. Several types of semiautomatic guns for submerged-arc welding are shown in Fig. 4-16.

Semiautomatic welding equipment appears

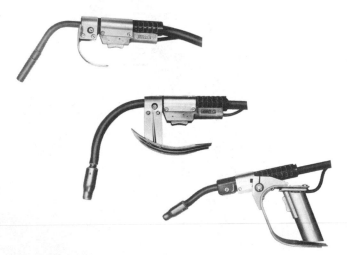

Fig. 4-15. Various designs of guns for semiautomatic self-shielded flux-cored electrode welding. The one at the top is rated at 350 amp, the middle one at 450 amp, and the lower one at 600 amp. The joint to be welded affects selection of nozzle curvature.

quite simple compared to full-automatic welding equipment, but possibly represents even a higher stage in mechanization in its simplicity. Semiautomatic welding attempts to put a degree of mechanization in the great bulk of welding work that is not subject to full mechanization. This work requires extreme flexibility, which is impossible with any full mechanized equipment. With semiautomatic welding, the operator still holds the equivalence of an electrode holder (the gun) in hand and travels and maneuvers it, but frequent electrode changing is eliminated and the pace of welding is established by the preset electrode feeding rate.

MECHANIZED TRAVEL UNITS

Semiautomatic welding takes a step toward full mechanization when devices and mechanisms are used with the semiautomatic gun to relieve the operator of holding, guiding, and traveling it. Thus, a small mechanized travel attachment mounted on the nozzle of the submerged-arc gun, shown in Fig. 4-17, establishes the rate of travel over a seam and

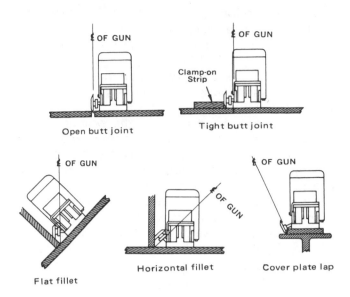

Fig. 4-19. These sketches show how the outboard guide wheels of the motorized unit shown in Fig. 4-18 are set to follow various types of joints.

supports the weight of the gun. Or, a small self-propelled trackless carriage, such as shown in Fig. 4-18, relieves the operator of holding and guiding the gun over the joint. His only function left is placing it on the work, starting and stopping its operation, and monitoring its performance. The sketches in Fig. 4-19 show how the spring-loaded guide rolls of the unit are set to maintain the desired path over the assembly.

FULL-AUTOMATIC WELDING HEADS

With fully mechanized welding, a great variety of equipment — much of it custom-designed — is used, but still all of this equipment may be viewed

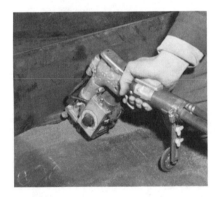

Fig. 4-17. A small motorized unit added to the submerged-arc gun establishes the travel rate and supports the gun as it travels the seam. Here, the weldor merely guides the semiautomatic gun and controls starting and stopping.

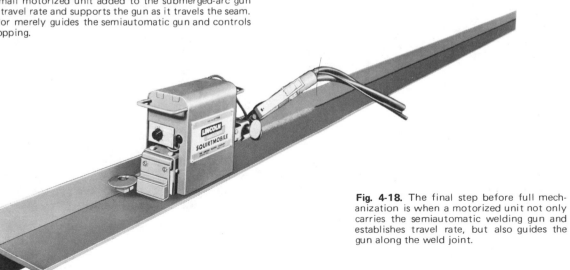

Fig. 4-18. The final step before full mechanization is when a motorized unit not only carries the semiautomatic welding gun and establishes travel rate, but also guides the gun along the weld joint.

as a substitute for the simple electrode holder used in stick-electrode welding. In a fully mechanized installation, the manual skill of the weldor is replaced entirely. Machines supply the skill — and the operators of such machines provide the instructions and watch over the machines to make sure that instructions are followed.

The welding head replaces the welding gun at the fully mechanized stage of arc-welding development. The head may be stationary with the work moving under it, or it may move across the work. The head may feed one wire (single-arc head) or two wires (Twinarc), and two or more heads may be used together (tandem-arc and multiarc).

Full-automatic welding is outside the scope of this text, yet the student of welding should be aware that many of the operations that can be done with the manual stick electrode or the hand-held semiautomatic gun will be fully mechanized in some industries. Full-automatic welding requires not only ingenious devices to move the welding arc or arcs over the work, or to move work under the arc or arcs, but also similarly ingenious fixtures for holding materials and manipulating both the movement of the work and the movement of the welding arcs. For introduction to full-automatic arc welding and the fixtures, manipulators, and positioners used with it, the reader is referred to *The Procedure Handbook of Arc Welding,* published by The Lincoln Electric Company. In following chapters, full-automatic welding will sometimes be alluded to, and, when this happens, the reader should bear in mind that full automation is merely the application of mechanized devices to perform the functions of the basic welding circuit.

Consumables In Arc Welding

In addition to the equipment used in arc welding, various types of electrodes, rods, wires, fluxes, and gases are also used. These are called "consumables" because they are consumed or "used up" during welding. All filler metals, whether supplied by a covered electrode, a rod, or a wire, are "consumed" during welding and become a part of the finished weldment. All shielding gases, such as argon, helium, or carbon dioxide used with a gas-shielded arc-welding process, are expended during welding. Similarly, granular fluxes such as used with submerged-arc welding are at least partially expended during welding. (Excess flux material is sometimes recovered for reuse.)

In discussing consumables, it is necessary to make reference to terms and processes that have not already been explained or defined. The reader may refer to following chapters for explanation of certain terms. The important thing to bear in mind is that arc welding, whether it be manual shielded metal-arc, gas-shielded metal-arc, self-shielded flux-cored-electrode, or submerged-arc, it "uses up" materials — and these are precisely prescribed for the welding process, the joint configuration, and the metallurgical requirements.

THE COVERED ELECTRODE

The first consumable that the student of welding will encounter is the covered electrode — popularly known as the "stick" electrode. This is the electrode used in ordinary electric-arc hand welding. It has the capacity for shielding the arc, providing filler metal, and giving the "fill", "follow", and "freeze" properties needed with the joint being welded. The covered electrode is actually a remarkable item, incorporating within its apparently simple structure decades of chemical and metallurgical technology.

The first electrodes used in arc welding were low-carbon bare steel wires. Usable only with direct current, they produced welds or poor quality by present standards. The arc was erratic and hard to control. The weld metal reacted with oxygen and nitrogen in the surrounding atmosphere. This resulted in the formation of oxides and nitrides in the deposits, which were detrimental to good weld deposits. There followed years in which the bare metal electrodes were lightly lime-coated by such means as dipping and spraying. The result was a somewhat better control over the welding operation, but the electrodes still lacked in many respects. One of the most noteworthy advancements was made by a European firm. A heavily covered electrode was produced with a wrapping of asbestos, fine aluminum wire, and lime. The resultant electrode had shielding, deoxidizing, and fluxing properties and gave welds of improved strength. Their high cost, however, prevented widespread acceptance.

By the early thirties American companies had started producing covered electrodes by an extrusion process. In this process, powders made up of substances to serve special functions are first mixed with a binder, resulting in an extrusion material of dough-like consistency. Under hydraulic pressure, the covering material is pressed on the core wire as it passes rapidly through a close-tolerance sizing die. This method of electrode production resulted in a covered electrode with advantages over former types and was quickly adopted by industry throughout the world.

CLASSIFICATION OF COVERED ELECTRODES

Mild-steel electrodes are classified on the basis of the mechanical properties of the deposited weld metal, the type of covering, the welding position in which the electrode is intended for use, and the type of current suitable for the electrode. Specifications require that the core wires cannot vary in diameter more than .002" from size, and coverings must be concentric with the core wire. For years, the identification system in use was a color spot near the grip end of the electrode. Now, some specifications require the classification number to be imprinted on the covering near the grip end.

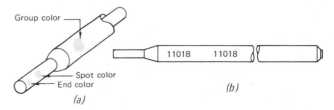

Fig. 5-1. (a) National Electrical Manufacturers Association color-code method to identify an electrode's classification; (b) American Welding Society imprint method.

TABLE 5-1. AWS A5.1-69 and A5.5-69 Designations for Manual Electrodes

a. The prefix "E" designates arc-welding electrode.
b. The first two digits of four-digit numbers and the first three digits of five-digit numbers indicate minimum tensile strength:

E60XX . . . .   60,000 psi Minimum Tensile Strength
    E70XX . . . .   70,000 psi Minimum Tensile Strength
    E110XX . . . .   110,000 psi Minimum Tensile Strength

c. The next-to-last digit indicates position:
EXX1X . . . .   All positions   EXX2X . . . .   Flat position and horizontal fillets
d. The suffix (Example: EXXXX-A1) indicates the approximate alloy in the weld deposit:

— A1 . . . .   0.5% Mo
    — B1 . . . .   0.5% Cr, 0.5% Mo
    — B2 . . . .   1.25% Cr, 0.5% Mo
    — B3 . . . .   2.25% Cr, 1% Mo
    — B4 . . . .   2% Cr, 0.5% Mo
    — B5 . . . .   0.5% Cr, 1% Mo
    — C1 . . . .   2.5% Ni
    — C2 . . . .   3.25% Ni
    — C3 . . . .   1% Ni, 0.35% Mo, 0.15% Cr
    — D1 and D2 . . . .   0.25 -0.45% Mo, 1.75% Mn
    — G . . . .   0.5% min. Ni, 0.3% min. Cr, 0.2% min. Mo, 0.1% min. V, 1% min. Mn (only one element required)

However, color coding (Fig. 5-1) is still used on electrodes that are too small to be legibly imprinted and on electrodes that can be extruded at rates too high for imprinting.

All mild and alloy-steel electrodes are classified with a four or five-digit number, prefaced by the letter E. The first two numbers stand for the minimum tensile strength of the deposited metal in thousands of pounds per square inch. The third digit indicates the position in which the electrode is capable of making satisfactory welds; 1 is for all positions, 2 for flat and horizontal positions only. The last digit indicates the type of current to be used and the type of covering (see Tables 5-1 and 5-2). Thus, an E7018 electrode would be one giving a weld deposit of 70,000 psi minimum tensile strength, usable in all welding positions with AC or DC-positive current, and having a low-hydrogen, iron-powder type of covering.

In the case of a five-digit number, such as E11018, the first three digits indicate the minimum tensile strength in thousands of pounds per square inch. A suffix, such as A1, B2, or C3, indicates the approximate alloy content of the weld metal deposited by an alloy-steel electrode (see Fig. 5-1d).

TABLE 5-2. AWS A5.1-69 Electrode Designations for Covered Arc-Welding Electrodes

Designation	Current	Covering Type
EXX10	DC(+) only	Organic
EXX11	AC or DC(+)	Organic
EXX12	AC or DC(−)	Rutile
EXX13	AC or DC(±)	Rutile
EXX14	AC or DC(±)	Rutile, iron-powder (approx. 30%)
EXX15	DC(+) only	Low-hydrogen
EXX16	AC or DC(+)	Low-hydrogen
EXX18	AC or DC(+)	Low-hydrogen, iron-powder (approx. 25%)
EXX20	AC or DC(±)	High iron-oxide
EXX24	AC or DC(±)	Rutile, iron-powder (approx. 50%)
EXX27	AC or DC(±)	Mineral, iron-powder (approx. 50%)
EXX28	AC or DC(+)	Low-hydrogen, iron-powder (approx. 50%)

SOME POPULAR STICK ELECTRODES

The student of welding should become acquainted first with a half-dozen of so E60XX and E70XX electrodes for the welding of mild steel. The following are brief descriptions of the most commonly used electrodes in mild-steel fabrication.

E6010 — The first commercially produced cellulose-covered electrode. Excellent for all positions. Gives deep penetration, thin slag, and X-ray-quality welds. Used with DC reverse polarity only.

E6011 — The AC counterpart to E6010. Good for all positions. Gives deep penetration, thin slag, and X-ray-quality welds. Used with either AC or DC reverse polarity.

E6012 — Has a rutile-type covering. Gives medium penetration, making it a good choice for poor fitup work. A general-purpose electrode, it can be used in all positions but gives best performance in the flat or horizontal position and vertical downhill. Used with AC or DC straight polarity.

E6013 — Similar in many ways to the E6012 electrode. Gives good performance in welding sheet metal, using low-amperage settings with light-duty transformer welders. Used with AC or DC straight or reverse polarity.

E6020 — An iron oxide-covered electrode that produces excellent welds with either AC or DC straight or reverse polarity in flat or horizontal fillets or flat groove welds. Produces a spray-type arc and a heavy slag that is easily removed.

E6027 — Similar to E6020 but contains as much as 50% iron powder in the covering, which results in very high deposition rates. Gives a spray-type arc and a heavy slag that is easily removed. Especially recommended for groove welds because of good wash-in along the side of the joint. Used with AC or DC straight polarity.

E7014 — This 70,000-psi electrode has a rutile and iron-powder covering, which gives it a relatively high deposition rate. Usable with AC or DC straight or reverse polarity and especially favored for inclined or short horizontal fillets.

E7015 — A low-hydrogen, all-position electrode for welding medium-carbon, low-alloy, and hard-to-weld steels with little or no preheat. Good for high-sulfur steels. Used with DC reversed polarity current only.

E7016 — Same characteristics as E7015, except can be used with AC current.

E7018 — A low-hydrogen iron-powder electrode for all-position use. Used with AC or DC reverse polarity.

E7024 — Covering contains about 50% iron powder. Has higher deposition rate than E7014. Excellent electrode for horizontal and flat fillets. Used with AC or DC straight or reverse polarity.

E7028 — A low-hydrogen electrode with a heavy iron-powder content in the covering. Used in welding flat and horizontal fillets, employing eigher AC or DC reverse polarity.

ELECTRODE COVERINGS

It can be seen by the foregoing that the electrode covering has a large effect on its performance characteristics. The third and fourth digits in a four-digit electrode designation (or fourth and fifth in a five-digit) tells the experienced weldor a lot about the use of the electrode.

The functions of the electrode covering include the following:

- Provides a vapor shield to protect the molten metal from reaction with the oxygen and nitrogen of the air.

- Provides an ionized path for conducting current from the electrode tip to the work and for maintenance of an arc.

- Provides a flux for cleansing the metal surface of oxides and tying up any oxides as slags that float to the top and may be removed from the finish weld.

- Controls the weld profile, especially on fillet welds.

- Controls the melt-off rate of the electrode.

- Controls the penetration properties of the arc.

- Provides filler metal, in addition to that supplied by the core wire.

- Adds alloy materials to the weld deposit where a particular chemical composition is required.

The covering substances creating shielding gases or vapors under the heat of the arc include cellulose materials, such as cotton cellulose and wood flour. The gases produced are carbon dioxide, carbon monoxide (small amounts), hydrogen (small amounts), and water vapor. E6010 and E6011 are cellulose-covered electrodes. Carbonates, such as calcium carbonate, are used in some electrodes. At arc temperatures, carbonates decompose liberating carbon dioxide gas for shielding.

Materials used in the electrode covering for fluxing and slag formation include rutile (a titanium dioxide mineral), asbestos, calcium carbonate, silica flour, aluminum oxide, manganese oxides, and feldspar. The chemical reactions of these substances in removing oxides and cleansing the molten pool are extremely complex and possibly not completely understood. Suffice it to say that not only do these materials remove undesirable elements, but also form slags that rise to the surface of the pool, freeze before the metal below freezes, and thus aid in the protection of the molten metal from reaction with the atmosphere.

Deoxidizers in the coverings serve to reduce oxides that might have been present on the work or inadvertently formed by oxidation of the molten metal through imperfect shielding or slagging. Oxides would tend to make the weld metal brittle. The most commonly used deoxidizing agents are silicon, aluminum, and manganese.

Arc stabilization is another important function of the electrode covering. With AC current, the flow reverses direction 60 times a second with 60-hertz power. Because of this, there is a tendency for the arc to "cut off" every time the current flow is reversed. This problem is solved with AC electrodes by incorporating potassium compounds, such as potassium titanate, in the covering. The potassium ion maintains a good electrical path between the electrode and workpiece in AC operation. The phenomenon of reversing current with AC explains why all DC electrodes are not usable with AC current — even though all AC electrodes are usable with DC current. Some DC electrodes don't have the arc-stabilization ingredients needed for the oscillating AC current.

Binders and extrusion aids are other substances found in the covering of electrodes for mild steel. These materials not only provide the consistency needed for extruding the mix around a core wire, but also protect the active covering ingredients from chemical changes during electrode manufacture and subsequent storage. Widely used binder materials include sodium silicate (water glass), potassium silicate (especially for AC electrodes), and various clays and minerals.

The electrode covering is also a vehicle for adding filler-metal ingredients to the weld deposit. Thus, iron powder is extensively used in electrode coverings — adding iron to the weld, in addition to the iron supplied by the core wire. Iron powder may be only a small percentage of the covering material or over half of it. In some E6010 electrodes, a small percentage added to the covering stabilizes and quiets the arc without loss of the penetrating characteristics. Iron powder added in large amounts increases the deposition rate, increases the optimum current, and with thick coverings facilitates the use of the drag technique in welding. The electrode covering can also be a source of alloying metals, such as manganese, nickel, chromium, and molybdenum. When mixed with the iron from the steel wire core, an alloy weld is created during the welding process.

Covered electrodes are produced in lengths from 6 to 18 inches. Standard core-wire diameters range from 1/16" to 5/16", with the 5/32" and 3/16" sizes being most popular.

Electrodes are sold by the pound, packed in special cardboard containers with moisture barriers, in hermetically sealed containers, or in various types of metal cans. Electrodes must be stored in dry areas and precautions taken to prevent moisture absorption.

The American Welding Society requires that covered electrodes give weld deposits meeting minimum mechanical-property and radiographic requirements. These are shown in Table 5-3. The

TABLE 5-3. AWS A5.1-69 Minimum Mechanical Property and Radiographic Requirements for Covered Arc-Welding Electrode Weld Metal

AWS Classification	Tensile Strength, min, psi	Yield Point, min, psi	Elongation in 2 in., min, percent	Radiographic Standard [a]	V-Notch Impact [d]
E60 Series [b]					
E6010	62,000	50,000	22	Grade II	20 ft/lb at −20°F
E6011	62,000	50,000	22	Grade II	20 ft/lb at −20°F
E6012	67,000	55,000	17	Not required	Not required
E6013	67,000	55,000	17	Grade II	Not required
E6020	62,000	50,000	25	Grade I	Not required
E6027	62,000	50,000	25	Grade II	20 ft/lb at −20°F
E70 Series [c]					
E7014			17	Grade II	Not required
E7015			22	Grade I	20 ft/lb at −20°F
E7016	72,000	60,000	22	Grade I	20 ft/lb at −20°F
E7018			22	Grade I	20 ft/lb at −20°F
E7024			17	Grade II	Not required
E7028			22	Grade II	20 ft/lb at 0°F

a   See AWS A5.1-69, Fig. 3

b   For each increase of one percentage point in elongation over the minimum, the yield point or tensile strength, or both, may decrease 1,000 psi to a minimum of 60,000 psi for the tensile strength and 48,000 psi for the yield point for all classifications of the 60-series except E6012 and E6013. For the E6012 and E6013 classifications the yield point and tensile strength may decrease to a minimum of 65,000 psi for the tensile strength and 53,000 psi for the yield point.

c   For each increase of one percentage point in elongation over the minimum, the yield point or tensile strength, or both, may decrease 1,000 psi to a minimum of 70,000 psi for the tensile strength and 58,000 psi for the yield point.

d   The extreme lowest value and the extreme highest value obtained in the test shall be disregarded. Two of the three remaining values shall be greater than the specified 20 ft/lb energy level; one of the three may be lower but shall not be less than 15 ft/lb. The computed average value of the three remaining values shall be equal to or greater than the 20 ft/lb energy level.

TABLE 5-4. Chemical Requirements of Deposited Weld Metal

AWS Classification	Chemical Composition, max. per cent[a]					
	Manganese	Silicon	Nickel	Chromium	Molybdenum	Vanadium
E7014, E7015, E7016, E7018, E7024, E7028	1.25*	0.90	0.30*	0.20*	0.30*	0.08*
E6010, E6011, E6012, E6013 E6020, E6027	No chemical requirements					

* The sum total of all elements with the asterisk shall not exceed 1.50 per cent.
a For obtaining the chemical composition, DC straight polarity only may be used where DC, both polarities, is specified.

TABLE 5-5. Composition Requirements of Low-Alloy Weld Metal, AWS A5.5-69.

Electrode Classification	Composition (%)								
	C	Mn	P	S	Si	Ni	Cr	Mo	V
Carbon-Molybdenum Steel									
E7010-A1		0.60			0.40				
E7011-A1		0.60			0.40				
E7015-A1		0.90			0.60				
E7016-A1	0.12	0.90	0.03	0.04	0.60	. . .	. . .	0.40 to 0.64	. . .
E7018-A1		0.90			0.80				
E7020-A1		0.60			0.40				
E7027-A1		1.00			0.40				
Chromium-Molybdenum Steel									
E8016-B1	0.12	0.90	0.03	0.04	0.60	. . .	0.40 to 0.65	0.40 to 0.65	. . .
E8018-B1					0.80				
E8015-B2L	0.05	0.90	0.03	0.04	1.00	. . .	1.00 to 1.50	0.40 to 0.65	. . .
E8016-B2	0.12	0.90	0.03	0.04	0.60	. . .	1.00 to 1.50	0.40 to 0.65	. . .
E8018-B2					0.80				
E8018-B2L	0.05	0.90	0.03	0.04	0.80	. . .	1.00 to 1.50	0.40 to 0.65	. . .
E9015-B3L	0.05	0.90	0.30	0.04	1.00	. . .	2.00 to 2.50	0.90 to 1.20	. . .
E9015-B3					0.60				
E9016-B3	0.12	0.90	0.03	0.04	0.60	. . .	2.00 to 2.50	0.90 to 1.20	. . .
E9018-B3					0.80				
E9018-B3L	0.05	0.90	0.03	0.04	0.80	. . .	2.00 to 2.50	0.90 to 1.20	. . .
E8015-B4L	0.05	0.90	0.03	0.04	1.00	. . .	1.75 to 2.25	0.40 to 0.65	. . .
E8016-B5	0.07 to 0.15	0.40 to 0.70	0.03	0.04	0.30 to 0.60	. . .	0.40 to 0.60	1.00 to 1.25	0.05
Nickel Steel									
E8016-C1	0.12	1.20	0.03	0.04	0.60	2.00 to 2.75	. . .	. . .	. . .
E8018-C1					0.80				
E8016-C2	0.12	1.20	0.03	0.04	0.60	3.00 to 3.75	. . .	. . .	. . .
E8018-C2					0.80				
E8016-C3	0.12	0.40 to 1.25	0.030	0.030	0.80	0.80 to 1.10	0.15	0.35	0.05
E8018-C3									
Manganese-Molybdenum Steel									
E9015-D1	0.12	1.25 to 1.75	0.03	0.04	0.60	. . .	. . .	0.25 to 0.45	. . .
E9018-D1					0.80				
E10015-D2					0.60				
E10016-D2	0.15	1.65 to 2.00	0.03	0.04	0.60	. . .	. . .	0.25 to 0.45	. . .
E10018-D2					0.80				
Other Low-Alloy Steel									
EXX10-G EXX11-G EXX13-G EXX15-G EXX16-G EXX18-G E7020-G	. . .	1.00 min	. . .	. . .	0.80 min	0.50 min	0.30 min	0.20 min	0.10 min
E9018-M	0.10	0.60 to 1.25	0.030	0.030	0.80	1.40 to 1.80	0.15	0.35	0.05
E10018-M	0.10	0.75 to 1.70	0.030	0.030	0.60	1.40 to 2.10	0.35	0.25 to 0.50	0.05
E11018-M	0.10	1.30 to 1.80	0.030	0.030	0.60	1.25 to 2.50	0.40	0.30 to 0.55	0.05
E12018-M	0.10	1.30 to 2.25	0.030	0.030	0.60	1.75 to 2.25	0.30 to 1.50	0.30 to 0.55	0.05

Note: Single values shown are maximum percentages except where otherwise specified.

chemical requirements of deposited weld metal are shown in Table 5-4.

LOW-ALLOY STEEL ELECTRODES

AWS specification A5.5-69 prescribes the chemical requirements for low-alloy shielded metal-arc weld metal (see Table 5-5). The same classification system is used as for mild-steel covered electrodes, with the addition of a suffix to indicate the alloy constituency of the deposited weld metal. The electrodes with the suffix "G" need have only one alloy above the minimum to qualify for the chemical requirements. Electrodes with the suffix "M" will meet or be similar to certain military requirements.

CHROMIUM AND CHROMIUM-NICKEL ELECTRODES AND RODS

The corrosion-resistant stainless steels are welded with electrodes or rods that give weld metal matching the corrosion resistance of the base metal. With the shielded metal-arc process, covered electrodes are used; with gas metal-arc processes, the stainless filler metal comes from a bare chromium or chromium-nickel electrode; and with the gas tungsten-arc process, a welding rod supplies the filler metal.

Table 5-6 shows the classification designations for stainless covered electrodes and the chemical composition for deposited weld metal. The deposited weld metal can be expected to have the same corrosion resistance as the base metal of the same composition. However, due to the heat of welding or subsequent heat treatment, metallurgical changes can occur that may affect the corrosion resistance of the weld and adjacent base metal. For this reason, corrosion tests should be made on critical applications.

Mechanical-property requirements for the weld metal deposited from these stainless covered electrodes are shown in Table 5-7.

Chromium and chromium-nickel steel welding rods and bare electrodes are classified on the basis of chemical composition of the filler metal as manufactured. Table 5-8 shows the required chemical composition. Rods and electrodes are available in a variety of diameters, lengths, and spool sizes, as shown in Table 5-9.

SUBMERGED-ARC ELECTRODES AND FLUXES

Whereas there is only one consumable with the shielded metal-arc process (the covered electrode),

TABLE 5-6. AWS A5.4-69 Chemical Requirements for Stainless Covered Electrode Weld Metal.

AWS Classification	Carbon,[a] percent	Chromium, percent	Nickel, percent	Molybdenum, percent	Columbium Plus Tantalum, percent	Manganese, percent	Silicon percent	Phosphorus, percent	Sulfur, percent	Tungsten, percent
E308	0.08	18.0 to 21.0	9.0 to 11.0	. . .	. . .	2.5	0.90	0.04	0.03	. . .
E308L	0.04	18.0 to 21.0	9.0 to 11.0	. . .	. . .	2.5	0.90	0.04	0.03	. . .
E309	0.15	22.0 to 25.0	12.0 to 14.0	. . .	. . .	2.5	0.90	0.04	0.03	. . .
E309Cb	0.12	22.0 to 25.0	12.0 to 14.0	. . .	0.70 to 1.00	2.5	0.90	0.04	0.03	. . .
E309Mo	0.12	22.0 to 25.0	12.0 to 14.0	2.0 to 3.0	. . .	2.5	0.90	0.04	0.03	. . .
E310	0.20	25.0 to 28.0	20.0 to 22.5	. . .	. . .	2.5	0.75	0.03	0.03	. . .
E310Cb	0.12	25.0 to 28.0	20.0 to 22.0	. . .	0.70 to 1.00	2.5	0.75	0.03	0.03	. . .
E310Mo	0.12	25.0 to 28.0	20.0 to 22.0	2.0 to 3.0	. . .	2.5	0.75	0.03	0.03	. . .
E312	0.15	28.0 to 32.0	8.0 to 10.5	. . .	. . .	2.5	0.90	0.04	0.03	. . .
E16-8-2	0.10	14.5 to 16 5	7.5 to 9.5	1.0 to 2.0	. . .	2.5	0.50	0.03	0.03	. . .
E316	0.08	17.0 to 20.u	11.0 to 14.0	2.0 to 2.5	. . .	2.5	0.90	0.04	0.03	. . .
E316L	0.04	17.0 to 20.0	11.0 to 14.0	2.0 to 2.5	. . .	2.5	0.90	0.04	0.03	. . .
E317	0.08	18.0 to 21.0	12.0 to 14.0	3.0 to 4.0	. . .	2.5	0.90	0.04	0.03	. . .
E318	0.08	17.0 to 20.0	11.0 to 14.0	2.0 to 2.5	6 x C, min. to 1.00 max.	2.5	0.90	0.04	0.03	. . .
E320 [e]	0.07	19.0 to 21.0	32.0 to 36.0	2.0 to 3.0	8 x C, min. to 1.00 max.	2.5	0.60	0.04	0.03	. . .
E330	0.25	14.0 to 17.0	33.0 to 37.0	. . .	. . .	2.5	0.90	0.04	0.03	. . .
E347 [b]	0.08	18.0 to 21.0	9.0 to 11.0	. . .	8 x C, min.[c] to 1.00 max.	2.5	0.90	0.04	0.03	. . .
E349 [d]	0.13	18.0 to 21.0	8.0 to 10.0	0.35 to 0.65	0.75 to 1.2	2.5	0.90	0.04	0.03	1.25 to 1.75
E410	0.12	11.0 to 13.5	0.60	. . .	. . .	1.0	0.90	0.04	0.03	. . .
E430	0.10	15.0 to 18.0	0.60	. . .	. . .	1.0	0.90	0.04	0.03	. . .
E502	0.10	4.0 to 6.0	0.40	0.45 to 0.65	. . .	1.0	0.90	0.04	0.03	. . .
E505	0.10	8.0 to 10.5	0.40	0.85 to 1.20	. . .	1.0	0.90	0.04	0.03	. . .
E7Cr	0.10	6.0 to 8.0	0.40	0.45 to 0.65	. . .	1.0	0.90	0.04	0.03	. . .

Note 1. — Analysis shall be made for the elements for which specific values are shown in the table. If, however, the presence of other elements is indicated in the course of routine analysis, further analysis shall be made to determine that the total of these other elements, except iron, is not present in excess of 0.70 percent.

Note 2. — Single values shown are maximum percentages except where otherwise specified.

a Carbon shall be analyzed to the nearest 0.01 percent.
b Chromium shall be 1.9 x Ni, min., when so specified.
c Tantalum shall be 0.10 max., when so specified.
d Titanium shall be 0.15 max.
e Copper shall be 3.0 to 4.0.

TABLE 5-7. AWS A5.4-69 Mechanical-Property Requirements for Stainless Covered Electrode Weld Metal

AWS Classification	Tensile Strength min, psi	Elongation in 2 in., min, percent	Heat Treatment
E308	80,000	35	none
E308L	75,000	35	none
E309	80,000	30	none
E309Cb	80,000	30	none
E309Mo	80,000	30	none
E310	80,000	30	none
E310Cb	80,000	25	none
E310Mo	80,000	30	none
E312	95,000	22	none
E16-8-2	80,000	35	none
E316	75,000	30	none
E316L	70,000	30	none
E317	80,000	30	none
E318	80,000	25	none
E320	80,000	30	none
E330	75,000	25	none
E347	80,000	30	none
E349	100,000	25	none
E410	70,000	20	a
E430	70,000	20	b
E502	60,000	20	a
E505	60,000	20	a
E7Cr	60,000	20	a

a Specimen shall be heated to between 1550 and 1600°F and held for 2 hr., furnace cooled at a rate not exceeding 100°F per hr., to 1100°F, and air-cooled.
b Specimen shall be heated to between 1400 and 1450°F and held for 4 hr., furnace-cooled at a rate not exceeding 100°F per hr. to 1100°F, and air-cooled.

there are two consumables with the submerged-arc process. The bare mild-steel electrodes and the fluxes for submerged-arc welding are covered in AWS A5.17-69.

Submerged-arc electrodes are classified on the basis of chemical composition, as shown in Table 5-10. In the classifying system, the letter "E" indicates an electrode, as in the other classifying systems, but here the similarity stops. The next letter "L," "M," or "H," indicates low, medium, or high-manganese, respectively. The following number or numbers indicate the approximate carbon content in hundredths of one percent. If there is a suffix "K," this indicates a silicon-killed steel.

Fluxes are classified on the basis of the mechanical properties of the weld deposit made with a particular electrode. (See Table 5-11.) The classification designation given to a flux consists of a prefix "F" (indicating a flux) followed by a two-digit number representative of the tensile-strength and impact requirements for test welds made in accordance with the specification. This is followed by a set of numbers corresponding to the classification of the electrode used with the flux. For example, considering F71-EM12K:

The prefix "F" indicates a flux (see Table 5-11). The "71" indicates a minimum tensile strength of 72,000 psi, yield strength of 60,000 psi, elongation of 22%, and impact strength of 20 ft./lb. at 0°F. This flux will produce weld metal that will meet the specified mechanical properties when used with the EM12K electrode (see Table 5-10).

There are two types of submerged-arc fluxes,

TABLE 5-8. AWS A5.9-69 Chemical Requirements for Bare Stainless Welding Rods and Electrodes

AWS Classification	Carbon, percent	Chromium, percent	Nickel, percent	Molybdenum percent	Columbium plus Tantalum, percent	Manganese percent	Silicon, percent	Phosphorus percent	Sulfur, percent	Tungsten, percent
ER308 [a,f]	0.08	19.5 to 22.0	9.0 to 11.0	. . .	. . .	1.0 to 2.5	0.25 to 0.60	0.03	0.03	. . .
ER308L [a,f]	0.03	19.5 to 22.0	9.0 to 11.0	. . .	. . .	1.0 to 2.5	0.25 to 0.60	0.03	0.03	. . .
ER309 [f]	0.12	23.0 to 25.0	12.0 to 14.0	. . .	. . .	1.0 to 2.5	0.25 to 0.60	0.03	0.03	. . .
ER310	0.08 to 0.15	25.0 to 28.0	20.0 to 22.5	. . .	. . .	1.0 to 2.5	0.25 to 0.60	0.03	0.03	. . .
ER312	0.15	28.0 to 32.0	8.0 to 10.5	. . .	. . .	1.0 to 2.5	0.25 to 0.60	0.03	0.03	. . .
ER316 [f]	0.08	18.0 to 20.0	11.0 to 14.0	2.0 to 3.0	. . .	1.0 to 2.5	0.25 to 0.60	0.03	0.03	. . .
ER316L [f]	0.03	18.0 to 20.0	11.0 to 14.0	2.0 to 3.0	. . .	1.0 to 2.5	0.25 to 0.60	0.03	0.03	. . .
ER317	0.08	18.5 to 20.5	13.0 to 15.0	3.0 to 4.0	. . .	1.0 to 2.5	0.25 to 0.60	0.03	0.03	. . .
ER318	0.08	18.0 to 20.0	11.0 to 14.0	2.0 to 3.0	8 x C, min. to 1.0, max.	1.0 to 2.5	0.25 to 0.60	0.03	0.03	. . .
ER320 [e]	0.07	19.0 to 21.0	32.0 to 36.0	2.0 to 3.0	8 x C, min. to 1.0, max.	2.5	0.60	0.04	0.03	. . .
ER321 [c]	0.08	18.5 to 20.5	9.0 to 10.5	0.5 max.	. . .	1.0 to 2.5	0.25 to 0.60	0.03	0.03	. . .
ER347 [a,f]	0.08	19.0 to 21.5	9.0 to 11.0	. . .	10 x C, min. to 1.0, max.	1.0 to 2.5	0.25 to 0.60	0.03	0.03	. . .
ER348 [a]	0.08	19.0 to 21.5	9.0 to 11.0	. . .	10 x C, min. to 1.0, max. [b]	1.0 to 2.5	0.25 to 0.60	0.03	0.03	. . .
ER349 [d]	0.07 to 0.13	19.0 to 21.5	8.0 to 9.5	0.35 to 0.65	1.0 to 1.4	1.0 to 2.5	0.25 to 0.60	0.03	0.03	1.25 to 1.75
ER410	0.12	11.5 to 13.5	0.6	0.6	. . .	0.6	0.50	0.03	0.03	. . .
ER420	0.25 to 0.40	12.0 to 14.0	0.6	. . .	. . .	0.6	0.50	0.03	0.03	. . .
ER430	0.10	15.5 to 17.0	0.6	. . .	. . .	0.6	0.50	0.03	0.03	. . .
ER502	0.10	4.5 to 6.0	0.6	0.45 to 0.65	. . .	0.6	0.25 to 0.60	0.03	0.03	. . .

Note 1. — Analysis shall be made for the elements for which specific values are shown in this table. If, however, the presence of other elements is indicated in the course of routine analysis, further analysis shall be made to determine that the total of these other elements, except iron, is not present in excess of 0.70 percent.

Note 2. — Single values shown are maximum percentages except where otherwise specified.

a   Chromium, min. = 1.9 x Nickel, when so specified.
b   Tantalum, max. = 0.10 percent.
c   Titanium = 9 x C, min. to 1.0, max.
d   Titanium = 0.10 to 0.30.
e   Copper = 3.0 to 4.0.
f   These grades are available in high-silicon classifications which shall have the same chemical-composition requirements as given above with the exception that the silicon content shall be 0.50 to 1.0 percent. These high-silicon classifications shall be designated by the addition of "Si" to the standard classification designations listed above. The fabricator should consider carefully the use of high-silicon filler metals in highly restrained or fully austenitic welds.

TABLE 5-9. AWS A5.9-69 Standard Sizes

Form	Diameter [a], in.
Welding rods in straight lengths	0.045, 1/16 (0.062), 5/64 (0.078), 3/32 (0.094), 1/8 (0.125), 5/32 (0.156), 3/16 (0.188)
Filler metal in coils with or without support	0.045, 1/16 (0.062), 5/64 (0.078), 3/32 (0.094), 7/64 (0.109), 1/8 (0.125), 5/32 (0.156), 3/16 (0.188), 1/4 (0.250)
Filler metal wound on standard 12-in. O.D. spools	0.030, 0.035, 0.045, 1/16 (0.062), 5/64 (0.078), 3/32 (0.094), 7/64 (0.109)
Electrodes wound on lightweight 1-1/2 and 2-1/2-lb 4-in. O.D. spools	0.020, 0.025, 0.030, 0.035, 0.045

a   Electrodes and welding rods of diameters up to and including 0.045 in. shall not vary more than ± 0.001 from the nominal. Diameters greater than 0.045 in. shall not vary more than ± 0.002 from the nominal.

Fused fluxes are manufactured by carefully mixing the raw chemicals and then melting them in an electric furnace. The resulting slag or "melt" is cooled to a glasslike material, ground, and screened to the proper mesh size for welding.

The bonded fluxes are manufactured by first grinding the chemicals, some of which may have already received some processing. The chemicals are then mixed with a bonding agent, typically sodium silicate, and heated in a kiln. The resulting material is ground and sized for welding.

Alloys, such as nickel, chromium, molybdenum, and vanadium, can be added to bonded fluxes and used to produce alloy-steel weld metal with mild-steel electrodes. Also fluxes are available for welding stainless steel. These fluxes are designed to compensate for the loss in chromium that normally occurs during welding.

depending on the method of manufacture. AWS specification A5.17-69 does not differentiate between the two, but both types with the same classification are generally interchangeable with a modification in the welding procedure.

FLUX-CORED ARC-WELDING ELECTRODES

Semiautomatic welding with the self-shielded flux-cored electrode process is widely used in the fabrication of steel products and in the erection of structural steel. To a lesser extent, the self-shielded

TABLE 5-10. AWS A5.17-69 Chemical-Composition Requirements for Submerged-Arc Electrodes

AWS Classification	Chemical Composition, percent						
	Carbon	Manganese	Silicon	Sulfur	Phosphorus	Copper [a]	Total other Elements
Low Manganese Classes							
EL8	0.10	0.30 to 0.55	0.05				
EL8K	0.10	0.30 to 0.55	0.10 to 0.20				
EL12	0.07 to 0.15	0.35 to 0.60	0.05				
Medium Manganese Classes				0.035	0.03	0.15	0.50
EM5K [b]	0.06	0.90 to 1.40	0.40 to 0.70				
EM12	0.07 to 0.15	0.85 to 1.25	0.05				
EM12K	0.07 to 0.15	0.85 to 1.25	0.15 to 0.35				
EM13K	0.07 to 0.19	0.90 to 1.40	0.45 to 0.70				
EM15K	0.12 to 0.20	0.85 to 1.25	0.15 to 0.35				
High Manganese Class							
EH14	0.10 to 0.18	1.75 to 2.25	0.05				

a   The copper limit is independent of any copper or other suitable coating which may be applied to the electrode.

b   This electrode contains 0.05 to 0.15 percent titanium, 0.02 to 0.12 percent zirconium, and 0.05 to 0.15 percent aluminum, which is exclusive of the "Total Other Elements" requirement.

Note 1 — Analysis shall be made for the elements for which specific values are shown in this table. If, however, the presence of other elements is indicated in the course of routine analysis, further analysis shall be made to determine that the total of these other elements is not present in excess of the limits specified for "Total Other Elements" in the last column of the table.

Note 2 — Single values shown are maximum percentages.

**TABLE 5-11. AWS A5.17-69 Mechanical-Property Requirements
for Submerged-Arc Flux Classification**

AWS Flux[a] Classification	Tensile Strength psi	Yield Strength at 0.2% Offset, min, psi	Elongation in 2 in., min, %	Charpy V-Notch Impact Strength[b]
F60-XXXX F61-XXXX[c] F62-XXXX[c] F63-XXXX[c] F64-XXXX[c]	62,000 to 80,000	50,000	22[d]	Not required 20 ft/lb at 0°F 20 ft/lb at −20°F 20 ft/lb at −40°F 20 ft/lb at −60°F
F70-XXXX F71-XXXX[c] F72-XXXX[c] F73-XXXX[c] F74-XXXX[c]	72,000 to 95,000	60,000	22[e]	Not required 20 ft/lb at 0°F 20 ft/lb at −20°F 20 ft/lb at −40°F 20 ft/lb at −60°F

a The letters "XXXX" as used in this table stand for the electrode designations EL8, EL8K, etc. (See Table 5-10).

b The extreme lowest value obtained, together with the extreme highest value obtained, shall be disregarded for this test. Two of the three remaining values shall be greater than the specified 20 ft/lb energy level; one of the three may be lower but shall not be less than 15 ft/lb. The computed average value of the three values shall be equal to or greater than the 20 ft/lb energy level.

c Note that if a specific flux-electrode combination meets the requirements of a given F6X-xxxx classification, this classification also meets the requirements of all lower numbered classifications in the F6X-xxxx series. For instance, a flux-electrode combination meeting the requirements of the F63-xxxx classification, also meets the requirements of the F62-xxxx, F61-xxxx, and F60-xxxx classifications. This applies to the F7X-xxxx series also.

d For each increase of one percentage point in elongation over the minimum, the yield strength or tensile strength, or both, may decrease 1000 psi to a minimum of 60,000 psi for the tensile strength and 48,000 psi for the yield strength.

e For each increase of one percentage point in elongation over the minimum, the yield strength or tensile strength, or both, may decrease 1000 psi to a minimum of 70,000 psi for the tensile strength and 58,000 psi for the yield strength.

flux-cored electrode process is used with fully mechanized equipment in such high-production industries as the automotive. Should the beginning weldor find application for his new skills in a company that fabricates steel, his first introduction to semiautomatic welding is likely to be with the self-shielded flux-cored electrode process. (See Chapter 12).

The electrodes used with this process are long lengths of tubular "wire", fed to the welding gun (or automatic welding head) continuously as the welding progresses. The electrode is usually packaged in 60-pound or smaller coils for semiautomatic welding or in 300 or 600-pound reels or drums for high-production full-automatic welding.

The flux-cored electrode contains within its tubular construction all the ingredients for shielding the arc and weld pool and fluxing, deoxidizing, and conditioning the molten metal. In its appearance, the tubular electrode looks like "wire", and it is called wire in industry. Essentially, the flux-cored electrode is a "long length of stick electrode with the covering put inside the filler metal". That is exactly what the developers had in mind — turning the stick electrode "outside-in" — so the stick-electrode process could be mechanized.

Flux-cored electrodes are produced in one technique by starting with a flat strip, passing it through forming rolls, which curve the strip into a trough, filling the trough with the desired powdered ingredients, closing the trough to form a flux-filled steel tube, and, through successive drawing dies, drawing the tube down to the desired diameter. The wires are cleaned and wound on reels. Wire diameters vary from 1/16 to 5/32 inch.

Specifications for flux-cored arc welding electrodes are given in AWS A5.20-69. Electrodes are classified on the basis of single or multiple-pass operation, chemical composition of the deposited weld metal, mechanical properties and whether or not carbon dioxide is required as a separate shielding gas. Table 5-12 and 5-13 show the minimum mechanical-property requirements.

The classification system follows as closely as possible the other AWS systems for classifying filler metal. For example, with E70T-1:

E denotes "electrode".

70 tells that the tensile strength is 70,000 psi.

T indicates that the electrode is tubular with flux in the tube.

TABLE 5-12. AWS A5.20-69 Mechanical-Property Requirements
for Flux-Cored Arc-Welding Weld Metal[a]

AWS Classification	Shielding Gas [b]	Current and Polarity [c]	Tensile Strength min.[f], psi	Yield Strength at 0.2% Offset, min.[f], psi	Elongation in 2 inches, min.[f], psi
E60T-7	None	DC, straight polarity	67,000	55,000	22
E60T-8	None		62,000	50,000	22
E70T-1	CO$_2$	DC	72,000	60,000	22
E70T-2	CO$_2$		72,000	Not required	
E70T-3	None		72,000	Not required	
E70T-4	None	reverse	72,000	60,000	22
E70T-5[g]	CO$_2$ None	polarity	72,000	60,000	22
E70T-6	None		72,000	60,000	22
E70T-G	not spec.	not spec.	72,000 [d]	Not required	
			72,000 [e]	60,000 [e]	22 [e]

a   As-welded mechanical properties.
b   Shielding gases are designated as follows:
    CO$_2$ = carbon dioxide
    None = no separate shielding gas
c   Reverse polarity means electrode is positive; straight polarity means electrode is negative.
d   Requirement for single-pass electrodes.
e   Requirement for multiple-pass electrodes.
f   For each increase of one percentage point in elongation over the minimum, the minimum required yield strength or the tensile strength, or both, may decrease 1000 psi, for a maximum reduction of 2000 psi in either the required minimum yield strength or the tensile strength, or both.
g   Where CO$_2$ and None are indicated as the shielding gases for a given classification, chemical analysis pads and test assemblies shall be prepared using both CO$_2$ and no separate shielding gas.

1   denotes a particular classification, based on the chemical analysis and mechanical properties of the deposited weld metal, the shielding gas used (if any), and the adaptability of the electrode for single or multiple-pass operations.

The AWS electrode types include the following:

E60T-7 electrodes are self-shielding and can be used for single and multiple-pass welds. The weld deposits have high crack resistance.

TABLE 5-13. AWS A5.18-69 Impact-Property Requirements for Gas Metal-Arc Welding Weld Metal

AWS Classification	Minimum V-Notch Impact Requirement [a]
E70S-2 E70S-6 E70S-1B E70U-1	20 ft/lb at −20°F
E70S-3	20 ft/lb at 0°F
E70S-1, E70S-4, E70S-5, E70S-G, E70S-GB	Not required

a   The extreme lowest value obtained, together with the extreme highest value obtained, shall be disregarded for this test. Two of the three remaining values shall be greater than the specified 20 ft/lb energy level; one of the three may be lower but shall not be less than 15 ft/lb. The computed average value of the three values shall be equal to or greater than the 20 ft/lb energy level.

E60T-8 electrodes are self-shielding and can be used for single and multiple-pass applications in the flat and horizontal positions. The weld deposits have high crack resistance and good notch toughness at 0°F.

E70T-1 electrodes are designed to be used with CO$_2$ shielding gas for making single and multiple-pass welds in the flat position and for horizontal fillets.

E70T-2 electrodes are designed to be used with CO$_2$ shielding gas and are intended primarily for single-pass welds in the flat position and for horizontal fillets. These electrodes will tolerate a greater amount of surface contamination than the E70T-1 grade.

E70T-3 electrodes are self-shielding and are characterized by their fast-follow characteristics. They are intended primarily for depositing single-pass, high-speed welds in the flat and horizontal positions on sheet steel and light plate. They should not be used on heavy sections or for multiple-pass welding.

E70T-4 electrodes are self-shielding and have fast-fill characteristics. They can be used for single and multiple-pass applications in the flat and horizontal positions. These electrodes are characterized by a high depositon rate, low spatter loss, flat to convex bead shape, and easily removed slag. Weld deposits have high crack resistance, even in restrained joints and in plate with high sulfur or carbon content. The weld metal is low in hydrogen, and X-ray quality is achieved with standard procedures. One of the practical advantages of these electrodes is their tolerance of poor fitup.

E70T-5 electrodes may be used with or without external gas and are primarily designed for flat fillet or groove welds. Horizontal fillet welds can be made satisfactorily, but at lower deposition rates than obtainable with flat groove welds. These electrodes can be used in single-pass applications with minimal surface preparation. Operating characteristics of E70T-5 electrodes include globular transfer, low penetration, slightly convex bead configuration, and a thin, easily removed slag. The weld deposit has good notch toughness at −20°F.

E70T-6 electrodes are similar to those of the E70T-5 classification. Chemical composition requirements are slightly different, however, because the electrodes are designed for use without externally applied gas.

E70T-G electrodes are those flux-cored electrodes that are not included in the preceding classifications. The electrode supplier must be consulted for the characteristics and proper use of these electrodes. They may be designed for multiple-pass work or limited to single-pass applications. E70T-G electrodes are not required to meet chemical, radiographic, bend-test, or impact requirements. They are, however, required to meet tension-test requirements and all other requirements of this classification.

SHIELDING GASES

Shielding gases are required with the metal inert-gas (MIG) and tungsten inert-gas (TIG) welding processes. The primary purpose of a shielding gas is to protect the molten weld metal from contamination by the oxygen and nitrogen in air. The factors, in addition to cost, that affect the suitability of a gas include the influence of the gas on the arcing and metal-transfer characteristics during welding, weld penetration, width of fusion and surface shape, welding speed, and the tendency to undercut. Among the inert gases — helium, argon, neon, krypton, and xenon — the only ones plentiful enough for practical use in welding are helium and argon. These gases provide satisfactory shielding for the more reactive metals, such as aluminum, magnesium, beryllium, columbium, tantalum, titanium, and zirconium.

Although pure inert gases protect metal at any temperature from reaction with constituents of the air, they are not suitable for all welding applications. Controlled quantities of reactive gases mixed with inert gases improve the arc action and metal-transfer characteristics when welding the steels, but such mixtures are not used for the reactive metals.

Oxygen, nitrogen, and carbon dioxide are reactive gases. With the exception of carbon dioxide, these gases are not generally used alone for arc shielding. Carbon dioxide can be used alone or mixed with an inert gas for welding many carbon and low-alloy steels. Oxygen is used in small quantities with one of the inert gases — usually argon. Nitrogen is occasionally used alone, but is usually mixed with argon, as a shielding gas to weld copper. The most extensive use of nitrogen is in Europe, where helium is relatively unavailable.

ARGON AND HELIUM AS SHIELDING GASES

The inert natures of argon and helium (chemically nonreactive) are not the only characteristic that makes them suitable for gas shielding. Other characteristics are important and are deciding factors in the choice of gas for TIG or MIG welding with specific materials. For a given arc length and current, arc voltage with helium is higher than with argon. Because more heat is produced with helium than with argon, helium is more effective for welding thick materials, particularly high-conductivity metals such as copper and aluminum alloys. Argon is more suitable for welding thin materials and those with lower heat conductivity, especially in welding positions other than flat.

The heavier a gas, the more effective it is for arc shielding. Helium is very light; argon is about 10 times heavier than helium and about 30% heavier than air. When argon is discharged from the welding nozzle it forms a protective blanket over the weld area, while helium rises and disperses rapidly. For this reason, higher flow rates are generally required with helium (or with mixtures high in helium) than with argon shielding.

Shape of a weld bead and penetration pattern are determined, to a large extent, by metal-transfer characteristics which, in turn, are affected by the shielding gas used.

Metal is generally deposited either by spray transfer or by globular transfer. Spray transfer (usually the more desirable) produces relatively deep penetration at the center of the bead and shallow penetration at the edges; globular transfer produces a broader and shallower penetration patter throughout the bead.

Argon generally promotes more spray transfer than helium and at lower current levels. But even with argon shielding, spray transfer cannot always be achieved at usable current levels — one of the problems in welding ferrous metals by the gas

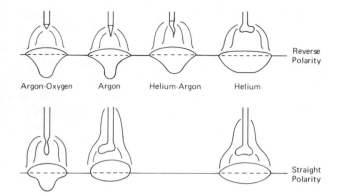

Fig. 5-2. Electrode tip shape, bead contour, and penetration patterns for various shielding gases.

metal-arc process.

The physics of metal transfer across an arc is not completely understood. In an argon atmosphere with DCRP, the size of the metal droplet crossing the arc decreases as the current increases. At a critical level of current the mode of transfer changes abruptly. The tip of the electrode becomes pointed, metal transfers from the electrode to the work in a fine spray, the arc becomes very stable, and there is little or no spatter. Fig. 5-2 illustrates the appearance of electrode tips in various shielding gases. A degree of spray transfer is possible with 20% argon and 80% helium. Here the argon has predominating effect because of its higher density.

INERT GASES WITH REACTIVE GAS ADDITIONS

Improved metal transfer, a more stable arc, and less spatter result from the addition of oxygen or carbon dioxide to an inert shielding gas. These additions when welding carbon and low-alloy steels also promote wetting and flow of weld metal, thus reducing or eliminating undercut. Effects on penetration and bead shape of oxygen additions are illustrated in Fig. 5-2.

Noticeable changes in arc action and metal-transfer characteristics in gas metal-arc welding result from addition of as little as 0.5% oxygen or carbon dioxide to argon. However, 1 to 5% oxygen is generally added. Oxygen or carbon dioxide are seldom added to helium or argon-helium mixtures.

Addition of 5% oxygen or 10 to 25% carbon dioxide to argon produces a significant pinch effect with a DC, straight-polarity arc. The filler wire tapers, the metal transfers in the form of a fast-moving stream of droplets, and the penetration pattern approaches that of reverse polarity. At the same time, melt-off rate is reduced considerably. With pure argon, melt-off rate with straight polarity is almost double that with reverse polarity.

However, most MIG welding with an inert gas or carbon dioxide is done with DCRP. Mixtures of 5% oxygen or 25% carbon dioxide with argon are commercially available.

Because of oxidizing effects, addition of oxygen or carbon dioxide to argon may cause porosity in some ferrous metals, as well as loss of such alloying elements as chromium, vanadium, aluminum, titanium, manganese, and silicon. Consequently, filler wires used with oxygen-containing shielding gas require additions of deoxidizers to counteract the effects of the oxygen.

CARBON DIOXIDE AS A SHIELDING GAS

Carbon dioxide may be used as a shielding gas for the MIG welding of carbon and low alloy steels, but since it is a reactive gas the electrodes used must contain sufficient deoxidizers to counteract the effects of oxygen. Recently, stainless steel electrodes with high silicon have been developed for use with argon-25% carbon dioxide mixtures.

The low cost of carbon dioxide makes its use as a shielding gas very attractive. With the development of better electrodes, sound weld deposits with good mechanical properties can be made.

Two types of metal transfer occur with carbon dioxide shielding gas — globular and short-circuiting. The spray transfer experienced with argon or argon-oxygen mixture does not occur. Globular transfer produces a harsh arc with excessive spatter. By control of welding conditions, the short-circuiting type of metal transfer is promoted.

To promote the short-circuiting type of transfer when welding carbon and low-alloy steels, argon is often used as the dominant gas in a mixture, with the carbon dioxide content cut to 20 to 30%. Other mixtures with higher percentages of carbon dioxide also give short-circuiting transfer, with its advantages of low penetration, all-position capability, and the ability to handle poor fitup on light-gage material without burnthrough.

In the short-circuiting type of transfer, a globule of molten metal collects on the end of the electrode. The electrode is being fed toward the work and, before the globule detaches from the end of the electrode, it contacts the molten crater and forms a short circuit. The high current due to the short circuit blasts the globule from the electrode into the crater. An arc then forms in the gap between the crater and the tip of the electrode, which starts another globule forming on the tip of the electrode. This cycle of metal transfer is repeated about 20 to 200 times per second.

SHIELDING GASES FOR TIG WELDING

Either argon, helium, or a mixture of the two is

TABLE 5-14. SHIELDING GASES AND GAS MIXTURES FOR GAS METAL-ARC WELDING

Shielding Gas	Chemical Behavior	Uses, Remarks
Argon	Inert	For welding most metals, except steel
Helium	Inert	Al and Cu alloys, for greater heat and to minimize porosity
A and He (20-80 to 50-50%)	Inert	Al and Cu alloys, for greater heat input and to minimize porosity. Quieter, more stable arc than with He alone.
A and Cl (trace Cl)	Essentially Inert	Al alloys, to minimize porosity
N_2	Reducing	On Cu, permits very powerful arc; used mostly in Europe.
A + 25-30% N_2	Reducing	On Cu, powerful but smoother operating, more readily controlled arc than N_2 alone; used mostly in Europe.
A + 1-2% O_2	Oxidizing	Stainless and alloy steels, also for some deoxidized copper alloys
A + 3-5% O_2	Oxidizing	Plain carbon, alloy, and stainless steels; requires deoxidized electrode
A + 20-30% CO_2	Oxidizing	Various steels; used principally with short-circuiting arc
A + 5% O_2 + 15% CO_2	Oxidizing	Various steels; requires deoxidized wire; used chiefly in Europe
CO_2	Oxidizing	Plain-carbon and low-alloy steels; deoxidized electrode is essential

TABLE 5-15. AWS A5.18-69 Mechanical-Property Requirements for Gas Metal-Arc Weld Metal[a]

AWS Classification	Shielding Gas[b]	Current and Polarity [c]	Tensile Strength min., psi	Yield Strength at 0.2% Offset, min.	Elongation in 2 inches, min. %
GROUP A — MILD STEEL ELECTRODES					
E70S-1	AO	DC reverse polarity	72,000 [e,f]	60,000[e,f]	22 [e,f]
E70S-2 E70S-3	AO & CO_2[d]				
E70S-4 E70S-5 E70S-6	CO_2				
E70S-G	not spec.	not spec.			
GROUP B — LOW-ALLOY STEEL ELECTRODES					
E70S-1B E70S-GB	CO_2 not spec.	DC, reverse polarity not spec.	72,000 [e,f] 72,000 [e,f]	60,000 [e,f] 60,000 [e,f]	17 [e,f] 22 [e,f]
GROUP C — EMISSIVE ELECTRODE					
E70U-1	AO & A [d]	DC, straight polarity	72,000 [e]	60,000 [e]	22 [e]

a As-welded mechanical properties
b Shielding gases are designated as follows:
     AO   = argon, plus 1 to 5 percent oxygen
     CO_2 = carbon dioxide
     A   = argon
c Reverse polarity means electrode is positive; straight polarity means electrode is negative.
d Where two gases are listed as interchangeable (that is, AO and CO_2 and AO & A) for classification of a specific electrode, the classification tests may be conducted using either gas.
e Mechanical properties as determined from an all-weld-metal tension-test specimen.
f For each increase of one percentage point in elongation over the minimum, the yield strength or tensile strength, or both, may decrease 1,000 psi to a minimum of 70,000 psi for the tensile strength and 58,000 psi for the yield strength.

TABLE 5-16. AWS A5.18-69 Impact-Property Requirements for Gas Metal-Arc Weld Metal

AWS Classification	Minimum V-Notch Impact Requirement [a]
E70T-5	20 ft/lb at −20°F
E60T-8 E70T-1 E70T-6	20 ft/lb at 0°F
E60T-7 E70T-2 E70T-3 E70T-4 E70T-G	Not required

a The extreme lowest value obtained, together with the extreme highest value obtained, shall be disregarded for this test. Two of the three remaining values shall be greater than the specified 20 ft/lb energy level; one of the three may be lower but shall not be less than 15 ft/lb. The computed average value of the three values shall be equal to or greater than the 20 ft/lb energy level.

commonly used in gas tungsten-arc welding. Argon provides the advantage of easier arc starting, smoother arc action, better cleaning action for the AC welding of aluminum and magnesium, and superior resistance to draft. In addition, argon costs less than helium and requires a lower arc voltage for comparable currents and arc lengths.

In the manual welding of thin material, argon is recommended because its lower arc-voltage characteristic reduces the tendency for burnthrough. In vertical or overhead welding, this same characteristic reduces the tendency for the metal to sag and run.

Helium's higher arc-voltage characteristic is desirable when welding thick material or metals with high heat conductivity and for the high-speed mechanized welding of stainless-steel tubing. Mixtures of argon and helium are used to balance the arc characteristics.

Mixtures of argon or helium with hydrogen provide higher arc voltage and heat in the welding region than helium alone. This reactive gas, however, can damage many metals and alloys, including aluminum, copper, and magnesium-base materials. Mixtures of inert gas with hydrogen can be used in welding only a few materials, such as certain stainless steels and nickel alloys.

The rate at which some metals are joined by gas tungsten-arc welding and the quality of the resulting welds are significantly affected by gas purity. The reactive metals particularly can be degraded by gas impurities of a few hundredths of one percent. Copper, carbon steel, and stainless steels can tolerate much higher levels of impurities with no adverse effects.

Purity of commercially available argon and helium averages over 99.95%, and in some cases exceeds 99.995%. Impurities in shielding gases usually consist of water vapor, oil, oxygen, or nitrogen — usually from sources other than the original gas supply. Water vapor or atmospheric gases can diffuse through the hose lines, or contaminants can be drawn in at leaks in the lines. Tubing that is not susceptible to gas diffusion should be used to supply shielding gas for welding of materials that are sensitive to impurities.

SHIELDING GASES FOR MIG WELDING

The most commonly used gases for gas metal-arc welding are given in Table 5-14.

Initially, only argon, helium, or a mixture of these inert gases were used for gas metal-arc welding. Other gases were not considered, because the primary use of the gas metal-arc process was for welding the more reactive metals, such as aluminum and magnesium, which require an inert gas shield. Today, however, the process is used for welding many metals that do not require inert-gas shielding.

Carbon dioxide shielding is widely used for MIG welding of carbon and low-alloy steels in conjunction with a deoxidized electrode. Its advantage over the inert gases is its lower cost.

MILD-STEEL ELECTRODES FOR GAS METAL-ARC WELDING

AWS A5.18-69 prescribes requirements for mild-steel solid electrodes for gas metal-arc welding of mild and low-alloy steel. The electrodes are classified on the basis of their chemical composition and the as-welded mechanical properties of the deposited weld metal (see Tables 5-15 and 5-16). For the chemical-composition requirements of the deposited weld metal, see Table 5-17.

Table 5-17 includes a Group B classification, entitled "Low-Alloy Steel Electrodes." The alloy additions here do not meet the accepted definitions of mild steel. The basis for including this classification in a mild-steel specification is that the alloy additions are for deoxidation and usability improvement and not for the purpose of upgrading the mechanical properties.

The classification system follows as closely as possible the pattern used in other AWS filler-metal specifications. However, the inherent nature of the process requires some changes in the system to better classify the electrodes. For example, consider E70S-1 and E70U-1. The prefix E designates an electrode. The number 70 refers to the required minimum as-welded tensile strength in 1000 psi. The letter S designates a bare, solid electrode. The letter U designates an emissive-coated solid electrode. The suffix number 1 indicates a particular as-manufactured chemical composition. The low-alloy group (Group B) has an additional suffix "B".

The characteristics of the steel electrode types are as follows:

E70S-1 — Low silicon content. May be used with CO_2 shielding gas when weld quality is not critical.

E70S-2 — Multiple deoxidized electrodes that produce sound welds in semikilled and rimmed steels as well as killed steels. Can be used to advantage on steels that have a rusty or dirty surface. Excellent for use with the short-circuiting-type transfer. May be used with various shielding gases.

E70S-3 — Similar to E70S-1 but with a high silicon content. Used primarily for single-pass welds. May be used with various shielding gases.

E70S-4 — Higher silicon content than E70S-3. Weld deposits have even higher tensile strength.

E70S-5 — These electrodes contain aluminum in addition to manganese and silicon for deoxidizers. Applicable to a wide variety of steels with CO_2 gas and high welding currents.

E70S-6 — Used with CO_2 gas shielding, these electrodes produce welds that meet the highest impact requirements.

E70S-G — A special classification of solid electrodes that are not required to meet chemical or impact requirements. Users should consult their electrode supplier for characteristics.

E70S1B — For single or multiple-pass welding of mild and low-alloy steel. Chemistry is designed to control porosity with CO_2 and give good radiographic quality welds in difficult-to-weld mild and

TABLE 5-17. AWS A5.18-69 Chemical-Composition Requirements for Gas Metal-Arc Electrodes

AWS Classification	Chemical Composition, percent											
	Carbon	Manganese	Silicon	Phosphorus	Sulfur	Nickel [a]	Chromium [a]	Molybdenum [a]	Vanadium [a]	Titanium	Zirconium	Aluminum
GROUP A — MILD STEEL ELECTRODES												
E70S-1	0.07 to 0.19		0.30 to 0.50									
E70S-2	0.06		0.40 to 0.70							0.05 to 0.15	0.02 to 0.12	0.05 to 0.15
E70S-3	0.06 to 0.15	0.90 to 1.40	0.45 to 0.70	0.025	0.035							
E70S-4	0.07 to 0.15		0.65 to 0.85									
E70S-5	0.07 to 0.19		0.30 to 0.60									0.50 to 0.90
E70S-6	0.07 to 0.15	1.40 to 1.85	0.80 to 1.15									
E70S-G	no chemical requirements [b]											
GROUP B — LOW-ALLOY STEEL ELECTRODES												
E70S-1B	0.07 to 0.12	1.60 to 2.10	0.50 to 0.80	0.025	0.035	0.15		0.40 to 0.60				
E70S-GB	no chemical requirements											
GROUP C — EMISSIVE ELECTRODE												
E70U-1	0.07 to 0.15	0.80 to 1.40	0.15 to 0.35	0.025	0.035							

Note — Single values shown are maximums.
a   For Groups A and C these elements may be present but are not intentionally added.
b   For this classification there are no chemical requirements for the elements listed with the exception that there shall be no intentional addition of Ni, Cr, Mo or V.

TABLE 5-18. AWS A5.9-69 Chemical Requirements for Bare Stainless Welding Rods and Electrodes

AWS Classification	Carbon, percent	Chromium, percent	Nickel, percent	Molybdenum percent	Columbium plus Tantalum, percent	Manganese percent	Silicon, percent	Phosphorus percent	Sulfur, percent	Tungsten, percent
ER308 [a,f]	0.08	19.5 to 22.0	9.0 to 11.0	. . .	. . .	1.0 to 2.5	0.25 to 0.60	0.03	0.03	. . .
ER308L [a,f]	0.03	19.5 to 22.0	9.0 to 11.0	. . .	. . .	1.0 to 2.5	0.25 to 0.60	0.03	0.03	. . .
ER309 [f]	0.12	23.0 to 25.0	12.0 to 14.0	. . .	. . .	1.0 to 2.5	0.25 to 0.60	0.03	0.03	. . .
ER310	0.08 to 0.15	25.0 to 28.0	20.0 to 22.5	. . .	. . .	1.0 to 2.5	0.25 to 0.60	0.03	0.03	. . .
ER312	0.15	28.0 to 32.0	8.0 to 10.5	. . .	. . .	1.0 to 2.5	0.25 to 0.60	0.03	0.03	. . .
ER316 [f]	0.08	18.0 to 20.0	11.0 to 14.0	2.0 to 3.0	. . .	1.0 to 2.5	0.25 to 0.60	0.03	0.03	. . .
ER316L [f]	0.03	18.0 to 20.0	11.0 to 14.0	2.0 to 3.0	. . .	1.0 to 2.5	0.25 to 0.60	0.03	0.03	. . .
ER317	0.08	18.5 to 20.5	13.0 to 15.0	3.0 to 4.0	. . .	1.0 to 2.5	0.25 to 0.60	0.03	0.03	. . .
ER318	0.08	18.0 to 20.0	11.0 to 14.0	2.0 to 3.0	8 x C, min. to 1.0, max.	1.0 to 2.5	0.25 to 0.60	0.03	0.03	. . .
ER320 [e]	0.07	19.0 to 21.0	32.0 to 36.0	2.0 to 3.0	8 x C, min. to 1.0, max.	2.5	0.60	0.04	0.03	. . .
ER321 [c]	0.08	18.5 to 20.5	9.0 to 10.5	0.5 max.	. . .	1.0 to 2.5	0.25 to 0.60	0.03	0.03	. . .
ER347 [a,f]	0.08	19.0 to 21.5	9.0 to 11.0	. . .	10 x C, min. to 1.0, max.	1.0 to 2.5	0.25 to 0.60	0.03	0.03	. . .
ER348 [a]	0.08	19.0 to 21.5	9.0 to 11.0	. . .	10 x C, min. to 1.0, max.[b]	1.0 to 2.5	0.25 to 0.60	0.03	0.03	. . .
ER349 [d]	0.07 to 0.13	19.0 to 21.5	8.0 to 9.5	0.35 to 0.65	1.0 to 1.4	1.0 to 2.5	0.25 to 0.60	0.03	0.03	1.25 to 1.75
ER410	0.12	11.5 to 13.5	0.6	0.6	. . .	0.6	0.50	0.03	0.03	. . .
ER420	0.25 to 0.40	12.0 to 14.0	0.6	. . .	. . .	0.6	0.50	0.03	0.03	. . .
ER430	0.10	15.5 to 17.0	0.6	. . .	. . .	0.6	0.50	0.03	0.03	. . .
ER502	0.10	4.5 to 6.0	0.6	0.45 to 0.65	. . .	0.6	0.25 to 0.60	0.03	0.03	. . .

Note 1. — Analysis shall be made for the elements for which specific values are shown in this table. If, however, the presence of other elements is indicated in the course of routine analysis, further analysis shall be made to determine that the total of these other elements, except iron, is not present in excess of 0.70 percent.

Note 2. — Single values shown are maximum percentages except where otherwise specified.

a   Chromium, min. = 1.9 x Nickel, when so specified.
b   Tantalum, max. = 0.10 percent.
c   Titanium = 9 x C, min. to 1.0, max.
d   Titanium = 0.10 to 0.30.
e   Copper = 3.0 to 4.0.
f   These grades are available in high-silicon classifications which shall have the same chemical-composition requirements as given above with the exception that the silicon content shall be 0.50 to 1.0 percent. These high-silicon classifications shall be designated by the addition of "Si" to the standard classification designations listed above. The fabricator should consider carefully the use of high-silicon filler metals in highly restrained or fully austenitic welds.

TABLE 5-19. AWS A5.10-69 Chemical Requirement for Bare Welding Rods and Electrodes for Aluminum and Aluminum Alloys

AWS Classification	Silicon, percent	Iron, percent	Copper percent	Manganese, percent	Magnesium, percent	Chromium, percent	Nickel, percent	Zinc, percent	Titanium, percent	Other Elements,[g] percent Each	Other Elements,[g] percent Total	Aluminum, percent
ER1100	b	b	0.05-0.20	0.05	. . .	. . .	. . .	0.10	. . .	0.05	0.15	99.00 min.[h]
ER1260	c	c	0.04	0.01	. . .	. . .	. . .	. . .	. . .	0.03	. . .	99.60 min.[h]
ER2319 [i]	0.20	0.30	5.8-6.8	0.20-0.40	0.02	. . .	. . .	0.10	0.10-0.20	0.05	0.15	remainder
ER4145	9.3-10.7	0.8	3.3-4.7	0.15	0.15	0.15	. . .	0.20	. . .	0.05	0.15	remainder
ER4043	4.5-6.0	0.8	0.30	0.05	0.05	. . .	. . .	0.10	0.20	0.05	0.15	remainder
ER4047	11.0-13.0	0.8	0.30	0.15	0.10	. . .	. . .	0.20	. . .	0.05	0.15	remainder
ER5039	0.10	0.40	0.03	0.30-0.50	3.3-4.3	0.10-0.20	. . .	2.4-3.2	0.10	0.05	0.10	remainder
ER5554	c	c	0.10	0.50-1.0	2.4-3.0	0.05-0.20	. . .	0.25	0.05-0.20	0.05	0.15	remainder
ER5654 [j]	d	d	0.05	0.01	3.1-3.9	0.15-0.35	. . .	0.20	0.05-0.15	0.05	0.15	remainder
ER5356	e	e	0.10	0.05-0.20	4.5-5.5	0.05-0.20	. . .	0.10	0.06-0.20	0.05	0.15	remainder
ER5556	c	c	0.10	0.50-1.0	4.7-5.5	0.05-0.20	. . .	0.25	0.05-0.20	0.05	0.15	remainder
ER5183	0.40	0.40	0.10	0.50-1.0	4.3-5.2	0.05-0.25	. . .	0.25	0.15	0.05	0.15	remainder
R-C4A [a]	1.5	1.0	4.0-5.0	0.35	0.03	. . .	. . .	0.35	0.25	0.05	0.15	remainder
R-CN42A [a]	0.7	1.0	3.5-4.5	0.35	1.2-1.8	0.25	1.7-2.3	0.35	0.25	0.05	0.15	remainder
R-SC51A [a]	4.5-5.5	0.8 [f]	1.0-1.5	0.50 [f]	0.40-0.60	0.25	. . .	0.35	0.25	0.05	0.15	remainder
R-SG70A [a]	6.5-7.5	0.6	0.25	0.35	0.20-0.40	. . .	. . .	0.35	0.25	0.05	0.15	remainder

Note 1 — Single values shown are maximum percentages, except where a minimum is specified.

Note 2 — For purposes of determining conformance to these limits, an observed value or a calculated value obtained from analysis shall be rounded off to the nearest unit in the last righthand place of figures used in expressing the specified limit, in accordance with Recommended Practices for Designating Significant Places in Specified Limiting Values (ASTM Designation: E29). 1968 Book of ASTM Standards, Part 32.

Note 3 — Analysis shall be made for the elements for which specific limits are shown. If, however, the presence of other elements is suspected, or indicated in the course of routine analysis, further analysis shall be made to determine that these other elements are not in excess of the limits specified for "other elements."

a   For repair of castings.
b   Silicon plus iron shall not exceed 1.0 percent.
c   Silicon plus iron shall not exceed 0.40 percent.
d   Silicon plus iron shall not exceed 0.45 percent.
e   Silicon plus iron shall not exceed 0.50 percent.
f   If iron exceeds 0.45 percent, manganese should be present in an amount equal to one half the iron.
g   Beryllium shall not exceed 0.0008 percent.
h   The aluminum content is the difference between 100.00 percent and the sum of all other metallic elements present in amounts of 0.010 percent or more each, expressed to the second decimal.
i   Vanadium content shall be 0.05-0.15 percent. Zirconium content shall be 0.10-0.25 percent.
j   Effective with the 1969 revision, ER5654 has replaced filler metal composition ER5154, ER5254, and ER5652.

low-alloy steels. Can also be used for out-of-position welds.

E70S-GB — These electrodes have alloy additions for deoxidation and usability improvement. Consult the supplier for characteristics and intended use.

E70U-1 — Gives spray-type transfer using argon gas and DC straight polarity. Used sparingly because of the wide variety of other types.

STAINLESS BARE ELECTRODES AND RODS

Corrosion-resisting chromium and chromium-nickel steel (stainless-steel) welding rods are used with the gas tungsten-arc process, and bare electrodes are used with submerged-arc and gas metal-arc welding processes. Both rods and electrodes are classified on the basis of the chemical composition of the filler metal as manufactured. (See Table 5-18.) The specification also provides for a composite rod or electrode. In this case, the chemical analysis is made on a pad of undiluted metal deposited from the filler metal by melting with the TIG process, using argon shielding gas.

ALUMINUM AND ALUMINUM-ALLOY BARE ELECTRODES AND RODS

Aluminum and aluminum-alloy welding rods and bare electrodes are made in accordance with AWS A5.10-69 specifications. These filler metals are classified on the basis of their chemical composition as-manufactured and their useability — while not consumed in such quantities as the mild-steel or the low-alloy steel filler metals, they nevertheless play an important role in industry.

The chemical requirments for welding rods and bare electrodes are shown in Table 5-19.

The specification classifies the materials as "R" or "E". The letter R indicates a welding rod and E indicates an electrode. ER indicates use as either an electrode or filler-metal rod. As Table 5-19 shows, there are 16 classifications of these filler materials. Types ER5356, ER4043 and ER5183 can be used for the widest variety of welding applications. Standard sizes of rods and wires range from 1/16 to 1/4-inch in diameter.

Weldability Of Carbon And Low-Alloy Steels

After his introduction to the basic principles of arc welding, power sources and equipment, and the materials consumed by each process, the student should know something about the weldability of metals and the problems likely to be encountered before exposure to the details of the specific arc-welding processes. On the assumption that the beginning weldor will work primarily with the carbon and low-alloy steels, this chapter will deal with such steels, their weldability, and the problem of weld cracking. The following Chapter 7 will discuss weld joint design, welding symbols, and welding costs, and Chapter 8 will take up other problems encountered in arc welding, such as distortion and arc blow. By this sequence, it is hoped that the student will have adequate background for understanding the application, capabilities, and limitations of the various arc-welding processes before they are detailed in subsequent chapters.

The reader of this book will find the slant heavy on the welding of carbon steels and lean on discussion of the welding of other metals. This is not only a needed editorial technique for minimizing the length of text, but also a requisite for giving the student proper perspective. In all probability, the beginning weldor will start his career with the welding of mild steels. This is where the greatest opportunities lie — and most weldors progress from simple stick-electrode welding of carbon steels to more exotic welding processes with specialty steels and nonferrous metals. However, becoming a competent weldor — capable of, say, using both stick-electrode and the various semiautomatic processes in the welding of structural steel — can be a goal in itself and one with exceptional career opportunities.

Carbon and low-alloy steels are the work-horse materials for construction and transportation equipment and for industrial and consumer products of many types. They comprise over 90% of total steel production, and more carbon steel is used in product manufacture than all other metals combined.

Most steels can be welded, but satisfactory joints cannot be produced in all grades with equal ease. A metal is considered to have good weldability if it can be welded without excessive difficulty or the need for special and costly procedures, and the weld joints are equal in all necessary respects to a similar piece of solid metal. Weldability varies with the grade, chemistry, and mechanical properties of the steel, and, when weld joining is to be a major factor in the attachment of steel parts, weldability should be given proper attention in specifying and ordering materials for the job.

Several methods are used to identify and specify steels. These are based on chemistry, on mechanical properties, on an ability to meet a standard specification or industry-accepted practice, or on an ability to be fabricated into a certain type of product.

SPECIFICATION BY CHEMISTRY

A desired composition can be produced in one of three ways: to a maximum limit, to a minimum limit, or to an acceptable range.

For economical, high-speed welding of carbon-steel plate, the composition of the steel should be within the "preferred-analysis" ranges indicated in Table 6-1. If one or more elements vary from the ranges shown, cost-increasing methods are usually

TABLE 6-1. Preferred Analyses for Steels
To Be Arc-Welded

Element	Composition (%)	
	Preferred	High*
Carbon	0.06 to 0.25	0.35
Manganese	0.35 to 0.80	1.40
Silicon	0.10 or less	0.30
Sulfur	0.035 or less	0.05
Phosphorus	0.030 or less	0.04

* Additional care is required in welding steels containing these amounts of the elements listed.

*A mill test report is usually based on a ladle analysis and is an average for an entire heat. Most low-carbon steels are rimmed steels, widely used because of their excellent forming and deep-drawing properties. The analysis of a rimmed steel varies from the first ingot to the last ingot of a single heat and also from the top to the bottom of a single ingot. Thus, a mill test report is an average and should be interpreted as such.

required to produce good welding results. Thus, steels within these ranges should be used whenever extensive welding is to be done unless their properties do not meet service requirements. Published welding procedures generally apply to normal welding conditions and to the more common preferred-analysis mild steels. Low-hydrogen electrodes and processes will generally tolerate a wider range of the elements than shown in Table 6-1.

If the chemical specification of a steel falls outside of the preferred-analysis range, it is usually not necessary to use special welding procedures based on the extremes allowed by the specification. The chemistry of a specific heat, under average mill-production conditions, may be considerably below the top limits indicated in the specification. Thus, for maximum economy, welding procedures for any type of steel should be based on actual rather than allowed chemistry values. A mill test report* can be obtained that gives the analysis of a heat of steel. From this information, a welding procedure can be established that ensures production of quality welds at lowest possible cost.

Standard carbon and alloy steels are identified by AISI (American Iron and Steel Institute), SAE (Society of Automotive Engineers), or ASTM (American Society for Testing Materials) designation systems. In the commonly used four-digit system of the AISI and SAE (Table 6-2), the last two digits indicate the middle of the carbon range. For example, in grade 1035, the 35 represents a carbon range from 0.32 to 0.38%. The first two digits indicate these carbon-steel grades:

10 xx	Nonresulfurized
11 xx	Resulfurized
12 xx	Resulfurized and rephosphorized

A prefix "B" indicates an acid Bessemer steel, an "E" indicates an electric-furnace steel. The E steels are usually alloy or stainless-steel grades. Steels without a prefix designation may be produced by basic open-hearth, basic-oxygen, or electric-furnace methods.

The letter "L" between the second and third digit indicates a leaded steel. The letter "B" in the same position designates a boron-treated steel. The suffix "H" refers to steels specially produced to narrow chemical and hardenability ranges.

These four-digit AISI or SAE standard steel designations apply primarily to sheet, strip, and bar products. ASTM specifications apply to most plates and structural shapes.

Some of the commonly specified elements and their effects on weldability and other characteristics of steel follow:

Carbon is the principal hardening element in steel. As carbon content increases, hardenability and tensile strength increase, and ductility and weldability decrease. In steels with a carbon content over 0.25%, rapid cooling from the welding temperature may produce a hard, brittle zone adjacent to the weld. Also, if considerable carbon is picked up in the weld puddle through admixture from the metal being welded, the weld deposit itself may be hard. Addition of small amounts of elements other than carbon can produce high tensile strengths without a detrimental effect on weldability. In general, carbon content should be low for best weldability.

Manganese increase hardenability and strength, but to a lesser extent than carbon. Properties of steels containing manganese depend principally on carbon content. Manganese content of less than 0.30% may promote internal porosity and cracking in the weld bead; cracking can also result if the content is over 0.80%.

For good weldability, the ratio of manganese to sulfur should be at least ten to one. If a steel has a low manganese content in combination with a low carbon content, it may not have been properly deoxidized. In steel, manganese combines with sulfur to form MnS, which is not harmful. However, a steel with a low Mn/S ratio may contain sulfur in the form of FeS, which can cause cracking (a "hot-short" condition) in the weld.

In general, manganese increases the rate of carbon penetration during carburizing and is beneficial to the surface finish of carbon steels.

Sulfur increases the machinability of steels, but reduces transverse ductility, impact toughness, and weldability. Sulfur in any amount promotes hot shortness in welding, and the tendency increases with increased sulfur. It can be tolerated up to

TABLE 6-2. AISI Designation
System for Alloy Steels

Alloy Series	Approximate Alloy Content (%)
13XX	Mn 1.60-1.90
40XX	Mo 0.15-0.30
41XX	Cr 0.40-1.10; Mo 0.08-0.35
43XX	Ni 1.65-2.00; Cr 0.40-0.90; Mo 0.20-0.30
44XX	Mo 0.45-0.60
46XX	Ni 0.70-2.00; Mo 0.15-0.30
47XX	Ni 0.90-1.20; Cr 0.35-0.55; Mo 0.15-0.40
48XX	Ni 3.25-3.75; Mo 0.20-0.30
50XX	Cr 0.30-0.50
51XX	Cr 0.70-1.15
E51100	C 1.00; Cr 0.90-1.15
E52100	C 1.00; Cr 0.90-1.15
61XX	Cr 0.50-1.10; Va 0.10-0.15 (min)
86XX	Ni 0.40-0.70; Cr 0.40-0.60; Mo 0.15-0.25
87XX	Ni 0.40-0.70; Cr 0.40-0.60; Mo 0.20-0.30
88XX	Ni 0.40-0.70; Cr 0.40-0.60; Mo 0.30-0.40
92XX	Si 1.80-2.20

Fig. 6-1. Sulfur segregations. Dark lines in etched section indicate areas of high sulfur concentration.

about 0.035% (with sufficient Mn); over 0.050% it can cause serious problems. Sulfur is also detrimental to surface quality in low-carbon and low-manganese steels.

A common cause of poor welding quality that is not apparent from analyses made in the usual way is segregated layers of sulfur in the form of iron sulfide. These layers, which cause cracks or other defects at the fusion line of an arc-welded joint, can be detected by examination of a deep-etched cross section as illustrated in Fig. 6-1.

Silicon is a deoxidizer that is added during the making of steel to improve soundness. Silicon increases strength and hardness, but to a lesser extent than manganese. It is detrimental to surface quality, especially in the low-carbon, resulfurized grades. If carbon content is fairly high, silicon aggravates cracking tendencies. For best welding conditions, silicon content should not exceed 0.10%, but amounts up to 0.30% are not as serious as high sulfur or phosphorus content.

Phosphorus, in large amounts, increases strength and hardness, but reduces ductility and impact strength, particularly in the higher-carbon grades. In low-carbon steels, phosphorus improves machinability and resistance to atmospheric corrosion.

As far as welding is concerned, phosphorus is an impurity, and should be kept as low as possible. Over 0.04% makes welds brittle and increases the tendency to crack. Phosphorus also lowers the surface tension of the molten weld metal, making it difficult to control.

Copper improves atmospheric corrosion resistance when present in excess of 0.15%. (A minimum of 0.20% is usually specified for this purpose.) Most carbon steels contain some copper as a "tramp element," up to about 0.15%. Copper content up to about 1.50% has little or no effect on the acetylene or arc-weldability of a steel, but it affects forge-weldability adversely. Copper content over 0.50% may reduce mechanical properties, however, if the steel is heat-treated.

Copper content is detrimental to surface quality, particularly in high-sulfur grades.

SPECIFYING BY MECHANICAL PROPERTIES

The producer of steels specified by mechanical properties is free to alter the chemistry of the steel (within limits) to obtain the required properties. Mechanical tests are usually specified under one of these conditions: 1) Mechanical test requirements only, with no limits on chemistry. 2) Mechanical test requirements, with limits on one or more elements.

Generally, these tests have been set up according to practices approved by the SAE or ASTM or to the requirements of other authorized code-writing organizations, such as the ASME (American Society of Mechanical Engineers) or the API (American Petroleum Institute).

The most common tests are bend tests, hardness tests, and a series of tensile tests that evaluate modulus of elasticity, yield strength, and tensile strength. Metallurgical tests are sometimes used to measure grain size, decarburization, or inclusions. Other tests relating to end-use requirements, such as burst tests for pressure tubing, may be included in some specifications.

Most carbon steels are produced to standard specifications established by regulating bodies concerned with public welfare and safety. The largest and most influential body of this type is the ASTM. Other major groups are the SAE, the ASME, the AAR (American Association of Railroads), and the AWWA (American Water Works Association). ASTM specifications are broad, covering requirements of many industries. Most other groups prepare steel specifications for the needs and interests of their particular industries.

SPECIFYING BY END PRODUCT

Often more important than exact mechanical properties or chemical analysis is the ability of a steel to be fabricated into a specific end product. Fabricating operations such as welding or deep drawing can change the as-delivered properties of a steel, and more than one chemical analysis or steel-making method can often produce a suitable material for the product. Consequently, many flat-rolled steel products such as plate, sheet and strip are specified to have adequate properties for fabrication into an "identified" end product.

A specification for an identified end product tells the steel producer which fabrication processes will be used, finish requirements, and the product's service requirements.

METALLURGY OF A WELD BEAD

The heat of welding brings about certain changes, both in the structure of the steel being welded and in the weld metal. Some of these changes occur during welding; others, after the metal has cooled.

During welding, the temperature of the molten weld metal reaches 3000°F or higher. A short distance from the weld, the temperature of the plate may be only about 600°F. When the steel reaches or exceeds certain critical temperatures between these values, changes occur that affect grain structure, hardness, and strength properties. These changes and the temperatures at which they occur are illustrated by Fig. 6-2, a schematic diagram of a section through a weld bead.

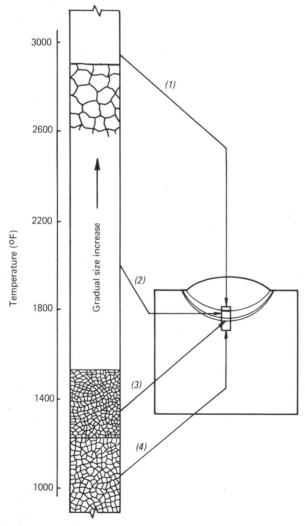

Fig. 6-2. Effect of welding heat on hardness and microstructure of an arc-welded 0.25% carbon-steel plate. The schematic diagram represents a strip cut vertically through the weld shown. Significance of the four numbered zones are: 1. Metal that has been melted and resolidified. Grain structure is coarse. 2. Metal that has been heated above the upper critical temperature (1525°F for 0.25% carbon steel) but has not been melted. This area of large grain growth is where underbead cracking can occur. 3. Metal that has been heated slightly above the lower critical temperature (1333°F) but not to the upper critical temperature. Grain refinement has taken place. 4. Metal that has been heated and cooled, but not to a high enough temperature for a structural change to occur.

The extent of change in structure depends on the maximum temperature to which the metal is subjected, the length of time the temperature is sustained, the composition of the metal, and the rate of cooling. The principal factor that controls these changes is the amount of heat that is put into the plate — both from preheating and from the welding process.

Cooling rate affects properties along with grain size. Rapid cooling rates produce stronger, harder, and less ductile steels; slow cooling rates produce the opposite properties. With low-carbon steels, the relatively small differences in cooling rates in normal practice have negligible effects on these properties. However, with steels of higher carbon contents or those with appreciable amounts of alloying elements, the effect can be significant.

Holding the plate material at a high temperature (above the upper critical temperature) for a long time produces a structure with large grain size. During welding, however, the metal adjacent to the weld (Zone 3 in Fig. 6-2) is at the high temperature for a very short time. The result is a slight decrease in grain size and an increase in strength and hardness, compared with the base metal.

In multipass weld joints, each bead produces a grain-refining action on the preceding bead as it is reheated. However, this refining is not likely to be uniform throughout the joint.

FACTORS CAUSING UNDERBEAD CRACKING

Except in some weld-surfacing operations cracks are considered deleterious. Cracking can occur either in the deposited metal or in the heat-affected zone of the base metal adjacent to the weld. The major cause of cracking in the base metal or in the weld metal is a high-carbon or alloy content that increases the hardenability. High hardenability, combined with a high cooling rate, produces the brittle condition that leads to cracking. Other causes of weld cracking are: joint restraint that produces high stresses in the weld, improper shape of the weld bead, hydrogen pickup, and contaminants on the plate or electrode.

Subsurface cracks in the base metal, under or near the weld, are known as underbead cracks. Underbead cracking in the heat-affected base metal is caused by: 1) A relatively high-carbon or alloy content steel that is allowed to cool too rapidly from the welding temperature. 2) Hydrogen pickup during welding.

Underbead cracking seldom occurs with the preferred-analysis steels (Table 6-1). With carbon steels above 0.35%-carbon content and with the low-alloy structural-grade steels, underbead cracking can be minimized by using a low-hydrogen welding process. The problem is most severe with materials such as the heat-treated structural steels having tensile strengths of 100,000 psi and higher.

The second factor that promotes underbead cracking — the pickup and retention of hydrogen — is also influenced by the cooling rate from the welding temperature. During welding, some hydrogen — a decomposition product of moisture from the air, electrode coating, wire, flux, shielding gas, or the surface of the plate — can dissolve into the molten weld metal and from there into the extremely hot (but not molten) base metal. If cooling occurs slowly, the process reverses, and the hydrogen has sufficient time to escape through the weld into the air. But if cooling is rapid, some hydrogen may be trapped in the heat-affected zone next to the weld metal, as illustrated by Fig. 6-3. The hydrogen is absorbed and produces a condition of low ductility known as hydrogen embrittlement.

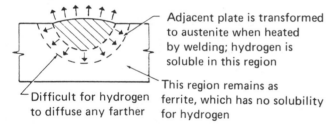

Most of the hydrogen escapes through the weld into the air

Adjacent plate is transformed to austenite when heated by welding; hydrogen is soluble in this region

This region remains as ferrite, which has no solubility for hydrogen

Difficult for hydrogen to diffuse any farther

Fig. 6-3. Austenitic heat-affected zone of a weld has high solubility for hydrogen. Upon cooling, the hydrogen builds up pressure that can cause underbead craking.

One theory suggests that the hydrogen produces a pressure, which — combined with shrinkage stresses and any hardening effect from the chemistry of the steel — causes tiny cracks in the metal immediately under the weld bead (Fig. 6-4). Similar cracks that appear on the plate surface adjacent to the weld are called "toe cracks."

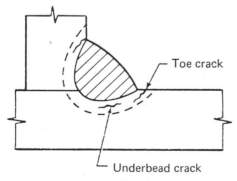

Toe crack

Underbead crack

Fig. 6-4. Underbead cracking and toe cracks caused by hydrogen pickup in heat-affected zone of plate.

Slower cooling (by welding slower, or by preheating) allows more of the hydrogen to escape and helps control the problem. In addition, the use of low-hydrogen welding materials eliminates the major source of hydrogen and usually eliminates underbead cracking.

Rapid cooling rates occur when the arc strikes on a cold plate — at the start of a weld with no previous weld bead to preheat the metal. The highest cooling rates occur on thick plate and in short tack welds. The effect of weld length on cooling rate can be illustrated by the time required to cool welds from 1600° to 200°F on a 3/4-in. steel plate:

2-1/2-in. weld	1.5 min
4-in. weld	5 min
9-in. weld	33 min

A 9-in.-long weld made on plate at 70°F has about the same cooling rate as a 3-in. weld on a plate that has been preheated to 300°F.

Welds with large cross sections require greater heat input than smaller ones. High welding current and slow travel rates reduce the rate of cooling and decrease the likelihood of cracking.

THE EFFECT OF SECTION THICKNESS

In a steel mill, billets are rolled into plates or shapes while red hot. The rolled members are then placed on finishing tables to cool. Because a thin plate has more surface area in proportion to its mass than a thick plate, it loses heat faster (by radiation) and cools more rapidly.

If a thick plate has the same chemistry as a thin one, its slower cooling rate results in lower tensile and yield strength, lower hardness, and higher elongation. In very thick plates, the cooling rate may be so low that the properties of the steel may not meet minimum specifications. Thus, to meet specified yield-strength levels, the mill increases the carbon or alloy content of the steels that are to be rolled into thick sections.

In welding, cooling rates of thin and thick plates are just the opposite. Because of the larger mass of plate, the weld area in a thick plate cools more rapidly than the weld area in a thin one. The heat input at the weld area is transferred, by conduction, to the large mass of relatively cool steel, thus cooling the weld area relatively rapidly. (Heat is transferred more rapidly by conduction than by radiation.) The thin plate has less mass to absorb the heat, and it cools at a slower rate. The faster cooling of the thicker plate produces higher tensile and yield strengths, higher hardness, and lower elongation.

Welds in structural-steel shapes and plate under 1/2-in. thick have less tendency toward cracking

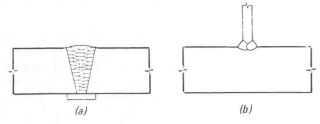

Fig. 6-5. A groove-welded butt joint in thick plate (a) requires a higher preheat, because of joint restraint, than a fillet-welded joint of a thin member and a thick plate (b).

than welds in thicker plate. In addition to the favorable (slower) cooling rate of thinner members, two other factors minimize causes of cracking: 1) Thinner plate weldments usually have a good ratio (high) of weld-throat-to-plate thickness. 2) Because they are less rigid, thinner plates can flex more as the weld cools, thus reducing restraint on the weld metal.

Thicker plates and rolled sections do not have these advantages. Because a weld cools faster on a thick member, and because the thick member probably has a higher carbon or alloy content, welds on a thick section have higher strength and hardness but lower ductility than similar welds on thin plate. If these properties are unacceptable, preheating (especially for the more critical root pass) may be necessary to reduce the cooling rate.

Because it increases cost, preheating should be used only when needed. For example, a thin web to be joined to thick flange plate by fillet welds may not require as much preheat as two highly restrained thick plates joined by a multiple-pass butt weld (Fig. 6-5).

THE EFFECT OF JOINT RESTRAINT

If metal-to-metal contact exists between thick plates prior to welding, the plates cannot move — the joint is restrained. As the weld cools and contracts, all shrinkage stress must be taken up in the weld, as illustrated in Fig. 6-6(a). This restraint may cause the weld to crack, especially in the first pass on the second side of the plate.

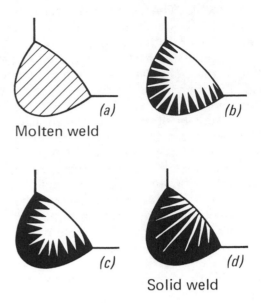

Molten weld

Solid weld

Fig. 6-7. A molten fillet weld (a) starts to solidify along the sides next to the plate (b). Solidification proceeds as shown in (c) and (d).

Joint restraint can be minimized by providing a space of 1/32 to 1/16 in. between the two members to allow movement during cooling. Such spaces or gaps can be incorporated by several simple means:

1. Soft steel wire spacers may be placed between the plates, as in Fig. 6-6(b). The wire flattens out as the weld shrinks, as shown in Fig. 6-6(c). (Copper wire should not be used because it may contaminate the weld metal).
2. Rough flame-cut edges on the plate. The peaks of the cut edge keep the plates apart, yet can deform and flatten out as the weld shrinks.
3. Upsetting the edge of the plate with a heavy center punch. Results are similar to those of the flame-cut edge.

Provision for a space between thick plates to be welded is particularly important for fillet welds.

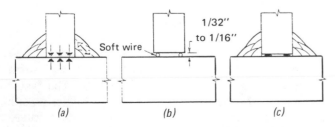

Fig. 6-6. In a restrained joint in thick plates (a), all shrinkage stress must be taken up in the weld. Separating the plates with soft wires (b) allows the plates to move slightly during cooling. The wires flatten (c) and remove most of the stress from the weld metal.

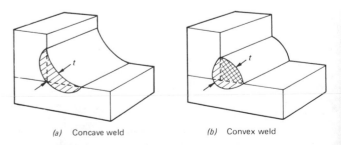

Fig. 6-8. The leg size and the surface of a concave fillet weld (a) may be larger than that of a convex bead (b), but its throat, t, may be considerably smaller.

Fillet Welds: A molten fillet weld starts to solidify, or freeze, along the sides of the joint, as in Fig. 6-7, because the heat is conducted to the adjacent plate, which is at a much lower temperature. Freezing progresses inward until the entire weld is solid. The last material to freeze is that at the center, near the surface of the weld.

Although a concave fillet weld may appear to be larger than a convex weld (Fig. 6-8), it may have less penetration into the welded plates and a smaller throat than the convex bead. Thus the convex weld may be the stronger of the two, even though it appears to be smaller.

In the past, the concave weld has been preferred by designers because of the smoother stress flow it offers to resist a load on the joint. Experience has shown, however, that single-pass concave fillet welds have a greater tendency to crack during cooling than do convex welds. This disadvantage usually outweighs the effect of improved stress distribution, especially in steels that require special welding procedures.

When a concave bead cools and shrinks, the outer surface is in tension and may crack. A convex bead has considerably reduced shrinkage stresses in the surface area, and the possibility of cracking during cooling is slight. For multiple-pass fillet welds only the first pass need be convex.

When design conditions require concave welds for smooth flow of stresses in thick plate, the first bead (usually three or more passes are required) should be slightly convex. The others are then built up to the required shape.

Groove Welds: The root pass of a groove weld in heavy plate usually requires special welding procedures. For example, the root pass on the first side of a double-V joint is susceptible to cracking because of the notch, as illustrated in Fig. 6-9(a), which is a crack starter. On high-quality work, this notch is backchipped, as in Fig. 6-9(b), to: 1) Remove slag or oxides from the bottom of the groove. 2) Remove any small cracks that may have occurred in the root bead. 3) Widen the groove at the bottom so that the first bead of the second side is large enough to resist the shrinkage that it must withstand due to the rigidity of the joint.

The weld metal tends to shrink in all directions as it cools, and restraint from the heavy plates produces tensile stresses within the weld. The metal yields plastically while hot to accommodate the stresses; if the internal stresses exceed the strength of the weld, it cracks, usually along the centerline.

The problem is greater if the plate material has a higher carbon content than the welding electrode. If this is the case, the weld metal usually picks up additional carbon through admixture with the base metal. Under such conditions, the root bead is usually less ductile than subsequent beads.

A concave root bead in a groove weld, as shown in Fig. 6-10(a), has the same tendency toward cracking as it does in a fillet weld. Increasing the throat dimension of the root pass, as in Fig. 6-10(b), helps to prevent cracking. Electrodes and procedures should be used that produce a convex bead shape. A low-hydrogen process usually reduces cracking tendencies; if not, preheating may be required.

Centerline cracking can also occur in subsequent passes of a multiple-pass weld if the passes are excessively wide or concave. This can be corrected by putting down narrower, slightly convex beads, making the weld two or more beads wide, as in Fig. 6-11.

Width/Depth Ratio: Cracks caused by joint restraint or material chemistry usually appear at the face of the weld. In some situations, however, internal cracks occur that do not reach the surface. These are usually caused by improper joint design (narrow, deep grooves or fillets) or by misuse of a welding process that can achieve deep penetration.

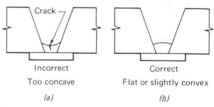

Fig. 6-10. A concave root pass (a) may crack because tensile stresses exceed the strength of the weld metal. A slightly convex root-pass bead (b) helps prevent cracking.

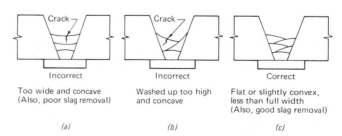

Fig. 6-11. Wide, concave passes (a and b) in a multiple-pass weld may crack. Slightly convex beads (c) are recommended.

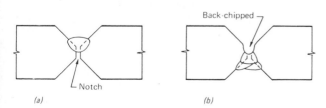

Fig. 6-9. The root pass of a double-V joint is susceptible to cracking because of the notch effect (a). On high-quality work, the notch is minimized by backchipping (b).

If the depth of fusion is much greater than the width of the weld face, the surface of the weld may freeze before the center does. When this happens, the shrinkage forces act on the almost-frozen center (the strength of which is lower than that of the frozen surface) and can cause a crack that does not extend to the surface. Fig. 6-12(a) is illustrative.

Internal cracks can also be caused by improper joint design or preparation. Results of combining thick plate, a deep-penetrating welding process,

and a 45° included angle are shown in Fig. 6-12(b). A similar result on a fillet weld made with deep penetration is shown in Fig. 6-12(c). A too-small bevel, and arc-gouging a groove too narrow for its depth on the second-pass side of a double-V groove weld, can cause the internal crack shown in Fig. 6-12(d).

Internal cracks are serious because they cannot be detected by visual inspection methods. But they can be eliminated if preventive measures are used. Penetration and volume of weld metal deposited in

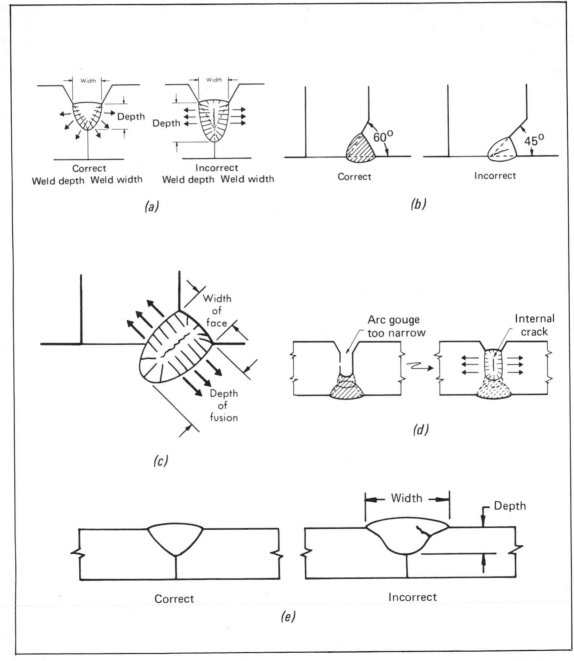

Fig. 6-12. Internal cracking can occur when weld penetration is greater than width. Correct and incorrect proportions are shown in (a), (b) and (c). Arc-gouging a groove too narrow for its depth can cause a similar internal crack (d). Cracks can also occur when depth is too shallow (e). Width of a weld should not exceed twice its depth.

each pass can be controlled by regulating welding speed and current and by using a joint design that establishes reasonable depth-of-fusion requirements. Recommended ratios of width of each individual bead to depth of fusion are between 1.2 to 1 and 2 to 1.

A different type of internal crack occurs in submerged-arc welding when the width-to-depth ratio is too large. Cracks in these so-called "hat-shaped" welds are especially dangerous because radiographic inspection may not detect them. The width-to-depth ratio of any individual bead should not exceed 2:1.

Lamellar cracking or tearing is illustrated in Fig. 6-13. In (a), the shrinkage forces on the upright member are perpendicular to the direction in which the plate was rolled at the steel mill. The inclusions within the plate are strung out in the direction of rolling. If the shrinkage stress should

become high enough, lamellar tear might occur by the progressive cracking from one inclusion to the next. A way to prevent this is illustrated in Fig. 6-13(b). Here, the bevel has been made in the upright plate. The weld now cuts across the inclusions, and the shrinkage forces are distributed, rather than applied to a single plane of inclusions.

FACTORS CONTRIBUTING TO CRACKING

Research studies have determined the factors contributing to weld cracking. These may be summarized as follows:

1. The contraction forces of multiple-pass welds tend to cause separations in the base metal and they generally increase with the strength and/or hardenability of the filler metal and base metals. Therefore, softer weld metal would tend to decrease not only weld metal cracks but also heat-affected zone cracks and lamellar tearing.
2. The susceptibility to delayed cracking is proportional to the hydrogen content of the welding atmosphere.
3. Greater crack sensitivity is exhibited by high-chemistry base metal and by heavier plate thicknesses.
4. In general, cracking will initiate in the heat-affected zone of the base metal, except in cases where the weld metal is of higher hardness.
5. With an open-arc or even a shielded-arc manual electrode, it can be assumed that in hot humid weather the arc atmosphere will contain more hydrogen as water vapor than in cool, dry weather. Any tendency to minimize the importance of preheat, of keeping the joint hot, or possibly of postheat in hot summer months, could be at the root of cracking problems on heavy restrained joints. This would be especially true if either the weld metal or the base metal is hardenable because of alloy or carbon content.

Low heat input with interruptions in the welding cycle tends to aggravate the problem.

The welding position and its influence on bead size, heat input, number of layers, etc., has a direct influence on the cracking tendency. For example, three-o'clock groove welds are more sensitive to cracking than flat-position groove welds.

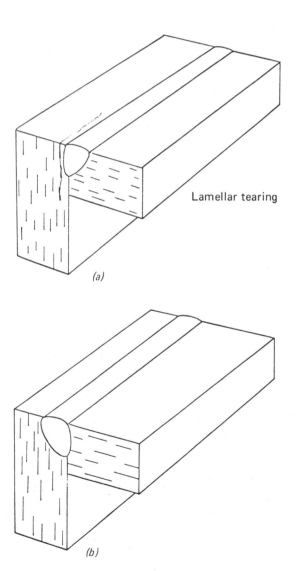

Fig. 6-13. Lamellar tearing (a) and a suggested solution (b).

WELDING RECOMMENDATIONS FOR THE CARBON STEELS

Classification of the carbon steels is based principally on carbon content. The groups are: low-carbon (to 0.30% carbon), medium-carbon (0.30 to 0.45%), and high-carbon (more than 0.45%). The first group is sometimes subdivided into the very-low-carbon steels (to 0.15%) and the mild steels (0.15 to 0.30%). Standard SAE compositions of carbon steels, applicable to structural shapes, plate, strip, sheet, and welded tubing are listed in Table 6-3.

Mechanical properties of hot-finished steels are influenced principally by chemical composition (particularly carbon content), but other factors — finishing temperature, section size, and the presence of residual elements — also affect properties. A 3/4-in. plate, for example, has higher tensile properties and lower elongation than a 1-1/2-in. plate of the same composition. This results from the higher rate of cooling of the 3/4-in. plate from the rolling temperature. Typical tensile properties of hot-rolled and cold-finished low-carbon steels are listed in Table 6-4.

Low-Carbon Steels: In general, steels with carbon contents to 0.30% are readily joined by all common arc-welding processes. These grades account for the greatest tonnage of steels used in welded structures. Typical applications include tanks, structural assemblies, vessels, machine bases, earth-moving and agricultural equipment, and general weldments.

Steels with very low carbon content — to 0.15% — are good welding steels, but they are not the best for high-speed production welding. The low carbon content and the low manganese content (to 0.30%) tend to produce internal porosity. This condition is usually corrected by modifying the welding procedure slightly — usually by using a slower speed. If the presence of some internal porosity has no detrimental effect on the service requirements of the assembly, standard high-speed welding procedures can be used.

Steels with very low carbon content are more ductile and easier to form than higher-carbon steels. They are used for applications requiring considerable cold forming, such as stampings or rolled or formed shapes.

Steels with 0.15 to 0.20% carbon content have excellent weldability. They seldom require anything beyond standard welding procedures, and they can be welded with all types of mild-steel electrodes. These steels should be used for maximum production speed on assemblies or structures that require extensive welding.

Steels at the upper end of the low-carbon range — the 0.25 to 0.30% carbon grades — have very good weldability, but when one or more of the elements is on the high side of permissible limits, cracking can result, particularly in fillet welds. With slightly reduced speeds and currents, any of the standard electrodes can be used for these steels.

In thicknesses to 5/16 in., standard procedures apply.

If some of the elements — particularly carbon, silicon, or sulfur — are on the high side of the limits, surface holes may form. Reducing current and speed minimizes this problem.

Although most welding applications of these steels require no preheating, heavy sections (2-in. or more) and certain joint configurations may require a preheat. Less preheating is required when

TABLE 6-3. Compositions of Carbon Steels

SAE Number	Chemical Composition Limits (%)			
	C	Mn	P, max.	S, max.
1005	0.06 max.	0.35 max.	0.040	0.050
1006	0.08 max.	0.25-0.40	0.040	0.050
1008	0.10 max.	0.30-0.50	0.040	0.050
1010	0.08-0.13	0.30-0.60	0.070	0.050
1011	0.08-0.13	0.60-0.90	0.040	0.050
1012	0.10-0.15	0.30-0.60	0.040	0.050
1013	0.11-0.16	0.50-0.80	0.040	0.050
1015	0.13-0.18	0.30-0.60	0.040	0.050
1016	0.13-0.18	0.60-0.90	0.040	0.050
1017	0.15-0.20	0.30-0.60	0.040	0.050
1018	0.15-0.20	0.60-0.90	0.040	0.050
1019	0.15-0.20	0.70-1.00	0.040	0.050
1020	0.18-0.23	0.30-0.60	0.040	0.050
1021	0.18-0.23	0.60-0.90	0.040	0.050
1022	0.18-0.23	0.70-1.00	0.040	0.050
1023	0.20-0.25	0.30-0.60	0.040	0.050
1025	0.22-0.28	0.30-0.60	0.040	0.050
1026	0.22-0.28	0.60-0.90	0.040	0.050
1029	0.25-0.31	0.60-0.90	0.040	0.050
1030	0.28-0.34	0.60-0.90	0.040	0.050
1035	0.32-0.38	0.60-0.90	0.040	0.050
1037	0.32-0.38	0.70-1.00	0.040	0.050
1038	0.35-0.42	0.60-0.90	0.040	0.050
1039	0.37-0.44	0.70-1.00	0.040	0.050
1040	0.37-0.44	0.60-0.90	0.040	0.050
1042	0.40-0.47	0.60-0.90	0.040	0.050
1043	0.40-0.47	0.70-1.00	0.040	0.050
1044	0.43-0.50	0.30-0.60	0.040	0.050
1045	0.43-0.50	0.60-0.90	0.040	0.050
1046	0.43-0.50	0.70-0.90	0.040	0.050
1049	0.46-0.53	0.60-0.90	0.040	0.050
1050	0.48-0.55	0.60-0.90	0.040	0.050
1053	0.48-0.55	0.70-1.00	0.040	0.050
1055	0.50-0.60	0.60-0.90	0.040	0.050
1060	0.55-0.65	0.60-0.90	0.040	0.050
1064	0.60-0.70	0.50-0.80	0.040	0.050
1065	0.60-0.70	0.60-0.90	0.040	0.050
1069	0.65-0.75	0.40-0.70	0.040	0.050
1070	0.65-0.75	0.60-0.90	0.040	0.050
1074	0.70-0.80	0.50-0.80	0.040	0.050
1075	0.70-0.80	0.40-0.70	0.040	0.050
1078	0.72-0.85	0.30-0.60	0.040	0.050
1080	0.75-0.88	0.60-0.90	0.040	0.050
1084	0.80-0.93	0.60-0.90	0.040	0.050
1085	0.80-0.93	0.70-1.00	0.040	0.050
1086	0.80-0.93	0.30-0.50	0.040	0.050
1090	0.85-0.98	0.60-0.90	0.040	0.050
1095	0.90-1.03	0.30-0.50	0.040	0.050

From the 1969 SAE Handbook. Some grades have wider ranges when producing steel for structural sheet and welded tubing.

TABLE 6-4. Typical Minimum Mechanical
Properties of Carbon-Steel Bars

AISI or SAE No.	Condition*	Tensile Strength (1000 psi)	Yield Strength (1000 psi)	Elongation in 2 in. (%)
1010	HR	47	26	28
	CF	53	44	20
1015	HR	50	28	28
	CF	56	47	18
1020	HR	55	30	25
	CF	61	51	15
1025	HR	58	32	25
	CF	64	54	15
1030	HR	68	38	20
	CF	76	64	12
1035	HR	72	40	18
	CF	80	67	12
1040	HR	76	42	18
	CF	85	71	12
1045	HR	82	45	16
	CF	91	77	12
1050	HR	90	50	15
	CF	100	84	10

* HR = hot rolled; CF = cold finished.
Data from ASM Metals Handbook, 8th Ed., Vol. 1.

low-hydrogen processes are used. In general, steels in the 0.25 to 0.30% carbon range should be welded with low-hydrogen electrodes or with a low-hydrogen process if the temperatures is below 50°F.

Medium and High-Carbon Steels: Because hardenability of steel increases with carbon content, the medium and high-carbon steels serve where hardness, wear resistance, or higher strength are needed. Important uses for medium-carbon steels (to 0.45%) include wear plates, springs, and components for railroad, agricultural, and earth-moving and materials-handling equipment.

Unfortunately, the same characteristics that make these steels so suitable for use in rugged parts and structures make them more difficult and costly to weld. The medium-carbon steels can be welded successfully, however, provided proper procedures and preheat and interpass temperatures are used. Sometimes, postweld stress relief may be required.

The high-carbon steels are almost always used in a hardened condition. Typical applications are for metalworking and woodworking tools, drills, dies, and knives, and for abrasion-resistant parts such as plowshares and scraper blades. Some farm equipment is built from rerolled rail stock (0.65% C), which is welded in the as-rolled condition, using preheating, interpass heating, and postweld stress relief.

Hardness of these steels can range from dead

soft in the annealed condition to Rockwell C 65 (with rapid quench treatment) for the higher-carbon grades. Although an AISI 1020 steel can be made as hard as Rc 50, hardness is very shallow. Increased carbon content increases depth of hardening and maximum attainable hardness to about Rc 65. Alloying elements increase depth of hardening but have little effect on maximum hardness possible.

It is advisable to make sample weld tests to determine cracking tendencies of steels containing 0.30% or more carbon. If such tendencies are apparent, preheating of the steel may be necessary to retard the cooling rate from the welding temperature. Required preheat temperature varies with analysis, size, and shape of the steel and with the amount of heat input from the welding process. In general, the higher the carbon or alloy content and the thicker the plate, the higher the preheat temperature needed to provide the slow cooling rate required to prevent hardening. For shop calculation, a Preheat Calculator — available from The Lincoln Electric Company at a nominal cost — is a handy tool for determining preheat requirements of various thicknesses of common-analysis steels.

Use of low-hydrogen processes can minimize the degree of preheating necessary and, in 14-gage and thinner materials, can eliminate the need for preheating entirely. As a rule of thumb, preheat temperatures used with low-hydrogen electrodes can be 100 to 200°F lower than those needed for electrodes other than low-hydrogen.

Structural Carbon Steels: Standard ASTM specifications that cover carbon-steel plates, shapes, and bars of structural quality are A283, A36, A515, and A516. These steels are used for bridges, buildings, pressure vessels and general structural use.

Other specifications, ASTM A7, A373, A212, and A201, were used formerly for the same types of structures. These specifications have been replaced by the four named above.

The A373 specification (obsolete, but still in use to some extent at the time of publication) stipulates maximum allowable carbon as 0.25 to 0.28% for various thicknesses and the range of manganese allowed as 0.60 to 0.90%. The A36 specification has the same limit on carbon, but the manganese content can be slightly higher — in the range of 0.60 to 1.20%.

Both specifications also limit sulfur and phosphorus content (0.05 and 0.04%), and both allow copper (0.20% or more) for improved corrosion resistance. The minimum yield for A373 steels is 32,000 psi, and for A36 steels, 36,000 psi. These requirements apply to all thicknesses up to 4 in.

for A373 and up to 8 in. for A36. The A373 and A36 steels are readily welded by manual and automatic submerged-arc methods, using standard procedures.

High-Strength Low-Alloy Structural Steels: Higher mechanical properties and, usually, better corrosion resistance than the structural carbon steels are characteristics of the high-strength low-alloy (HSLA) steels. These improved properties are achieved by additions of small amounts of alloying elements. Some of the HSLA types are carbon-manganese steels; others contain different alloy additions, governed by requirements for weldability, formability, toughness, or economy. Strength of these steels is between those of structural carbon steels and the high-strength quenched-and-tempered steels.

High-strength low-alloy steels are usually used in the as-rolled condition, although some are available that require heat treatment after fabrication. These steels are produced to specific mechanical-property requirements rather than to chemical compositions. Minimum mechanical properties available in the as-rolled condition vary among the grades and, within most grades, with thickness. Ranges of properties available in this group of steels are:

1. Minimum yield point from 42,000 to 70,000 psi.
2. Minimum tensile strength from 60,000 to 85,000 psi.
3. Resistance to corrosion, classed as: equal to that of carbon steels, twice that of carbon steels, or four to six times that of carbon steels.

The HSLA steels are available in most commercial wrought forms and are used extensively in products and structures that require higher strength-to-weight ratios than the carbon structural steels offer. Typical applications are supports and panels for truck bodies, railway cars, mobile homes, and other transportation equipment; components for tractors, threshers, fertilizer spreaders, and other agricultural machinery; materials-handling and storage equipment; and buildings, bridge decks, and similar structures.

The high-strength low-alloy steels should not be confused with the high-strength quenched-and-tempered alloy steels. Both groups are sold primarily on a trade-name basis, and they frequently share the same trade name, with different letters or numbers being used to identify each. The quenched-and-tempered steels are full-alloy steels that are heat-treated at the mill to develop optimum properties. They are generally martensitic in structure, whereas the HSLA steels are mainly ferritic steels; this is the clue to the metallurgical and fabri-

cating differences between the two types. In the as-rolled condition, ferritic steels are composed of relatively soft, ductile constituents; martensitic steels have hard, brittle constituents that require heat treatment to produce their high-strength properties.

Strength in the HSLA steels is achieved instead by relatively small amounts of alloying elements

TABLE 6-5. Specifications for High-Strength Low-Alloy Steels

Specification or Practice	Coverage
ASTM	
A-242	42,000 to 50,000-psi yield-point steels with atmospheric corrosion resistance equal to twice (with copper) or four or more times that of structural carbon steels. The more corrosion-resistant grades are used as "weathering steels."
A-374	Cold-rolled sheets and strip with 45,000-psi yield point; similar in many respects to A-242.
A-375	Hot-rolled sheets and strip with 50,000-psi yield point; similar in many respects to A-242.
A-440	Intermediate-manganese steels with 42,000 to 50,000-psi yield points. Copper additions provide atmospheric corrosion resistance double that of carbon steel. Good abrasion resistance; only fair weldability. Used primarily for riveted or bolted products.
A-441	Manganese-vanadium steels with 40,000 to 50,000-psi yield points. Copper additions provide atmospheric corrosion resistance double that of carbon steel. Lower manganese and carbon; therefore, improved weldability over A-440 steels.
A-572	Columbium-vanadium-nitrogen grades with six yield points from 42,000 to 65,000 psi. Grades with copper additions for improved atmospheric corrosion resistance are available. Modifications high in columbium may have excellent low-temperature notch toughness when produced to fine-grain practice (by roller quenching or normalizing).
A-588	Similar in most respects to A-242 steels, except that a 50,000-psi yield-point minimum is provided up to 4 in. thick and material up to 8 in. thick and is covered in the specification. Has four times the atmospheric corrosion resistance of carbon steel.
SAE (Recommended Practice — not a specification)	
J410b	Covers all major HSLA types, with yield strengths from 42,000 to 70,000 psi. Unlike ASTM, SAE gives greater attention to formability, toughness, and weldability. However, ASTM specs give wider coverage of mill forms and larger section thicknesses.
DoD	
Mil-S-7809A (May 3, 1963)	Covers HSLA steels in bars, shapes, sheets, strip, and plates.
Mil-S-13281B (Oct. 10, 1966)	Covers carbon, alloy, and HSLA steels for welded structures.

Source: "High-Strength Low-Alloy Steels", *Machine Design*, Feb. 17, 1972.

dissolved in a ferritic structure. Carbon content rarely exceeds 0.28% and is usually between 0.15 and 0.22%. Manganese content ranges from 0.85 to 1.60%, depending on grade, and other alloy additions — chromium, nickel, silicon, phosphorus, copper, vanadium, columbium, and nitrogen — are used in amounts less than one percent. Welding, forming, and machining characteristics of most grades do not differ markedly from those of the low-carbon steels.

To be weldable, the high-strength steels must have enough ductility to avoid cracking from the rapid cooling inherent in welding processes. Weldable HSLA steels must be sufficiently low in carbon, manganese, and all "deep-hardening" elements to ensure that appreciable amounts of martensite are not formed upon rapid cooling. Superior strength is provided by solution of alloying elements in the ferrite of the as-rolled steel. Corrosion resistance is also increased in certain of the HSLA steels by the alloying additions.

Addition of a minimum of 0.20% copper usually produces steels with about twice the atmospheric corrosion resistance of structural carbon steels. Steels with four to six times the atmospheric corrosion resistance of structural carbon steels are obtained in many ways, but, typically, with additions of nickel and/or chromium, often with more than 0.10% phosphorus. These alloys are usually used in addition to the copper.

Standard specifications or recommended practices covering the major types of HSLA steels are available from the American Society for Testing and Materials, the Society of Automotive Engineers, and the Department of Defense. These standards are summarized in Table 6-5.

Other standardizing organizations such as the American Institute of Steel Construction, The American Association of Railroads, and the Department of Transportation have established specifications or practices for the use of HSLA steels in certain industries and applications.

ASTM's specifications are oriented principally to mill form and mechanical properties; SAE's recommended practices include, in addition, information on fabrication characteristics — toughness, weldability, and formability.

ASTM Specifications for Low-Alloy Steels: Five ASTM specifications cover the high-strength low-alloy structural steels. They are: A242, A440, A441, A572, and A588. Specifications A374 and A375 cover similar steels in sheet and strip form.

ASTM A242 covers HSLA structural steel shapes, plates, and bars for welded, riveted, or bolted construction. Maximum carbon content of these steels is 0.24%; typical content is from 0.09 to 0.17%. Materials produced to this specification are intended primarily for structural members where light weight and durability are important.

Some producers can supply copper-bearing steels (0.20% minimum copper) with about twice the atmospheric corrosion resistance of carbon steels. Steels meeting the general requirements of ASTM A242 but modified to give four times the atmospheric corrosion resistance of structural steels are also available. These latter grades — sometimes called "weathering steels" — are used for architectural and other structural purposes where it is desirable to avoid painting for either esthetic or economic reasons.

Welding characteristics vary according to the type of steel; producers can recommend the most weldable material and offer welding advice if the conditions under which the welding will be done are known.

ASTM A440 covers high-strength intermediate-manganese copper-bearing HSLA steels used principally for riveted or bolted structures. These steels are not generally recommended for welding because of their relatively high carbon and manganese contents. ASTM A440 and its companion, A441, have the same minimum mechanical properties as A242.

ASTM A440 steels have about twice the atmospheric corrosion resistance of structural carbon steel and very good abrasion resistance. The high manganese content (typically, about 1.45%) tends to cause weld metal to air-harden — a condition that may produce high stresses and cracks in the weld. If these steels must be welded, careful preheating (higher than for A441) is necessary.

ASTM A441 covers the intermediate-manganese HSLA steels that are readily weldable with proper procedures. The specification calls for additions of vanadium and a lower manganese content (1.25% maximum) than ASTM A440. Minimum mechanical properties are the same as A242 and A440 steels, except that plates and bars from 4 to 8-in. thick are covered in A441.

Atmospheric corrosion resistance of this steel is approximately twice that of structural carbon steel. Another property of ASTM A441 steel is its superior toughness at low temperatures. Only shapes, plates, and bars are covered by the specification, but weldable sheets and strip can be supplied by some producers with approximately the same minimum mechanical properties.

ASTM A572 includes six grades of high-strength low-alloy structural steels in shapes, plates, and bars. These steels offer a choice of strength levels ranging from 42,000 to 65,000-psi yields.

Proprietary HSLA steels of this type with 70,000 and 75,000-psi yield points are also available. Increasing care is required for welding these steels as strength level increases.

A572 steels are distinguished from other HSLA steels by their columbium, vanadium, and nitrogen content. Copper additions above a minimum of 0.20% may be specified for atmospheric corrosion resistance about double that of structural carbon steels.

A supplementary requirement is included in the specification that permits designating the specific alloying elements required in the steel. Examples are the Type 1 designation, for columbium; Type 2, for vanadium; Type 3, for columbium and vanadium; and Type 4, for vanadium and nitrogen. Specific grade designations must accompany this type of requirement.

ASTM A588 provides for a steel similar in most respects to A242 weathering steel, except that the 50,000-psi yield point is available in thicknesses to at least 4 in.

SAE Specifications for Low-Alloy Steels: High-strength low-alloy steels are also covered in the SAE Recommended Practice J410b. This is not a standard. Rather, it is a recommended practice — a guide or memorandum from SAE to its members to help standardize their engineering practices. SAE J410b was written long before most of the HSLA steels had ASTM specifications. Its content is more general than the ASTM documents, and its intent is to guide material selection in the light of fabrication requirements. Now that ASTM has defined almost all of the HSLA steels in standard specifications, SAE J410b is seldom used as a material specification. But the SAE document is still valuable as a general guide to using the HSLA steels.

The SAE document addresses itself primarily to the specific needs of fabricators of automobiles, trucks, trailers, agricultural equipment, and aircraft. This is why SAE J410b does not cover the thicker plates and heavier structural shapes. Minimum mechanical properties of commonly used steels covered by SAE J410b are listed in Table 6-6.

For mechanical-property data on materials thicker than those listed in the table, suppliers should be consulted. SAE J410b high-strength low-alloy steels may be specified as annealed, normalized, or otherwise specially prepared for forming. When this is done, mechanical properties are agreed upon between supplier and purchaser.

Each grade has chemical composition limits to control welding characteristics in a manner similar to ASTM designations. Table 6-7 lists relative formability, weldability, and toughness of the J410b steels.

Grade 945A has excellent arc and resistance-welding characteristics and the best formability, weldability, and low-temperature notch toughness. It is available in sheets, strip, and light plate.

Grade 945C is a carbon-manganese steel with satisfactory arc-welding properties if proper procedures are used to prevent hardening of the weld metal. Moderate preheat is usually required, especially for thick sections. It is similar to Grade 950C, but has lower carbon and manganese content to improve arc-welding characteristics, formability, and low-temperature notch toughness, at some sacrifice in strength.

TABLE 6-6. Minimum Mechanical Properties for SAE J410b HSLA Steels

Grade, Form, and Thickness	Tensile Strength (1000 psi)	Yield Strength 0.2% Offset (1000 psi)	Elongation (%)	
			2 in.	8 in.
945 A, C				
Sheet, strip	60	45	22	. . .
Plate, bar				
To 1/2 in.	65	45	22	18
1/2 to 1-1/2 in.	62	42	24	19
1-1/2 to 3 in.	62	40	24	19
950 A, B, C, D				
Sheet, strip	70	50	22	. . .
Plate, bar				
To 1/2 in.	70	50	22	18
1/2 to 1-1/2 in.	67	45	24	19
1-1/2 in. to 3 in.	63	42	24	19
945X*	60	45	22	18
950X*	65	50	22	18
955X	70	55		
960X	75	60		
965X	80	65		
970X	85	70		

* To 3/8 in. thick.

TABLE 6-7. Fabrication Characteristics of SAE J410b Steels

Formability	Weldability	Toughness
945A	945A	945A
950A	950A	950A
945C, 945X	950D	950B
950B, 950X	945X	950D
950D	950B, 950X	945X, 350X
950C	945C	945C, 950C
	950C	

Alloys are listed in order of decreasing excellence; most formable, most weldable, and toughest alloys at the top.

Source: *Machine Design,* Metals Reference Issue, Dec. 14, 1967.

Grade 945X is a columbium or vanadium-treated carbon-manganese steel similar to 945C except for improved toughness and weldability.

Grade 950A has good weldability, low-temperature notch toughness, and formability. It is normally available only in sheet, strip, and light plate.

Grade 950B has satisfactory arc-welding properties and fairly good low-temperature notch toughness and formability.

Grade 950C is a carbon-manganese steel that can be arc welded if the cooling rate is controlled, but is unsuitable for resistance welding. Formability and toughness are fair.

Grade 950D has good weldability and fairly good formability. Its phosphorus content reduces its low-temperature properties.

Grade 950X is a columbium or vanadium-treated carbon-manganese steel similar to 950C except for somewhat improved welding and forming properties.

Several other grades are also covered by SAE J410b — higher-strength steels that have reduced formability and weldability.

Modifications of standard SAE-grade designations are also available. For example, fully killed steels made to fine-grain practice are indicated by the suffix "K." Thus, 945AK is a fully killed, fine-grain, HSLA steel with maximum ladle analysis of 0.15% carbon and a yield strength of about 45,000 psi. All grades made to K practice may not be available from all suppliers. This fine-grain practice is usually specified when low-temperature notch toughness is important.

Steels designated by the suffix "X" contain strengthening elements, such as columbium or vanadium (with or without nitrogen) added singly or in combination. These are usually made semi-killed. However, killed steel may be specified by indicating both suffixes, such as SAE 950XK.

Available HSLA-steel grades often have characteristics in excess of the specification minimums. Literature from producer companies contains information on physical and mechanical property ranges and suggested fabricating and welding practices.

Joint Design And Welding Instructions

The designer specifies the type of joint to be used in joining two pieces of metal. Through welding symbols on the drawing or other instructions, he tells the weldor how the welding of the joint is to be executed. The job of the weldor is to follow instructions — even when they seem questionable — since the designer has probably put considerable thought into his instructions, often making extensive mathematical calculations.

The weldor who conscientiously tries to do a good job by adding a "little bit" to the fillet leg size to "assure safety" is actually doing his employer a disservice. By his good intentions, he may be doubling the weld costs; in most cases the safety factor he deems desirable has already been incorporated in the weld by the designer. A first rule in being a weldor of most value to the employer is to follow welding instructions to the letter.

The details of joint design — with the massive mathematical calculations frequently involved — are outside the interests of the professional weldor. However, knowledge of the types of joints, the reasons for their usage, their advantages and limitations is helpful to the weldor in obtaining overall job perspective. How to execute various joints, of course, is mandatory knowledge for the weldor's job.

A weld joint is the part of an assembly through which loads of various types are transferred from one member to another. The designer determines what loads are to be transferred, the joint configuration deemed practical for transferring the loads, and the type and size of welds to use at the joint. The terms "joint" and "weld" are not synonomous. As Fig. 7-1 shows, there are five different types of joints, but 12 different types of welds. And a butt joint (B in Fig. 7-1) can be made with 10 different types of welds (all of the single and double welds in Fig. 7-1 except the two fillets). Furthermore, a weld that one may normally consider a weld for a butt joint can also be used for corners or T joints; thus in Fig. 7-2 a single-bevel weld is used in a T and corner joint and a single-V groove weld is used in a corner joint.

FILLET-WELDED JOINTS

The fillet weld, requiring no groove preparation, is one of the most commonly used welds. Corner welds are also widely use in machine design. Various corner arrangements are illustrated in Fig. 7-3. The corner-to-corner joint, as in Fig. 7-3(a), is difficult to assemble because neither plate can be supported by the other. A small electrode with low welding current must be used so that the first welding pass does not burn through. The joint requires a large amount of metal. The corner joint shown in Fig. 7-3(b) is easy to assemble, does not easily burn through, and requires just half the amount of the weld metal as the joint in Fig. 7-3(a). However, by

TYPES of JOINTS   TYPES of WELDS

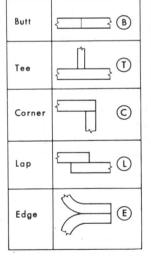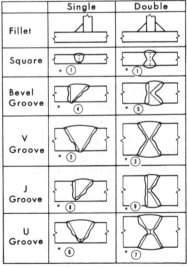

Fig. 7-1. Joint designs (left); weld types (right).

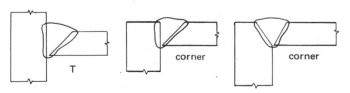

Fig. 7-2. Single-bevel weld used in T joint (left) and corner joint (center); single-V in corner joint (right).

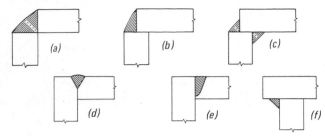

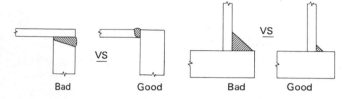

Fig. 7-3. Various corner joints.

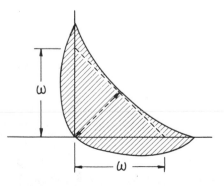

Fig. 7-4. Size of weld should be determined with reference to thinner member.

using half the weld size, but placing two welds, one outside and the other inside, as in Fig. 7-3(c), it is possible to obtain the same total throat as with the first weld. Only half the weld metal need be used.

With thick plates, a partial-penetration groove joint, as in Fig. 7-3(d) is often used. This requires beveling. For a deeper joint, a J preparation, as in Fig. 7-3(e), may be used in preference to a bevel. The fillet weld in Fig. 7-3(f) is out of sight and makes a neat and economical corner.

In good practice, the size of the weld will always be designed with reference to the size of the thinner member. The joint cannot be made any stronger by using the thicker member for the weld size, and much more weld metal will be required, as illustrated in Fig. 7-4.

In the United States, a fillet weld is measured by the leg size of the largest right triangle that may be inscribed within the cross-sectional area (Fig. 7-5). The throat, a better index to strength, is the shortest distance between the root of the joint and

the face of the diagrammatical weld. As Fig. 7-5 shows, the leg size used may be shorter than the actual leg of the weld. With convex fillets, the actual throat may be longer than the throat of the inscribed triangle.

GROOVE AND FILLET COMBINATIONS

A combination of a partial-penetration groove weld and a fillet weld (Fig. 7-6) is used for many joints. The AWS prequalified, single-bevel groove T joint is reinforced with a fillet weld.

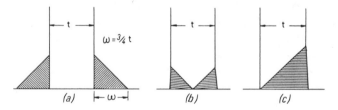

Fig. 7-6. Combined groove and fillet-welded joints.

The designer is frequently faced with the question of whether to use fillet or groove welds (Fig. 7-7). Here cost becomes a major consideration. The fillet welds in Fig. 7-7(a) are easy to apply and require no special plate preparation. They can be made using large-diameter electrodes with high welding currents, and, as a consequence, the deposition rate is high. The cost of the welds increases as the square of the leg size.

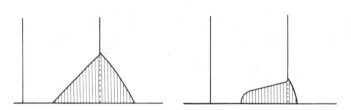

Fig. 7-7. Comparison of fillet welds and groove welds.

In comparison, the double-bevel groove weld in Fig. 7-7(b), has about one-half the weld area of the fillet welds. However, it requires extra preparation and the use of smaller-diameter electrodes with lower welding currents to place the initial pass without burning through. As plate thickness increases, this initial low-deposition region becomes a less important factor, and the higher cost factor decreases in significance. The construction of a curve based on the best possible determination of the actual cost of welding, cutting, and assembling, such as illustrated in Fig. 7-8, is a possible technique for deciding at what point in plate thickness the double-bevel groove weld becomes less costly. The point of intersection of the fillet curve with a

Fig. 7-5. Leg size, ω, of a fillet weld.

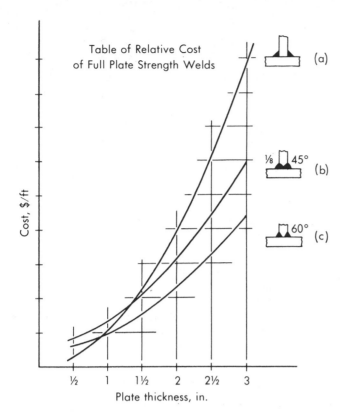

Fig. 7-8. Relative costs of welds having the full strength of the plate.

fatigue loading. Although the illustrated full-strength fillet weld, having leg sizes equal to three-quarters the plate thickness, would be sufficient, some codes have lower allowable limits for fillet welds and may require a leg size equal to the plate thickness. In this case, the cost of the fillet-welded joint may exceed the cost of the single-bevel groove in thicker plates. Also, if the joint is so positioned that the weld can be made in the flat position, a single-bevel groove weld would be less expensive than if fillet welds were specified. As can be seen in Fig. 7-9, one of the fillets would have to be made in the overhead position — a costly operation.

The partial-penetration double-bevel groove joint shown in Fig. 7-10 has been suggested as a full-strength weld. The plate is beveled at 60° on both sides to give a penetration of at least 29% of the thickness of the plate (.29t). After the groove is filled, it is reinforced with a fillet weld of equal cross-sectional area and shape. This partial-penetration double-bevel groove joint has 57.8% the weld metal of the full-strength fillet weld. It requires joint preparation; however, the 60° angle allows the use of large electrodes and high welding current.

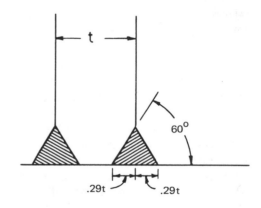

Fig. 7-10. Partial-penetration double-bevel groove joint.

groove-weld curve is the point of interest. The accuracy of this device is dependent on the accuracy of the cost data used in constructing the curves.

Referring to Fig. 7-7(c), it will be noted that the single-bevel groove weld requires about the same amount of weld metal as the fillet welds deposited in Fig. 7-7(a). Thus, there is no apparent economic advantage. There are some disadvantages, though. The single-bevel joint requires bevel preparation and initially a lower deposition rate at the root of the joint. From a design standpoint, however, it offers a direct transfer of force through the joint, which means that it is probably better under

Full-strength welds are not always required in the design, and economies can often be achieved by using partial-strength welds where these are applicable and permissible. Referring to Fig. 7-11, it can be seen that on the basis of an unreinforced 1-in. throat, a 45° partial-penetration, single-bevel groove weld requires just one-half the weld area needed for a fillet weld. Such a weld may not be as economical as the same strength fillet weld, however, because of the cost of edge preparation and need to use a smaller electrode and lower current on the initial pass.

If the single-bevel groove joint were reinforced with an equal-leg fillet weld, the cross-sectional area for the same throat size would still be one-half

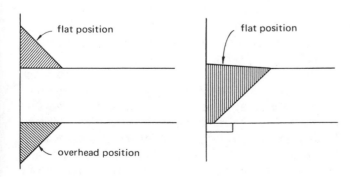

Fig. 7-9. In the flat position, a single-bevel groove joint is less expensive than fillet welds in making a T joint.

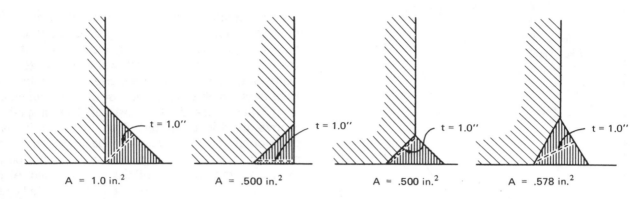

Fig. 7-11. Comparison of weld joints having equal throats.

the area of the fillet, and less beveling would be required. The single-bevel 60° groove joint with an equal fillet weld reinforcement for the same throat size would have an area of 57.8% of the simple fillet weld. This joint has the benefit of smaller cross-sectional area — yet the 60° included angle allows the use of higher welding current and larger electrodes. The only disadvantage is the extra cost of preparation.

From this discussion, it is apparent that the simple fillet-welded joint is the easiest to make, but may require excessive weld metal for larger sizes. The single-bevel 45°-included-angle joint is a good choice for the larger weld sizes. However, one would miss opportunities by selecting the two extreme conditions of these two joints. The joints between these two should be considered. Referring to Fig. 7-12, one may start with the single-bevel 45° joint without the reinforcing fillet weld, gradually add a reinforcement, and finallly increase the lower leg of the fillet reinforcement until a full 45° fillet weld is reached. In this figure, p = length of preparation; ω = leg of reinforcing fillet.

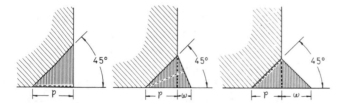

Fig. 7-12. Comparison of weld joints with and without reinforcing fillet welds.

EFFECT OF FILLET SIZE ON WELDING COSTS

The foregoing indicates how rapidly the amount of weld metal increases with increasing leg size of a fillet — and, thus, how welding costs can become excessive with even a small amount of fil-

let oversize. Although the weldor has no influence on the design of the fillet, he can help reduce excessive costs by not oversizing the fillet — depositing it closely to the specified size. Table 7-1 shows how rapidly electrode consumption and welding time increases with increased leg size of a fillet.

TABLE 7-1. Electrode and Welding Time With Increased Leg Sizes of Fillet Weld

Leg Size (in)	Electrode Required (lbs/ft)	Welding Time (hrs/ft)
1/4	0.21	0.0118
5/16	0.30	0.0148
3/8	0.41	0.0182
1/2	0.73	0.0356
5/8	1.15	0.0582
3/4	1.62	0.0822

Inspecting this table, one can see that if a 1/4" fillet is specified and the weldor deposits 3/8" "for good measure", he virtually doubles the amount of weld metal used and increases the welding time by 54%. This slight deviation from specification could possibly turn a profitable job into a losing job for the weldor's employer, depending on how closely welding costs were originally calculated.

GROOVE-WELDED JOINTS

Groove welds are commonly used for butt joints and some T and corner joints where maximum strength and reliability are required. Fig. 7-13 and 7-14 show the various types of groove preparations for butt joints.

The square groove is the most economical, since it requires no edge preparation. With relatively thin material, one merely places the pieces at prescribed distances apart and welds from one or both sides, depending on whether the weld is to be single or double. In some instances, the material is abutted and penetration and reinforcement alone depended on to effect adequate joining. If the material is over 3/8" thick, however, and the shielded

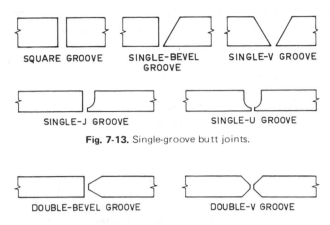

Fig. 7-13. Single-groove butt joints.

Fig. 7-14. Double-groove butt joints.

metal-arc process is used, it may be necessary to prepare the edges if 100% penetration is required. Edges of plate over 3/8″ thick may be prepared for single-bevel, double-bevel, single-V, double-V, single-J, or single-U welds. Single-groove welds are used when the welding is done from one side only; double-groove welds when the weldment can be turned over and welding done from both sides. Double-groove welds are the most economical — use less weld metal and welding time — especially on thick sections. Joints designed for welding with a deep-penetration process — such as submerged-arc — require less bevel angle and, thus, less electrode metal for fill.

Groove welds should be designed so that complete penetration is possible with the least amount of welding. Welds must extend completely through the cross section of the plates being joined. Also, complete fusion without slag entrapment, excessive porosity, or cracking must be obtained for a satisfactory weld. Bevel angles should not exceed 30 degrees for single-V groove welds in order to minimize the amount of filler metal required. Note the difference in required weld metal per foot for each of the three joint preparations in Fig. 7-15.

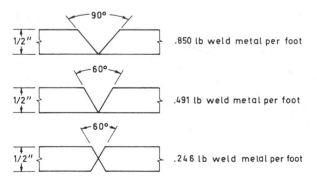

Fig. 7-15. Comparison of the amount of weld metal to fill three types of groove preparations.

Fig. 7-16 indicates that the root opening (R) is the separation between the members to be joined.

A root opening is used for electrode accessibility to the base or root of the joint. The smaller the angle of the bevel, the larger the root opening must be to get good fusion at the root.

If the root opening is too small, root fusion is more difficult to obtain, and smaller electrodes must be used, thus slowing down the welding process.

If the root opening is too large, weld quality does not suffer but more weld metal is required; this increases welding cost and will tend to increase distortion.

Fig. 7-17 indicates how the root opening must be increased as the included angle of the bevel is

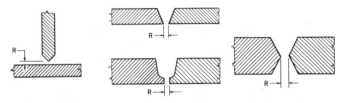

Fig. 7-16. Root openings with various joint preparations.

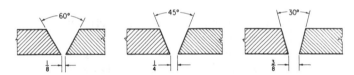

Fig. 7-17. How the root opening must be increased as the bevel angle is decreased.

decreased. Backup strips are used on larger root openings. All three preparations are acceptable; all are conducive to good welding procedure and good weld quality. Selection, therefore, it's usually based on cost.

Root opening and joint preparation will directly affect weld cost (pounds of metal required), and choice should be made with this in mind. Joint preparation involves the work required on plate edges prior to welding and includes beveling and providing a root face.

Using a double-groove joint in preference to a single-groove (Fig. 7-18) cuts in half the amount of welding. This reduces distortion and makes possi-

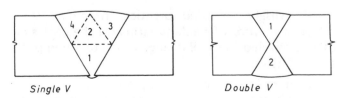

Fig. 7-18. Using double-groove joint in place of single-groove joint reduces amount of welding.

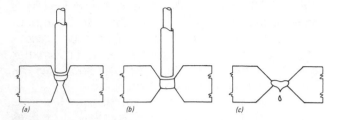

Fig. 7-19. (a) If the gap is too small, the weld will bridge the gap, leaving slag at the root; (b) a proper joint preparation; (c) a root opening too large will result in burnthrough.

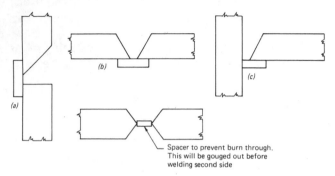

Spacer to prevent burn through. This will be gouged out before welding second side

Fig. 7-20. Backup strips — (a), (b) and (c) — are used when all welding is done from one side or, when the root opening is excessive, a spacer to prevent burnthrough (d) will be gouged out before welding the second side.

ble alternating the weld passes on each side of the joint, again reducing distortion.

In Fig. 7-19(a), if the bevel or gap is too small, the weld will bridge the gap leaving slag at the root. Excessive back-gouging is then required.

Figure 7-19(b) shows how proper joint preparation and procedure will produce good root fusion and will minimize back-gouging.

In Fig. 7-19(c), a large root opening will result in burnthrough. Spacer strip may be used, in which case the joint must be back-gouged.

Backup strips are commonly used when all welding must be done from one side, or when the root opening is excessive. Backup strips, shown in Fig 7-20(a), (b), and (c), are generally left in place and become an integral part of the joint.

Spacer strips may be used especially in the case of double-V joints to prevent burnthrough. The spacer in Fig. 7-20(d) to prevent burnthrough will be gouged out before welding the second side.

THE USE OF BACKUP STRIPS

A widely accepted practice in joining steel plates is the use of backing strips on the root side of the beveled joint. Backing is used to accomplish the following:

1. Alignment and spacing of plate edges.
2. Aid to the operator in producing a sound root weld without burnthrough.

3. Assure complete penetration through the joint.
4. Act as a heat sink to distribute more evenly the welding heat.
5. Aid in shaping the root side of the joint when a grooved copper bar is used.
6. Aid in assuring adequate inert gas coverage on underside of weld on certain materials when using the gas tungsten-arc or gas metal-arc processes.

Materials most generally used for weld backing include flat steel bars (usually about 3/16-inch thick by one-inch wide), copper bars, or special glass-fiber backing tape. The latter is especially good for use on odd shapes that may be very difficult to prepare with flat metal bars. The steel bar is the most widely used. In Fig. 7-21, the steel backing strip could become a part of the joint or could be removed, usually by chipping, followed by back-gouging into the root area to sound material and weld filling. When copper backing strips are used, the molten steel does not adhere to the copper. If a groove is machined in the surface of the copper strip, it will act as a "mold" to shape the underside of the weld bead, as illustrated in Fig. 7-22.

Fig. 7-21. The steel backup strip could become a part of the finished joint or could be removed, followed by back-gouging and weld filling.

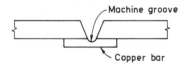

Machine groove

Copper bar

Fig. 7-22. A machined groove in a copper backup acts as a mold to shape the underside of the root weld bead.

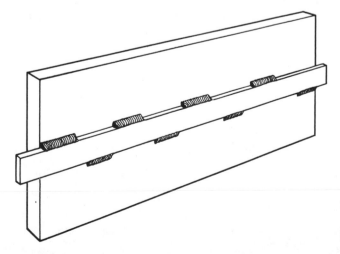

Fig. 7-23. Short intermittent tack welds should be used to hold the backup strip in place.

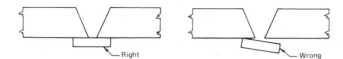

Fig. 7-24. The backup strip should be in intimate contact with both edges of plate.

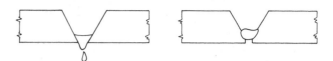

Fig. 7-26. A feather edge is more prone to burnthrough than a joint with a root face.

Backup strip material should conform to the base metal. Feather edges of the plate are recommended when using a backup strip.

Short intermittent tack welds should be used to hold the backup strip in place, and these should preferably be staggered to reduce any initial restraint of the joint. They should not be directly opposite one another (Fig. 7-23).

The backup strip should be in intimate contact with both plate edges to avoid trapped slag at the root (Fig. 7-24).

PLATE EDGE PREPARATION

Plate edges may be prepared for welding by any of the following methods:

1. Oxyacetylene cutting.
2. Machining.
3. Air carbon-arc gouging.
4. Chipping (pneumatic chipping guns).
5. Grinding.

Oxyacetylene cutting is by far the most widely used method on steel plates, due to its speed, economy, and adaptability. Machining may be economically used on work calling for considerable repetition or where the accuracy of machined parts may be an important factor. Preparation for J or U grooves is often done by machining. The edges of other than flat sections, such as parts of castings, may be beveled by chipping. Even on flat plates the edges may be beveled by chipping in areas where machining would be impossible or where oxyacetylene cutting might be dangerous or impractical. Grinding should be used only on small sections not lending themselves to the faster methods. Air carbon-arc gouging is widely used in welding plants working on materials such as stainless steel or cast iron, as well as on ordinary carbon steel.

Edge preparation frequently requires a root face. The main purpose of a root face (Fig. 7-25) is

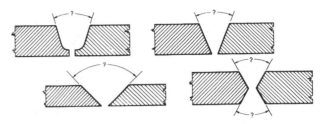

Fig. 7-27. Accessibility is gained by compromising between bevel and root opening.

to provide an additional thickness of metal, as opposed to a feather edge, in order to minimize any burnthrough tendency. A feather-edge preparation is more prone to burnthrough than a joint with a root face, especially if the gap gets a little too large (Fig. 7-26).

A root face is not as easily obtained as a feather edge. A feather edge is generally a matter of one cut with a torch, while a root face will usually require two cuts or possibly a torch cut plus machining.

A root face usually requires back-gouging if a 100% weld is required. A root face is not recommended when welding into a backup strip, since a gas pocket would be formed.

Plate edges are beveled to permit accessibility to all parts of the joint and insure good fusion throughout the entire weld cross section. Accessibility can be gained by compromising between maximum bevel and minimum root opening (Fig. 7-27).

Degree of bevel may be dictated by the importance of maintaining proper electrode angle in confined quarters (Fig. 7-28). For the joint illustrated, the minimum recommended bevel is 45°.

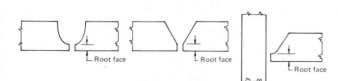

Fig. 7-25. A root face minimizes tendency to burnthrough.

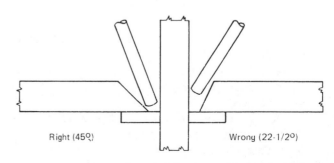

Fig. 7-28. Degree of bevel may be dictated by the need for maintaining proper electrode angle.

Fig. 7-29. Without back-gouging, penetration is incomplete.

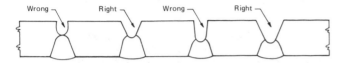

Fig. 7-30. Proper back-gouging should be deep enough to expose sound weld metal.

J and U preparations are excellent to work with, but economically they may have little to offer because preparation requires machining as opposed to simple torch cutting. Also a J or U groove requires a root face and thus back-gouging.

To consistently obtain complete fusion when welding a plate, back-gouging is required on virtually all joints except bevel joints with feather edge. This may be done by any convenient means, grinding, chipping, or gouging. The latter method is generally the most economical and leaves an ideal contour for subsequent beads.

Without back-gouging, penetration is incomplete (Fig. 7-29). Proper back-gouging should be deep enough to expose sound weld metal, and the contour should permit the electrode complete accessibility (Fig. 7-30).

POINTS TO REMEMBER ABOUT GROOVE WELDS

In a production company, the designer will specify the weld — tell how he wants grooves prepared and welded. But in the small shop, the weldor will have to do his own designing. The following are points to remember about groove welds:

1. Bevel edges of plate over 1/4-inch thick to assure 100% penetration but not enough to cause overwelding. Bevel should not exceed 30 degrees on each plate edge.
2. A single-V groove should be used on plates up to 3/8-inch thick.
3. A double-V groove should be used on plates over 3/4-inch thick. This will require less filler metal, is faster, and will control any distortion by the alternate welding on both sides of the neutral axis.
4. Avoid excessive build-up on the weld surface. This is not only costly but may cause points of severe stress concentration.
5. Use backing bars to speed work and assure sound root area.

6. When joining two edges of unequal thickness, it may be necessary to bevel the thick section near the joint area in order to match the lighter section. This is a good way to reduce severe stress concentration.
7. Avoid placing the joints at points of maximum stress.
8. Weld in the flat position if possible.

WELDING COSTS

In the foregoing, the cost of welding has been mentioned frequently. Designs are created and welding processes and procedures are selected to minimize welding costs. If the weldor on the job follows the instructions given him, he will perform in a way as to minimize costs — as opportunities for cost minimization are foreseen by the designer and others at the engineering level. But the weldor-owner of a small shop needs to know something about cost estimation — and many weldors operate small shops as a primary business or supplementary to their corporate employment.

A comprehensive method for evaluating arc welding costs is given in *The Procedure Handbook of Arc Welding,* Twelfth Edition, published by The Lincoln Electric Company, Cleveland, Ohio. This handbook also gives a "quick method for estimating weld costs", which is presented in the following text.

As pointed out in the Lincoln handbook, some situations do not require the accuracy of a careful cost analysis. For example, preliminary estimates would be satisfactory for comparing two welding processes doing the same job. Also, for estimating jobs in a small welding shop — to the estimated cost of which an arbitrary profit will be added — there is no point in calculations to a fraction of a dollar. A quick method for comparison purposes is to disregard the cost of consumables and calculate the cost only on the labor and overhead. The following equation may be used for this purpose:

$$CL = \frac{CR}{(S)\,(OF)}$$

Where —

CL = Cost of labor and overhead per linear foot of weld in dollars per foot.

CR = Cost of labor and overhead in dollars per hour.

S = Speed of electrode travel, feet per hour.

OF = Operating factor, ratio of the productive time to the total time involved.

The equation states that the estimated cost per foot of weld (dollars/foot) is the labor and overhead rate divided by the welding speed (feet/hour) and the operating factor. To use it, one must have values for CR, S, and OF. The cost of labor will be known and the cost of overhead will be established by the management of the business. Frequently, overhead is rated at a percentage of labor, for instance 50%, 80%, or 100%. Operating factor (OF) is largely dependent on the process used and the time for materials handling and other nonwelding operations. With stick-electrode welding, operating factor is frequently 30 to 40%. Speed of electrode travel (S) depends on the weld size, welding process, and other variables. A typical speed in running a 1/4" fillet with E7024 stick electrode is 85 feet per hour.

Use of the cost formula is illustrated by the following example:

A particular job requires making a 1/4" horizontal fillet weld with 7/32" E7024 electrode. Arc speed tables (see the procedure tables in Lincoln's *The Procedure Handbook Arc Welding*) show the value for (S) to be 85 feet per hour. The shop owner has determined that his labor plus overhead (CR) is $7.00 per hour, and since the work is a type that requires considerable time for changing electrodes and handling material, he judges the operating factor to be 30% — or .30 as it would be expressed mathematically. Putting these values into the formula:

$$CL = \frac{CR}{(S)\,(OF)}$$

$$CL = \frac{7.00}{85 \times .30} = \$.274/ft.$$

The shop owner, can, thus, expect his cost of labor and overhead to run about 27-1/2 cents per foot of 1/4" horizontal fillet weld. He may add 5 cents per foot for cost of consumables, which at the time of publication was reasonable for shielded metal-arc welding. To this he can add desired profit and make an intelligent job estimate.

WELDING SYMBOLS

The instructions to the weldor from the design engineer are given on the drawing by standardized welding symbols. These symbols are the "shorthand" by which considerable information is conveyed with positive clarity by a few lines.

Welding symbols show:

- The type of weld.
- The location of the weld.

- The welding process to be used.
- How the parts are to be prepared for welding.
- The size of the weld.
- Whether the weld is to be continuous or intermittent.
- Where any machining, grinding, or other weld-surface finishing is required.
- Whether the weld is to be made in the fabricating plant or on the erection site.

The welding symbols illustrated on the following pages have been standarized and adopted by the American Welding Society. An individual symbol consists of basic elements, joined together to give a precise description of the weld. Any type of weld can be described by the proper combination of these elements.

The fundamental components are the arrow and the reference line to which other symbols are added.

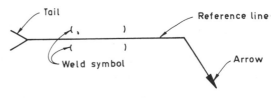

Fig. 7-31

Welding symbols have four distinct parts (see Fig. 7-31). The arrow points to the joint, the reference line is a base for locating the small weld symbols, and the tail is a place to put special procedures or notes. The weld symbols define the type of weld that is required (see Fig. 7-32). The perpendicular leg of the weld symbol is always to the left. Additional information concerning size, length, finish, etc. is placed on the reference line.

TYPE OF WELD							
		PLUG OR SLOT	GROOVE				
BEAD	FILLET		SQUARE	V	BEVEL	U	J
◠	◺	▱	‖	⋁	⋁	⋃	⋃

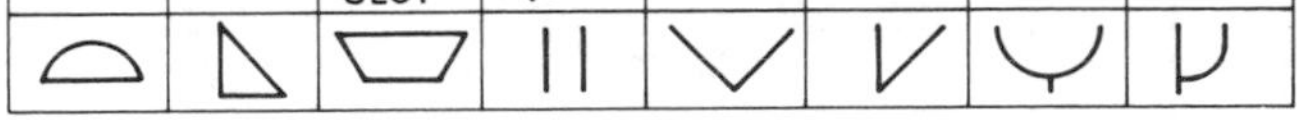

Fig. 7-32

Each joint has two sides; the "arrow" side to which the tip of the arrow points, and the "other" side. It is possible to designate which side is to be welded. If the small weld symbol is below the reference line, the weld is to be made on the "arrow" side; when the symbol is on top of the reference line, the weld is to be made on the "other" side.

It may be difficult to tell from a drawing just what the "other" side is. Fig. 7-33 below, illustrates

AMERICAN WELDING SOCIETY

Basic Welding Symbols and Their Location Significance

Location Significance	Fillet	Plug or Slot	Spot or Projection	Seam	Back or backing	Surfacing	Flange (Edge)	Flange (Corner)
Arrow side					Groove weld symbol			
Other side					Groove weld symbol	Not Used		
Both sides		Not used	Not used	Not used	Not used	Not used	Not used	Not used
No arrow side or other side significance	Not used	Not used			Not used	Not used	Not used	Not used

Supplementary Symbols Used with Welding Symbols

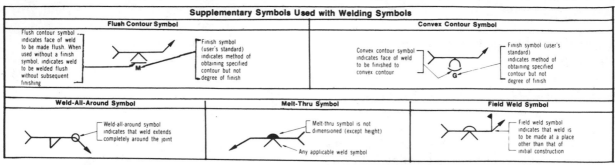

Flush Contour Symbol — Flush contour symbol indicates face of weld to be made flush. When used without a finish symbol, indicates weld to be welded flush without subsequent finishing. Finish symbol (user's standard) indicates method of obtaining specified contour but not degree of finish.

Convex Contour Symbol — Convex contour symbol indicates face of weld to be finished to convex contour. Finish symbol (user's standard) indicates method of obtaining specified contour but not degree of finish.

Weld-All-Around Symbol — Weld-all-around symbol indicates that weld extends completely around the joint.

Melt-Thru Symbol — Melt-thru symbol is not dimensioned (except height). Any applicable weld symbol.

Field Weld Symbol — Field weld symbol indicates that weld is to be made at a place other than that of initial construction.

Basic Joints—Identification of Arrow Side and Other Side of Joint

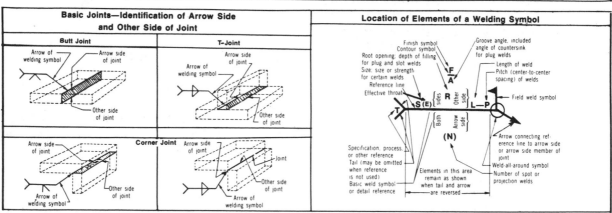

Butt Joint — Arrow of welding symbol; Arrow side of joint; Other side of joint.

T–Joint — Arrow side of joint; Arrow of welding symbol; Other side of joint.

Corner Joint — Arrow side of joint; Joint; Other side of joint; Arrow of welding symbol.

Location of Elements of a Welding Symbol

Finish symbol; Contour symbol; Root opening; depth of filling for plug and slot welds; Size: size or strength for certain welds; Reference line; Effective throat; Groove angle, included angle of countersink for plug welds; Length of weld; Pitch (center-to-center spacing) of welds; Field weld symbol; Specification, process, or other reference; Tail (may be omitted when reference is not used); Basic weld symbol or detail reference; Elements in this area remain as shown when tail and arrow are reversed; Arrow connecting reference line to arrow side or arrow side member of joint; Weld-all-around symbol; Number of spot or projection welds.

Arrow Side and Other Side Member of Joint

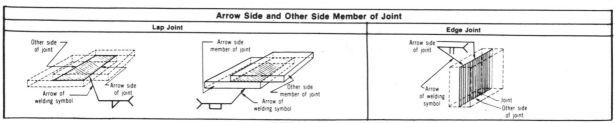

Lap Joint — Other side of joint; Arrow side member of joint; Arrow of welding symbol; Arrow side of joint; Other side member of joint; Arrow of welding symbol.

Edge Joint — Arrow side of joint; Arrow of welding symbol; Joint; Other side of joint.

Designation of Welding and Allied Processes by Letters

AAC . . . air carbon arc cutting	B . . . brazing	CW . . . cold welding	ESW . . . electroslag welding
AAW . . . air acetylene welding	BB . . . block brazing	DB . . . dip brazing	EXW . . . explosion welding
ABD . . . adhesive bonding	BMAW . . . bare metal arc welding	DFB . . . diffusion brazing	FB . . . furnace brazing
AB . . . arc brazing	CAC . . . carbon arc cutting	DFW . . . diffusion welding	FCAW . . . flux cored arc welding
AC . . . arc cutting	CAW . . . carbon arc welding	DS . . . dip soldering	FCAW-EG . . . flux cored arc welding—electrogas
AHW . . . atomic hydrogen welding	CAW-G . . . gas carbon arc welding	EASP . . . electric arc spraying	FLB . . . flow brazing
AOC . . . oxygen arc cutting	CAW-S . . . shielded carbon arc welding	EBC . . . electron beam cutting	FLOW . . . flow welding
AW . . . arc welding	CAW-T . . . twin carbon arc welding	EBW . . . electron beam welding	FLSP . . . flame spraying

FOC . . . chemical flux cutting
FOW . . . forge welding
FRW . . . friction welding
FS . . . furnace soldering
FW . . . flash welding
GMAC . . . gas metal arc cutting
GMAW . . . gas metal arc welding
GMAW-EG . . . gas metal arc welding—electrogas

STANDARD WELDING SYMBOLS

Basic Welding Symbols and Their Location Significance

Supplementary Symbols

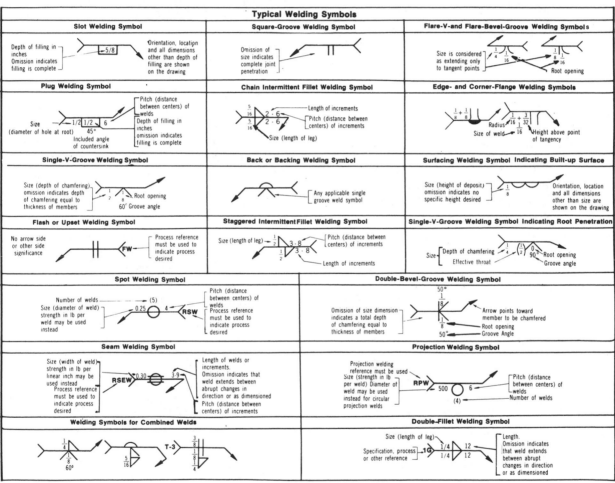

	Groove						Weld-all-Around	Field Weld	Melt-thru
Square	**V**	**Bevel**	**U**	**J**	**Flare-V**	**Flare-bevel**			
								Contour	
	Not used	Not used	Not used	Not used	Not used	Not used	Flush	Convex	Concave

Typical Welding Symbols

Slot Welding Symbol — Depth of filling in inches. Omission indicates filling is complete. −5/8. Orientation, location and all dimensions other than depth of filling are shown on the drawing

Square-Groove Welding Symbol — Omission of size indicates complete joint penetration

Flare-V- and Flare-Bevel-Groove Welding Symbols — Size is considered as extending only to tangent points. Root opening

Plug Welding Symbol — Size (diameter of hole at root) −1/2 1/2 6. 45° Included angle of countersink. Pitch (distance between centers) of welds. Depth of filling in inches, omission indicates filling is complete.

Chain Intermittent Fillet Welding Symbol — Length of increments. Pitch (distance between centers) of increments. Size (length of leg)

Edge- and Corner-Flange Welding Symbols — Radius. Size of weld. Height above point of tangency

Single-V-Groove Welding Symbol — Size (depth of chamfering), omission indicates depth of chamfering equal to thickness of members. 60° Groove angle. Root opening

Back or Backing Welding Symbol — Any applicable single groove weld symbol

Surfacing Welding Symbol Indicating Built-up Surface — Size (height of deposit), omission indicates no specific height desired. Orientation, location and all dimensions other than size are shown on the drawing

Flash or Upset Welding Symbol — No arrow side or other side significance. FW. Process reference must be used to indicate process desired

Staggered Intermittent Fillet Welding Symbol — Size (length of leg). 3-8. Pitch (distance between centers) of increments. Length of increments

Single-V-Groove Welding Symbol Indicating Root Penetration — Size: Depth of chamfering. Effective throat. Root opening. Groove angle. 90°

Spot Welding Symbol — Number of welds (5). Size (diameter of weld) strength in lb per weld may be used instead. 0.25 4 RSW. Pitch (distance between centers) of welds. Process reference must be used to indicate process desired

Double-Bevel-Groove Welding Symbol — 50°. Omission of size dimension indicates a total depth of chamfering equal to thickness of members. Arrow points toward member to be chamfered. Root opening. Groove Angle. 50°

Seam Welding Symbol — Size (width of weld) strength in lb per linear inch may be used instead. RSEW 0.30 3-9. Process reference must be used to indicate process desired. Length of welds or increments. Omission indicates that weld extends between abrupt changes in direction or as dimensioned. Pitch (distance between centers) of increments

Projection Welding Symbol — Projection welding reference must be used. Size (strength in lb per weld) Diameter of weld may be used instead for circular projection welds. RPW 500 6. (4). Pitch (distance between centers) of welds. Number of welds

Welding Symbols for Combined Welds — 1/4. 1/8 60°. 5/16. T-3 3/8 1/8 1/4

Double-Fillet Welding Symbol — Size (length of leg). Specification, process or other reference. 1/4 12, 1/4 12. Length. Omission indicates that weld extends between abrupt changes in direction or as dimensioned

Designation of Welding and Allied Processes by Letters

GMAW-P ...gas metal arc welding—pulsed arc	IB ...... induction brazing	LOC .... oxygen lance cutting	OFC-P .... oxypropane cutting	PSP .... plasma spraying	S .... soldering
GMAW-S .... gas metal arc welding— short circuiting arc	INS ..... iron soldering	MAC .... metal arc cutting	OFW ....oxyfuel gas welding	RB .... resistance brazing	SAW ...... submerged arc welding
GTAC .... gas tungsten arc cutting	IRB .... infrared brazing	OAW ....oxyacetylene welding	OHW .... oxyhydrogen welding	RPW ....projection welding	SAW-S ... series submerged arc welding
GTAW ....gas tungsten arc welding	IRS .... infrared soldering	OC .... oxygen cutting	PAC .... plasma arc cutting	RS ....resistance soldering	SMAC .....shielded metal arc cutting
GTAW-P ..gas tungsten arc welding—pulsed arc	IS ..... induction soldering	OFC ....oxyfuel gas cutting	PAW ... plasma arc welding	RSEW ... resistance seam welding	SMAW .... shielded metal arc welding
HFRW ....high frequency resistance welding	IW ...... induction welding	OFC-A ....oxyacetylene cutting	PEW .... percussion welding	RSW ... resistance spot welding	SSW ...... solid state welding
HPW ....hot pressure welding	LBC ...laser beam cutting	OFC-H ....oxyhydrogen cutting	PGW ....pressure gas welding	ROW .... roll welding	SW ....stud arc welding
	LBW ...laser beam welding	OFC-N ....oxynatural gas cutting	POC .... metal powder cutting	RW ....resistance welding	TB .... torch brazing

a simple method for properly determining this. If you mentally "look" through the joint, you can "see" the "other" side. If you try to "look" the wrong way you will be "looking" at solid metal and will not be able to "see" through it. Always look through the joint. Remember that the arrow does not necessarily point to the "other" side. This can be clearly seen in Fig. 7-33 where the arrow points through solid metal and does not point to the "other" side. Therefore, in this case, one can not use the direction of the arrow as a guide to finding the "other" side.

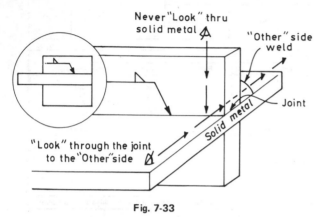

Fig. 7-33

The size and length of the desired weld are frequently specified on drawings. This information is placed on either side of the basic symbol. On the left side is the size of the weld, and on the right is the length and spacing (see Fig. 7-34).

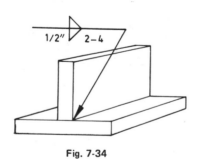

Fig. 7-34

Plate preparation such as beveling can also be indicated by welding symbols together with required dimensions.

Since fillet welds and simple butt welds comprise 95% of the work in steel fabrication, the student would do well to study these and commit them to memory. When, on the job, doubt arises as to the meaning of welding symbols, reference to a symbol chart is desirable. Only with time and experience will the weldor be able to understand all AWS symbols at first glance.

Figure 7-1 in the preceding text shows types of joints and types of welds. In a joint, the adjoining members may contact each other in several ways, as illustrated by the butt, T, corner, lap, and edge joints. These general descriptions of the joint geometry, however, do not define the weld joint configuration, since it can be made in various ways. Plate condition and preparation can also be indicated by welding symbols together with the required dimensions. Thus, a welded butt joint can be made square, double-square, single-bevel, single-V, double-V, or by four other joint configurations. A "T" connection can be made with a double fillet, as shown, or it may be made with a single or double bevel or single or double J. V and U weld joints are feasible only for butt and corner welds because of the need for the preparation of both surfaces.

Weld symbols are described in the following two pages, headed "American Welding Society Standard Welding Symbols", and their application to various joints and welds is given on the two pages that follow the AWS symbols charts.

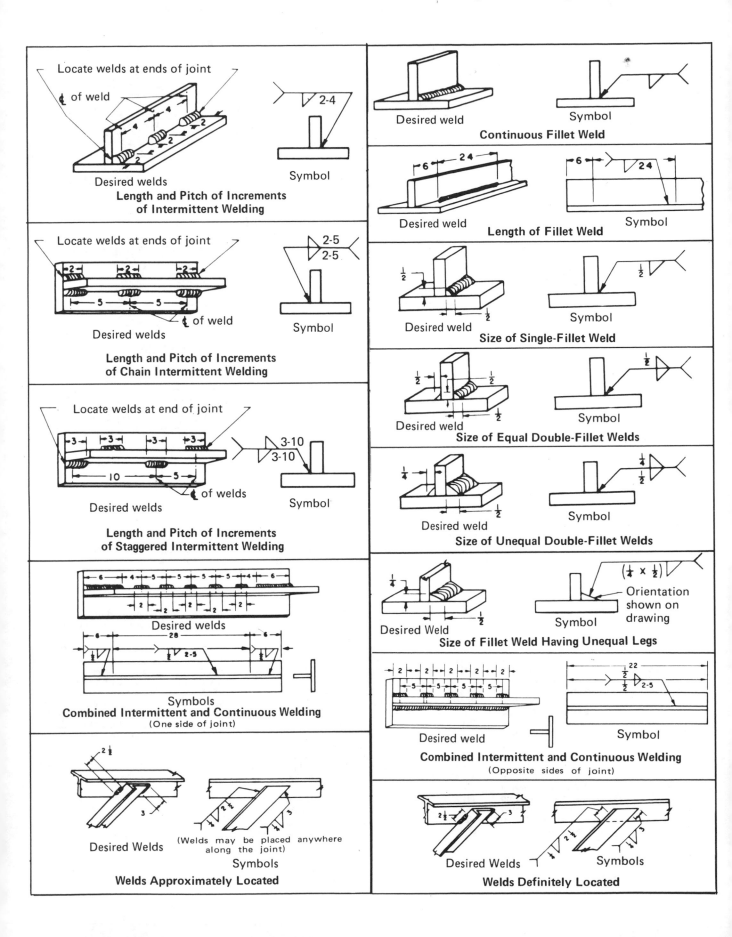

Length and Pitch of Increments of Intermittent Welding

Locate welds at ends of joint

℄ of weld

Desired welds

Symbol

Length and Pitch of Increments of Chain Intermittent Welding

Locate welds at ends of joint

℄ of weld

Desired welds

Symbol

Length and Pitch of Increments of Staggered Intermittent Welding

Locate welds at end of joint

℄ of welds

Desired welds

Symbol

Combined Intermittent and Continuous Welding
(One side of joint)

Desired welds

Symbols

Welds Approximately Located

Desired Welds

(Welds may be placed anywhere along the joint)

Symbols

Continuous Fillet Weld

Desired weld

Symbol

Length of Fillet Weld

Desired weld

Symbol

Size of Single-Fillet Weld

Desired weld

Symbol

Size of Equal Double-Fillet Welds

Desired weld

Symbol

Size of Unequal Double-Fillet Welds

Desired weld

Symbol

Size of Fillet Weld Having Unequal Legs

Desired Weld

Symbol

Orientation shown on drawing

Combined Intermittent and Continuous Welding
(Opposite sides of joint)

Desired weld

Symbol

Welds Definitely Located

Desired Welds

Symbols

Basic Joints — Identification of Arrow Side and Other Side of Joint

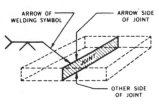

BUTT JOINT

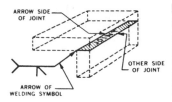

CORNER JOINT

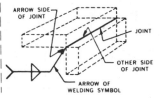

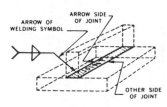

TEE JOINT

Arrow-Side and Other-Side Member of Joint

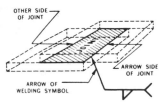

LAP JOINT

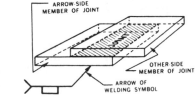

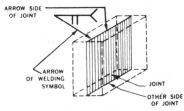

EDGE JOINT

Fillet	Plug or Slot	Spot or Projection	Seam	Groove							Back or Backing	Sur-facing	Flange	
				Square	V	Bevel	U	J	Flare V	Flare-bevel			Edge	Corner
△	▭	○	⊕	‖	∨	V	⋃	⊍	⋎	⎰	⌣	⌣⌣	⅃�	⅃⌐

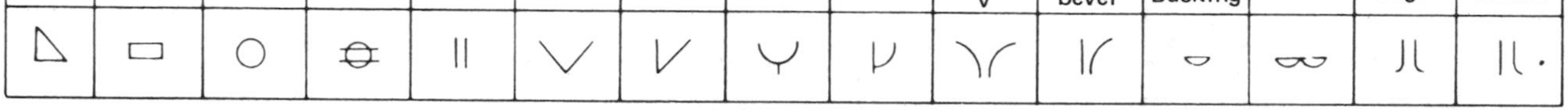

ARC-SEAM OR ARC-SPOT	RESIS-TANCE SPOT	PROJEC-TION	RESIS-TANCE SEAM	FLASH OR UPSET
	✳	✕	XXX	❘

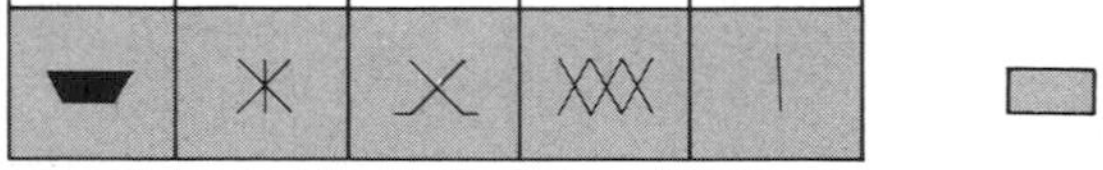

NONPREFERRED SYMBOLS: USE PREFERRED SYMBOL WITH PROCESS REFERENCE IN THE TAIL

Designation of Welding Processes by Letters

CAW . . . . Carbon-Arc Welding
CW . . . . Cold Welding
DB . . . . Dip Brazing
DFW . . . . Diffusion Welding
EBW . . . . . Electron Beam Welding
EW . . . . Electroslag Welding
EXW . . . . Explosion Welding
FB . . . . Furnace Brazing
FCAW . . . . Flux-Cored Arc Welding
FOW . . . . Forge Welding
FRW . . . . Friction Welding

FW . . . . Flash Welding
GMAW . . . . . Gas Metal-Arc Welding
GTAW . . . . Gas Tungsten-Arc Welding
IB . . . . Induction Brazing
IRB . . . . Infrared Brazing
IW . . . . Induction Welding

LBW . . . . Laser Beam Welding
OAW . . . . . .Oxyacetylene Welding
OHW . . . . . . .Oxyhydrogen Welding
PAW . . . . Plasma-Arc Welding
PEW . . . . Percussion Welding
PGW . . . . . . Pressure Gas Welding

RB . . . . .Resistance Brazing
RPW . . . . .Projection Welding
RSEW . . . . . Resistance-Seam Welding
RSW . . . . . . Resistance-Spot Welding
SAW . . . . .Submerged-Arc Welding
SMAW . . . Shielded Metal-Arc Welding
SW . . . . .Stud Welding
TB . . . . Torch Brazing
TW . . . . .Thermit Welding
USW . . . . .Ultrasonic Welding
UW . . . . Upset Welding

Designation of Cutting Processes by Letters

AAC . . . . Air Carbon-Arc Cutting
AC . . . . .Arc Cutting
AOC . . . . .Oxygen-Arc Cutting
CAC . . . . Carbon-Arc Cutting
FOC . . . . Chemical Flux Cutting
MAC . . . . Metal-Arc Cutting
OC . . . . Oxygen Cutting
PAC . . . . Plasma-Arc Cutting
POC . . . . .Metal Powder Cutting

Problems In Arc Welding

The beginner in arc welding will encounter a number of practical problems — such as striking the arc without sticking the electrode to the work — that will be solved and overcome with practice and experience. However, there are two problems — namely how to deal with arc blow and how to minimize weldment distortion — that require special knowledge for handling. Arc blow, of course, pertains to arc welding only. Distortion is a problem that can be encountered in all types of fusion welding.

ARC BLOW

Arc blow is a phenomenon encountered in DC arc welding when the arc stream does not follow the shortest path between the electrode and the workpiece, but is deflected forward or backward from the direction of travel or, less frequently, to one side. Unless controlled, arc blow can be the cause of difficulties in handling the molten pool and slag, excessive spatter, incomplete fusion, reduced welding speed, porosity, and lowered weld quality.

Back blow occurs when welding toward the ground connection, end of a joint, or into a corner. Forward blow is encountered when welding away from the ground or at the start of the joint. Forward blow can be especially troublesome with iron-powder or other electrodes that produce large slage coverings, where the effect is to drag the heavy slag or the crater forward and under the arc.

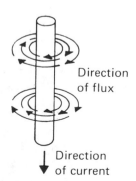

Fig. 8-1. A current through a conductor sets up a magnetic field that may be represented by planes of concentric circles — "flux lines."

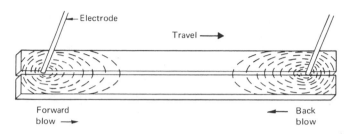

Fig. 8-2. Concentration of magnetic flux behind the arc at start of joint forces the arc forward. Flux concentration ahead of the arc at the end of the joint forces the arc backwards.

There are two types of arc blow of concern to the weldor. Their designations — magnetic and thermal — are indicative of their origins. Of the two, magnetic arc blow is the type causing most welding problems.

MAGNETIC ARC BLOW

Magnetic arc blow is caused by an unbalanced condition in the magnetic field surrounding the arc. Unbalanced conditions result from the fact that at most times the arc will be farther from one end of the joint than another and will be at varying distances from the ground connection. Imbalance also always exists because of the change in direction of the current as it flows from the electrode, through the arc, and into and through the workpiece.

To understand arc blow, it is helpful to visualize a magnetic field. Fig. 8-1 shows a DC current passing through a conductor, which could be an electrode or the ionized gas stream between an electrode and a weld joint. Around the conductor a magnetic field, or flux, is set up, with lines of force that can be represented by concentric circles in planes at right angle to the direction of the current. These circular lines of force diminish in intensity the farther they are from the electrical conductor.

They remain circular when they can stay in one medium, say air or metal, expansive enough to contain them until they diminish to essentially nothing in intensity. But if the medium changes, say from steel plate to air, the circular lines of forces are distorted; the forces tend to concentrate in the steel where they encounter less resistance. At a boundary between the edges of a steel plate and air, there is a squeezing of the magnetic flux lines, with deformation in the circular planes of force. This squeezing can result in a heavy concentration of flux behind or ahead of a welding arc. The arc then tends to move in the direction that would relieve the squeezing — would tend to restore flux balance. It veers away from the side of flux concentration — and this veering is the observed phenomenon of arc blow.

Fig. 8-2 illustrates the squeezing and distortion of flux fields at the start and finish of a seam weld. At the start, the flux lines are concentrated behind the electrode. (One might say the flux lines balk at leaving the steel plate and moving out into the air.) The arc tries to compensate for this imbalance by moving forward, creating forward arc blow. As the electrode approaches the end of the seam, the squeezing is ahead of the arc, with a resultant movement of the arc backwards, and the development of back blow. At the middle of a seam in two members of the same width, the flux field would be symmetrical, and there would be no back or forward arc blow. If one member should be wide and the other narrow, however, side blow could occur at the midpoint of the weld.

The representations in Fig. 8-2 are only partly descriptive of what really happens. Another "squeezing" phenomenon also has effect on the observed arc blow. This secondary effect results from the ground current within the workpiece. As shown in Fig. 8-3, a magnetic flux is also set up by the electrical current passing through the workpiece to the ground. The heavy line represents the path of the welding current and the light lines the magnetic field set up by the current. As the current changes direction, or turns the corner from the arc to the work, a concentration of flux occurs at x, which causes the arc to blow, as indicated, away from the ground. This is called the "ground effect."

The movement of the arc because of the ground effect will combine with the movement re-

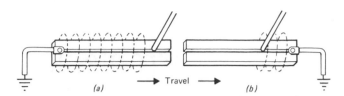

Fig. 8-4. Flux set up by ground current is behind the arc in (a), and ahead of the arc in (b).

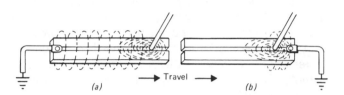

Fig. 8-5. Superimposed magnetic fields. Magnetic blow at the finish end of the joint (a) is reduced because the two flux fields tend to offset one another. At (b) the two fields are additive and cause a strong back blow.

sulting from the concentration previously described to give the observed arc blow. Since the two movements are algebraically additive, ground effect may diminish or increase the arc blow caused by the magnetic flux of the arc. In fact, control of the ground effect is one way to control arc blow especially useful with automatic welding processes.

In Fig. 8-4 (a), the ground is connected to the starting end of the seam, and the flux resulting from the ground current in the work is behind the arc. The arc movement resulting from the ground effect would, thus, be forward. At the start of the weld, this would be additive to the arc movement shown in Fig. 8-2. Near the end of the seam, however, the forward movement from the ground effect would diminish the total arc blow by cancelling some of the back blow resulting from concentration of the flux from the arc at the end of the workpiece. Fir. 8-5 (a) is illustrative.

In Fig. 8-4 (b), the ground is connected to the finish end of the seam, and the ground effect results in back blow. Here, it would increase the back blow of the arc flux at the finish of the weld. The combination of "squeezed" magnetic fluxes is illustrated in Fig. 8-5 (b). A ground at the finish of the weld, however, may be what the weldor needs to reduce excessive forward blow at the start of the weld.

Because ground effect is less forceful than concentrations of arc-derived magnetic flux at the ends of workpieces, positioning of the ground connection is only moderately effective in controlling arc blow. Other measures must also be used to reduce the difficulties caused by arc blow when welding.

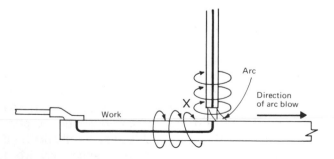

Fig. 8-3. Arc blow caused by ground effect. The magnetic flux set up by the ground current combines with the flux around the electrode causing a high flux concentration at (x) that blows the arc away from the ground connection.

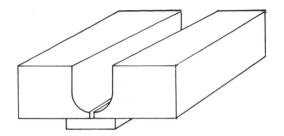

Fig. 8-6. Arc-blow problems are frequently encountered when welding with high DC current in deep groove joints such as this. The use of AC current may be an expedient solution.

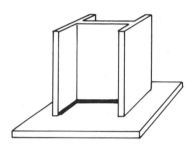

Fig. 8-7. Considerable arc blow can be expected when placing this "inside" fillet, using DC current. AC may be the solution.

Arc blow is also encountered in corners and in deep V joints. Although analysis of these situations is complicated, the cause is exactly the same as when welding a straight seam — concentrations of lines of magnetic flux and the movememnt of the arc to relieve such concentrations. Fig. 8-6.

Fig. 8-7 illustrate situations in which arc blow with DC current is likely to be a problem.

There is less arc blow with low current than with high current. This is because the intensity of the magnetic field a given distance from the conductor of electric current is proportional to the current. Usually, serious arc-blow problems do not occur when stick-electrode welding with DC up to about 250 amperes, but this is not an exact parameter since joint fitup and geometry could have major influence. With submerged-arc welding, still higher currents can often be used without creating arc-blow problems. The granular flux used with the submerged-arc process tends to dampen the arc-blow caused by magnetic fields.

The use of AC current markedly reduces arc blow. The rapid reversal of the current induces eddy currents in the base metal, and the fields set up by the eddy currents greatly reduce the strength of the magnetic fields that cause arc blow.

THERMAL ARC BLOW

The physics of the electric arc requires a hot spot on both the electrode and plate to maintain a continuous flow of current in the arc stream. As the electrode is advanced along the work, the arc will tend to lag behind. This natural lag of the arc is caused by the reluctance of the arc to move to the colder plate. The space between the end of the electrode and the hot surface of the molten crater is ionized and, therefore, is a more conductive path than from the electrode to the colder plate. When the welding is done manually, the small amount of "thermal back blow" due to the arc lag is not detrimental, but it may become a problem with the higher speeds of automatic welding or when the thermal back blow is added to magnetic back blow.

ARC BLOW WITH MULTIPLE ARCS

When two arcs are close to each other, their magnetic fields react to cause arc blow on both arcs. Multiple arcs are often used to increase the welding speed of the submerged-arc process, and usually the arcs are less than one inch apart.

When two arcs are close and are of opposite polarities, as in Fig. 8-8 (a), the magnetic fields

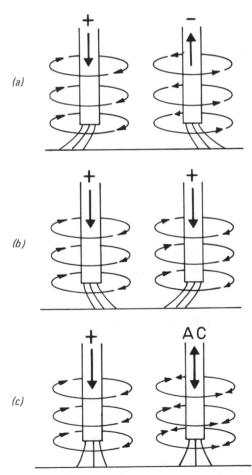

Fig. 8-8. Reactions of the magnetic fields when two arcs are close together: (a) arcs are of different polarities; the magnetic fields are additive and the arcs blow outward; (b) arcs are same polarity; magnetic fields oppose and the arcs blow inward; (c) arcs are DC and AC; little magnetic blow occurs.

between the arcs add to each other. The strong field between the arcs causes the arcs to blow away from each other.

If the arcs are the same polarity, as in Fig. 8-8 (b), the magnetic fields between the arcs oppose each other. This results in a weaker field between the arcs, causing the arcs to blow toward each other.

Usually, when two arcs are used, one is DC and the other AC, as shown in Fig. 8-8(c). The flux field of the AC arc completely reverses for each cycle, and the effect on the DC field is small. Very little arc blow results.

Another commonly used arrangement is two AC arcs. Arc-blow interference here is avoided to a large extent by phase-shifting the current of one arc 80 to 90 degrees from the other arc. A so-called "Scott" connection accomplishes this automatically. With the phase shift, the current and magnetic fields of one arc reach a maximum when the current and magnetic fields of the other arc are at or near minimum. As a result there is very little arc blow.

HOW TO REDUCE ARC BLOW

All arc blow is not detrimental. In fact, a small amount of arc blow can sometimes be used beneficially to help form the bead shape, control molten slag, and control penetration.

When arc blow is causing or contributing to such defects as undercut, inconsistent penetration, crooked beads, beads of irregular width, porosity, wavy beads, and excessive spatter, it must be controlled. Possible corrective measures have already been suggested in the preceding text. In general, here are some methods that might be considered:

- If DC current is being used with the shielded metal-arc process — especially at rates above 250 amperes — a change to AC current may eliminate problems.

- Hold as short an arc as possible to help the arc force counteract the arc blow.

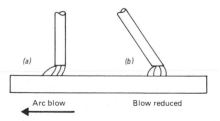

Fig. 8-9. Arc blow, as in (a), can sometimes be corrected by angling the electrode, as in (b).

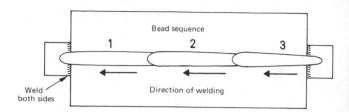

Fig. 8-10. Direction of welding and the sequence of beads for the back-step technique. Note tabs on both ends of the seam. Tabs should be the same thickness as the work.

- Reduce the welding current — which may require a reduction in arc speed.

- Angle the electrode with the work opposite the direction of arc blow, as illustrated in Fig. 8-9.

- Make a heavy tack weld on both ends of the seam; apply frequent tack welds along the seam, especially if the fitup is not tight.

- Weld toward a heavy tack or toward a weld already made.

- Use a back-step welding technique, as shown in Fig. 8-10.

- Weld away from the ground to reduce back blow; weld toward the ground to reduce forward blow.

- With processes where a heavy slag is involved, a small amount of back blow may be desirable; to get this, weld toward the ground.

- Wrap ground cable around the workpiece and pass ground current through it is such a direction that the magnetic field set up will tend to neutralize the magnetic field causing the arc blow.

The direction of the arc blow can be observed with an open-arc process, but with the submerged-arc process must be determined by the type of weld defect.

Back blow is indicated by the following:

- Spatter.

- Undercut, either continuous or intermittent.

- Narrow, high bead, usually with undercut.

- An increase in penetration.

- Surface porosity at the finish end of welds on sheet metal.

Forward blow is indicated by:

- A wide bead, irregular in width.

- Wavy bead.

- Undercut, usually intermittent.

- A decrease in penetration.

EFFECTS OF FIXTURING ON ARC BLOW

Steel fixtures for holding the work pieces may have an effect on the magnetic field around the arc and, thus, on arc blow. Usually, the fixturing causes no problem with stick-electrode welding when the current does not exceed 250 amperes. Fixtures for use with higher currents and with mechanized welding should be designed with precautions taken so that an arc-blow-promoting situation is not built into the fixture.

Each fixturing device may require special study to ascertain the best way to prevent the fixture from interfering deleteriously with the magnetic fields. The following are some points to note:

- Fixtures for welding the longitudinal seam of cylinders (Fig. 8-11) should be designed for a minimum of 1-in. clearance between the supporting beam and the work. The clamping fingers or bars that hold the work should be nonmagnetic. Do not attach the ground cable to the copper backup bar; ground directly to the work if possible.

- Fabricate the fixture from low-carbon steel. This is to prevent the buildup of permanent magnetism in the fixture.

- Welding toward the closed end of "horn type" fixtures reduces back blow.

- Design the fixture long enough so that end tabs can be used if necessary.

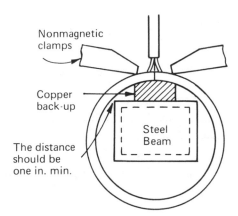

Fig. 8-11. Welding fixtures for clamping cylindrical work should have at least 1 in. of clearance between work and supporting beam. Clamps near the arc should be nonmagnetic.

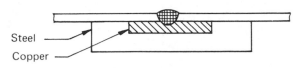

Fig. 8-12. A copper insert in a steel backup bar should not be used. The steel of the backup bar will increase arc blow.

- Do not use a copper strip inserted in a steel bar for a backing, as in Fig. 8-12. The steel part of the backup bar will increase arc blow.

- Provide for continuous or close clamping of parts to be seam-welded. Wide, intermittent clamping may cause seams to gap between clamping points, resulting in arc blow over the gaps.

- Do not build into the fixture large masses of steel on one side of the seam only. Counterbalance with a similar mass on the other side.

WELDMENT DISTORTION

Distortion is a problem common to all welding processes and may become serious if the proper control techniques are not applied. However, there are some general rules to follow that will control distortion to a tolerable amount even on complicated weldments.

Distortion is caused by the nonuniform expansion and contraction of the weld metal and adjacent base metal during the heating and cooling cycle of the welding process. Analysis of the changes occuring during this cycle is extremely complex because of attendant changes that occur in the physical and mechanical properties of metals with temperature change. For practical purposes, it is sufficient to recognize that metals "move" when they are heated or cooled and this movement can result in the distortion of a configuration from the intended shape.

To understand how and why distortion occurs during heating and cooling of a metal, consider the bar of steel shown in Fig. 8-13. As the bar is uniformly heated, it expands in all directions, as shown in Fig. 8-13 (a). As the metal cools to room temperature it contracts uniformly to its original dimensions.

But if the steel bar is restrained — say, in a vise — while it is heated, as shown in Fig. 8-13 (b), lateral expansion cannot take place, Volume expansion must occur, however, so the bar expands a greater amount in the vertical direction (thickness). As the deformed bar returns to room temperature, it will still tend to contract uniformly in all directions, as in Fig. 8-13 (c). The bar is now narrower but thicker. It has been permanently deformed, or distorted. For simplification, the sketches show this distortion occurring in thickness only. Actually, of course, length is similarly affected.

In a welded joint, these same expansion and contraction forces act on the weld metal and on the base metal. As the weld metal solidifies and fuses with the base metal, it is in its maximum expanded state — it occupies the greatest possible

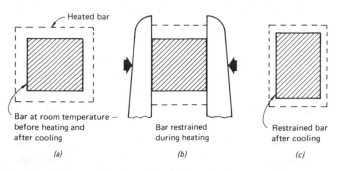

Fig. 8-13. If a steel bar is uniformly heated while unrestrained, as in (a), it will expand in all directions and return to its original dimensions on cooling. If restrained, as in (b), during heating, it can expand only in the vertical direction — become thicker. On cooling, the deformed bar contracts uniformly, as shown in (c), and, thus, is permanently deformed. This is a simplified explanation of a basic cause of distortion in welded assemblies.

volume as a solid. On cooling, it attempts to contract to the volume it would normally occupy at the lower temperature, but it is restrained from doing so by the adjacent base metal. Stresses develop within the weld, finally reaching the yield strength of the weld metal. At this point, the weld stretches, or yields, and thins out, thus adjusting to the volume requirements of the lower temperature. But only those stresses that exceed the yield strength of the weld metal are relieved by this accommodation. By the time the weld reaches room temperature — assuming complete restraint of the base metal so that it cannot move — the weld will contain locked-in tensile stresses approximately equal to the yield strength of the metal. If the restraints (clamps that hold the work piece or an opposing shrinkage force) are removed, the locked-in stresses are partially relieved as they cause the base metal to move, thus distorting the weldment.

Another approach to understanding internal stresses in a weld is shown in Fig. 8-14. Fillet welds

that join two heavy plates contain residual longitudinal and transverse stresses, as indicated in Fig. 8-14 (a). To visualize how these stresses got into the weld, imagine the situation depicted in Fig. 8-14 (b). Here the fillets have been separated from the base plates. The same amount of weld metal is assumed to exist in both situations. In its unattached condition, the weld metal has shrunk to the volume it would normally occupy at room temperature. It is under no restraint and is stress-free.

To get this unattached weld back to the condition in Fig. 8-14 (a), it would be necessary to pull it lengthwise — to impose longitudinal forces — and to stretch it transversely — to impose transverse forces. The weld metal has to give, or yield, in order to stretch, but at the time it reaches the needed dimensions, it is still under stress equivalent to its yield strength. This residual stress attempts to deform the weldment. In the case shown, it is unlikely that the plates would be deformed significantly because they are very rigid, and the weld is relatively small. When the first fillet is laid, however, angular distortion is likely to occur unless the plates are rigidly clamped or tacked.

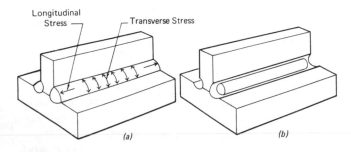

Fig. 8-14. The fillet welds in (a) have internal longitudinal and transverse stresses, and these welds would shrink to the dimensions of those shown in (b) if they could be unattached from the base plate. To re-establish the condition shown in (a), the fillets in (b) would have to be stretched longitudinally and transversely by forces that exceeded their yield strength.

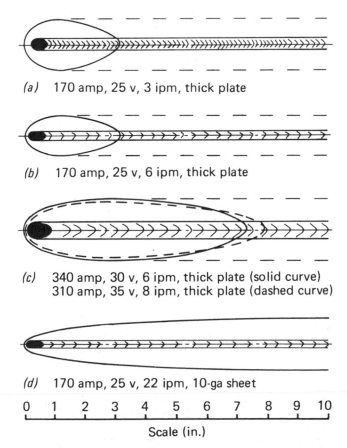

(a) 170 amp, 25 v, 3 ipm, thick plate

(b) 170 amp, 25 v, 6 ipm, thick plate

(c) 340 amp, 30 v, 6 ipm, thick plate (solid curve)
310 amp, 35 v, 8 ipm, thick plate (dashed curve)

(d) 170 amp, 25 v, 22 ipm, 10-ga sheet

Scale (in.)

Fig. 8-15. Higher welding speeds reduce the size of the adjacent base metal zone that shrinks along with the weld and help to minimize distortion.

Shrinkage in the base metal adjacent to the weld adds to the stresses that lead to distortion. During welding, the base metal adjacent to the weld is heated almost to its melting point. The temperature of the base metal a few inches from the weld is substantially lower. This large temperature differential causes nonuniform expansion followed by base metal movement, or metal displacement, if the parts being joined are restrained. As the arc passes on down the joint, the base metal cools and shrinks just like the weld metal. If the surrounding metal restrains the heated base metal from contracting normally, internal stresses develop. These, in combination with the stresses developed in the weld metal, increase the tendency of the weldment to distort.

The volume of adjacent base metal that contributes to distortion can be controlled somewhat by welding procedures. Higher welding speeds, for example, reduce the size of the adjacent base metal zone that shrinks along with the weld. An indication of these effects for some typical welds is shown in Fig. 8-15.

Controlled expansion and contraction is applied usefully in flame-straightening or flame-shrinking of a plate or weldment. For example, to shrink the center portion of a distorted plate, the flame from a torch is directed on a small, centrally located area. The area heats up rapidly and must expand. But the surrounding plate, which is cooler, prevents the spot from expanding along the plane of the plate. The only alternative is for the spot to expand in thickness, Fig. 8-16. In essence, the plate thickens where the heat is applied. Upon cooling, it tends to contract uniformly in all directions. When carefully done, spot heating produces shrinkage that is effective in correcting distortion caused by previous heating and cooling cycles.

BUTT WELDS

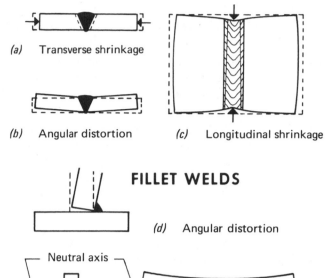

(a) Transverse shrinkage

(b) Angular distortion   *(c)* Longitudinal shrinkage

FILLET WELDS

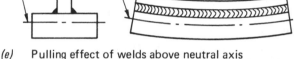

(d) Angular distortion

Neutral axis

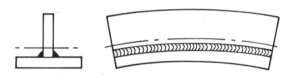

(e) Pulling effect of welds above neutral axis

(f) Pulling effect of welds below neutral axis

Fig. 8-17. How welds tend to distort and cause dimensional changes in assemblies.

Shrinkage of a weld causes various types of distortion and dimensional changes. A butt weld between two pieces of plate, by shrinking transversely, changes the width of the assembly, as in Fig. 8-17 (a). It also causes angular distortion, as in Fig. 8-17 (b). Here, the greater amount of weld metal and heat at the top of the joint produces greater shrinkage at the upper surface, causing the edges of the plate to lift. Longitudinal shrinkage of the same weld would tend to deform the joined plate, as shown in Fig. 8-17 (c).

Angular distortion is also a problem with fillets, as illustrated in Fig. 8-17 (d). If fillet welds in a T-shaped assembly are above the neutral axis (center of gravity) of the assembly, the ends of the member tend to bend upward, as in Fig. 8-17 (e). If the welds are below the neutral axis, the ends bend down, as in Fig 8-17 (f).

Since distortion is caused by the effects of heating and cooling and involves stiffness and metal yielding, the related mechanical and physical

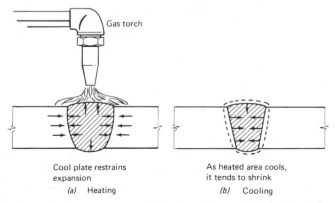

Gas torch

Cool plate restrains expansion
(a) Heating

As heated area cools, it tends to shrink
(b) Cooling

Fig. 8-16. The expansion and shrinkage phenomenon that produces distortion in weldments can be used constructively to remove distortion from steel plate. In (a), the heat from the torch causes a thickening of the spot heated. In (b), the cooled spot has a lesser volume within the thickness of the plate. A buckle that may have existed is now replaced with a slight bulge at the spot that was flame-shrunk.

properties of metals affect the degree of distortion. In general, it can be said that:

- Metals with a high coefficient of thermal expansion are likely to cause distortion problems in welded assemblies.

- Metals with a low thermal conductivity (stainless steel, for example) are likely to cause more distortion problems than metals with high thermal conductivity (aluminum or copper).

- As the yield strength of metals increase, distortion problems become more pronounced.

- As the modulus of elasticity (stiffness) increases the possibility of distortion decreases.

HOW TO CONTROL DISTORTION

If distortion in a weldment is to be prevented or minimized, methods must be used both in the design and in the welding shop to reduce or control shrinkage. The designer is primarily responsible for shrinkage-control measures, but the weldor can also help minimize the problem — especially by refraining from overwelding. The following methods for controlling shrinkage are presented for the weldor's information, with full recognition that some are outside his province and are measures that the designer should have taken into account before finalizing the working drawings:

Method 1 — Do not overweld. The more metal placed in a joint, the greater the shrinkage forces. Correctly sizing a joint is the responsibility of the designer, but following his instructions and not overwelding is the responsibility of the weldor.

The amount of weld metal in a fillet can be minimized by use of a flat or slightly convex bead, and in a butt joint by proper edge preparation and fitup. Only the effective throat, dimension T in Fig. 8-18 (a), in a conventional fillet can be used in calculating the design strength of the weld. The excess weld metal in a highly convex bead does not increase the allowable strength in code work, but it does increase shrinkage forces.

Proper edge preparation and fitup of butt welds, Fig. 8-18 (b), help to force the use of minimum amounts of weld metal. For maximum economy, the plates should be spaced from 1/32" to 1/16" apart. A bevel of 30 degrees on each side provides proper fusion at the root of the weld, yet requires minimal weld metal. In relatively thick plates, the angle of bevel can be decreased if the root opening is increased, or a J or U preparation can be used to decrease the amount of weld metal used in the joint. A double-V joint requires about one-half the weld metal of a single-V joint in the same plate thickness.

In general, if distortion is not a problem, the most economical joint should be selected. If distortion is a problem, either a joint in which the weld stresses balance each other or a joint requiring the least amount of weld metal should be selected.

Method 2 — Use intermittent welding, as in Fig. 8-18 (c), — which minimizes the amount of weld metal. When attaching stiffeners to plate, for example, intermittent welds can reduce the amount of weld metal by as much as 75%, yet provide needed strength.

Method 3 — Use as few weld passes as possible. Fewer passes with large electrodes, Fig. 8-18 (d), are preferable to a greater number of passes with small electrodes when transverse distortion could be a problem. Shrinkage caused by each pass tends to be cumulative, thereby increasing total shrinkage when many passes are used.

Method 4 — Place welds near the neutral axis. Distortion is minimized by providing a smaller leverage for the shrinkage forces to pull the plates out of alignment. Fig. 8-18 (e) is illustrative. Both design of the weldment and welding sequence can be used effectively to control distortion.

Method 5 — Balance welds around the neutral axis. This practice, shown in Fig. 8-18 (f), offsets one shrinkage force with another to effectively minimize distortion of the weldment. Here, too, design of the assembly and proper sequence of welding are important factors.

Method 6 — Use backstep welding. In the backstep technique, the general progression of welding may be, say, from left to right, but each bead segment is deposited from right to left as in Fig. 8-18 (g). As each bead segment is placed, the heated edges expand, which temporarily separates the plates at B. But as the heat moves out across the plate to C, expansion along outer edges CD brings the plates back together. This separation is most pronounced as the first bead is laid. With successive beads, the plates expand less and less because of the restraint of prior welds. Backstepping may not be effective in all applications, and it cannot be used economically in automatic welding.

Method 7 — Anticipate the shrinkage forces. Placing parts out of position before welding can make shrinkage perform constructive work. Several assemblies, preset in this manner, are shown in Fig. 8-18 (h). The required amount of preset for shrinkage to pull the plates into alignment can be determined from a few trial welds.

Prebending or prespringing the parts to be welded, Fig. 8-18 (i), is a simple example of the use of opposing mechanical forces to counteract distortion due to welding. The top of the weld groove —

which will contain the bulk of the weld metal — is lengthened when the plates are sprung. Thus, the completed weld is slightly longer than it would be if it had been made on the flat plate. When the clamps are released after welding, the plates return to the flat shape, allowing the weld to relieve its longitudinal shrinkage stresses by shortening to a straight line. The two actions coincide, and the welded plates assume the desired flatness.

Another common practice for balancing shrinkage forces is to position identical weldments back to back, Fig. 8-18 (j), clamping them tightly together. The welds are completed on both assemblies and allowed to cool before the clamps are released. Prebending can be combined with this method by inserting wedges at suitable positions between the parts before clamping.

In heavy weldments, particularly, the rigidity of the members and their arrangement relative to each other may provide the balancing forces needed. If these natural balancing forces are not present, it is necessary to use other means to counteract the shrinkage forces in the weld metal. This can be accomplished by balancing one shrinkage force against another or by creating an opposing force through the fixturing. The opposing forces may be: other shrinkage forces; restraining forces imposed by clamps, jigs, or fixtures; restraining forces arising from the arrangement of members in the assembly; or the force from the sag in a member due to gravity.

Method 8 — Plan the welding sequence. A well-planned welding sequence involves placing weld

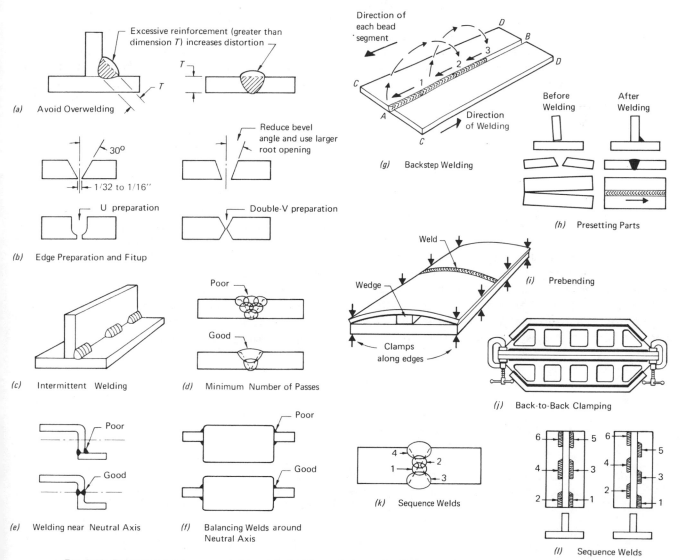

Fig. 8-18. Distortion can be prevented or minimized by techniques that defeat — or use constructively — the effects of the heating and cooling cycle.

metal at different points about the assembly so that, as the structure shrinks in one place, it counteracts the shrinkage forces of welds already made. An example of this is welding alternately on both sides of the neutral axis in making a butt weld, as in Fig. 8-18 (k). Another example, in a fillet weld, consists of making intermittent welds according to the sequences shown in Fig. 8-18 (l). In these examples, the shrinkage in weld No. 1 is balanced by the shrinkage in weld No. 2, and so on.

Clamps, jigs, and fixtures that lock parts into a desired position and hold them until welding is finished are probaby the most widely used means for controlling distortion in small assemblies or components. The restraining force provided by clamps increases internal stresses in the weldment until the yield point of the weld metal is reached. For typical welds on low-carbon plate, this stress level would approximate 45,000 psi. One might expect this stress to cause considerable movement or distortion after the welded part is removed from the jig or clamps. This does not occur, however, since the strain (unit contraction) from this stress is very low compared to the amount of movement that would occur if no restraint were used during welding. For example:

$$\text{Modulus of elasticity (E)} = \frac{\text{Stress } (\sigma)}{\text{Strain } (\epsilon)}$$

$$\epsilon = \frac{\sigma}{E \text{ steel}}$$

$$\epsilon = \frac{45,000}{30,000,000}$$

$$\text{Strain} = 0.0015 \text{ in./in.}$$

Method 9 — Remove shrinkage forces after welding. Peening is one way to counteract the shrinkage forces of a weld bead as it cools. Essentially, peening the bead stretches it and makes it thinner, thus relieving (by plastic deformation) the stresses induced by contraction as the metal cools. But this method must be used with care. For example, a root bead should never be peened, because of the danger of either concealing a crack or causing one. Generally, peening is not permitted on the final pass, because of the possibility of covering a crack and interfering with inspection, and because of the undesirable workhardening effect. Thus, the utility of the technique is limited, even though there have been instances where between-pass peening proved to be the only solution for a distortion or cracking problem. Before peening is used on a job, engineering approval should be obtained.

Another method for removing shrinkage forces is by stress relief — controlled heating of the weldment to an elevated temperature, followed by controlled cooling. Sometimes two identical weldments are clamped back to back, welded, and then stress relieved while being held in this straight condition. The residual stresses that would tend to distort the weldments are thus removed.

Method 10 — Minimize welding time. Since complex cycles of heating and cooling take place during welding, and since time is required for heat transmission, the time factor affects distortion. In general, it is desirable to finish the weld quickly, before a large volume of surrounding metal heats up and expands. The welding process used, type and size of electrode, welding current, and speed of travel, thus, affect the degree of shrinkage and distortion of a weldment. The use of iron-powder manual electrodes or mechanized welding equipment reduces welding time and the amount of metal affected by heat and, consequently, distortion. For example, depositing a given-size weld in thick plate with a process operating at 175 amp, 25 v, and 3 ipm requires 87,500 joules of energy per linear inch of weld. The same size weld, produced with a process operating at 310 amp, 35 v, and 8 ipm requires 81,400 joules per linear inch. The difference represents "excessive" heat, which expands the surrounding metal more than necessary.

Arc-Welding Procedures

In practice sessions with the arc-welding electrode — and in subsequent industrial work — the student will hear much about "procedures." In the words of the American Welding Society, a procedure is "the detailed elements (with prescribed values or ranges of values) of a process or method used to produce a specific result." In simpler language, an arc-welding procedure is how you set the controls on your welding machine when you are making a certain weld in a certain thickness of metal with a certain electrode — and how you proceed to execute that weld. By following a prescribed procedure, the skilled weldor ends up with the weld specified for the joint.

Typical procedures, as taken from *The Procedure Handbook of Arc Welding,* published by The Lincoln Electric Company, are shown in Figs. 9-1 and 9-2. Both are for manual shielded metal-arc (stick-electrode) welding of steel plate. By following the tabulated procedural specifications in Fig. 9-1, a weld of commercial quality should result; by following the specifications in Fig. 9-2, a butt weld meeting code quality should result.

Note that even though a number of variables are contemplated in the procedures — varying thickness of plate, varying electrode types and sizes, varying currents, varying number of passes, and so forth — the tabulation gives precise instructive information for every circumstance encompassed in the procedure. Thus, referring to Fig. 9-1, if the plates were 3/8" thick, a 9/32" weld size could be placed in one pass with a 1/4" E7024 electrode operating at 375 amperes AC, with the arc traveling at the rate of 17 to 19 inches per minute. On steel of good weldability, this procedure would give a weld meeting commercial standards of quality when executed by a skilled weldor.

The procedure, thus, is a detailed explanation of how to execute a specific weld. When presented such as those in Figs. 9-1 and 9-2, it gives the information needed to account for a large number of variables.

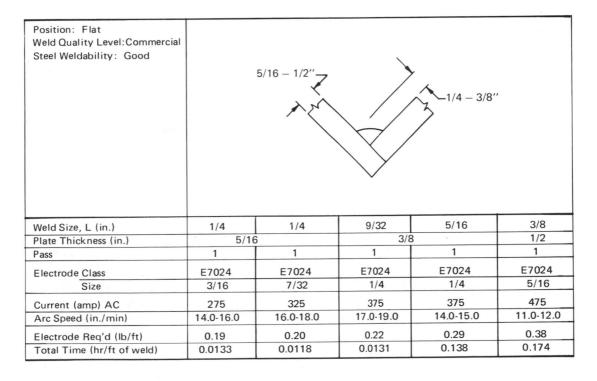

Position: Flat Weld Quality Level: Commercial Steel Weldability: Good					
Weld Size, L (in.)	1/4	1/4	9/32	5/16	3/8
Plate Thickness (in.)	5/16		3/8		1/2
Pass	1	1	1	1	1
Electrode Class	E7024	E7024	E7024	E7024	E7024
Size	3/16	7/32	1/4	1/4	5/16
Current (amp) AC	275	325	375	375	475
Arc Speed (in./min)	14.0-16.0	16.0-18.0	17.0-19.0	14.0-15.0	11.0-12.0
Electrode Req'd (lb/ft)	0.19	0.20	0.22	0.29	0.38
Total Time (hr/ft of weld)	0.0133	0.0118	0.0131	0.138	0.174

Fig. 9-1. Procedures for a flat fillet weld with 1/4" to 1/2" plate.

All welding in code work must be based on approved procedures. If the proposed welding is to be done with an innovation in process or technique — say, erection welding on a structural steel joint with a semiautomatic process to replace a standard stick-electrode procedure — the contractor must prepare a written procedure and demonstrate that it will produce satisfactory joints.

Much of the welding in industry does not require the high quality specified in structural codes. For example, welds that are subject to very low stress can tolerate minor defects and still be satisfactory. The application, thus, is a factor in selection of welding procedure. There are code-quality procedures, and there are commercial-quality procedures. It is futile and wasteful to use the more costly code-quality procedure where commercial-quality work would satisfy the requirement perfectly. Thus, in welding a fender to the framework of a farm tractor there is no good accomplished by using a stringent procedure meant for use in bridge or pressure-tank construction. At critical joints in the tractor framing, however, code-quality work may be mandatory.

CODE-QUALITY PROCEDURES

Code-quality procedures are intended to provide the highest level of quality and appearance. To accomplish this, conservative currents and travel speeds are recommended.

These procedures are aimed at producing welds that will meet the requirements of the commonly used codes: AWS Structural, AISC Buildings and Bridges, ASME Pressure Vessels, AASHO Bridges, and others. Code-quality welds are intended to be defect-free to the extent that they will measure up to the nondestructive testing requirements normally imposed by these codes. This implies crack-free, pressure-tight welds, with little or no porosity or undercut.

The specific requirements of codes are so numerous and varied that code-quality procedures may not satisfy every detail of a specific code. Procedure qualification tests are then used to confirm the acceptability of chosen procedures.

All butt welds made to code quality are full-penetration; fillet welds are full-size, as required by most codes. (The theoretical throat, rather than the true throat, is used as the basis of calculating strength.)

COMMERCIAL-QUALITY PROCEDURES

Commercial quality implies a level of quality and appearance that will meet the nominal requirements imposed on most of the welding done commercially. These welds will be pressure-tight and crack-free. They will have good appearance, and they will meet the normal strength requirements of the joint.

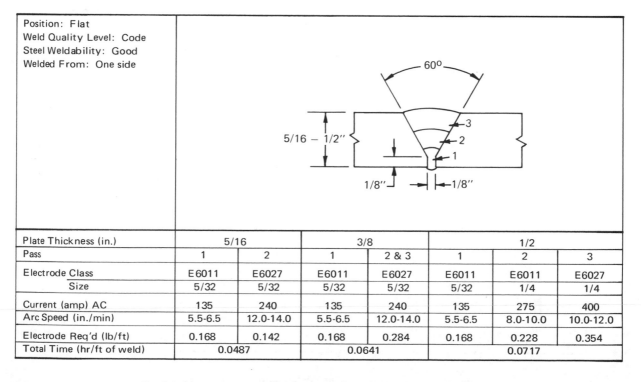

Position: Flat
Weld Quality Level: Code
Steel Weldability: Good
Welded From: One side

Plate Thickness (in.)	5/16		3/8		1/2		
Pass	1	2	1	2 & 3	1	2	3
Electrode Class	E6011	E6027	E6011	E6027	E6011	E6011	E6027
Size	5/32	5/32	5/32	5/32	5/32	1/4	1/4
Current (amp) AC	135	240	135	240	135	275	400
Arc Speed (in./min)	5.5-6.5	12.0-14.0	5.5-6.5	12.0-14.0	5.5-6.5	8.0-10.0	10.0-12.0
Electrode Req'd (lb/ft)	0.168	0.142	0.168	0.284	0.168	0.228	0.354
Total Time (hr/ft of weld)	0.0487		0.0641		0.0717		

Fig. 9-2. Procedures for a V-groove butt weld in 5/16'' to 1/2'' steel plate.

Procedures for commercial-quality welds are not as conservative as code-quality procedures: speeds and currents are generally higher. Welds made according to these procedures may have minor defects that would be objectionable to the more demanding codes.

It is recommended that appropriate tests be performed to confirm the acceptability of the selected procedure for the application at hand prior to putting it into production.

WELDABILITY OF MATERIAL

Weldability (see Chapter 6) of a steel has a considerable effect on the welding procedure. For some joints, more than one procedure is offered because of the marginal weldability of the steel.

Good weldability indicates a steel with a composition that is within the preferred range — one whose chemistry does not limit the welding speed.

Fair weldability indicates a steel with one or more elements outside the preferred range or one that contains one or more alloys. These steels require a lower welding speed or a mild preheat, or both, to minimize defects such as porosity, cracking, and undercut.

Poor weldability steels are those with compositions outside the preferred range, alloy additions, segregations, previous heat-treatment, or some other condition that makes them difficult to weld. These steels require still lower welding speeds, preheat, possibly a postheat, and careful electrode selection to obtain a satisfactory weld.

The addition of alloys to steel that enhance the mechanical properties or hardenability usually have an adverse effect on weldability. In general, the weldability of low-alloy steels is never better than "fair."

SOME POINTERS ON PROCEDURE CHARTS

In procedure charts, the student will find that fillet size is associated with a certain plate thickness. This relationship is solely for the purpose of designing a welding procedure and does not imply that a certain size fillet is the only size applicable to that plate thickness. In some procedures, the fillet size shown is larger than necessary to meet code requirements for the plate thickness. In such instances, the procedure for the proper weld size and quality should be selected. If the thickness of the plate being welded is appreciably greater than that specified in the procedure, a reduction in welding speed and current will probably be required.

The procedure data given in charts, such as those in Figs. 9-1 and 9-2 and those in subsequent chapters, have been developed to provide the most economical procedures for various applications. In some cases, more than one type or size of electrode is recommended for the same joint. In small shops, electrode selection may depend on the available power source; consequently, some joints have procedures for either AC or DC welders.

With some joints, procedures for two different types of electrodes are given — for example, E7014 or E7024, E7018 or E7028. This allows a choice of electrodes so the one with the better usability characteristics can be selected.

Any procedure for a poor or fair welding quality steel may be used on a steel of a better welding quality. Travel speed is given as a range. The electrode required and the total time are based on the middle of the range. Unless otherwise indicated in the chart, both members of the joint are the same thickness.

Pounds-of-electrode data usually include all ordinary deposition losses. These values are in terms of pounds of electrode needed to be purchased. Total time is the arc time only and does not allow for operating factor.

After a satisfactory welding procedure has been established for a specific job, all the data should be recorded and filed for future reference. This information is invaluable if the same job or a similar job occurs at a later date.

The Shielded Metal-Arc Process

The student will be introduced to arc welding via the shielded metal-arc process. This process — commonly called "stick-electrode" welding or "manual" welding — is the most widely used of all arc-welding processes. It is characterized by application versatility and flexibility and relative simplicity in the equipment. It is the process used by the small welding shop, by the home mechanic, by the farmer for repair of equipment — as well as a process having extensive application in industrial fabrication, structural steel erection, weldment manufacture, and other commercial metals joining. Arc welding to persons only casually acquainted with welding usually means shielded metal-arc welding.

With this process, an electric arc is struck between the electrically grounded work and a 9 to 18-in. length of covered metal rod — the electrode. The electrode is clamped in an electrode holder, which is joined by a cable to the power source. The weldor grips the insulated handle of the electrode holder (see Chapter 4) and maneuvers the tip of the electrode in respect to the weld joint. When he touches the tip of the electrode against the work, and then withdraws it to establish the arc, the welding circuit is completed. The heat of the arc melts base metal in the immediate area, the electrode's metal core, and any metal particles that may be in the electrode's covering. It also melts, vaporizes, or breaks down chemically nonmetallic substances incorporated in the covering for arc shielding, metal-protection, or metal-conditioning purposes. The mixing of molten base metal and filler metal from the electrode provides the coalescence required to effect joining.

As welding progresses, the covered rod becomes shorter and shorter. Finally, the welding must be stopped to remove the stub and replace it with a new electrode. This periodic changing of electrodes is one of the major disadvantages of the process in production welding. It decreases the operating factor, or the percent of the weldor's time spent in the actual operation of laying weld beads.

Another disadvantage of shielded metal-arc welding is the limitation placed on the current that can be used. High amperages, such as those used with semiautomatic guns or automatic welding heads, are impractical because of the long (and varying) length of electrode between the arc and the point of electrical contact in the jaws of the electrode holder. The welding current is limited by the resistance heating of the electrode. The electrode temperature must not exceed the "breakdown" temperature of the covering. If the temperature is too high the covering chemicals react with each other or with air and therefore do not function properly at the arc. Coverings with organics break down at lower temperatures than mineral or low-hydrogen coverings.

The versatility of the process, however — plus the simplicity of equipment — are viewed by many users whose work would permit some degree of mechanized welding — as overriding its inherent disadvantages. This point of view was formerly well taken, but now that semiautomatic self-shielded flux-cored arc welding has been developed to a similar (or even superior) degree of versatility and flexibility in welding (see Chapter 12), there is less justification for adhering to stick-electrode welding in steel fabrication and erection wherever substantial amounts of weld metal must be placed. In fact, the replacement of shielded metal-arc welding with semiautomatic processes has been a primary means by which steel fabricators and erectors have met cost-price squeezes in their welding operations.

Notwithstanding the limitations of shielded metal-arc welding, it is certain to remain a primary arc-welding process. It is the one well suited by minimal cost of equipment and broad application possibilities for the home mechanic, the farmer, the repair shop, the garage, the trailer-hitch installer, and many others who are concerned entirely with getting a welding job done.

OPERATIONAL PRINCIPLES

Chapter 3 describes the basic welding circuit, and in Chapters 4 and 5 items of equipment and electrodes for shielded metal-arc welding are discussed. As noted, welding begins when the arc is struck between the work and the tip of the electrode. The heat of the arc melts the electrode and the surface of the work near the arc. Tiny globules of molten metal form on the tip of the electrode and transfer through the arc into the molten weld "pool" or "puddle" on the work surface.

The transfer through the arc stream is brought about by electrical and magnetic forces. Movement of the arc along the work (or movement of the work under the arc) accomplishes progressive melting and mixing of molten metal, followed by solidification, and, thus, the unification of parts.

It would be possible to clamp a bare mild-steel electrode into the electrode holder and fuse-join two steel parts. The resulting weld would lack ductility and soundness if judged by the present standards of weld quality. The weld metal so deposited would contain oxides and nitrides resulting from reaction of the molten metal with oxygen and nitrogen of the atmosphere. An essential feature of the electrode used in the shielded metal-arc process is a covering or coating, applied to the core metal by extrusion or dipping, that contains ingredients to shield the arc and protect the hot metal from chemical reaction with constituents of the atmosphere.

The shielding ingredients have various functions. One is to shield the arc — provide a dense, impenetrable envelope of vapor or gas around the arc and the molten metal to prevent the pickup of oxygen and nitrogen and the chemical formation of oxides and nitrides in the weld puddle. Another is to provide scavengers and deoxidizers to refine the weld metal. A third is to produce a slag coating over molten globules of metal during their transfer through the arc stream and a slag blanket over the molten puddle and the newly solidified weld. Figure 10-1 illustrates the decomposition of an electrode covering and the manner in which the arc

stream and the weld metal are shielded from the air.

Another function of the shield is to provide the ionization needed for AC welding. With alternating current, the arc goes out 120 times a second. For it to be reignited each time it goes out, an electrically conductive path must be maintained in the arc stream. Potassium compounds in the electrode covering provide ionized gaseous particles that remain ionized during the fraction of a second that the arc is extinguished with AC cycle reversal. An electrical path for reignition of the arc is thus maintained.

The mechanics of arc shielding varies with the electrode type. Some types of electrodes depend largely on a "disappearing" gaseous shield to protect the arc stream and the weld metal. With these electrodes, only a light covering of slag will be found on the finished weld. Other electrode types depend largely on slag for shielding. The explanation for the protective action is that the tiny globules of metal being transferred in the arc stream are entirely coated with a thin film of molten slag. Presumably, the globules become coated with slag as vaporized slag condenses on them — so the protective action still arises from gasification. In any event, the slag deposits with these types of electrodes is heavy, completely covering the finished weld. Between these extremes are electrodes that depend on various combinations of gas and slag for shielding.

The performance characteristics of the electrodes (see Chapter 5) are related to their slag-forming properties. Electrodes with heavy slag formation have high deposition rates and are suitable for making large welds downhand. Electrodes that develop a gaseous shield that disappears into the atmosphere and give a light slag covering are low-deposition and best suited for making welds in the vertical or overhead positions.

A solid wire core is the main source of filler metal in electrodes for the shielded metal-arc process. However, the so-called iron-powder electrodes also supply filler metal from iron powder contained in the electrode covering or within a tubular core wire. Iron powder in the covering increases the efficiency of use of the arc heat and thus the deposition rate. With thickly covered iron-powder electrodes, it is possible to drag the electrode over the joint without the electrode freezing to the work or shorting out. Even though the heavy covering makes contact with the work, the electrical path through the contained powder particles is not adequate in conductivity to short the arc, and any resistance heating that occurs supplements the heat of the arc in melting the electrode. Because heavily-covered iron-powder electrodes can be dragged

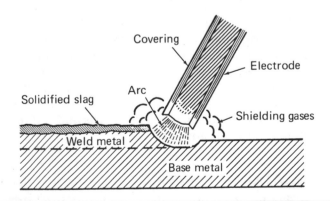

Fig 10-1. Schematic representation of shielded metal-arc welding. Gases generated by the decomposition and vaporization of materials in the electrode covering — including vaporized slag — provide a dense shield around the arc stream and over the molten puddle. Molten and solidified slag above the newly formed weld metal protects it from the atmosphere while it is hot enough to be chemically reactive with oxygen and nitrogen.

along the joint, less skill is required in their use.

Some electrodes for the shielded metal-arc process are fabricated with a tubular wire that contains alloying materials in the core. These are used in producing high-alloy deposits. Just as the conventional electrodes, they have an extruded or dipped covering.

POWER SOURCES FOR SHIELDED METAL-ARC WELDING

Shielded metal-arc welding requires relatively low currents (10 to 500 amp) and voltages (17 to 45), depending on the type and size electrode used. The current may be either AC or DC; thus, the power source may be either AC or DC or a combination AC/DC welder (see Chapter 4). For most work, a variable-voltage power source is preferred, since it is difficult for the weldor to hold a constant arc length. With the variable-voltage source and the machine set to give a steep volt-ampere curve, the voltage increases or decreases with variations in the arc length to maintain the current fairly constant. The equipment compensates for the inability of the operator to hold an exact arc length, and he is able to obtain a uniform deposition rate.

In some welding, however, it may be desirable for the weldor to have control over the deposition rate — such as when depositing root passes in joints with varying fitup or in out-of-position work. In these cases variable-voltage performance with a flatter voltage-amperage curve is desirable, so that the weldor can decrease the deposition rate by increasing his arc length or increase it by shortening the arc length.

Fig. 10-2 illustrates typical volt-ampere curves possible with a variable-voltage power source. The change from one type of voltage-ampere curve to another is made by changing the open-circuit voltage and current settings of the machine.

The fact that the shielded metal-arc process can be used with so many electrode types and sizes — in all positions — on a great variety of materials — and with flexibility in operator control makes it the most versatile of all welding processes. These advantages are enhanced further by the low cost of equipment. The total advantages of the process, however, must be weighed against the cost of per foot of weld when a process is to be selected for a particular job. Shielded metal-arc welding is a well recognized way of getting the job done, but too faithful adherence to it often leads to getting the job done at excessive welding costs.

SELECTION OF ELECTRODES

For economy and best performance, electrodes should be selected not only on chemical and mechanical compatibility with the base metal but also on their suitability for the joint. As was noted in the description of classifications of mild-steel electrodes in Chapter 5, some types are for all-position welding, while others give best performance in flat or horizontal joints. The joint, thus, is a determining factor in selection of electrodes, and it can be defined in terms of weld-metal requirements. A joint is said to make demands for either "fast-freeze", "fast-fill", or "fast-follow" electrode types. If an electrode provides weld metal that freezes fast where freezing fast will facilitate running the weld it will give maximum weld quality and welding economy. The same logic pertains to fast-fill and fast-follow electrodes.

Electrode selection for joint requirements (see Fig. 10-3) requires a definition of the type of joints:

Freeze joints are joints welded vertically and overhead. The weld metal must freeze quickly to keep the molten metal from spilling from the joint.

Fill joints are exemplified by groove, flat and horizontal fillet, and lap welds in plate over 3/16" thick. With such joints, the objective is to supply weld-metal fill in the shortest time.

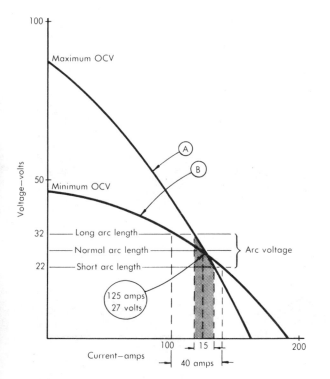

Fig. 10-2. Typical volt-ampere curves possible with a variable-voltage power source. The steep curve (A) allows minimum current change. The flatter curve (B) permits the weldor to control current by changing the length of the arc.

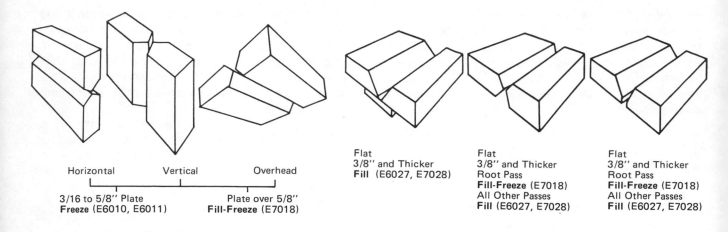

Horizontal   Vertical   Overhead

3/16 to 5/8'' Plate   Plate over 5/8''
Freeze (E6010, E6011)   **Fill-Freeze** (E7018)

Flat
3/8'' and Thicker
Fill (E6027, E7028)

Flat
3/8'' and Thicker
Root Pass
Fill-Freeze (E7018)
All Other Passes
Fill (E6027, E7028)

Flat
3/8'' and Thicker
Root Pass
Fill-Freeze (E7018)
All Other Passes
Fill (E6027, E7028)

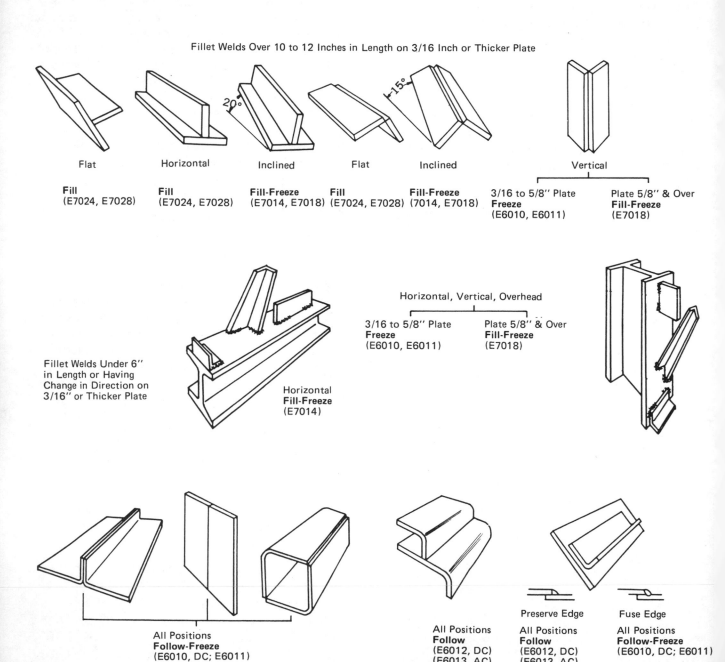

Fillet Welds Over 10 to 12 Inches in Length on 3/16 Inch or Thicker Plate

Flat
Fill
(E7024, E7028)

Horizontal
Fill
(E7024, E7028)

Inclined
Fill-Freeze
(E7014, E7018)

Flat
Fill
(E7024, E7028)

Inclined
Fill-Freeze
(7014, E7018)

Vertical

3/16 to 5/8'' Plate   Plate 5/8'' & Over
Freeze   **Fill-Freeze**
(E6010, E6011)   (E7018)

Fillet Welds Under 6''
in Length or Having
Change in Direction on
3/16'' or Thicker Plate

Horizontal
Fill-Freeze
(E7014)

Horizontal, Vertical, Overhead

3/16 to 5/8'' Plate   Plate 5/8'' & Over
Freeze   **Fill-Freeze**
(E6010, E6011)   (E7018)

All Positions
Follow-Freeze
(E6010, DC; E6011)

All Positions
Follow
(E6012, DC)
(E6013, AC)

Preserve Edge

All Positions
Follow
(E6012, DC)
(E6013, AC)

Fuse Edge

All Positions
Follow-Freeze
(E6010, DC; E6011)

Fig. 10-3. Guide to selection of electrodes.

Follow joints usually means joints in sheet metal. Welding sheet steel under 3/16" thick requires electrodes that weld at high travel speeds with minimum skips, misses, slag entrapment, and undercut.

The electrodes for carbon and low-alloy steel can be classified as fast-freeze, fast-fill, and fast-follow (also called "fill-freeze").

FAST-FREEZE ELECTRODES

Fast-freeze electrodes are compounded to deposit weld metal that solidifies rapidly after being melted by the arc, and are thus intended specifically for welding in the vertical and overhead positions. Although deposition rates are not as high as with other types of electrodes, the fast-freeze type can also be used for flat welding and is, thus, considered an "all-purpose" electrode that can be used for any weld in mild steel. However, welds made with any fast-freeze electrodes are slow and require a high degree of operator skill. Therefore, wherever possible, work should be positioned for flat welding, which permits the use of fast-fill electrodes.

Fast-freeze electrodes provide deep penetration and maximum admixture. The weld bead is flat with distinct ripples. Slag formation is light, and the arc is easy to control.

Applications for fast-feeze electrodes are:

- General-purpose fabrication and maintenance welding.
- Vertical-up and overhead plate welds requiring X-ray quality.
- Pipe welding, including cross-country, in-plant, and noncritical small-diameter piping.
- Welds to be made on galvanized, plated, painted, or unclean surfaces.
- Joints requiring deep penetration, such as square-edge butt welds.
- Sheet-metal welds, including edge, corner, and butt welds.

The commonly used fast-freeze electrodes in the welding of steel are E6010, E6011, E7010-A-1, and E7010-G.

E6010: This is the basic fast-freeze electrode for general-purpose DC welding. Light slag and good wash-in permit excellent control of the arc. The E6010 electrode is particularly valuable for critical out-of-position applications, such as with pipe welding.

E6011: A general fast-freeze electrode for use with industrial AC welders, E6011 is also the preferred electrode for sheet-metal edge, corner, and butt welds with DCSP. The electrode is also used for vertical-down welding, and for applications requiring exceptionally low silicon deposit. Special grades are available for general-purpose shop use with small, low open-circuit voltage AC welders (not suitable for X-ray quality). E6011 is also available in a special grade producing little slag, that is designed especially for tack welding.

E7010-A-1: This fast-freeze electrode is designed for welding high-strength pipe, such as X52 or X56, and for other out-of-position welding where high strength or control of alloy in the weld are important. It produces a 70,000-psi deposit containing 0.5% molybdenum. Operation is similar to E6010.

E7010-G: This electrode is similar to E7010-A1, but is designed specifically to avoid any surface-hole tendency in fill and cover-pass welds on high-strength pipe. Special grades are available for welding all passes on X60 and X65 high-strength line pipe.

Suggested welding techniques with fast-freeze electrodes involve proper selection of current and polarity, electrode size, and manipulative motions.

Current and Polarity: Unless otherwise specified, use DCRP with Exx10, and use AC with Exx11. Exx11 electrodes can be used on DCRP with a current about 10% below normal AC values. Always adjust current for proper arc action and control of the weld puddle.

Flat Welding: Hold an arc of 1/8 in. or less, or touch the work lightly with the electrode tip. Move fast enough to stay ahead of the molten pool. Use currents in the middle and high portion of the range.

Vertical Welding: Use an electrode of 3/16 in. or smaller. Vertical-down techniques are used by pipeliners and for single-pass welds on thin steel.

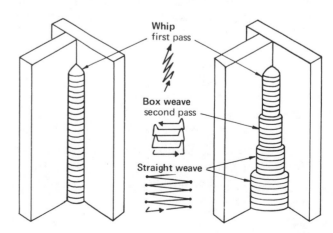

Fig. 10-4. Technique for vertical welding with fast-freeze electrodes.

Vertical-up is used for most plate welding. Make the first vertical-up pass with either a whipping technique for fillet welds, or with a circular motion for V-butt joints (Fig. 10-4). Apply succeeding passes with a weave, pausing slightly at the edges to insure penetration and proper wash-in. Use currents in the low portion of the range.

Overhead and Horizontal Butt Welds: Use an electrode of 3/16 in. or smaller. These welds (Fig. 10-5) are best made with a series of stringer beads, using a technique similar to those described for first-pass vertical-up welds.

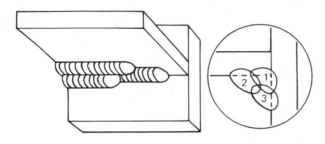

Fig. 10-5. Technique for overhead and horizontal butt welds with fast-freeze electrodes. These welds are best made with a series of stringer beads.

Sheet-Metal Edge and Butt Welds: Use DCSP. Hold an arc of 3/16 in. or more. Move as fast as possible while maintaining good fusion. Position the work 45° downhill for fastest welding. Use currents in the middle range.

FAST-FILL ELECTRODES

Fast-fill electrodes are compounded to deposit metal rapidly in the heat of the arc and are, thus, well suited to high-speed welding on horizontal surfaces. The weld metal solidifies somewhat slowly; therefore this type of electrode is not well suited for out-of-position welds. However, a slight downhill positioning is permissible. Joints normally considered fast-fill include butt, fillet, lap, and corner welds in plate 3/16 in. or thicker. These joints are capable of holding a large molten pool of weld metal as it freezes.

Arc penetration is shallow with minimum admixture. The bead is smooth, free of ripples, and flat or slightly convex. Spatter is negligible. Slag formation is heavy, and the slag peels off readily. Application for fast-fill electrodes are:

- Production welds on plate having a thickness of 3/16 in. or more.
- Flat and horizontal fillets, laps, and deep-groove butt welds.
- Welds on medium-carbon crack-sensitive steel when low-hydrogen electrodes are not available. (Preheat may be required.)

The coverings of fast-fill electrodes contain approximately 50% iron powder. This powder increases deposition rate by helping to contain the arc heat at the electrode, by melting to add to deposited weld metal, and by permitting currents higher than those permitted by other types of coverings. The thick, iron-bearing covering also facilitates use of the drag technique in welding..

The commonly used fast-fill electrodes in the welding of steel are E7024, E6027, E7020-A1.

E7024: This is a general-purpose fast-fill electrode. Special grades provide exceptionally high deposition rates and particularly good operating characteristics.

E6027: Used principally for flat deep-groove joints and for flat and horizontal fillets, the electrode has excellent wash-in characteristics. A friable slag permits easy slag removal in deep grooves. This electrode is sometimes used as an alternative to E7024 when X-ray quality or high notch toughness are required.

E7020-A1: The electrode is used in place of E6027 when a 70,000-psi strength or 0.5% molybdenum deposit is required.

The welding techniques used with these fast-fill electrodes are designed to take full advantage of their fast deposition rates. Recommended techniques follow.

Polarity: Use AC for highest speeds and best operating characteristics. DCRP can be used, but this type of current promotes arc blow and complicates control of the molten puddle.

Flat Welding: Use a drag technique; tip the electrode 10 to 30° in the direction of travel and make stringer beads. Weld with the electrode tip lightly dragging on the work so that molten metal is forced out from under the tip, thereby promoting penetration. The resulting smooth weld is similar in appearance to an automatic weld. Travel rapidly, but not too fast for good slag coverage. Stay about 1/4 to 3/8 in. ahead of the molten slag, as illustrated in Fig. 10-6. If travel speed is too slow, a small ball of molten slag may form and roll ahead of the arc, causing spatter, poor penetration, and erratic bead shape. Optimum current usually is 5 to 10 amp above the center of the range for a given electrode. Do not exceed the center of the range if the weld is to be of X-ray quality.

Horizontal Fillets and Laps: Point the electrode into the joint at an angle of 45° from horizontal and use the "flat" technique described above. The tip of the electrode must touch both horizontal and vertical members of the joint. If the

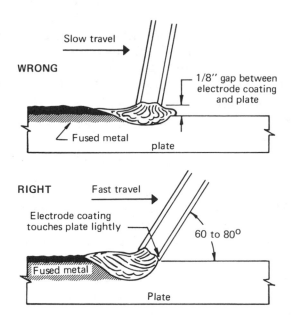

Fig. 10-6. Technique for flat welds with fast-fill electrodes. An incorrect technique is included for comparison.

45° angle between plates is not maintained, the fillet legs will be of different sizes. When two passes are needed, deposit the first bead mostly on the bottom plate. To weld the second pass hold the electrode at about 45°, fusing into the vertical plate and the first bead. Make multiple-pass horizontal fillets as shown in Fig. 10-7. Put the first bead in the corner with fairly high current, disregarding undercut. Deposit the second bead on the horizontal plate, fusing into the first bead. Hold the electrode angle needed to deposit the filler beads as shown, putting the final bead against the vertical plate.

Deep-Groove Butt Welds: To hold the large pool of molten weld metal produced by fast-fill electrodes, either a backup plate or a stringer bead made with a deeper-penetrating fast-freeze electrode is required. Deposit fast-fill beads with a stringer technique until a slight weave is required to obtain fusion of both plates. Split-weave welds

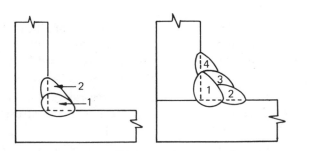

Fig. 10-7. Technique for multi-pass horizontal fillet welds with fast-fill electrodes. Beads should be deposited in the order indicated.

are better than a wide weave near the top of deep grooves. When welding the second to last pass, leave enough room so that the last pass will not exceed a 1/16 in. buildup. A slight undercut on all but the last pass creates no problems, because it is burned out with each succeeding pass.

FAST-FOLLOW ELECTRODES

Fast-follow or "fill-freeze" electrodes are compounded to provide a compromise between fast-freeze and fast-fill characteristics, and thus provide medium deposition rates and medium penetration. They permit welding at relatively high speed with minimal skip, misses, and undercut, and with minimum slag entrapment. These electrodes are particularly suited to the welding of sheet metal and are, thus, often called "sheet-metal" electrodes. Bead appearance with the fast-follow electrodes varies from smooth and ripple-free to wavy with distinct ripples. The electrodes can be used in all welding positions, but are most widely used in the level or downhill positions.

Applications for fast-follow electrodes include:

- Downhill fillet and lap welds.
- Irregular or short welds that change direction or position.
- Sheet-metal lap and fillet welds.
- Fast-fill joints having poor fitup.
- General-purpose welding in all positions.

The commonly used fast-follow electrodes in the welding of steel are E6012, E6013, and E7014.

E6012: The basic fast-follow electrode for general-purpose and production welding, this electrode provides a more forceful arc than other electrodes in the group. Special types are available for improved arc stability, minimum spatter, and easier slag removal. Some types contain iron powder in the coatings for greater mileage, better AC operation, and a smoother, quieter arc. These types are excellent for low-current applications, such as sheet-metal welding.

E6013: This electrode is used in place of E6012 for sheet-metal welding where appearance and ease of operation are more important than speed. AC operation is excellent. It is recommended for general-purpose welding with small AC transformer welding machines having low open-circuit voltage.

E7014: The electrode has highest iron-powder content in the group, and thus provides highest deposition (or maximum fast-fill) capability among the fast-follow electrodes. It has exceptionally good operating characteristics and is often preferred by weldors. It is frequently used for production welding on short, irregular, or downhill fast-fill types of joints.

The welding techniques on steel plate with these fast-follow electrodes may be summarized as follows.

Polarity: Use DCSP for best performance on all applications except when arc blow is a problem. To control arc blow, use AC.

Flat and Downhill: Use stringer beads for the first pass except when poor fitup requires a slight weave. Use either stringer or weave beads for succeeding passes. Touch the tip of the electrode to the work or hold an arc length of 1/8 in. or less. Move as fast as possible consistent with desired bead size. Use currents in the middle to higher portion of the range.

Electrode Size: Use electrodes of 3/16 in. or smaller diameter for vertical and overhead welding.

Vertical-Down: Use stringer beads or a slight weave. A drag technique must be used with some E6012 electrodes. Make small beads. Point the electrode upward so that arc force pushes molten metal back up the joint. Move fast enough to stay ahead of the molten pool. Use currents in the higher portion of the range.

Vertical-Up: Use a triangular weave. Weld a shelf at the bottom of the joint and add layer upon layer. Do not whip or take the electrode out of the molten pool. Point the electrode slightly upward so that arc force helps control the puddle. travel slow enough to maintain the shelf without spilling. Use currents in the lower portion of the range.

Overhead: Make stringer beads using a whipping technique with a slight circular motion in the crater. Do not weave. Travel fast enough to avoid spilling. Use currents in the lower portion of the range.

As the student will find during his work with fast-follow electrodes on sheet metal, the ability to adjust current while welding is important, particularly when fitup or material thickness varies. Motor-generator weldors equipped with foot-operated remote current controls are useful for this purpose.

Generally, use the highest current that does not cause burnthrough, does not undercut, or does not melt the edges of lap, corner, or edge welds. For fast welding, the operator must stay precisely on the joint and must travel at a uniform speed. Welding on sheet metal, thus, requires more than average skill, and a good weldor may need a few days of practice when first attempting this type of weld.

For maximum welding speed, minimum distor-

tion, or for welding in the flat position, joints generally should be positioned 45° to 75° downhill. Use copper backup strips where possible to decreased the danger of burnthrough. Procedure tables assume tight fitup and adequate clamping or tacking. Where poor fitup is encountered:

1. Reduce current.
2. Tilt the electrode into the direction of travel more than normally.

Deposit the entire weld in one pass using stringer beads or a slight weave. Drag the electrode on the joint and stay ahead of the molten pool. Tip the electrode well into the direction of travel so the arc force pushes the weld metal back into the joint. Use currents in the high portion of the range.

LOW-HYDROGEN ELECTRODES

Conventional welding electrodes may not be suitable where X-ray quality is required, where the base metal has a tendency to crack, where thick sections are to be welded, or where the base metal has an alloy content higher than that of mild steel. In these applications, a low-hydrogen electrode may be required.

Low-hydrogen electrodes are available with either fast-fill or fill-freeze characteristics. They are compounded to produce dense welds of X-ray quality with excellent notch toughness and high ductility. Low-hydrogen electrodes reduce the danger of underbead and microcracking on thick weldments and on high-carbon and low-alloy steels. Preheat requirements are less than for other electrodes.

Low-hydrogen electrodes are shipped in hermetically sealed containers, which normally can be stored indifinitely without danger of moisture pickup. But once the container is opened, the electrodes should be used promptly or stored in a heated cabinet. Details on electrode storage and on redrying moisture-contaminated electrodes are presented later in this chapter.

Applications for low-hydrogen electrodes include:

- X-ray-quality welds or welds requiring high mechanical properties.

- Crack-resistant welds in medium-carbon to high-carbon steels; welds that resist hot-short cracking in phosphorus steels; and welds that minimize porosity in sulfur-bearing steels.

- Welds in thick sections or in restrained joints in mild and alloy steels where shrinkage stresses might promote weld cracking.

- Welds in alloy steel requiring a strength of 70,000 psi or more.

- Multiple-pass, vertical, and overhead welds in mild steel.

Two low-hydrogen electrodes give the weldor ability to match all joint requirements in welding steel — E7018 and E7028.

E7018: This electrode has fill-freeze or fast-follow characteristics and is suitable for all-position operation. Iron powder in the electrode coating promotes rapid deposition. Moderately heavy slag is easy to remove. (Weld metal freezes rapidly even though slag remains somewhat fluid.) Beads are flat or slightly convex and have distinct ripples, with little spatter.

E7028: The electrode has fast-fill characteristics applicable to high-production welds where low-hydrogen quality is required. It performs best on flat fillets and deep-groove joints, but is also suitable for horizontal fillet and lap welds. Excellent restriking qualities permit efficient skip and tack welding.

Techniques for E7028 are the same as those described for conventional fast-fill electrodes. However, special care should be taken to clean the slag from every bead on multiple-pass welds to avoid slag inclusions that would appear on X-ray inspection. The ensuing discussion pertains to the techniques recommended for E7018 electrodes.

Polarity: Use DCRP whenever possible if the electrode size is 5/32 in. or less. For larger electrodes, use AC for best operating characteristics (but DCRP can also be used).

Flat: Use low current on the first pass, or whenever it is desirable to reduce admixture with a base metal of poor weldability. On succeeding passes, use currents that provide best operating characteristics. Drag the electrode lightly or hold an arc of 1/8 in. or less. Do not use a long arc at any time, since E7018 electrodes rely principally on molten slag for shielding. Stringer beads or small weave passes are preferred to wide weave passes. When starting a new electrode, strike the arc ahead of the crater, move back into the crater, and then proceed in the normal direction. On AC, use currents about 10% higher than those used with DC. Govern travel speed by the desired bead size.

Vertical: Weld vertical-up with electrode sizes of 5/32 in. or less. Use a triangular weave for heavy single-pass welds. For multipass welds, first deposit a stringer bead by using a slight weave. Deposit additional layers with a side-to-side weave, hesitating at the sides long enough to fuse out any small slag pockets and to minimize undercut. Do not use a whip technique or take the electrode out of the molten pool. Travel slowly enough to maintain the

shelf without causing metal to spill. Use currents in the lower portion of the range.

Overhead: Use electrodes of 5/32 in. or smaller. Deposit stringer beads by using a slight circular motion in the crater. Maintain a short arc. Motions should be slow and deliberate. Move fast enough to avoid spilling weld metal, but do not be alarmed if some slag spills. Use currents in the lower portion of the range.

REDRYING LOW-HYDROGEN ELECTRODES

Low-hydrogen electrodes must be dry if they are to perform properly. Electrodes in unopened, hermetically sealed containers remain dry indefinitely in good storage condtions. Opened cans should be stored in a cabinet at 250 to 300°F. Supplying weldors with electrodes twice a shift — at the start of the shift and at lunch, for example — minimizes the danger of moisture pickup. Return electrodes to the heated cabinet for overnight storage.

When containers are punctured or opened so that the electrode is exposed to the air for a few days, or when containers are stored under unusually wet conditions, low-hydrogen electrodes pick up moisture. The moisture, depending upon the amount absorbed, impairs weld quality in the following ways:

1. A small amount of moisture may cause internal porosity. Detection of this porosity requires X-ray inspection or destructive testing. If the

**TABLE 10-1. Procedures for
Drying Low-Hydrogen Electrodes**

	Drying Temperatures	
Nature of Moisture Pickup	**E7018-28**	**E8018-X, E9018-X, E11018-X**
Electrodes exposed to air for less than one week; no direct contact with water. Welds not subject to X-ray inspection.	300°F	300°F
Electrodes exposed to air for less than one week; no direct contact with water. Welds subject to X-ray inspection.	700°F	750°F
Electrodes have come in direct contact with water, or have been exposed to extremely humid conditions as indicated by core wire rusting at the holder end. Before redrying at 700 — 750F, predry electrodes in this condition at 180°F for 1 to 2 hours. This minimizes the tendency for coating cracks or oxidation of the alloys in the coating.	700°F	750°F

Note: One hour at the listed temperatures is satisfactory. Do not dry electrodes at higher temperatures or for more than 8 hours. Several hours at lower temperature are not equivalent to using the specified temperatures. Remove the electrodes from the can and spread them out in the furnace. Each electrode must reach the drying temperature. (Cardboard can liners char at about 350°F.)

base metal has high hardenability, even a small amount of moisture can contribute to underbead cracking.

2. A high amount of moisture causes visible external porosity in addition to internal porosity.

3. Severe moisture pickup can cause weld cracks or underbead cracking in addition to severe porosity.

Redrying completely restores ability to deposit quality welds. The proper redrying temperature depends upon the type of electrode and its condition. Drying procedures are listed in Table 10-1.

GENERAL CONSIDERATIONS IN WELDING

As noted earlier, joint position is often the primary factor in electrode selection and is therefore largely responsible for the speed and cost of welding. Where possible, work should be positioned flat for fastest welding speed.

Sheet-Metal Welds: In sheet steel from 10 to 18 gage, welds are usually larger than needed for joint strength. Thus, the primary objective is to avoid burnthrough while welding at fast travel speeds with minimum skips and misses. Fastest speeds are obtained with the work positioned 45 to 75° downhill.

Welds on Mild Steel Plate: Plates having a thickness of 3/16 in. or greater are welded most rapidly in the flat position. This position permits easiest manipulation of the electrode and allows use of high-deposition fast-fill electrodes. Variations in welding speed with different joint positions are illustrated in Fig. 10-8.

Welds on High-Carbon and Low-Alloy Steel: These steels can be welded most readily in the level position. Refer to the discussion on low-hydrogen electrodes.

Joint Geometry and Fitup: Joint dimensions specified in procedure tables are chosen for fast welding speeds consistent with weld quality. Departure from the recommended joint geometry may reduce welding speed or cause welding problems.

Fitup must be consistent for the entire joint. Sheet metal and most fillet and lap joints must be clamped tightly their entire length. Gaps or bevels must be accurately controlled over the entire joint. Any variations in a joint make it necessary for the operator to reduce the welding speed to avoid burnthrough and force him to make time-consuming manipulations of the electrodes.

Sufficient bevel is required for good bead shape and adequate penetration (Fig. 10-9). Insufficient bevel prevents adequate entry of the electrode into the joint. A deep, narrow bead also has a tendency

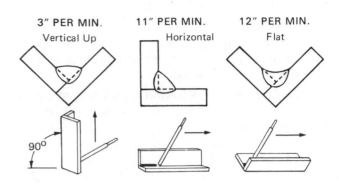

Fig. 10-8. Variations in welding speed with different joint positions.

to crack. However, excess bevel wastes material. Sufficient gap is needed for full penetration (Fig. 10-10). Excessive gap wastes metal and slows welding speed. Either a 1/8 in. root face or a backup strip is required for fast welding and good quality with thick plate (Fig. 10-11).

Feather-edge preparations require a slow costly seal bead. However, double-V butt joints without a root face are practical when the seal bead cost is offset by easier edge preparation and the gap can be limited to about 3/32 in.

Weld seal beads on flat work with 3/16-in. E6010 electrodes at about 150 amps DCRP. Use 1/8-in. electrode at about 90 amp DCRP for vertical, overhead, and horizontal butt welds. Employ a combination whipping technique and circulating motion in the crater.

When low-hydrogen seal beads are required, use the appropriate EXX18 electrode. Weld with the same electrode sizes and about 20 amp higher current than recommended for E6010. Employ stringer bead technique with a slight weave when needed.

Back-gouging from the second side is needed:

1. For X-ray quality.

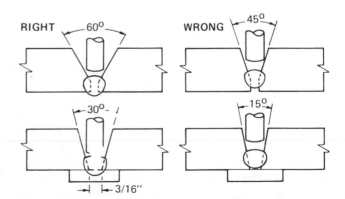

Fig. 10-9. Correct and incorrect bevels for good bead shape and adequate penetration.

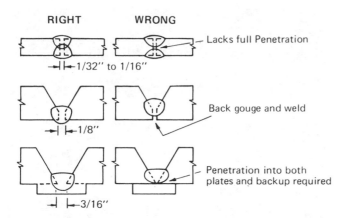

Fig. 10-10. Correct and incorrect gaps for proper penetration.

2. When irregular gap or poor technique produces a poor bead.

3. When a heavy bead is needed to prevent burn-through of semiautomatic fill beads.

Joint Cleanliness: To avoid porosity and attain the speeds indicated in procedure tables, remove excessive scale, rust, moisture, paint, oil, and grease from the surface of the joints.

If paint, dirt, or rust cannot be removed — as is sometimes the case in maintenance welding — use E6010 or E6011 electrodes to penetrate through the contaminants deeply into the base metal. Slow the travel speed to allow time for gas bubbles to boil out of the molten weld before it freezes.

Electrode Size: Large electrodes permit welding at high currents and high deposition rates. Therefore, use the largest electrode practical con-

sistent with good weld quality. Electrode size is limited by many factors, but the most important considerations usually are:

1. High currents increase penetration. Therefore, electrode size is limited on sheet metal and with root passes where burnthrough can occur.

2. The maximum electrode size practical for vertical and overhead welding is 3/16-in. The 5/32-in. electrode is the maximum size for low-hydrogen electrodes.

3. High DC current increases arc blow. When arc blow is a problem, either use AC or limit the current.

4. Joint dimensions sometimes limit the electrode diameter that will fit into the joint.

Preheat and Interpass Temperature: The use of preheat and minimum interpass temperatures may be dictated by the composition of the steel, by the thickness of the material, or by the degree of joint restraint. Preheating may be mandatory if the welding is done according to a code.

TROUBLE SHOOTING

Many operating variables can affect the quality and appearance of the weld. The effects produced by the most important of these variables are illustrated in Fig. 10-12. Common undesirable effects are shown in Figs. 10-13 through 10-15. Methods for correcting undesirable characteristics are discussed in the following paragraphs. Not discussed here is arc blow, which is covered in Chapter 8.

Weld Spatter: Spatter does not affect weld strength but does produce a poor appearance and

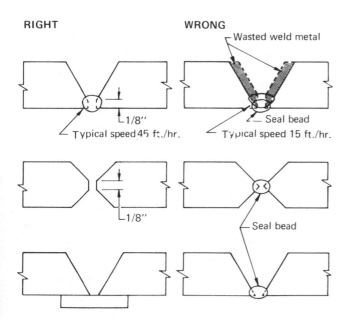

Fig. 10-11. Proper joint geometry for thick-plate welding.

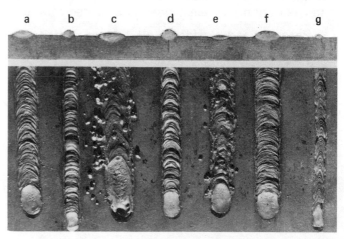

Fig. 10-12. Effect of welding variables on bead characteristics. Proper current, travel speed, and arc length (a). Current too low (b). Current too high (c). Arc length too short (d). Arc length too long (e). Travel speed too slow (f). Travel speed too fast (g).

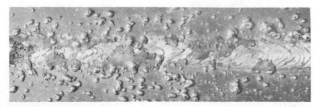

Fig. 10-13. Undesirable bead appearance caused by weld spatter.

increases cleaning costs. To control excessive spatter:

1. Try lowering the current. Be sure the current is within the recommended range for the type and size electrode.

2. Be sure the polarity is correct for the electrode type.

3. Try a shorter arc length.

4. If the molten metal is running in front of the arc, change the electrode angle.

5. Watch for arc blow.

6. Be sure the electrode is not too wet.

Undercut: Generally, the only harm from undercutting is impaired appearance. However, undercutting may also impair weld strength, particularly when the weld is loaded in tension or subjected to fatigue. To minimize undercut:

1. Reduce current, travel speed, or electrode size until the puddle is manageable.

2. Change electrode angle so the arc force holds the metal in the corners. Use a uniform travel speed and avoid excessive weaving.

Rough Welding: If polarity and current are within the electrode manufacturer's recommendations but the arc action is rough and erratic, the electrodes may be wet. Try electrodes from a fresh container. If the problem occurs frequently, store open containers of electrodes in a heated cabinet.

Porosity and Surface Holes: Most porosity is not visible. But severe porosity can weaken the weld. The following practices minimize porosity:

1. Remove scale, rust, paint, moisture, or dirt from the joint. Generally use an E6010 or E6011 electrode for dirty steel.

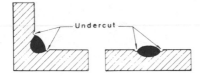

Fig. 10-14. Undercut in a weld. The effect is undesirable from the appearance standpoint and may weaken the joint.

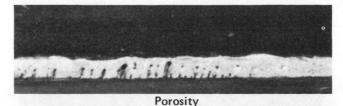

Porosity

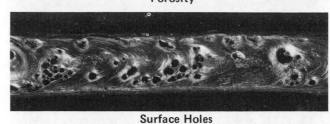

Surface Holes

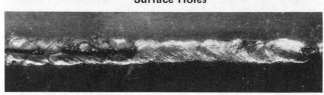

Poor Fusion

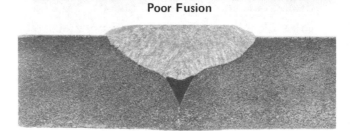

Shallow Penetration

Fig. 10-15. Undesirable effects caused by improper procedures and techniques.

2. Keep the puddle molten for a long time, so that gases may boil out before the metal freezes.

3. Steels very low in carbon or manganese or those high in sulfur or phosphorus should be welded with a low-hydrogen electrode. Minimize admixture of base metal with weld metal by using low currents and fast travel speeds for less penetration.

4. Try using a short arc length; short arcs are required for low-hydrogen electrodes.

Surface holes can be avoided by many of the practices used to minimize porosity.

Poor Fusion: Proper fusion exists when the weld bonds to both walls of the joint and forms a solid bead across the joint. Lack of fusion is often visible and must be avoided for a sound weld. To correct poor fusion:

1. Try a higher current and a stringer-bead technique.

2. Be sure the edges of the joint are clean, or use an E6010 or E6011 electrode.

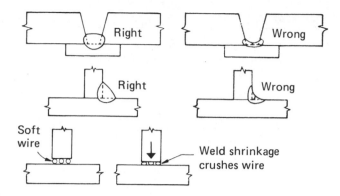

Fig. 10-16. Factors in controlling weld cracking. Illustrated are correct and incorrect joint geometries and bead shapes and a technique to permit stress relaxation in an otherwise rigid joint.

3. If gap is excessive, provide better fitup or use a weave technique to fill the gap.

Shallow Penetration: Penetration refers to the depth the weld enters into the base metal. For full-strength welds, penetration to the bottom of the joint is required. To overcome shallow penetration:

1. Try higher currents or slower travel.

2. Use small electrodes to reach into deep, narrow grooves.

3. Allow some gap (free space) at the bottom of the joint.

Cracking: Many different types of cracks may occur throughout a weld. Some are visible and some are not. However, all cracks are potentially serious, because they can lead to complete failure of the weld. The following suggestions may help control potential cracking. Practices to minimize cracks are shown in Fig. 10-16.

Most cracking is attributed to high-carbon or alloy content or high-sulfur content in the base metal. To control this type of cracking:

1. Use low-hydrogen electrodes.

2. Preheat. Use high preheats for heavier plate and rigid joints.

3. Reduce penetration by using low currents and small electrodes. This reduces the amount of alloy added to the weld from melted base metal.

To control crater cracking, fill each crater before breaking the arc. Use a back-stepping technique so as to end each weld on the crater of the previous weld.

On multiple-pass or fillet welds, be sure the first bead is of sufficient size and of flat or convex shape to resist cracking until the later beads can be added for support. To increase bead size, use slower travel speed, a short arc, or weld 5° uphill. Always continue welding while the plate is hot.

Rigid parts are more prone to cracking. If possible, weld toward the unrestrained end. Leave a 1/32-in. gap between plates for free shrinkage movement as the weld cools. Peen each bead while it is still hot to relieve stresses.

SHIELDED METAL-ARC PROCEDURES FOR CARBON AND LOW-ALLOY STEELS

The following procedure tables for shielded metal-arc welding of carbon and low-alloy steels are extracted from The Lincoln Electric Company's *Procedure Handbook of Arc Welding*. Reference should be made to Chapter 9 for information on how to use procedure tables.

SHIELDED METAL-ARC (MANUAL)

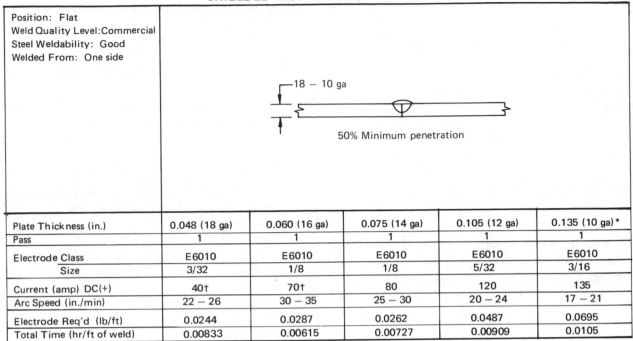

Position: Flat
Weld Quality Level: Commercial
Steel Weldability: Good
Welded From: One side

18 — 10 ga

50% Minimum penetration

Plate Thickness (in.)	0.048 (18 ga)	0.060 (16 ga)	0.075 (14 ga)	0.105 (12 ga)	0.135 (10 ga) *
Pass	1	1	1	1	1
Electrode Class	E6010	E6010	E6010	E6010	E6010
Size	3/32	1/8	1/8	5/32	3/16
Current (amp) DC(+)	40†	70†	80	120	135
Arc Speed (in./min)	22 — 26	30 — 35	25 — 30	20 — 24	17 — 21
Electrode Req'd (lb/ft)	0.0244	0.0287	0.0262	0.0487	0.0695
Total Time (hr/ft of weld)	0.00833	0.00615	0.00727	0.00909	0.0105

* Use 1/16 in. gap and whip the electrode.
† DC(—)

SHIELDED METAL-ARC (MANUAL)

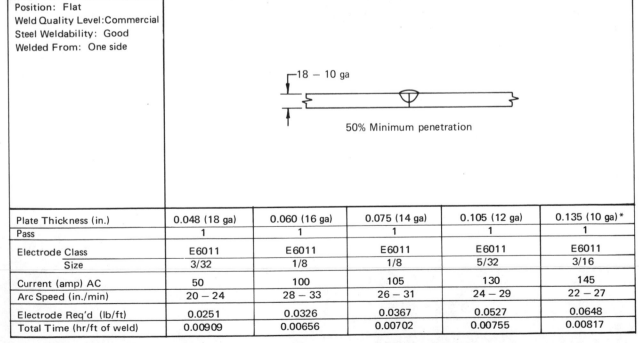

Position: Flat
Weld Quality Level: Commercial
Steel Weldability: Good
Welded From: One side

18 — 10 ga

50% Minimum penetration

Plate Thickness (in.)	0.048 (18 ga)	0.060 (16 ga)	0.075 (14 ga)	0.105 (12 ga)	0.135 (10 ga) *
Pass	1	1	1	1	1
Electrode Class	E6011	E6011	E6011	E6011	E6011
Size	3/32	1/8	1/8	5/32	3/16
Current (amp) AC	50	100	105	130	145
Arc Speed (in./min)	20 — 24	28 — 33	26 — 31	24 — 29	22 — 27
Electrode Req'd (lb/ft)	0.0251	0.0326	0.0367	0.0527	0.0648
Total Time (hr/ft of weld)	0.00909	0.00656	0.00702	0.00755	0.00817

* Use 1/16 in. gap and whip the electrode.

SHIELDED METAL-ARC (MANUAL)

Position: Flat
Weld Quality Level: Code
Steel Weldability: Good
Welded From: One side

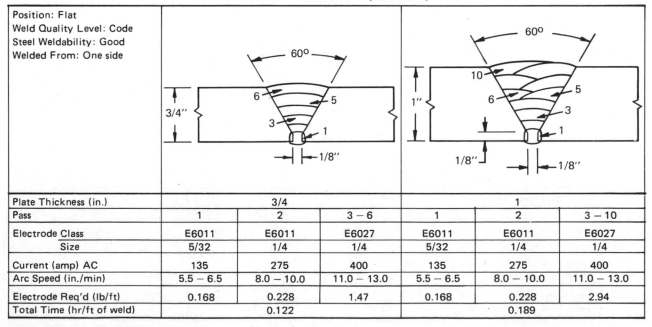

Plate Thickness (in.)	5/16		3/8		1/2		
Pass	1	2	1	2 & 3	1	2	3
Electrode Class	E6011	E6027	E6011	E6027	E6011	E6011	E6027
Size	5/32	5/32	5/32	5/32	5/32	1/4	1/4
Current (amp) AC	135	240	135	240	135	275	400
Arc Speed (in./min)	5.5-6.5	12.0-14.0	5.5-6.5	12.0-14.0	5.5-6.5	8.0-10.0	10.0-12.0
Electrode Req'd (lb/ft)	0.168	0.142	0.168	0.284	0.168	0.228	0.354
Total Time (hr/ft of weld)	0.0487		0.0641		0.0717		

SHIELDED METAL-ARC (MANUAL)

Position: Flat
Weld Quality Level: Code
Steel Weldability: Good
Welded From: One side

Plate Thickness (in.)	3/4			1		
Pass	1	2	3 – 6	1	2	3 – 10
Electrode Class	E6011	E6011	E6027	E6011	E6011	E6027
Size	5/32	1/4	1/4	5/32	1/4	1/4
Current (amp) AC	135	275	400	135	275	400
Arc Speed (in./min)	5.5 – 6.5	8.0 – 10.0	11.0 – 13.0	5.5 – 6.5	8.0 – 10.0	11.0 – 13.0
Electrode Req'd (lb/ft)	0.168	0.228	1.47	0.168	0.228	2.94
Total Time (hr/ft of weld)	0.122			0.189		

SHIELDED METAL-ARC (MANUAL)

Position: Flat
Weld Quality Level: Commercial
Steel Weldability: Good
Welded From: One side

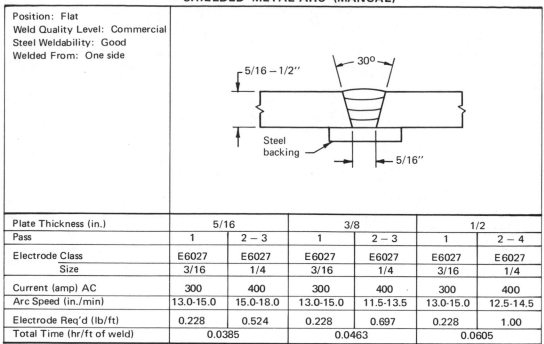

Plate Thickness (in.)	5/16		3/8		1/2	
Pass	1	2 – 3	1	2 – 3	1	2 – 4
Electrode Class	E6027	E6027	E6027	E6027	E6027	E6027
Size	3/16	1/4	3/16	1/4	3/16	1/4
Current (amp) AC	300	400	300	400	300	400
Arc Speed (in./min)	13.0-15.0	15.0-18.0	13.0-15.0	11.5-13.5	13.0-15.0	12.5-14.5
Electrode Req'd (lb/ft)	0.228	0.524	0.228	0.697	0.228	1.00
Total Time (hr/ft of weld)	0.0385		0.0463		0.0605	

SHIELDED METAL-ARC (MANUAL)

Position: Flat
Weld Quality Level: Commercial
Steel Weldability: Good
Welded From: One side

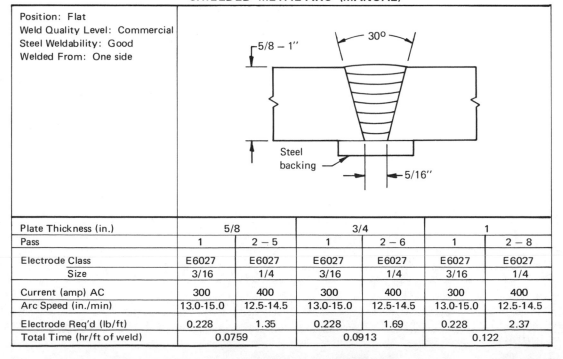

Plate Thickness (in.)	5/8		3/4		1	
Pass	1	2 – 5	1	2 – 6	1	2 – 8
Electrode Class	E6027	E6027	E6027	E6027	E6027	E6027
Size	3/16	1/4	3/16	1/4	3/16	1/4
Current (amp) AC	300	400	300	400	300	400
Arc Speed (in./min)	13.0-15.0	12.5-14.5	13.0-15.0	12.5-14.5	13.0-15.0	12.5-14.5
Electrode Req'd (lb/ft)	0.228	1.35	0.228	1.69	0.228	2.37
Total Time (hr/ft of weld)	0.0759		0.0913		0.122	

SHIELDED METAL-ARC (MANUAL)

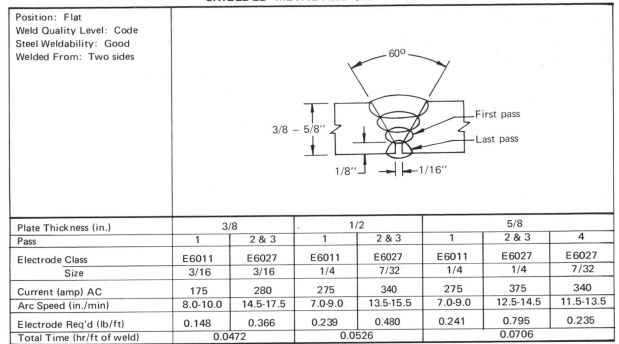

Position: Flat
Weld Quality Level: Code
Steel Weldability: Good
Welded From: Two sides

Plate Thickness (in.)	3/8		1/2		5/8		
Pass	1	2 & 3	1	2 & 3	1	2 & 3	4
Electrode Class	E6011	E6027	E6011	E6027	E6011	E6027	E6027
Size	3/16	3/16	1/4	7/32	1/4	1/4	7/32
Current (amp) AC	175	280	275	340	275	375	340
Arc Speed (in./min)	8.0-10.0	14.5-17.5	7.0-9.0	13.5-15.5	7.0-9.0	12.5-14.5	11.5-13.5
Electrode Req'd (lb/ft)	0.148	0.366	0.239	0.480	0.241	0.795	0.235
Total Time (hr/ft of weld)	0.0472		0.0526		0.0706		

Back gouge first pass before welding last pass.

SHIELDED METAL-ARC (MANUAL)

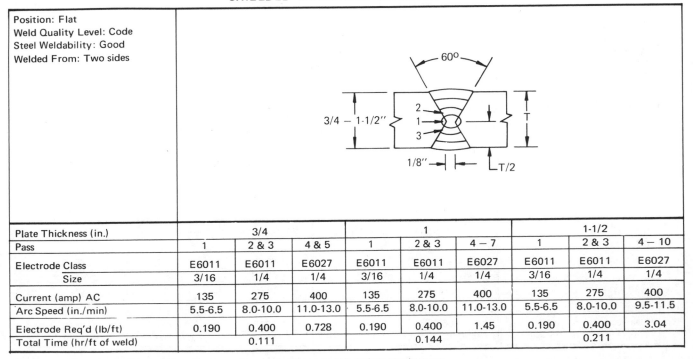

Position: Flat
Weld Quality Level: Code
Steel Weldability: Good
Welded From: Two sides

Plate Thickness (in.)	3/4			1			1-1/2		
Pass	1	2 & 3	4 & 5	1	2 & 3	4 – 7	1	2 & 3	4 – 10
Electrode Class	E6011	E6011	E6027	E6011	E6011	E6027	E6011	E6011	E6027
Size	3/16	1/4	1/4	3/16	1/4	1/4	3/16	1/4	1/4
Current (amp) AC	135	275	400	135	275	400	135	275	400
Arc Speed (in./min)	5.5-6.5	8.0-10.0	11.0-13.0	5.5-6.5	8.0-10.0	11.0-13.0	5.5-6.5	8.0-10.0	9.5-11.5
Electrode Req'd (lb/ft)	0.190	0.400	0.728	0.190	0.400	1.45	0.190	0.400	3.04
Total Time (hr/ft of weld)	0.111			0.144			0.211		

Back gouge first pass before welding third pass. Complete third pass side before turning over.

SHIELDED METAL-ARC (MANUAL)

Position: Vertical down Weld Quality Level:Commercial Steel Weldability: Good Welded From: One side	
	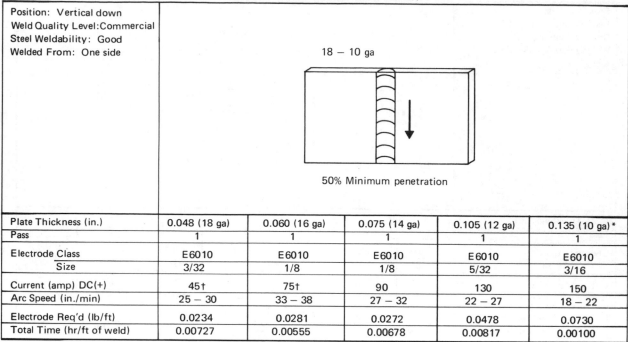18 — 10 ga 50% Minimum penetration

Plate Thickness (in.)	0.048 (18 ga)	0.060 (16 ga)	0.075 (14 ga)	0.105 (12 ga)	0.135 (10 ga) *
Pass	1	1	1	1	1
Electrode Class	E6010	E6010	E6010	E6010	E6010
Size	3/32	1/8	1/8	5/32	3/16
Current (amp) DC(+)	45†	75†	90	130	150
Arc Speed (in./min)	25 — 30	33 — 38	27 — 32	22 — 27	18 — 22
Electrode Req'd (lb/ft)	0.0234	0.0281	0.0272	0.0478	0.0730
Total Time (hr/ft of weld)	0.00727	0.00555	0.00678	0.00817	0.00100

* Use 1/16 in. gap and whip the electrode.

† Use DC(−)

SHIELDED METAL-ARC (MANUAL)

Position: Vertical down Weld Quality Level:Commercial Steel Weldability: Good Welded From: One side	
	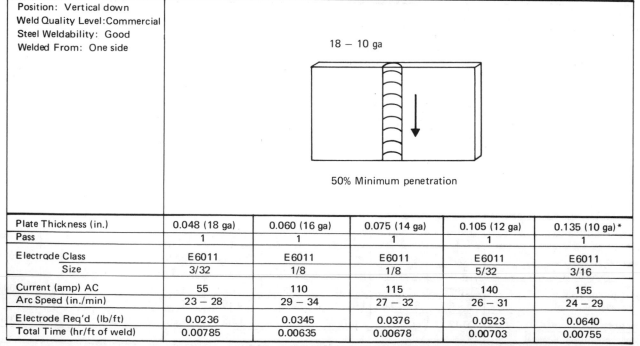18 — 10 ga 50% Minimum penetration

Plate Thickness (in.)	0.048 (18 ga)	0.060 (16 ga)	0.075 (14 ga)	0.105 (12 ga)	0.135 (10 ga) *
Pass	1	1	1	1	1
Electrode Class	E6011	E6011	E6011	E6011	E6011
Size	3/32	1/8	1/8	5/32	3/16
Current (amp) AC	55	110	115	140	155
Arc Speed (in./min)	23 — 28	29 — 34	27 — 32	26 — 31	24 — 29
Electrode Req'd (lb/ft)	0.0236	0.0345	0.0376	0.0523	0.0640
Total Time (hr/ft of weld)	0.00785	0.00635	0.00678	0.00703	0.00755

* Use 1/16 in. gap and whip the electrode.

SHIELDED METAL-ARC (MANUAL)

Position: Vertical up
Weld Quality Level: Code
Steel Weldability: Good
Welded From: One side

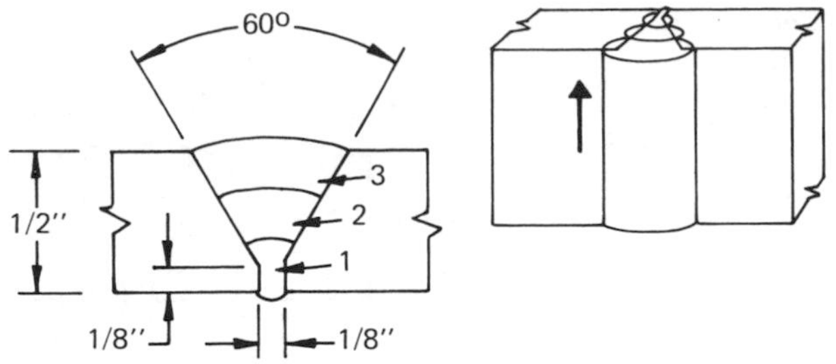

Plate Thickness (in.)	1/4	.5/16	3/8	1/2
Pass	1 & 2	1 & 2	1 & 2	1 — 3
Electrode Class	E6010	E6010	E6010	E6010
Size	5/32	5/32	3/16	3/16
Current (amp) DC(+)	110	120	150	170
Arc Speed (in./min)*	5.2-5.8	3.8-4.2	4.8-5.3	3.8-4.2
Electrode Req'd (lb/ft)	0.323	0.440	0.586	0.990
Total Time (hr/ft of weld)	0.0901	0.118	0.130	0.152

* First pass only. Vary speed on succeeding passes to obtain proper weld size.

SHIELDED METAL-ARC (MANUAL)

Position: Vertical up
Weld Quality Level: Code
Steel Weldability: Good
Welded From: One side

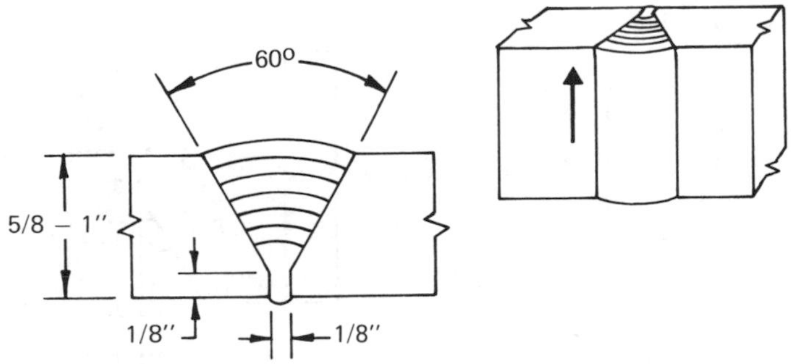

Plate Thickness (in.)	5/8	3/4	1
Pass	1 — 4	1 — 6	1 — 10
Electrode Class	E6010	E6010	E6010
Size	3/16	3/16	3/16
Current (amp) DC(+)	170	170	170
Arc Speed (in./min)*	3.8 — 4.2	3.8 — 4.2	3.8 — 4.2
Electrode Req'd (lb/ft)	1.48	2.08	3.56
Total Time (hr/ft of weld)	0.228	0.318	0.547

* First pass only. Vary speed on succeeding passes to obtain proper weld size.

SHIELDED METAL-ARC (MANUAL)

Position: Vertical up
Weld Quality Level: Code
Steel Weldability: Fair
Welded From: One side

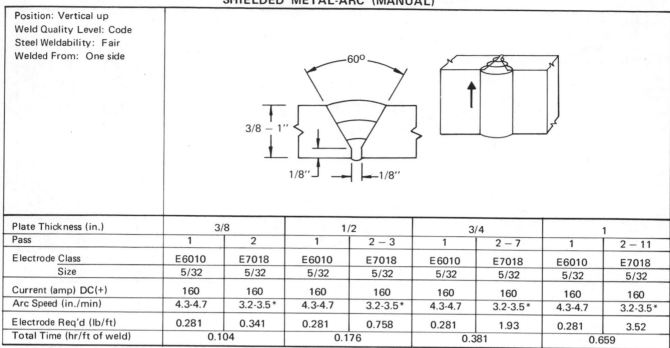

Plate Thickness (in.)	3/8		1/2		3/4		1	
Pass	1	2	1	2 – 3	1	2 – 7	1	2 – 11
Electrode Class	E6010	E7018	E6010	E7018	E6010	E7018	E6010	E7018
Size	5/32	5/32	5/32	5/32	5/32	5/32	5/32	5/32
Current (amp) DC(+)	160	160	160	160	160	160	160	160
Arc Speed (in./min)	4.3-4.7	3.2-3.5*	4.3-4.7	3.2-3.5*	4.3-4.7	3.2-3.5*	4.3-4.7	3.2-3.5*
Electrode Req'd (lb/ft)	0.281	0.341	0.281	0.758	0.281	1.93	0.281	3.52
Total Time (hr/ft of weld)	0.104		0.176		0.381		0.659	

* Second pass only. Vary speed on succeeding passes to obtain proper weld size.

SHIELDED METAL-ARC (MANUAL)

Position: Vertical up
Weld Quality Level: Code
Steel Weldability: Good
Welded From: Two sides

Plate Thickness (in.)	3/4		1		1-1/4		1-1/2	
Pass	1	2 – 5	1	2 – 7	1	2 – 7	1	2 – 9
Electrode Class	E6010	E7018	E6010	E7018	E6010	E7018	E6010	E7018
Size	5/32	5/32	5/32	5/32	5/32	5/32	5/32	5/32
Current (amp) DC(+)	140	160	140	160	140	160	140	160
Arc Speed (in./min)	3.5-4.1	4.1-4.9	3.5-4.1	3.5-4.1	3.9-4.1	2.3-2.9	3.5-4.1	2.4-3.0
Electrode Req'd (lb/ft)	0.240	0.900	0.240	1.66	0.240	2.40	0.240	3.16
Total Time (hr/ft of weld)	0.230		0.367		0.514		0.645	

Gouge out seam for first pass on second side.

SHIELDED METAL-ARC (MANUAL)

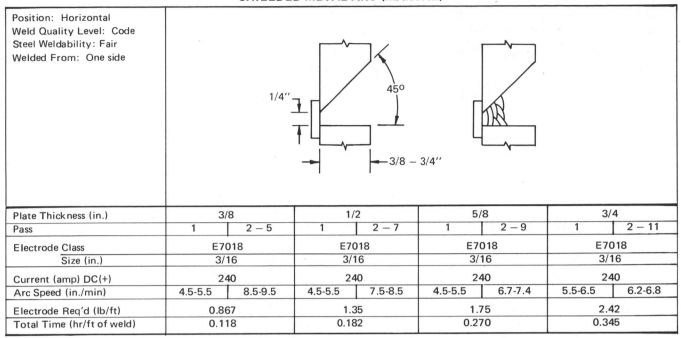

Position: Horizontal
Weld Quality Level: Code
Steel Weldability: Fair
Welded From: One side

Plate Thickness (in.)	3/8		1/2		5/8		3/4	
Pass	1	2 — 5	1	2 — 7	1	2 — 9	1	2 — 11
Electrode Class	E7018		E7018		E7018		E7018	
Size (in.)	3/16		3/16		3/16		3/16	
Current (amp) DC(+)	240		240		240		240	
Arc Speed (in./min)	4.5-5.5	8.5-9.5	4.5-5.5	7.5-8.5	4.5-5.5	6.7-7.4	5.5-6.5	6.2-6.8
Electrode Req'd (lb/ft)	0.867		1.35		1.75		2.42	
Total Time (hr/ft of weld)	0.118		0.182		0.270		0.345	

SHIELDED METAL-ARC (MANUAL)

Position: Horizontal
Weld Quality Level: Code
Steel Weldability: Fair
Welded From: One side

Plate Thickness (in.)		1		1-1/4		1-1/2	
Pass	1*	2 — 13	14 — 19†	2 — 17	18 — 24†	2 — 22	23 — 31†
Electrode Class	E7018	E7018		E7018		E7018	
Size (in.)	3/16	7/32	3/16	7/32	3/16	7/32	3/16
Current (amp) DC(+)	240	280	240	280	240	280	240
Arc Speed (in./min)	5 — 6	6.2-6.8	9.5-10.5	5.7-6.3	9.5-10.5	5.2-5.8	9.5-10.5
Electrode Req'd (lb/ft)		3.39	.994	4.82	1.23	6.40	1.60
Total Time (hr/ft of weld)		0.526		.714		1.00	

* First pass for all thicknesses

† Cover passes.

SHIELDED METAL-ARC (MANUAL)

Position: Horizontal
Weld Quality Level: Commercial
Steel Weldability: Fair
Welded From: Two sides

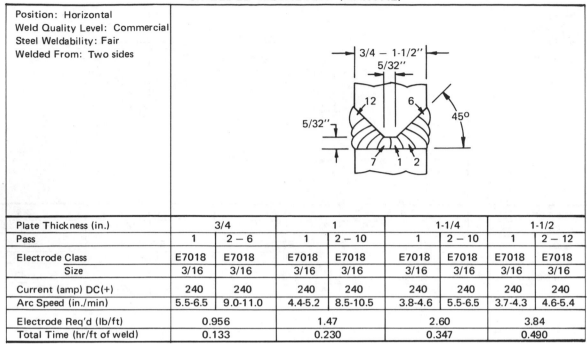

Plate Thickness (in.)	3/4		1		1-1/4		1-1/2	
Pass	1	2 – 6	1	2 – 10	1	2 – 10	1	2 – 12
Electrode Class	E7018	E7018	E7018	E7018	E7018	E7018	E7018	E7018
Size	3/16	3/16	3/16	3/16	3/16	3/16	3/16	3/16
Current (amp) DC(+)	240	240	240	240	240	240	240	240
Arc Speed (in./min)	5.5-6.5	9.0-11.0	4.4-5.2	8.5-10.5	3.8-4.6	5.5-6.5	3.7-4.3	4.6-5.4
Electrode Req'd (lb/ft)	0.956		1.47		2.60		3.84	
Total Time (hr/ft of weld)	0.133		0.230		0.347		0.490	

Fill first pass side. Back gouge as required before welding second side.

SHIELDED METAL-ARC (MANUAL)

Position: Horizontal
Weld Quality Level: Code
Steel Weldability: Fair
Welded From: One side

Plate Thickness (in.)		3/4	1	1-1/4	1-1/2
Pass	1*	2 – 3	2 – 5	2 – 5	2 – 6
Electrode Class	E7018	E7018	E7018	E7018	E7018
Size (in.)	3/16	3/16	3/16	3/16	3/16
Current (amp) DC(+)	240	240	240	240	240
Arc Speed (in./min)	4.0-6.0	9.5-10.5	9.0-10.0	5.7-6.3	4.7-5.3
Electrode Req'd (lb/ft)		0.470	0.740	1.80	1.92
Total Time (hr/ft of weld)		0.0800	0.116	0.178	0.250

* First pass for all thicknesses.

SHIELDED METAL-ARC (MANUAL)

Position: Overhead
Weld Quality Level: Code
Steel Weldability: Fair
Welded From: One side

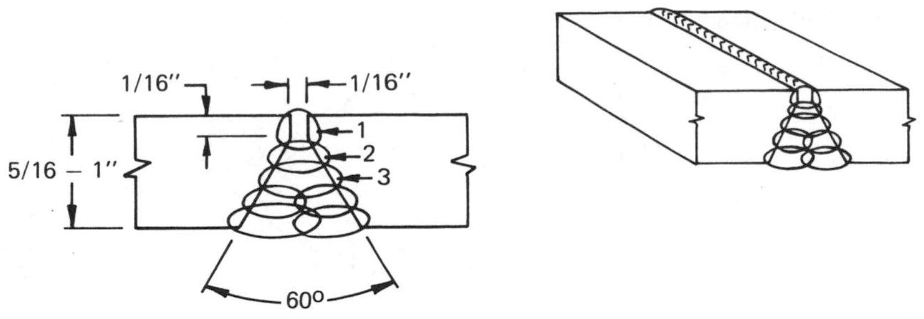

Plate Thickness (in.)	5/16		3/8		1/2		3/4		1	
Pass	1	2	1	2 − 3	1	2 − 5	1	2 − 9	1	2 − 13
Electrode Class	E6010	E7018	E6010	E7018	E6010	E7018	E6010	E7018	E6010	E7018
Size	1/8	5/32	1/8	5/32	1/8	5/32	1/8	5/32	1/8	5/32
Current (amp) DC(+)	110	170	110	170	110	170	110	170	110	170
Arc Speed (in./min)	4.3 − 4.7	3.4 − 3.8	4.3 − 4.7	3.3 − 3.7	4.3 − 4.7	3.6 − 4.0	4.3 − 4.7	4.3 − 4.7	4.3 − 4.7	3.6 − 4.0
Electrode Req'd (lb/ft)	0.155	0.327	0.155	0.671	0.155	0.918	0.155	2.08	0.155	3.70
Total Time (hr/ft of weld)	0.0999		0.158		0.202		0.399		0.575	

Split layers after third pass, as shown in sketch.

SHIELDED METAL-ARC (MANUAL)

Position: Flat and horizontal
Weld Quality Level: Commercial
Steel Weldability: Good

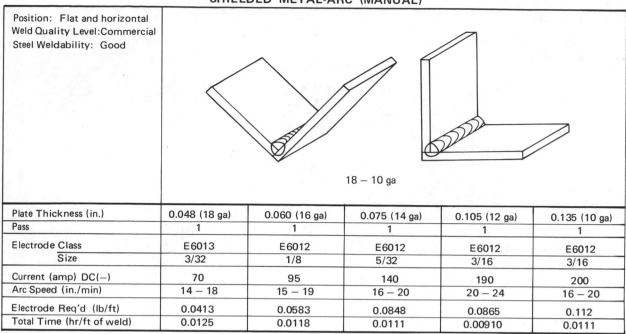

18 — 10 ga

Plate Thickness (in.)	0.048 (18 ga)	0.060 (16 ga)	0.075 (14 ga)	0.105 (12 ga)	0.135 (10 ga)
Pass	1	1	1	1	1
Electrode Class	E6013	E6012	E6012	E6012	E6012
Size	3/32	1/8	5/32	3/16	3/16
Current (amp) DC(−)	70	95	140	190	200
Arc Speed (in./min)	14 — 18	15 — 19	16 — 20	20 — 24	16 — 20
Electrode Req'd (lb/ft)	0.0413	0.0583	0.0848	0.0865	0.112
Total Time (hr/ft of weld)	0.0125	0.0118	0.0111	0.00910	0.0111

SHIELDED METAL-ARC (MANUAL)

Position: Flat and horizontal
Weld Quality Level: Commercial
Steel Weldability: Good

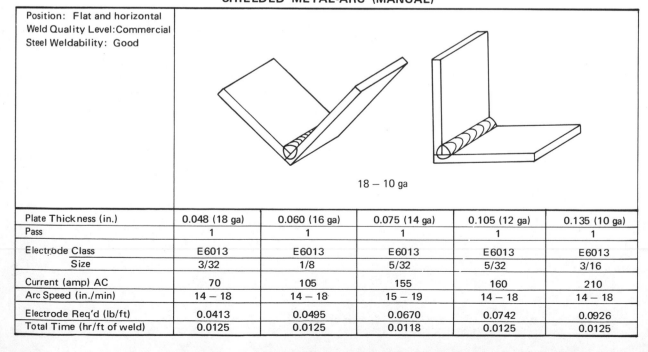

18 — 10 ga

Plate Thickness (in.)	0.048 (18 ga)	0.060 (16 ga)	0.075 (14 ga)	0.105 (12 ga)	0.135 (10 ga)
Pass	1	1	1	1	1
Electrode Class	E6013	E6013	E6013	E6013	E6013
Size	3/32	1/8	5/32	5/32	3/16
Current (amp) AC	70	105	155	160	210
Arc Speed (in./min)	14 — 18	14 — 18	15 — 19	14 — 18	14 — 18
Electrode Req'd (lb/ft)	0.0413	0.0495	0.0670	0.0742	0.0926
Total Time (hr/ft of weld)	0.0125	0.0125	0.0118	0.0125	0.0125

SHIELDED METAL-ARC (MANUAL)

Position: Flat
Weld Quality Level: Commercial
Steel Weldability: Good

14 ga — 1/4" to 3/16"

Weld Size, L (in.)				5/32	5/32	3/16	3/16
Plate Thickness (in.)	0.075 (14 ga)	0.105 (12 ga)	0.135 (10 ga)	3/16		1/4	
Pass	1	1	1	1	1	1	1
Electrode Class	E7024	E7024	E7024	E7024	E7024	E7024	E7024
Size	3/32	1/8	1/8	1/8	5/32	5/32	3/16
Current (amp) AC	95	150	160	180	210	230	270
Arc Speed (in./min)	14.5-16.0	16.5-18.5	16.5-18.5	15.0-16.5	16.0-18.0	14.0-15.5	15.5-17.5
Electrode Req'd (lb/ft)	0.0485	0.0760	0.0822	0.102	0.117	0.144	0.162
Total Time (hr/ft of weld)	0.0131	0.0114	0.0114	0.0127	0.0117	0.0136	0.0121

SHIELDED METAL-ARC (MANUAL)

Position: Flat
Weld Quality Level: Commercial
Steel Weldability: Good

5/16 — 1/2" 1/4 — 3/8"

Weld Size, L (in.)	1/4	1/4	9/32	5/16	3/8
Plate Thickness (in.)	5/16		3/8		1/2
Pass	1	1	1	1	1
Electrode Class	E7024	E7024	E7024	E7024	E7024
Size	3/16	7/32	1/4	1/4	5/16
Current (amp) AC	275	325	375	375	475
Arc Speed (in./min)	14.0-16.0	16.0-18.0	17.0-19.0	14.0-15.0	11.0-12.0
Electrode Req'd (lb/ft)	0.19	0.20	0.22	0.29	0.38
Total Time (hr/ft of weld)	0.0133	0.0118	0.0131	0.138	0.174

SHIELDED METAL-ARC (MANUAL)

Position: Flat
Weld Quality Level: Commercial
Weldability: Good

Weld Size, L (in.)	1/2		9/16		5/8		3/4	
Plate Thickness (in.)	5/8		3/4		3/4		1	
Pass	1	2	1	2	1	2 & 3	1	2 – 4
Electrode Class	E7024	E7024	E7024	E7024	E7024	E7024	E7024	E7024
Size	5/16	5/16	5/16	5/16	5/16	5/16	5/16	5/16
Current (amp) AC	475	550	475	550	475	550	475	550
Arc Speed (in./min)	13.0-15.0	14.0-16.0	13.0-15.0	10.0-11.0	13.0-15.0	14.0-15.0	13.0-15.0	13.0-14.0
Electrode Req'd (lb/ft)	0.67		0.85		1.07		1.46	
Total Time (hr/ft of weld)	0.0276		0.0333		0.0429		0.587	

SHIELDED METAL-ARC (MANUAL)

Position: Flat
Weld Quality Level: Commercial
Steel Weldability: Good

Weld Size, L (in.)	5/32 [1]	3/16 [2]	1/4 [3]	5/16 [3]	3/8
Plate Thickness (in.)	3/16	1/4	5/16	3/8	1/2
Pass	1	1	1	1	1
Electrode Class	E7014	E7014	E7014	E7014	E7014
Size	5/32	3/16	7/32	1/4	5/16
Current (amp) AC	200	250	310	370	450
Arc Speed (in./min)	12.5-13.5	12.0-13.0	11.0-12.0	9.0-10.0	7.5-8.5
Electrode Req'd (lb/ft)	0.0980	0.121	0.191	0.270	0.375
Total Time (hr/ft of weld)	0.0154	0.0160	0.0174	0.0211	0.0250

(1) Flat to 60° downhill.
(2) Flat to 30° downhill.
(3) Flat to 10° downhill.

SHIELDED METAL-ARC (MANUAL)

Position: Flat Weld Quality Level: Code Steel Weldability: Good								

3/16 — 1/2"

5/32 — 3/8"

Weld Size, L (in.)	5/32	3/16		1/4		9/32	5/16	3/8
Plate Thickness (in.)	3/16	1/4		5/16		3/8		1/2
Pass	1	1	1	1	1	1	1	1
Electrode Class	E6027	E6027	E6027	E6027	E6027	E6027	E6027	E6027
Size	5/32	5/32	3/16	3/16	7/32	1/4	1/4	1/4
Current (amp) AC	210	220	260	270	335	380	390	400
Arc Speed (in./min)	15.5-17.0	13.5-15.0	15.5-17.0	12.5-14.0	14.5-16.0	14.0-15.5	11.0-12.0	9.5-10.5
Electrode Req'd (lb/ft)	0.119	0.146	0.167	0.215	0.228	0.269	0.343	0.428
Total Time (hr/ft of weld)	0.0123	0.0140	0.0123	0.0151	0.0131	0.0136	0.0174	0.0200

SHIELDED METAL-ARC (MANUAL)

Position: Flat Weld Quality Level: Code Steel Weldability: Good								

5/8 — 3/4"

1/2 — 9/16"

3/4 — 1"

5/8 — 3/4"

Weld Size, L (in.)	1/2		9/16		5/8		3/4	
Plate Thickness (in.)	5/8		3/4		3/4		1	
Pass	1	2	1	2	1	2 & 3	1	2 — 4
Electrode Class	E6027	E6027	E6027	E6027	E6027	E6027	E6027	E6027
Size	1/4	1/4	1/4	1/4	1/4	1/4	1/4	1/4
Current (amp) AC	400	400	400	400	400	400	400	400
Arc Speed (in./min)	11.5-12.5	11.5-12.5	11.5-12.5	7.5-8.5	11.5-12.5	11.0-12.0	11.5-12.5	10.0-11.0
Electrode Req'd (lb/ft)	0.727		0.936		1.12		1.58	
Total Time (hr/ft of weld)	0.0333		0.0417		0.512		0.0737	

SHIELDED METAL-ARC (MANUAL)

Position: Flat
Weld Quality Level: Code
Steel Weldability: Poor

Weld Size, L (in.)	5/32	3/16	1/4	5/16	3/8
Plate Thickness (in.)	3/16	1/4	5/16	3/8	1/2
Pass	1	1	1	1	1
Electrode Class	E7028	E7028	E7028	E7028	E7028
Size	5/32	3/16	3/16	7/32	1/4
Current (amp) AC	215	260	280	330	400
Arc Speed (in./min)	13.5-15.0	13.5-15.0	11.0-12.0	10.0-12.0	8.5-9.5
Electrode Req'd (lb/ft)	0.104	0.147	0.208	0.285	0.437
Total Time (hr/ft of weld)	0.0140	0.0140	0.0175	0.0175	0.222

Preheat may be necessary depending on plate material.

SHIELDED METAL-ARC (MANUAL)

Position: Flat
Weld Quality Level: Code
Steel Weldability: Poor

Weld Size, L (in.)	5/32	3/16	1/4	5/16	3/8
Plate Thickness (in.)	3/16	1/4	5/16	3/8	1/2
Pass	1	1	1	1	1
Electrode Class	E7018	E7018	E7018	E7018	E7018
Size	3/16	7/32	7/32	1/4	1/4
Current (amp) AC	240	275	275	350	350
Arc Speed (in./min)	13.5-15.0	13.0-14.0	9.0-10.0	7.0-8.0	6.0-6.8
Electrode Req'd (lb/ft)	0.109	0.132	0.195	0.272	0.409
Total Time (hr/ft of weld)	0.0140	0.0149	0.0202	0.0270	0.0313

Preheat may be necessary depending on plate material.

SHIELDED METAL-ARC (MANUAL)

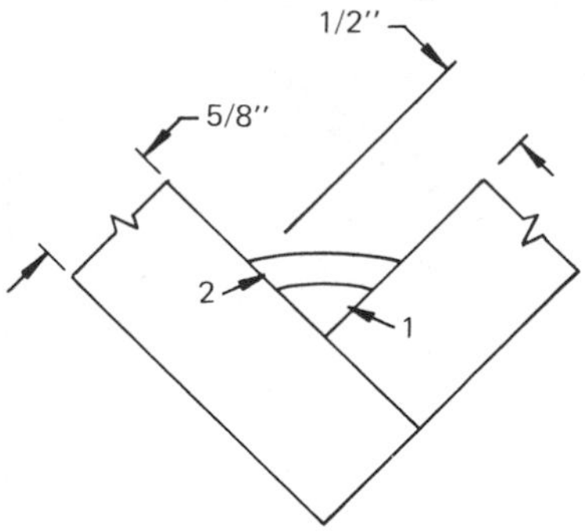

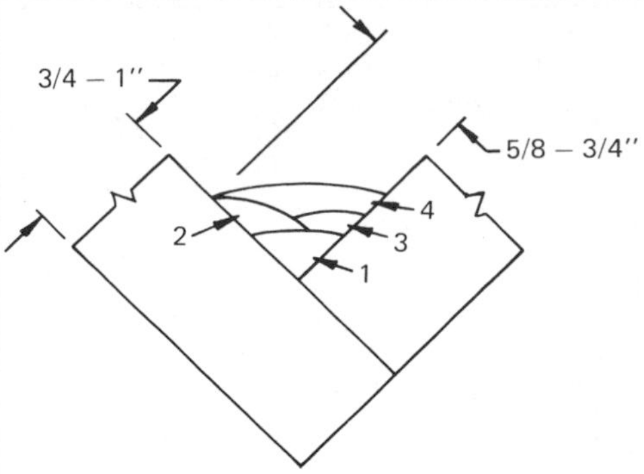

Position: Flat
Weld Quality Level: Code
Steel Weldability: Poor

Weld Size, L (in.)	1/2	5/8	3/4
Plate Thickness (in.)	5/8	3/4	1
Pass	1 & 2	1 — 3	1 — 4
Electrode Class	E7028	E7028	E7028
Size	1/4	1/4	1/4
Current (amp) AC	400	400	400
Arc Speed (in./min)	9.5 — 11.5	9.0 — 11.0	9.0 — 11.0
Electrode Req'd (lb/ft)	0.776	1.24	1.79
Total Time (ht/ft of weld)	0.0384	0.0615	0.0887

Preheat may be necessary depending on plate material.

SHIELDED METAL-ARC (MANUAL)

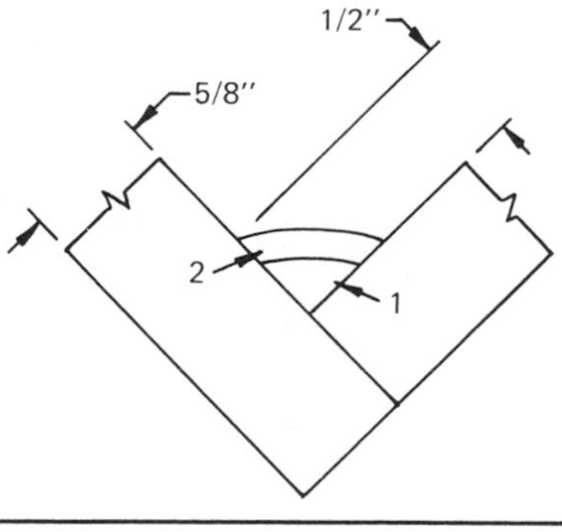

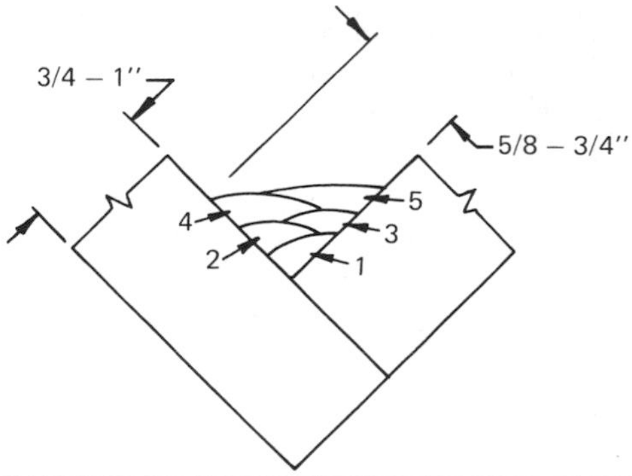

Position: Flat
Weld Quality Level: Code
Steel Weldability: Poor

Weld Size, L (in.)	1/2	5/8	3/4
Plate Thickness (in.)	5/8	3/4	1
Pass	1 & 2	1 — 4	1 — 5
Electrode Class	E7018	E7018	E7018
Size	1/4	1/4	1/4
Current (amp) AC	350	350	350
Arc Speed (in./min)	6.9 — 7.6	6.7 — 7.5	6.6 — 7.4
Electrode Req'd (lb/ft)	0.727	1.14	1.50
Total Time (hr/ft of weld)	0.0555	0.114	0.123

Preheat may be necessary depending on plate material.

SHIELDED METAL-ARC (MANUAL)

Position: Vertical down
Weld Quality Level: Commercial
Steel Weldability: Good

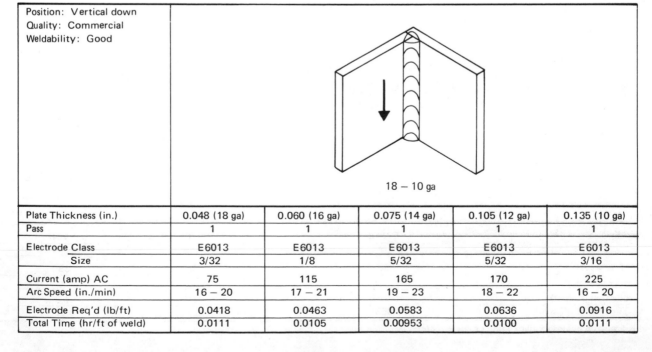

18 — 10 ga

Plate Thickness (in.)	0.048 (18 ga)	0.060 (16 ga)	0.075 (14 ga)	0.105 (12 ga)	0.135 (10 ga)
Pass	1	1	1	1	1
Electrode Class	E6013	E6012	E6012	E6012	E6012
Size	3/32	1/8	5/32	3/16	3/16
Current (amp) DC(—)	70	105	150	200	210
Arc Speed (in./min)	17 — 21	18 — 22	21 — 25	23 — 28	21 — 25
Electrode Req'd (lb/ft)	0.0374	0.0542	0.0713	0.0792	0.0930
Total Time (hr/ft of weld)	0.0105	0.0100	0.00870	0.00785	0.00870

SHIELDED METAL-ARC (MANUAL)

Position: Vertical down
Quality: Commercial
Weldability: Good

18 — 10 ga

Plate Thickness (in.)	0.048 (18 ga)	0.060 (16 ga)	0.075 (14 ga)	0.105 (12 ga)	0.135 (10 ga)
Pass	1	1	1	1	1
Electrode Class	E6013	E6013	E6013	E6013	E6013
Size	3/32	1/8	5/32	5/32	3/16
Current (amp) AC	75	115	165	170	225
Arc Speed (in./min)	16 — 20	17 — 21	19 — 23	18 — 22	16 — 20
Electrode Req'd (lb/ft)	0.0418	0.0463	0.0583	0.0636	0.0916
Total Time (hr/ft of weld)	0.0111	0.0105	0.00953	0.0100	0.0111

SHIELDED METAL-ARC (MANUAL)

Position: Vertical Weld Quality Level: Code Steel Weldability: Good

3/16 − 1''

5/32 − 3/4''

Weld Size, L (in.)	5/32	3/16	1/4	5/16	3/8	1/2	5/8	3/4
Plate Thickness (in.)	3/16	1/4	5/16	3/8	1/2	5/8	3/4	1
Pass	1	1	1	1	1	1 − 2	1 − 3	1 − 4
Electrode Class	E6010	E6010	E6010	E6010	E6010	E6010	E6010	E6010
Size	5/32	3/16	3/16	3/16	3/16	3/16	3/16	3/16
Current (amp) DC(+)	120	150	155	155	155	160	160	160
Arc Speed (in./min)	10.5-11.5	7.4-8.2	5.0-5.5	3.0-3.3	2.0-2.2	4.3-4.7*	4.3-4.7*	4.3-4.7*
Electrode Req'd (lb/ft)	0.0712	0.137	0.211	0.346	0.514	0.850	1.31	1.93
Total Time (hr/ft of weld)	0.0182	0.0256	0.0381	0.0635	0.0952	0.147	0.227	0.333
Direction of welding	Down	Up	Up	Up	Up	Up	Up	Up

* First pass only. Vary speed on succeeding passes to obtain proper weld size.

SHIELDED METAL-ARC (MANUAL)

Position: Vertical Weld Quality Level: Code Steel Weldability: Fair

1/4 − 1''

3/16 − 3/4''

Weld Size, L (in.)	3/16	1/4	5/16	3/8	1/2	5/8	3/4
Plate Thickness (in.)	1/4	5/16	3/8	1/2	5/8	3/4	1
Pass	1	1	1	1	1	1 − 2	1 − 3
Electrode Class	E7018	E7018	E7018	E7018	E7018	E7018	E7018
Size	1/8	1/8	1/8	5/32	5/32	5/32	5/32
Current (amp) DC(+)	135	140	140	150	150	150	150
Arc Speed (in./min)	5.4-5.8	3.8-4.2	2.3-2.5	1.8-2.0	1.1-1.3	1.9-2.1*	1.9-2.1*
Electrode Req'd (lb/ft)	0.155	0.231	0.371	0.556	0.925	1.41	2.11
Total Time (hr/ft of weld)	0.0357	0.0500	0.0833	0.105	0.167	0.261	0.389

* First pass only. Vary speed on succeeding passes to obtain proper size.

SHIELDED METAL-ARC (MANUAL)

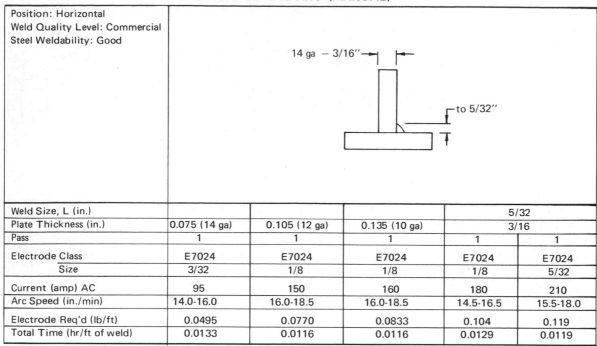

Position: Horizontal
Weld Quality Level: Commercial
Steel Weldability: Good

14 ga — 3/16''

to 5/32''

Weld Size, L (in.)				5/32	
Plate Thickness (in.)	0.075 (14 ga)	0.105 (12 ga)	0.135 (10 ga)	3/16	
Pass	1	1	1	1	1
Electrode Class	E7024	E7024	E7024	E7024	E7024
Size	3/32	1/8	1/8	1/8	5/32
Current (amp) AC	95	150	160	180	210
Arc Speed (in./min)	14.0-16.0	16.0-18.5	16.0-18.5	14.5-16.5	15.5-18.0
Electrode Req'd (lb/ft)	0.0495	0.0770	0.0833	0.104	0.119
Total Time (hr/ft of weld)	0.0133	0.0116	0.0116	0.0129	0.0119

SHIELDED METAL-ARC (MANUAL)

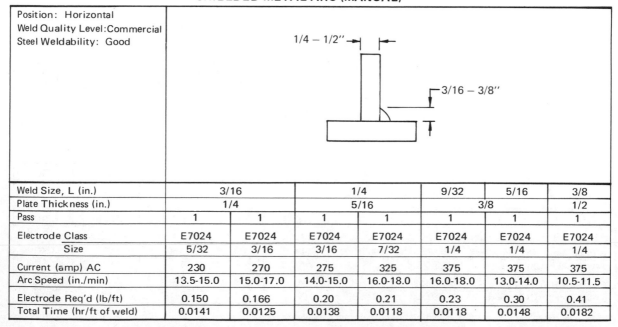

Position: Horizontal
Weld Quality Level: Commercial
Steel Weldability: Good

1/4 — 1/2''

3/16 — 3/8''

Weld Size, L (in.)	3/16		1/4		9/32	5/16	3/8
Plate Thickness (in.)	1/4		5/16		3/8		1/2
Pass	1	1	1	1	1	1	1
Electrode Class	E7024	E7024	E7024	E7024	E7024	E7024	E7024
Size	5/32	3/16	3/16	7/32	1/4	1/4	1/4
Current (amp) AC	230	270	275	325	375	375	375
Arc Speed (in./min)	13.5-15.0	15.0-17.0	14.0-15.0	16.0-18.0	16.0-18.0	13.0-14.0	10.5-11.5
Electrode Req'd (lb/ft)	0.150	0.166	0.20	0.21	0.23	0.30	0.41
Total Time (hr/ft of weld)	0.0141	0.0125	0.0138	0.0118	0.0118	0.0148	0.0182

SHIELDED METAL-ARC (MANUAL)

Position: Horizontal
Weld Quality Level: Commercial
Steel Weldability: Good

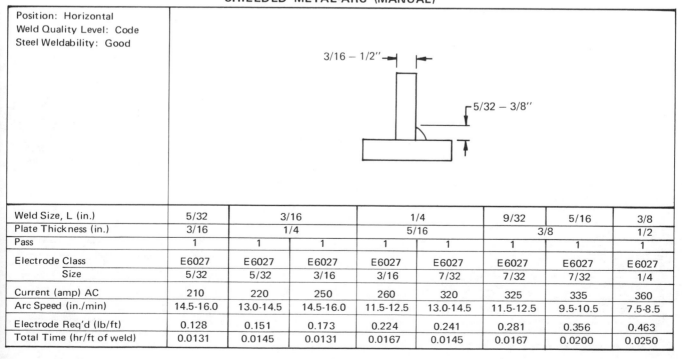

Weld Size, L (in.)	1/2		9/16		5/8		3/4	
Plate Thickness (in.)	5/8		3/4		3/4		1	
Pass	1	2 & 3	1	2 & 3	1	2 – 4	1	2 – 5
Electrode Class	E7024	E7024	E7024	E7024	E7024	E7024	E7024	E7024
Size	1/4	1/4	1/4	1/4	1/4	1/4	1/4	1/4
Current (amp) AC	375	375	375	375	375	375	375	375
Arc Speed (in./min)	10.5-11.5	11.0-12.0	10.5-11.5	14.0-16.0	10.5-11.5	14.0-16.0	10.5-11.5	12.0-13.0
Electrode Req'd (lb/ft)	0.73		0.92		1.15		1.62	
Total Time (hr/ft of weld)	0.0356		0.0449		0.0582		0.0822	

SHIELDED METAL-ARC (MANUAL)

Position: Horizontal
Weld Quality Level: Code
Steel Weldability: Good

Weld Size, L (in.)	5/32	3/16		1/4		9/32	5/16	3/8
Plate Thickness (in.)	3/16	1/4		5/16		3/8		1/2
Pass	1	1	1	1	1	1	1	1
Electrode Class	E6027	E6027	E6027	E6027	E6027	E6027	E6027	E6027
Size	5/32	5/32	3/16	3/16	7/32	7/32	7/32	1/4
Current (amp) AC	210	220	250	260	320	325	335	360
Arc Speed (in./min)	14.5-16.0	13.0-14.5	14.5-16.0	11.5-12.5	13.0-14.5	11.5-12.5	9.5-10.5	7.5-8.5
Electrode Req'd (lb/ft)	0.128	0.151	0.173	0.224	0.241	0.281	0.356	0.463
Total Time (hr/ft of weld)	0.0131	0.0145	0.0131	0.0167	0.0145	0.0167	0.0200	0.0250

SHIELDED METAL-ARC (MANUAL)

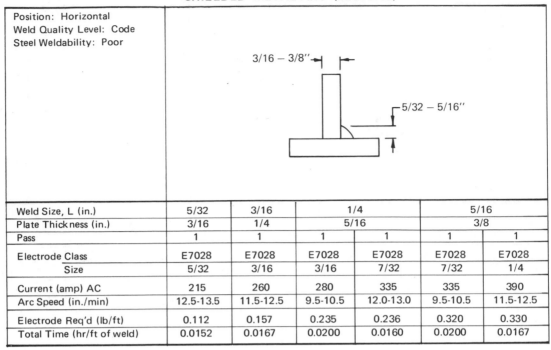

Position: Horizontal
Weld Quality Level: Code
Steel Weldability: Poor

Weld Size, L (in.)	5/32	3/16	1/4		5/16	
Plate Thickness (in.)	3/16	1/4	5/16		3/8	
Pass	1	1	1	1	1	1
Electrode Class	E7028	E7028	E7028	E7028	E7028	E7028
Size	5/32	3/16	3/16	7/32	7/32	1/4
Current (amp) AC	215	260	280	335	335	390
Arc Speed (in./min)	12.5-13.5	11.5-12.5	9.5-10.5	12.0-13.0	9.5-10.5	11.5-12.5
Electrode Req'd (lb/ft)	0.112	0.157	0.235	0.236	0.320	0.330
Total Time (hr/ft of weld)	0.0152	0.0167	0.0200	0.0160	0.0200	0.0167

Preheat may be necessary depending on plate material.

SHIELDED METAL-ARC (MANUAL)

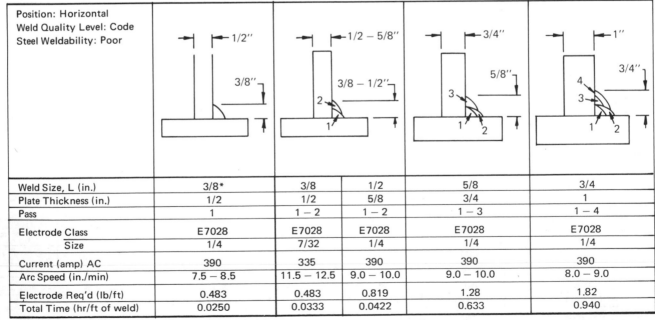

Position: Horizontal
Weld Quality Level: Code
Steel Weldability: Poor

Weld Size, L (in.)	3/8*	3/8	1/2	5/8	3/4
Plate Thickness (in.)	1/2	1/2	5/8	3/4	1
Pass	1	1 – 2	1 – 2	1 – 3	1 – 4
Electrode Class	E7028	E7028	E7028	E7028	E7028
Size	1/4	7/32	1/4	1/4	1/4
Current (amp) AC	390	335	390	390	390
Arc Speed (in./min)	7.5 – 8.5	11.5 – 12.5	9.0 – 10.0	9.0 – 10.0	8.0 – 9.0
Electrode Req'd (lb/ft)	0.483	0.483	0.819	1.28	1.82
Total Time (hr/ft of weld)	0.0250	0.0333	0.0422	0.633	0.940

Preheat may be necessary depending on plate material.

* May not be full 3/8 in. on the vertical leg.

SHIELDED METAL-ARC (MANUAL)

Position: Horizontal
Weld Quality Level: Code
Steel Weldability: Poor

3/16 — 3/8''

5/32 — 5/16''

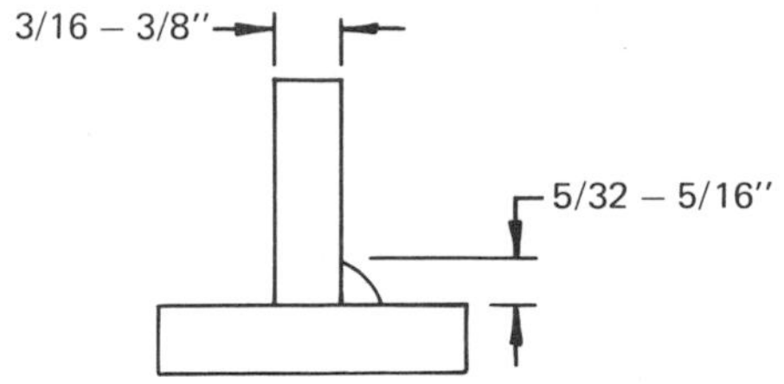

Weld Size, L (in.)	5/32	3/16	1/4	5/16
Plate Thickness (in.)	3/16	1/4	5/16	3/8
Pass	1	1	1	1
Electrode Class	E7018	E7018	E7018	E7018
Size	3/16	7/32	7/32	1/4
Current (amp) AC	240	275	275	350
Arc Speed (in./min)	12.5 — 13.5	11.0 — 12.0	8.5 — 9.5	6.5 — 7.5
Electrode Req'd (lb/ft)	0.111	0.140	0.203	0.335
Total Time (hr/ft of weld)	0.0154	0.0174	0.0222	0.0286

Preheat may be necessary depending on plate material.

SHIELDED METAL-ARC (MANUAL)

Position: Horizontal
Weld Quality Level: Code
Steel Weldability: Poor

1/2''   5/8''   3/4''   1''

3/8''   1/2''   5/8''   3/4''

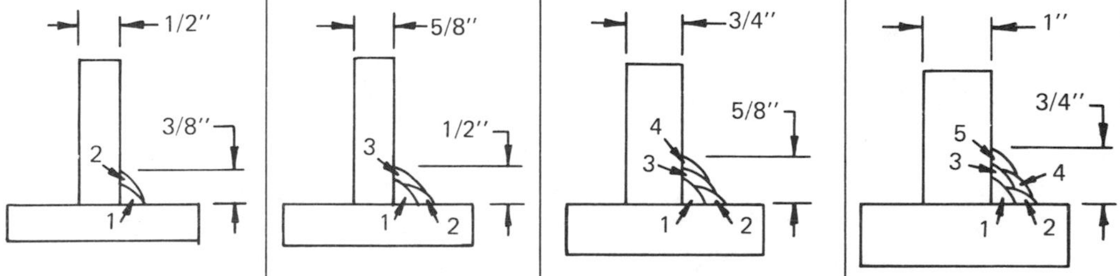

Weld Size, L (in.)	3/8	1/2	5/8	3/4
Plate Thickness (in.)	1/2	5/8	3/4	1
Pass	1 & 2	1 — 3	1 — 4	1 — 5
Electrode Class	E7018	E7018	E7018	E7018
Size	1/4	1/4	1/4	1/4
Current (amp) AC	350	350	350	350
Arc Speed (in./min)	9.5 — 11.5	9.5 — 10.5	8.0 — 9.0	7.0 — 8.0
Electrode Req'd (lb/ft)	0.480	0.785	1.18	1.62
Total Time (hr/ft of weld)	0.0390	0.0600	0.0940	0.133

Preheat may be necessary depending on plate material.

SHIELDED METAL-ARC (MANUAL)

Position: Horizontal
Weld Quality Level:Commercial
Steel Weldability: Good

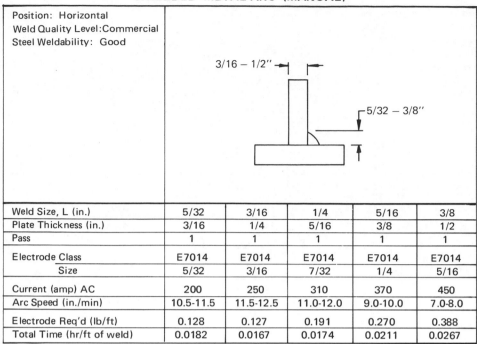

3/16 — 1/2"

5/32 — 3/8"

Weld Size, L (in.)	5/32	3/16	1/4	5/16	3/8
Plate Thickness (in.)	3/16	1/4	5/16	3/8	1/2
Pass	1	1	1	1	1
Electrode Class	E7014	E7014	E7014	E7014	E7014
Size	5/32	3/16	7/32	1/4	5/16
Current (amp) AC	200	250	310	370	450
Arc Speed (in./min)	10.5-11.5	11.5-12.5	11.0-12.0	9.0-10.0	7.0-8.0
Electrode Req'd (lb/ft)	0.128	0.127	0.191	0.270	0.388
Total Time (hr/ft of weld)	0.0182	0.0167	0.0174	0.0211	0.0267

SHIELDED METAL-ARC (MANUAL)

Position: Overhead
Weld Quality Level: Code
Steel Weldability: Good

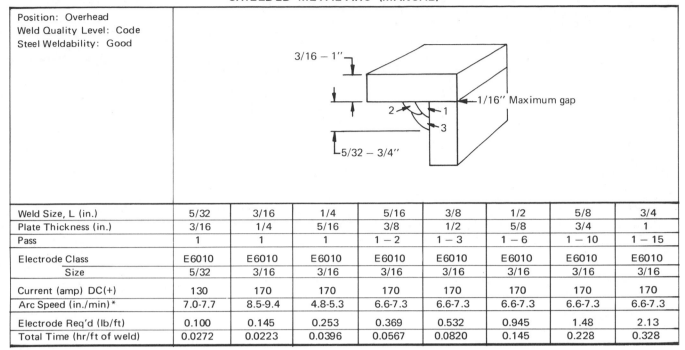

3/16 – 1"
1/16" Maximum gap
2   1
3
5/32 – 3/4"

Weld Size, L (in.)	5/32	3/16	1/4	5/16	3/8	1/2	5/8	3/4
Plate Thickness (in.)	3/16	1/4	5/16	3/8	1/2	5/8	3/4	1
Pass	1	1	1	1 – 2	1 – 3	1 – 6	1 – 10	1 – 15
Electrode Class	E6010	E6010	E6010	E6010	E6010	E6010	E6010	E6010
Size	5/32	3/16	3/16	3/16	3/16	3/16	3/16	3/16
Current (amp) DC(+)	130	170	170	170	170	170	170	170
Arc Speed (in./min)*	7.0-7.7	8.5-9.4	4.8-5.3	6.6-7.3	6.6-7.3	6.6-7.3	6.6-7.3	6.6-7.3
Electrode Req'd (lb/ft)	0.100	0.145	0.253	0.369	0.532	0.945	1.48	2.13
Total Time (hr/ft of weld)	0.0272	0.0223	0.0396	0.0567	0.0820	0.145	0.228	0.328

On 1/2 in. plate and thicker, place the first pass of each layer on the top plate.

* First pass only. Vary speed on succeeding passes to obtain proper weld size.

SHIELDED METAL-ARC (MANUAL)

Position: Overhead
Weld Quality Level: Code
Steel Weldability: Fair

3/16 – 1"
1/16" Maximum gap
2   1
3
5/32 – 3/4"

Weld Size, L (in.)	5/32	3/16	1/4	5/16	3/8	1/2	5/8	3/4
Plate Thickness (in.)	3/16	1/4	5/16	3/8	1/2	5/8	3/4	1
Pass	1	1	1 – 2	1 – 3	1 – 4	1 – 6	1 – 10	1 – 15
Electrode Class	E7018	E7018	E7018	E7018	E7018	E7018	E7018	E7018
Size	5/32	5/32	5/32	5/32	5/32	5/32	5/32	5/32
Current (amp) DC(+)	170	170	170	170	170	170	170	170
Arc Speed (in./min)*	10.5-11.5	7.2-8.0	8.2-9.1	8.2-9.1	8.5-9.4	7.0-7.7	7.2-8.0	8.1-8.9
Electrode Req'd (lb/ft)	0.107	0.155	0.277	0.394	0.570	1.01	1.59	2.29
Total Time (hr/ft of weld)	0.0182	0.0264	0.0463	0.0670	0.0967	0.172	0.269	0.388

On 3/8 in. plate and thicker place the first pass of each layer on the top plate.

* First pass only. Vary succeeding passes to obtain proper weld size.

SHIELDED METAL-ARC (MANUAL)

Position: Horizontal
Weld Quality Level: Commercial
Steel Weldability: Good

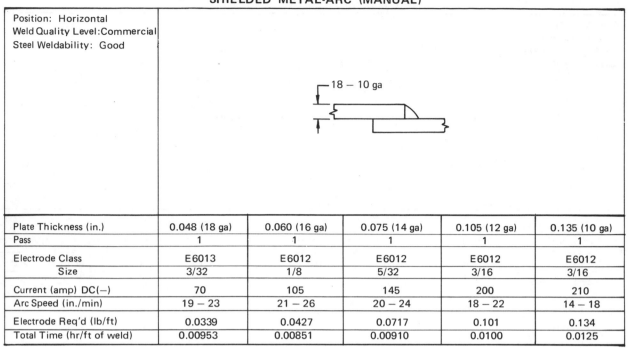

18 — 10 ga

Plate Thickness (in.)	0.048 (18 ga)	0.060 (16 ga)	0.075 (14 ga)	0.105 (12 ga)	0.135 (10 ga)
Pass	1	1	1	1	1
Electrode Class	E6013	E6012	E6012	E6012	E6012
Size	3/32	1/8	5/32	3/16	3/16
Current (amp) DC(−)	70	105	145	200	210
Arc Speed (in./min)	19 — 23	21 — 26	20 — 24	18 — 22	14 — 18
Electrode Req'd (lb/ft)	0.0339	0.0427	0.0717	0.101	0.134
Total Time (hr/ft of weld)	0.00953	0.00851	0.00910	0.0100	0.0125

SHIELDED METAL-ARC (MANUAL)

Position: Horizontal
Weld Quality Level: Commercial
Steel Weldability: Good

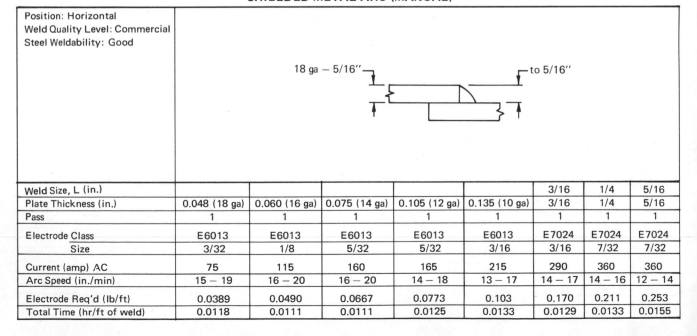

18 ga — 5/16"   to 5/16"

Weld Size, L (in.)						3/16	1/4	5/16
Plate Thickness (in.)	0.048 (18 ga)	0.060 (16 ga)	0.075 (14 ga)	0.105 (12 ga)	0.135 (10 ga)	3/16	1/4	5/16
Pass	1	1	1	1	1	1	1	1
Electrode Class	E6013	E6013	E6013	E6013	E6013	E7024	E7024	E7024
Size	3/32	1/8	5/32	5/32	3/16	3/16	7/32	7/32
Current (amp) AC	75	115	160	165	215	290	360	360
Arc Speed (in./min)	15 — 19	16 — 20	16 — 20	14 — 18	13 — 17	14 — 17	14 — 16	12 — 14
Electrode Req'd (lb/ft)	0.0389	0.0490	0.0667	0.0773	0.103	0.170	0.211	0.253
Total Time (hr/ft of weld)	0.0118	0.0111	0.0111	0.0125	0.0133	0.0129	0.0133	0.0155

SHIELDED METAL-ARC (MANUAL)

Position: Vertical down
Weld Quality Level: Commercial
Steel Weldability: Good

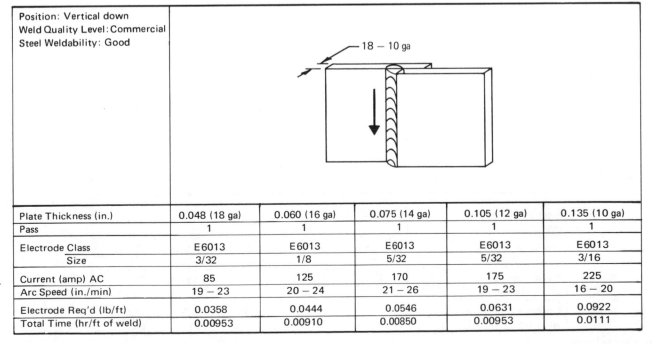

18 — 10 ga

Plate Thickness (in.)	0.048 (18 ga)	0.060 (16 ga)	0.075 (14 ga)	0.105 (12 ga)	0.135 (10 ga)
Pass	1	1	1	1	1
Electrode Class	E6013	E6012	E6012	E6012	E6012
Size	3/32	1/8	5/32	3/16	3/16
Current (amp) DC(—)	75	115	155	210	220
Arc Speed (in./min)	22 — 27	27 — 32	27 — 32	25 — 30	22 — 27
Electrode Req'd (lb/ft)	0.0316	0.0375	0.0576	0.0781	0.0930
Total Time (hr/ft of weld)	0.00817	0.00678	0.00678	0.00728	0.00817

SHIELDED METAL-ARC (MANUAL)

Position: Vertical down
Weld Quality Level: Commercial
Steel Weldability: Good

18 — 10 ga

Plate Thickness (in.)	0.048 (18 ga)	0.060 (16 ga)	0.075 (14 ga)	0.105 (12 ga)	0.135 (10 ga)
Pass	1	1	1	1	1
Electrode Class	E6013	E6013	E6013	E6013	E6013
Size	3/32	1/8	5/32	5/32	3/16
Current (amp) AC	85	125	170	175	225
Arc Speed (in./min)	19 — 23	20 — 24	21 — 26	19 — 23	16 — 20
Electrode Req'd (lb/ft)	0.0358	0.0444	0.0546	0.0631	0.0922
Total Time (hr/ft of weld)	0.00953	0.00910	0.00850	0.00953	0.0111

SHIELDED METAL-ARC (MANUAL)

Position: Flat
Weld Quality Level: Commercial
Steel Weldability: Good
Welded From: One side

All thicknesses

Also permissible
for 18 and 16 ga

18 — 10 ga

Plate Thickness (in.)	0.048 (18 ga)	0.060 (16 ga)	0.075 (14 ga)	0.105 (12 ga)	0.135 (10 ga)
Pass	1	1	1	1	1
Electrode Class	E6010	E6010	E6010	E6010	E6010
Size	3/32	1/8	1/8	5/32	3/16
Current (amp) DC(−)	45	80	85	110	155*
Arc Speed (in./min)	30 — 35	35 — 40	35 — 40	33 — 38	27 — 32
Electrode Req'd (lb/ft)	0.0197	0.0282	0.0300	0.0432	0.0505
Total Time (hr/ft of weld)	0.00616	0.00533	0.00533	0.00563	0.00678

* Use DC(+)

SHIELDED METAL-ARC (MANUAL)

Position: Flat
Weld Quality Level: Commercial
Steel Weldability: Good
Welded From: One side

3/16 — 1/2″

3/32 — 1/4″

Weld Size, L (in.)	3/32	1/8	5/32	3/16	1/4
Plate Thickness (in.)	3/16	1/4	5/16	3/8	1/2
Pass	1	1	1	1	1
Electrode Class	E7024	E7024	E7024	E7024	E7024
Size	5/32	3/16	7/32	7/32	1/4
Current (amp) AC	215	275	350	360	410
Arc Speed (in./min)	22.0-27.0	19.0-23.0	18.5-22.5	16.5-19.5	14 — 17
Electrode Req'd (lb/ft)	0.0750	0.114	0.152	0.175	0.250
Total Time (hr/ft of weld)	0.00820	0.00952	0.00975	0.0111	0.0130

SHIELDED METAL-ARC (MANUAL)

Position: Flat Weld Quality Level: Commercial Steel Weldability: Good Welded From: One side					
Weld Size, L (in.)	3/16	1/4	5/16	3/8	1/2
Plate Thickness (in.)	3/16	1/4	5/16	3/8	1/2
Pass	1	1	1	1	1 & 2
Electrode Class	E7024	E7024	E7024	E7024	E7024
Size	3/16	7/32	7/32	1/4	1/4
Current (amp) AC	250	320	350	400	410
Arc Speed (in./min)	21.0 — 25.0	18.0 — 22.0	14.5 — 17.5	13.0 — 16.0	11.5 — 14.5
Electrode Req'd (lb/ft)	0.101	0.133	0.198	0.240	0.530
Total Time (hr/ft of weld)	0.00870	0.0100	0.0125	0.0139	0.0308

SHIELDED METAL-ARC (MANUAL)

Position: Vertical down Weld Quality Level: Commercial Steel Weldability: Good Welded From: One side					
Plate Thickness (in.)	0.048 (18 ga)	0.060 (16 ga)	0.075 (14 ga)	0.105 (12 ga)	0.135 (10 ga)
Pass	1	1	1	1	1
Electrode Class	E6010	E6010	E6010	E6010	E6010
Size	3/32	1/8	1/8	5/32	3/16
Current (amp) DC(−)	50	90	95	120	170*
Arc Speed (in./min)	35 — 40	40 — 45	40 — 45	37 — 42	33 — 38
Electrode Req'd (lb/ft)	0.0184	0.0278	0.0293	0.0436	0.0461
Total Time (hr/ft of weld)	0.00533	0.00471	0.00471	0.00507	0.00563

* DC(+)

SHIELDED METAL-ARC (MANUAL)

Position: Flat
Weld Quality Level: Commercial
Steel Weldability: Good

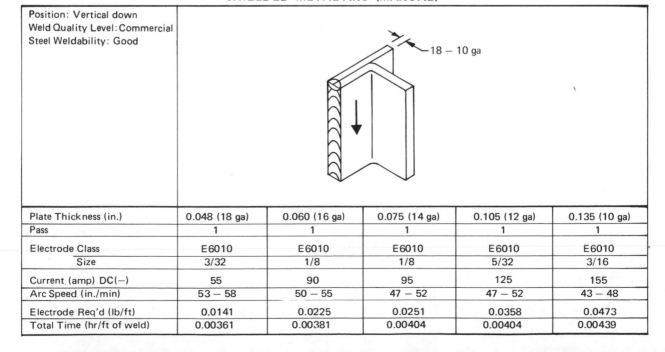

18 — 10 ga

Plate Thickness (in.)	0.048 (18 ga)	0.060 (16 ga)	0.075 (14 ga)	0.105 (12 ga)	0.135 (10 ga)
Pass	1	1	1	1	1
Electrode Class	E6010	E6010	E6010	E6010	E6010
Size	3/32	1/8	1/8	5/32	3/16
Current (amp) DC(−)	50	80	85	115	140
Arc Speed (in/min)	45 — 50	43 — 48	40 — 45	40 — 45	37 — 42
Electrode Req'd (lb/ft)	0.0145	0.0232	0.0263	0.0382	0.0476
Total Time (hr/ft of weld)	0.00421	0.00439	0.00471	0.00471	0.00505

SHIELDED METAL-ARC (MANUAL)

Position: Vertical down
Weld Quality Level: Commercial
Steel Weldability: Good

18 — 10 ga

Plate Thickness (in.)	0.048 (18 ga)	0.060 (16 ga)	0.075 (14 ga)	0.105 (12 ga)	0.135 (10 ga)
Pass	1	1	1	1	1
Electrode Class	E6010	E6010	E6010	E6010	E6010
Size	3/32	1/8	1/8	5/32	3/16
Current (amp) DC(−)	55	90	95	125	155
Arc Speed (in./min)	53 — 58	50 — 55	47 — 52	47 — 52	43 — 48
Electrode Req'd (lb/ft)	0.0141	0.0225	0.0251	0.0358	0.0473
Total Time (hr/ft of weld)	0.00361	0.00381	0.00404	0.00404	0.00439

SHIELDED METAL-ARC (MANUAL)

Positon: Flat
Weld Quality Level: Commercial
Steel Weldability: Good

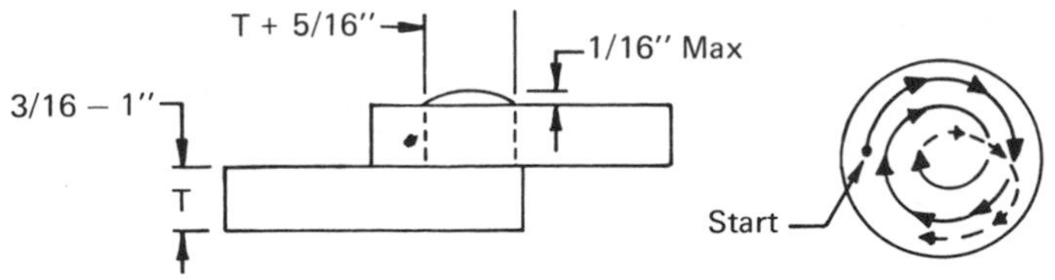

T + 5/16''   1/16'' Max

3/16 – 1''

T

Start

Plate Thickness (in.)	3/16	5/16	3/8	1/2	3/4	1
Electrode Class	E7018	E7018	E7018	E7018	E7018	E7018
Size	1/8	3/16	3/16	7/32	1/4	1/4
Current (amp) AC	140	250	250	300	350	350
Arc Speed (in./min)						
Electrode Req'd*	0.0154	0.0440	0.0642	0.113	0.300	0.605
Total Time* (hr)	0.00417	0.00500	0.00731	0.0118	0.0236	0.0475

Weld with spiral motion and continue as long as slag can be kept molten or until the weld is completed.

* Per weld

SHIELDED METAL-ARC (MANUAL)
Special Procedures for ASTM A203 and A537 Steels

Position: Flat
Weld Quality Level: Code
Steel Weldability: Poor
Welded From: Two sides

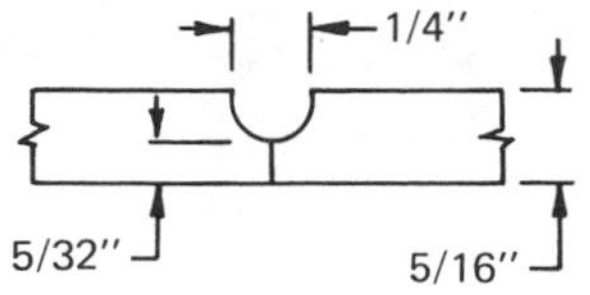

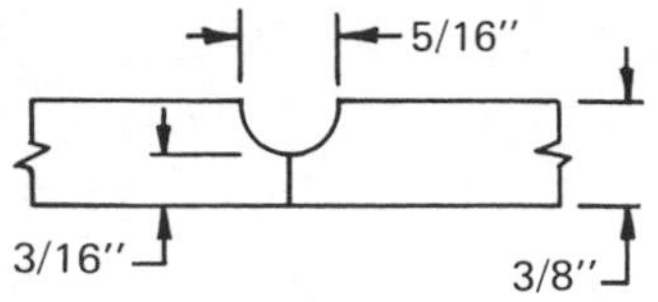

Plate Thickness (in.)	5/16		3/8	
Pass	1 & 2	3 & 4*	1 − 3	4 − 6*
Electrode Class†				
Size	5/32	5/32	5/32	5/32
Current (amp) DC(+)	150	150	150	150
Arc Speed (in./min)	9 − 11	8 − 10	9 − 11	8 − 10
Electrode Req'd (lb/ft)	0.48		0.65	
Total Time (hr/ft of weld)	0.0844		0.127	
Interpass Temperature, Max. (°F)	150		150	

Position: Flat
Weld Quality Level: Code
Steel Weldability: Poor
Welded From: Two sides

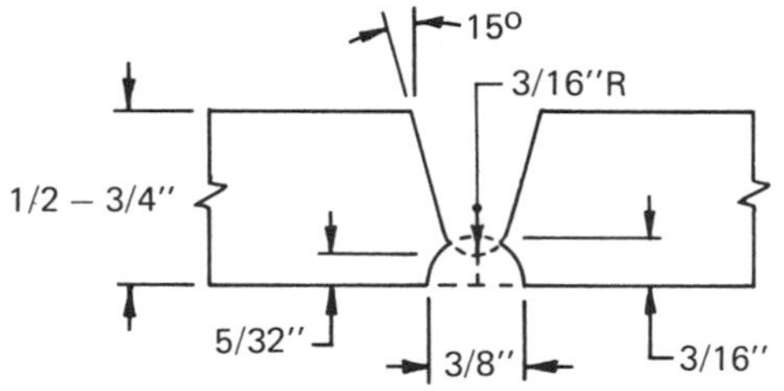

Plate Thickness (in.)	1/2		5/8		3/4	
Pass	1 − 5	6 − 8*	1 − 7	8 − 10*	1 − 10	11 − 13*
Electrode Class†						
Size	5/32	5/32	5/32	5/32	5/32	5/32
Current (amp) DC(+)	150	150	150	150	150	150
Arc Speed (in./min)	7 − 9	8 − 10	7 − 9	8 − 10	7 − 9	8 − 10
Electrode Req'd (lb/ft)	1.40		1.79		2.25	
Total Time (hr/ft of weld)	0.188		0.238		0.313	
Interpass Temperature, Max. (°F)	175		200		225	

* Second side is gouged after first side is completed.

† See Tables 6-13 and 6-17.

Submerged-Arc Welding

In submerged-arc welding, a bare coiled electrode wire is automatically fed into the weld joint (Fig. 11-1), where the arc (either AC or DC) melts it under a layer of granular flux that is metered into the weld zone by gravity flow through a nozzle. Fusion takes place beneath the flux without sparks, spatter, or flash. This means that arc-welding helmets or shields are not required, although most operators wear light goggles to protect themselves from an occasional flash.

Because both granular and molten flux is subject to the attraction of gravity, the submerged-arc process is essentially limited to the flat position and for horizontal fillets. With special equipment and techniques, it can be used in the vertical-up position, but it cannot be used for overhead welding.

When cold, the granular flux is a nonconductor, but as the arc is started, the flux melts and becomes a conductor and carries some of the current to the weld pool. The flux has important metallurgical, as well as shielding functions to perform, such as supplying deoxidizers or alloying elements. After cooling, the fused flux forms a hard, glassy, and easily removed slag layer over the deposit. Unfused flux is frequently recovered by a vacuum hose attachment, screened, and reused.

Submerged-arc fluxes always have a melting temperature lower than that of the metal. This insures that no solid flux particles will be trapped within the molten weld metal. Being lighter than molten weld metal, the molten flux arises to the top of the pool. To properly perform its shielding of the molten weld metal, the molten flux must have low enough viscosity to quickly "run together", but yet must not be so fluid as to run off the pool. Widely used ingredients in granular fluxes include lime, silica, manganese oxides, and calcium fluoride. Specialty fluxes may contain alloying elements to give desired properties to the weld metal, and some fluxes contain iron, which acts as "added" filler metal much as the iron powder in covered stick electrodes. Fluxes are usually sold in 100-pound sacks. It is important that these materials be stored in a dry atmosphere. See Chapter 5 for additional information on submerged-arc fluxes.

The electrodes for submerged arc welding are also described in Chapter 5. Electrode wire is produced in diameters from 1/16" to 3/8" and wound in coils, on rims, or in drums in such a manner that it will unwind without restriction. Most popular packaging weights are 60, 200, and 1000-pound lots.

Electrodes in the form of flat strips are sometimes used to make wide flat deposits, as in cladding or surfacing the inside of large vessels used in the chemical or petroleum industries. Tubular flux-cored electrodes may be used to deposit special alloys when welding special high-strength or stainless steels.

ADVANTAGES OF SUBMERGED-ARC WELDING

In the production welding of steel, semiautomatic and, especially, full-automatic submerged-arc welding are favored methods. The reasons are

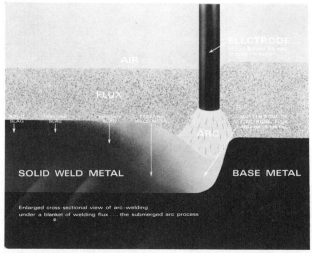

Fig. 11-1. The mechanics of the submerged-arc process. The arc and the molten weld metal are buried in the layer of flux, which protects the weld metal from contamination and concentrates the heat into the joint. The molten flux arises through the pool, deoxidizing and cleansing the molten metal, and forms a protective slag over the newly deposited weld.

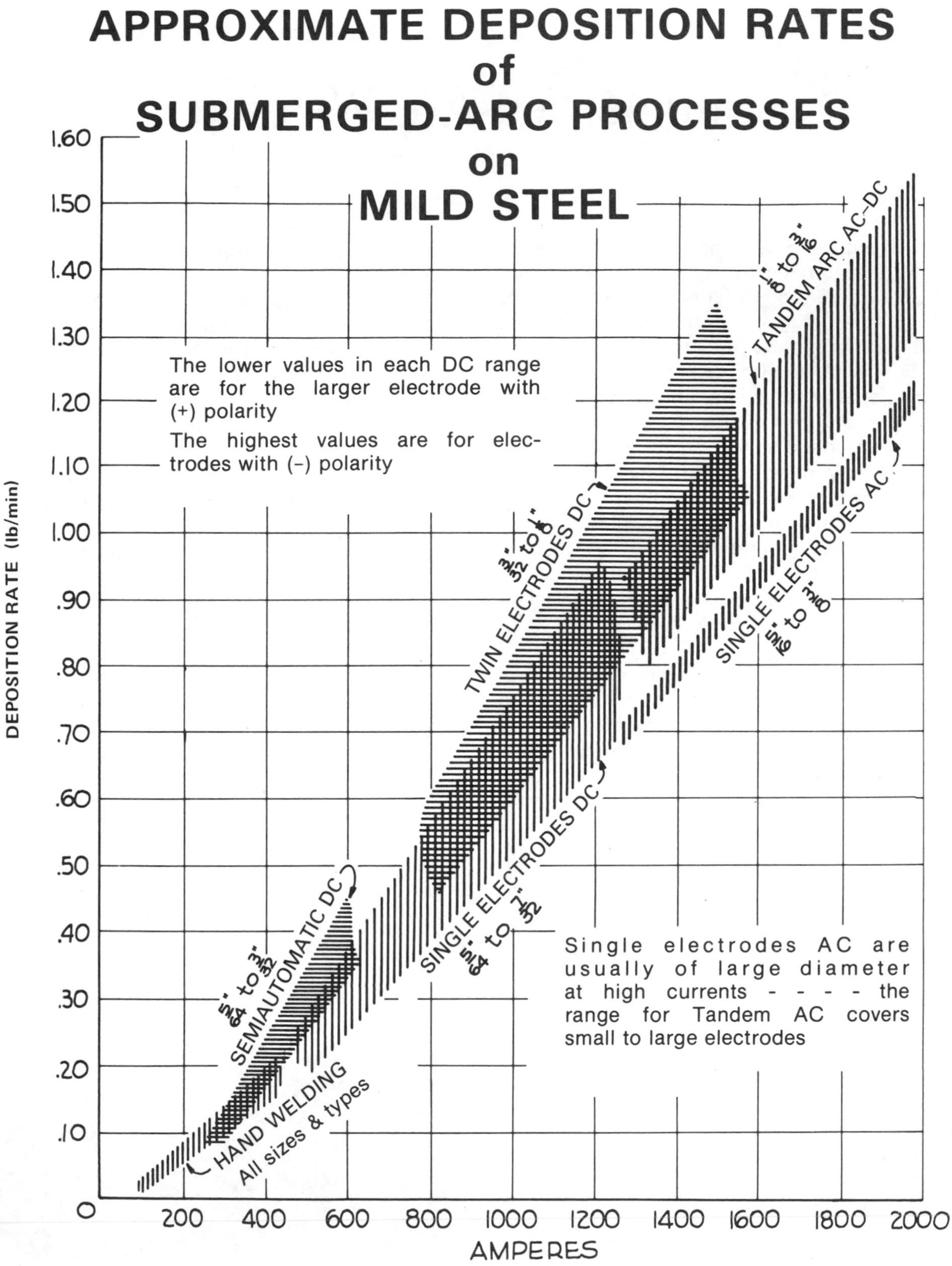
APPROXIMATE DEPOSITION RATES
of
SUBMERGED-ARC PROCESSES
on
MILD STEEL
DEPOSITION RATE (lb/min)
AMPERES
0
.10
.20
.30
.40
.50
.60
.70
.80
.90
1.00
1.10
1.20
1.30
1.40
1.50
1.60
200
400
600
800
1000
1200
1400
1600
1800
2000
The lower values in each DC range are for the larger electrode with (+) polarity
The highest values are for electrodes with (-) polarity
Single electrodes AC are usually of large diameter at high currents - - - - the range for Tandem AC covers small to large electrodes
HAND WELDING
All sizes & types
SEMIAUTOMATIC DC
5/64" to 3/32"
SINGLE ELECTRODES DC
5/64" to 7/32"
TWIN ELECTRODES DC
3/32" to 1/8"
SINGLE ELECTRODES AC
5/16" to 3/8"
TANDEM ARC AC-DC
1/8" to 3/16"

Fig. 11-2. Approximate deposition rates of various submerged-arc arrangements, compared with the deposition rates of stick-electrode welding.

several, including the speed of the process, its deep penetration, the excellent quality of the weld, and the lack of flash — which adds to worker comfort.

High currents can be used in submerged-arc welding and extremely high heat developed. Because the current is applied to the electrode a short distance above its tip, relatively high amperages can be used on small diameter electrodes. This results in extremely high current densities on relatively small cross sections of electrode. Currents as high as 600 amperes can be carried on electrodes as small as 5/64", giving a density in the order of 125,000 amperes per square inch — six to ten times that carried on stick electrodes. Fig. 11-2 shows approximate deposition rates for various submerged-arc arrangements, with comparable deposition rates for manual welding with covered electrodes.

Because of the high current density, the melt-off rate is much higher for a given electrode diameter than with stick-electrode welding. The melt-off rate is affected by the electrode material, the flux, type of current, polarity, and length of wire beyond the point of electrical contact in the gun or head.

The insulating blanket of flux above the arc prevents rapid escape of heat and concentrates it in the welding zone. Not only are the electrode and base metal melted rapidly, but the fusion is deep into the base metal. The deep penetration allows the use of small welding grooves, thus minimizing the amount of filler metal per foot of joint and permitting fast travel speeds. Fast welding, in turn, minimizes the total heat input into the assembly and, this, tends to reduce problems of heat distortion. Even relatively thick joints can be welded in one pass by submerged-arc.

Welds made under the protective layer of flux have good ductility and impact resistance and uniformity in bead appearance. Mechanical properties at least equal to those of the base metal are consistently obtained. In single-pass welds, the fused base material is large compared to the amount of filler metal used. Thus, in such welds the base metal may greatly influence the chemical and mechanical properties of the weld. For this reason, it is sometimes unnecessary to use electrodes of the same composition as the base metal for welding many of the low-alloy steels. The chemical compostion and properties of multipass welds are less affected by the base metal and depend to a greater extent on the composition of the electrode, the activity of the flux, and the welding conditions.

Through regulation of current, voltage, and travel speed, the operator can exercise close control over penetration to provide any depth, ranging

from deep and narrow with high-crown reinforcement, to wide, nearly flat beads with shallow penetration. Beads with deep penetration may contain on the order of 70% melted base metal, while shallow beads may contain as little as 10% base metal. In some instances, the deep-penetration properties of submerged-arc can be used to eliminate or reduce the expense of edge preparation.

Submerged-arc welding may be done with either DC or AC power. Direct current gives better control of bead shape, penetration, and welding speed, and arc starting is easier. Bead shape is usually best with DC reverse polarity (electrode positive), which also provides maximum penetration. Highest deposition rates and minimum penetration are obtained with DC straight polarity. Alternating current has the advantage of minimizing magnetic arc blow and gives penetration betweeen that of DCRP and DCSP.

ELECTRODE FEEDING AND CONTROL EQUIPMENT

Semiautomatic Welding: Semiautomatic equipment, commonly called manual "Squirt", maintains a preset current and voltage. The operator must strike the arc, guide the welding gun along the seam, and manually pace the travel speed. A remote electrode-feeding mechanism (Fig. 11-3) feeds the electrode and automatically controls the current and voltage. A typical gun, shown in Fig. 11-4, is hand-held by the operator. In Fig. 11-5, a

Fig. 11-3. A typical electrode-feeding unit for semiautomatic submerged-arc welding. The flux tank holds approximately 100 lbs of flux, which feeds by dry fluidization through a hose to the gun.

Fig. 11-4. Typical gun for semiautomatic submerged-arc welding. The gun is designed for fluidized flux feeding.

Fig. 11-5. Gun with a travel mechanism attached.

Fig. 11-6. Gun mounted on a small tractor, which relieves the operator of holding and guiding the gun.

Multiple Automatic Heads: For higher welding speeds two or three heads may be combined to weld simultaneously on the same joint. This is known as multiple-electrode or tandem-arc welding. Each welding head is powered by a separate power source, as distinguished from twin-electrode welding, in which both electrodes are powered by the same power source.

LONG-STICKOUT WELDING

The fast deposition rate of submerged-arc welding is enhanced by the applicability of the "long-

travel-speed device is added to the gun, but the operator must hold the gun and guide it along the seam. In Fig. 11-6, the gun is mounted on a small tractor that rides on the work and follows the joint. This relieves the operator from holding and guiding the gun, and reduces his function to setting the guide rolls for the joint, starting the welding, and monitoring the progress as the tractor rides the seam. Equipment shown in Fig. 11-5 and 11-6 is called mechanized squirt-welding equipment.

Automatic Welding: A typical fully automatic head is shown in Fig. 11-7. The head shown is equipped to feed a single electrode. The same head will feed two electrodes by changing to a contact nozzle as shown in Fig. 11-8 and changing the wire drive rolls. This modification is known as twin-electrode submerged-arc welding. The electrical control system maintains the preset current and voltage, strikes the arc, starts the travel and controls the travel speed. Either the head is stationary and the work moves, or the work is stationary and the head moves.

Fig. 11-7. Typical submerged-arc welding head for fully automatic welding.

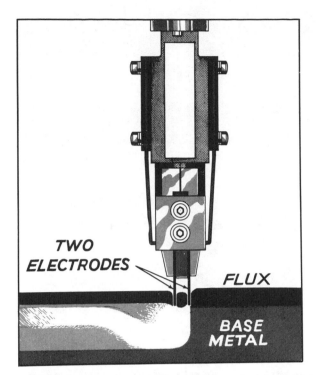

Fig. 11-8. Twin-electrode nozzle for converting a single-arc head for welding with two wires simultaneously.

stickout" principle to the process. This principle, which is also widely used with the self-shielded flux-cored electrode process, enables increasing the welding speed by as much as 50%.

In semiautomatic and full-automatic welding, electric current is fed into the electrode at the point of electrical contact within the gun or nozzle. The current must then travel to the tip of the electrode to reach the arc. The distance between the point of electrical contact and the electrode tip is referred to as "stickout" or "electrical stickout" (Fig. 11-9).

This entire length of electrode — not just the visible portion protruding from the nozzle — is subject to resistance heating as the current passes

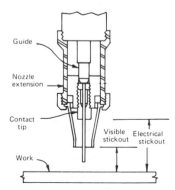

Fig. 11-9. Long electrical stickout — used to increase melt-off rate through resistance heating of the electrode. The term, applied to the distance between the point of electrical contact within the nozzle and the tip of the electrode, is distinct from visible stickout, which denotes the length of electrode extending beyond the guide tip.

through it. The longer the projection of the electrode from the point of electrical contact, the greater the heat build-up within it. This heat can be used to good advantage to increase the melting rate and reduce penetration. Special attachments can be added to standard welding equipment to take advantage of the higher melt-off rates and attendant increase in deposition rates.

Deposition rates with long-stickout welding are typically increased some 25% to 50% with no increase in welding current. With single-electrode, fully automatic submerged-arc welding, the deposition rate may approach that of two-wire welding with a multiple-power source.

There are, however, side effects that must be anticipated. A change to long-stickout welding is similar to a change from reverse to straight polarity. Increase in deposition rate is accompanied by a decrease in penetration. This decrease generally is not large enough to prevent the use of long stickout except on applications where positive polarity is used for the express purpose of producing maximum penetration. Long-stickout welding also results in less tendency for burnthrough, which can be advantageous when the fitup is imperfect, and reduces the heat-affected zone.

A voltage drop accompanies the resistance heating of the extra length of projecting electrode. When the operator sets the voltage control of the wire-feeding equipment, he must compensate for this voltage drop to avoid having the arc operate at less than optimum voltage.

Long-stickout welding provides the greatest economies in fast-fill applications that require a large volume of weld metal, as, for example, in flat-fillet and groove butt welds. The reduction in heat-affected zone is particularly beneficial in the welding of quenched and tempered steels. In some instances, the heat-affected zone is reduced 25%.

Long-stickout techniques can also be used to good advantage in build-up and hardsurfacing applications. Here the benefits include greater speed, improved quality of deposit, and better appearance.

Flux and electrode types are selected for long stickout on the same basis as for standard stickout.

SUBMERGED-ARC WELDING OF STEELS

The multiplicity of arrangements for the welding of carbon and low-alloy steels by semiautomatic and full-automatic submerged-arc welding makes detailed description too ponderous for a text of this type. The fabricator of steel products usually works with the supplier of equipment, electrodes, and fluxes in designing the submerged-arc system and procedures giving the best results with his product. The fixtures and manipulators, as well as the welding equipment itself, are components of integrated systems. Systems can be extremely complex with as many as a dozen or more submerged-arc heads depositing weld metal simultaneously. Reference to The Lincoln Electric Company's *Procedure Handbook of Arc Welding* will give the student some understanding of the multiplicity of arrangements used by industry in the submerged-arc welding of steel, but only after the student is employed in a company using a complex automated submerged-arc welding system will he have exposure to the special techniques, requirements, procedures, and problems.

Generalizations, however, about the latter — the problems — can be made, and these apply to submerged-arc welding with the hand-held semiautomatic gun that will likely be the tool for the weldor's initiation to the process, as well as to complex automated welding. In all submerged-arc welding, steps must be taken to prevent weld porosity and weld cracking in order to achieve the high-quality welds possible with the process.

PREVENTING WELD POROSITY

Porosity due to the entrapment of gas in the weld metal is not desirable, although the strength of the weld is not lowered appreciably unless the porosity is very severe. Porosity may be evident on the surface, as in Fig. 11-10, or may occur beneath

Rusty plate before welding

Weld on uncleaned rusty plate

Weld on torch heated rusty plate

Weld on rusty plate that has been
wire brushed before tacking

Weld on rusty plate, wire brushed
before tacking and torch heated

Fig. 11-11. Effect of various rust-removal methods on weld porosity. Power wire-brushing combined with torch-heating results in minimum porosity.

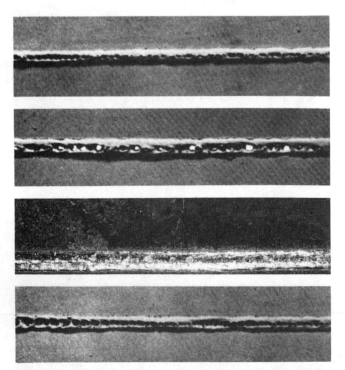

Fig. 11-10. Severe porosity apparent on the surface of the weld bead. Causes of the porosity are (from the top down) oily workpiece, dirty flux, insufficient flux, and backward arc blow.

a sound surface. Various factors are causes of weld porosity. These factors and their control are discussed in the following text.

Contaminants in the Joint: The most common cause of porosity is the presence of organic materials or other gas-producing contaminants in the joint. Weld joints, thus, must be free of foreign matter, such as rust, dirt, oil, and moisture for porosity-free welds. Although cleaning the exterior surfaces (top and bottom of the plate) helps reduce porosity, the abutting edges of the workpieces must be cleaned for best results.

It is not necessary, however, to clean every edge that is to be welded by submerged-arc. Edges that have been prepared by machining or flame-cutting can be welded without further cleaning if they are not rusty or oil-coated. Also, edges with ordinary mill scale can be welded if the scale is not loose or flaky. Even heavy "blue" mill scale can be welded satisfactorily if a silicon-killed electrode is used. Blue mill scale is dark gray or black in color and has no detrimental effect in welding. "Red" mill scale, however, which is reddish brown in color, has the same detrimental effect as rust.

Power wire-brushing and torch-heating are used

to clean rust and red mill scale from edges (Fig. 11-11). Either method, used individually, greatly reduces the porosity normally produced by these contaminants. For best results, however, both cleaning techniques should be used in combination.

Joints should be brushed clean before they are fitted together, then a flame torch should be played on the joint about a foot or two in front of the arc during welding to drive off residual moisture. If there is red mill scale or rust on the plate, the surface of the plate edges must be heated to about 400 to 600°F to drive off the moisture. Some moisture will remain to cause porosity if this temperature range is not reached.

Oil, grease, and die lubricants should be removed by degreasing and washing operations. The washing compound must be rinsed away completely, and the work must be dry before welding begins.

Wire Contamination: Welding electrodes sometimes become rusty during storage. This rust may cause porosity, especially in high-speed welds on light-gage sheet metal. Rusty wire also may not feed properly through the feed cables of semiautomatic welders, and the rust causes excessive wear and arcing at the contact nozzle. Do not attempt to use rusty wire.

Wire that has become contaminated with oil, grease, or dirt should be cleaned prior to welding. Sometimes, a small amount of lubricant is put on the wire for semiautomatic welding to improve feed through the cable. If too much is applied, it will cause porosity.

Insufficient Flux: If an inadequate amount of flux is used, the arc flashes through the flux and causes scattered surface porosity. On the other hand, too much flux causes an undesirable bead shape. The correct amount is indicated when the light of the arc reflects on the wire.

Insufficient flux coverage is more common on circumferential welds than on flat welds. On small circumferential welds, the flux must be contained around the arc by mechanical support. The weld may contain surface porosity if the slag spills off the weld before it has solidified. The danger of slag spillage is especially great with corner welds and with multiple-pass horizontal fillet welds.

Contaminants in the Flux: Contaminants may be picked up by the flux-recovery system and deposited in subsequent welds. The flux should be discarded if these contaminants cannot be removed by the recovery equipment (by magnetic separation or heating, for example).

Welding flux in factory-sealed moisture-resistant bags can be stored for several months in a dry area without picking up moisture. Flux exposed to

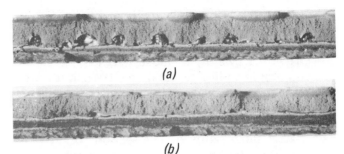

Fig. 11-12. Porosity caused by entrapped flux (a), and sound weld (b) produced by reducing penetration. Penetration in (a) came within 5/32 in. of the backup bead, but missed the backup bead in (b) by 3/16 in.

the atmosphere will pick up moisture by condensation especially in a humid location. Flux can be dried by heating to 500°F for a period long enough to ensure that the entire bulk has reached that temperature. For a long exposure period in a humid atmosphere, 750°F may be necessary.

Dirt must be kept out of the flux. The flux-recovery system should be equipped to remove dust from the flux. Collected dust should be removed from the recovery equipment regularly. If it is not removed frequently, slugs of dust may fall into the recovered flux and cause large holes in the weld.

On some joints, such as those inside tanks, pieces of mill scale may fall onto the joint and contaminate the weld. This scale also may reach the weld through the flux-recovery system. However, mill scale can easily be removed from recovered flux by a magnetic separator.

Entrapped Flux: There is a possibility of porosity wherever there is an opportunity for flux to become trapped between the bottom of the bead and the opposite side of the joint. This porosity may either be subsurface or may come through to the surface as large holes. The solution to this problem is to leave at least 5/32 in. between the root of the weld and the other side, or to penetrate completely into the other side so that no unwelded space remains (Fig. 11-12).

Porosity from entrapped flux is most commonly encountered in butt welds. If the gap between the plate edges is 1/32 in. or more, flux may spill into the gap ahead of the arc. The remedy is to

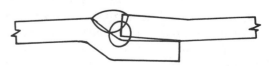

Fig. 11-13. An offset lap weld, which tends to trap flux at the bottom of the joint. The first pass may be porous, but the second pass will be sound.

back the joint with a manual or semiautomatic weld or a backup strip. The bead must penetrate the backup, or clear the backup by at least 5/32-in.

Offset lap welds, as illustrated in Fig. 11-13, are vulnerable to flux entrapment. Here, it is necessary to penetrate beyond the corner of the joint to produce porosity-free welds. Such penetration frequently cannot be obtained with a single pass, so two passes must be used. The second pass remelts most of the first, and the resultant deposit is clean and porosity-free.

Segregation: The composition of the base metal has a bearing on the porosity occurring in the weld. Even when composition is within acceptable limits, possible local segregation of constituents may promote porosity. Sulfur in particular tends to segregate within steel alloys. These sulfur segregations can be detected by a deep etch of the cross section, or by other chemical processes. Severe segregations may appear as laminations and cause large holes in the weld.

When it is necessary to weld steels with sulfur segregation, use procedures that give minimum admixture (low current, negative polarity, and large electrode diameters), and travel as slowly as possible to allow gases to escape through the molten pool. On joints that are normally square-edge butts, scarf the joint; and on joints that are normally beveled, increase the scarf. Also use multiple passes where possible.

Press-Fit Lubricants: Parts to be joined by a press-fit are usually coated with a lubricant, such as white lead, prior to mating. If a weld is then made in the vicinity of the press fit, the lubricant gives off gases that cause porosity, usually large holes at or near the end of the weld. Preferred practice is to avoid press fits in joints to be welded and to allow a gap of up to 1/32 in. But if press fits must be used, one piece should be knurled to allow a path for gases to escape.

Inappropriate Polarity: Though the effect of polarity on porosity is slight and not normally an important factor, positive polarity generally produces less porosity than negative polarity. Negative polarity, however, results in less porosity with sulphur-bearing steels or with other alloys where penetration and admixture are to be minimized.

Excessive Travel Speed: Reducing travel speed reduces porosity, since slow speed allow gaseous materials to boil out of the molten weld metal. But a reduction in speed generally increases costs, so other solutions should be investigated first. The effect of speed on porosity is particularly strong with light-gage sheet, where rapid travel tends to increase porosity by increasing arc blow. Reducing speed may substantially reduce porosity here, if

other means of controlling arc blow are not effective.

Slag Residue from Tack Welds: Slag from some types of electrodes may cause porosity where tack welds are covered with a submerged-arc bead. To avoid this problem the manual electrodes used for tack welding should be of the E6010, E6011, E7016, or E7018 classes. These electrodes do not leave a residue that causes porosity in subsequent cover welds.

PREVENTING WELD CRACKING

Weld cracking with mild steel is seldom a problem in material less than 3/8 in. thick. With thicker material, welds are subjected to rapid cooling rates, which frequently induce high stresses and lead to cracking. Low ambient temperature increases the cooling rate and produces a similar effect. Constrained shapes not free to flex or deflect under thermal stresses also have a tendency to crack, as do steels of high hardenability or "hot-shortness." The term "weldability," used to indicate the relative ease with which steels can be welded without cracking, is discussed in Chapter 6.

Cracking in fillet welds is more common than in butt welds because both legs of a fillet joint are rigidly fixed. This rigidity prevents deflections that normally absorb thermal stresses. The following factors influence the crack resistance of fillet welds.

Gap: When any part to be welded is more than 1 in. thick, a gap of 1/32 to 1/16 in. should be used to allow the weld to shrink during cooling. Grooving the plate edges or inserting a compressible material between the workpieces minimize the shrinkage stresses.

Polarity: Positive polarity is normally recommended for fillet welds to obtain greatest penetration and minimum tendency for porosity at high speeds. But if the chemical composition of the workpiece promotes cracking, negative polarity should be used to reduce penetration and minimize admixture with plate metal. Also, the 20 to 30% increase in melt-off-rate with negative polarity helps build up an adequate bead with the preferred convex shape.

Electrode Size: Large-diameter electrodes should be used when cracking is a problem to reduce penetration and decrease admixture with the parent plate.

Flux Coverage: Flux thickness should be just adequate to cover the arc.

Number of Arcs: Twin electrodes, frequently used on flat fillets, produce less penetration, less admixture, and more melt-off compared to a single arc. For a given arc speed, twin electrodes thus

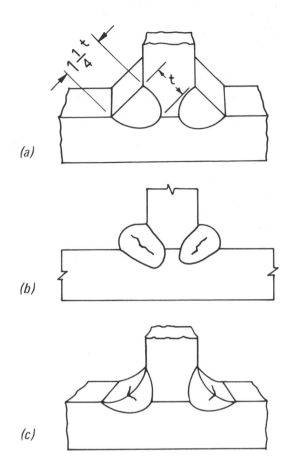

(a)

(b)

(c)

Fig. 11-14. Influence of bead shape on weld cracking in fillet welds. Welds least likely to crack are those (a) with a width that exceeds the depth. The minimum recommended ration of width to depth is 1.25 to 1. Beads with greater depth than width (b) may crack internally. Regardless of bead shape, concave bead surfaces (c) should be avoided, because they promote surface cracks.

reduce tendencies toward porosity and cracking. Twin electrodes also produce less arc blow.

Type of First Pass: A manual first pass with an E7018 electrode reduces admixture and thereby minimizes cracking tendencies. This practice is also good assurance against burnthrough where poor fitup is encountered.

Bead Shape: Width of the weld cross section should be 1-1/4 times the depth to reduce stresses caused by internal shrinkage, as illustrated in Fig. 11-14(a). This rule-of-thumb is especially important on steels with high cracking tendencies. Beads that are too deep may crack internally, Fig. 11-14(b). Slag removal also is difficult with deep beads. The bead surface must not be concave. Although concave welds have a pleasing appearance, the resulting surface stresses promote surface cracks.

Edge Preparation: Internal cracking and slag inclusions are possible if the prepared angle on single-pass welds is too acute. Bevel joints should not be used unless they have included angles of at least 60°, so that the width is greater than the depth. If 100% penetration T joints are specified on heavy

plate, the first pass on each side should be made with E7018 electrode, or the joint should be prepared in a manner to avoid excessive penetration and the resultant possibility of beads having greater depth than width.

Angle of Electrode: When two steels to be welded are of differing chemical analyses, arc movement should be toward the more weldable alloy to minimize admixture with the less weldable alloy.

Electrode Stickout: As electrical stickout (distance from point of electrical contact to electrode tip) is increased, melt-off rate increases while penetration and admixture decrease. Increased stickout thus reduces cracking tendencies, but also increases the difficulty of controlling the bead shape.

Grounding: The workpiece should be grounded at the "start" end of the weld, except on short welds, which should be grounded at both ends of the joint.

Speed and Current: Travel speed and welding current should be decreased as the proportions of carbon and other alloy consituents in the steel increase. This measure reduces cracking tendencies by reducing penetration and minimizing the size of the molten puddle.

Cracking in butt welds is less common than in fillet welds because butt joints are less constrained and can generally deflect enough to absorb thermal stresses. But when cracking is encountered in butt welds, the following factors should be reviewed.

Bead Shape: "Hat-shaped" beads, caused by excessively high voltage or slow travel speed, may promote cracks at the change in bead contour where the "crown" joins the "brim" (Fig. 11-15). A reduction in voltage is usually sufficient to avoid such cracks, but an increase in travel speed may also be required in some cases. These measures may require that the weld be made with two passes instead of one.

Bead shape may also promote cracking in seams that have been back-chipped or back-gouged. Cracking, therefore, is often a concern in the first pass on the second side of a double-beveled joint. Since the groove produced by back-gouging or back-chipping is deep and narrow, the bead placed

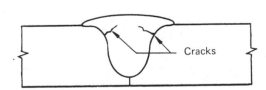

Fig. 11-15. A hat-shaped bead produced by excessive voltage. Similar effect is produced by travel speeds that are too slow. Such beads have a tendency to crack in locations indicated by the arrows.

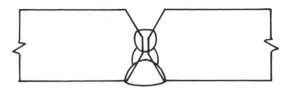

Fig. 11-16. Deep, narrow beads in a back-chipped butt joint are prone to cracking. Beads should be wider than they are deep.

in this trough often has a tendency to crack (Fig. 11-16). The appropriate measure in this case is to produce a groove that is wider than it is deep.

Admixture: Butt joints made in steels of poor weldability may have a tendency to crack. The appropriate remedy, as described in the prior paragraphs pertaining to fillet welds, is to reduce admixture with the base metal. This is usually best accomplished by using negative polarity, large electrodes, twin electrodes, a manual first pass, long electrode stickout, slow travel speeds, or low currents.

Alloy Pick-Up from the Flux: Excessively high arc voltages cause substantial pick-up of manganese and silicon from some fluxes. This pick-up usually can be avoided by not exceeding voltages recommended in standard procedures tables.

PROCEDURES FOR SUBMERGED-ARC WELDING OF CARBON AND LOW-ALLOY STEELS

The following procedures for the welding of carbon and low-alloy steels by the submerged-arc process are applicable only to semiautomatic manual and semiautomatic mechanized welding. It is highly unlikely that the student of welding will have opportunity to work with full-automatic equipment in his training courses. However, should such opportunities occur later on the job, The Lincoln Electric Company's *Procedure Handbook of Arc Welding* will be a source of information on full-automatic procedures.

For explanation of procedure tables generally — and how to use the following tables — the student should refer to Chapter 9 of this text.

SUBMERGED-ARC (SEMIAUTOMATIC) MANUAL

Welding Position: Flat
Weld Quality Level: Commercial
Steel Weldability: Good

Plate Thickness (in.)	0.075 (14 ga)	0.105 (12 ga)	0.135 (10 ga)	3/16	1/4
Pass	1	1	1	1	1
Electrode Size	1/16	1/16	1/16	1/16	1/16
Current (amp) DC(+)	275	325	375	425	425
Volts	25	27	29	33	36
Arc Speed (in./min)	44 — 50	40 — 46	35 — 40	26 — 30	14 — 18
Electrode Req'd (lb/ft)	0.037	0.047	0.065	0.108	0.190
Flux Req'd (lb/ft)	0.09 — 0.13	0.10 — 0.14	0.12 — 0.16	0.14 — 0.18	0.15 — 0.21
Total Time (hr/ft of weld)	0.00426	0.00465	0.00534	0.00715	0.0125
Backing, minimum size (in.)	12 ga x 3/8	12 ga x 1/2	10 ga x 5/8	3/16 x 3/4	1/4 x 1
Gap (in.)	1/16	1/16	3/32	3/32	1/8

SUBMERGED-ARC (SEMIAUTOMATIC) MANUAL

Welding Position: Flat
Weld Quality Level: Commercial
Steel Weldability: Good

Plate Thickness (in.)	3/16	1/4	5/16	3/8
Pass	1	1	1	1
Electrode Size	5/64	5/64	5/64	5/64
Current (amp) DC(+)	425	450	475	500
Volts	31	32	34	35
Arc Speed (in./min)	20 — 22	15 — 17	13 — 15	10 — 12
Electrode Req'd (lb/ft)	0.12	0.18	0.22	0.30
Flux Req'd (lb/ft)	0.13 — 0.17	0.21 — 0.27	0.25 — 0.32	0.34 — 0.43
Total Time (hr/ft of weld)	0.00952	0.0125	0.0143	0.0182
Backing, minimum size (in.)	3/16 x 3/4	1/4 x 3/4	1/4 x 1	1/4 x 1
Gap (in.)	1/8	5/32	5/32	3/16

SUBMERGED-ARC (SEMIAUTOMATIC) MANUAL

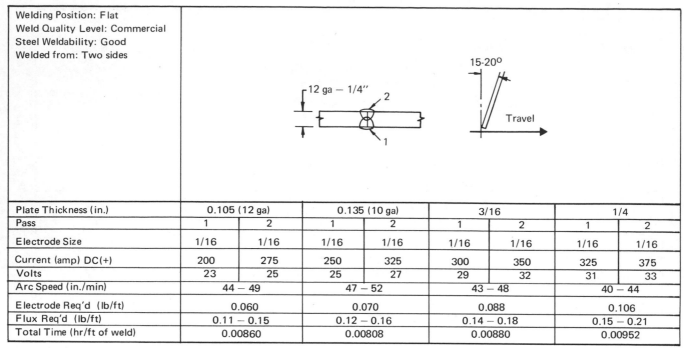

Welding Position: Flat
Weld Quality Level: Commercial
Steel Weldability: Good
Welded from: Two sides

Plate Thickness (in.)	0.105 (12 ga)		0.135 (10 ga)		3/16		1/4	
Pass	1	2	1	2	1	2	1	2
Electrode Size	1/16	1/16	1/16	1/16	1/16	1/16	1/16	1/16
Current (amp) DC(+)	200	275	250	325	300	350	325	375
Volts	23	25	25	27	29	32	31	33
Arc Speed (in./min)	44 — 49		47 — 52		43 — 48		40 — 44	
Electrode Req'd (lb/ft)	0.060		0.070		0.088		0.106	
Flux Req'd (lb/ft)	0.11 — 0.15		0.12 — 0.16		0.14 — 0.18		0.15 — 0.21	
Total Time (hr/ft of weld)	0.00860		0.00808		0.00880		0.00952	

See introductory notes.

SUBMERGED-ARC (SEMIAUTOMATIC) MANUAL

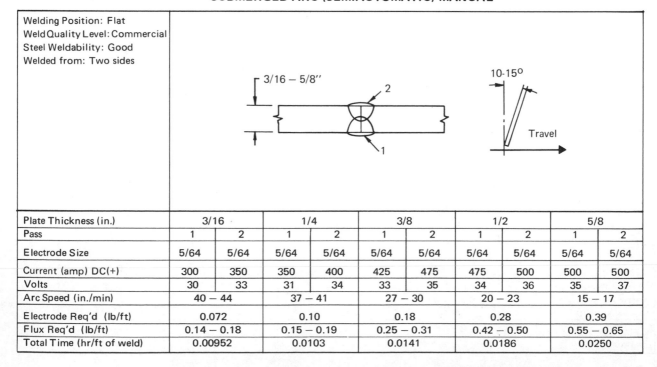

Welding Position: Flat
Weld Quality Level: Commercial
Steel Weldability: Good
Welded from: Two sides

Plate Thickness (in.)	3/16		1/4		3/8		1/2		5/8	
Pass	1	2	1	2	1	2	1	2	1	2
Electrode Size	5/64	5/64	5/64	5/64	5/64	5/64	5/64	5/64	5/64	5/64
Current (amp) DC(+)	300	350	350	400	425	475	475	500	500	500
Volts	30	33	31	34	33	35	34	36	35	37
Arc Speed (in./min)	40 — 44		37 — 41		27 — 30		20 — 23		15 — 17	
Electrode Req'd (lb/ft)	0.072		0.10		0.18		0.28		0.39	
Flux Req'd (lb/ft)	0.14 — 0.18		0.15 — 0.19		0.25 — 0.31		0.42 — 0.50		0.55 — 0.65	
Total Time (hr/ft of weld)	0.00952		0.0103		0.0141		0.0186		0.0250	

SUBMERGED-ARC (SEMIAUTOMATIC) MANUAL

Welding Position: Flat
Weld Quality Level: Commercial
Steel Weldability: Good
Welded from: Two sides

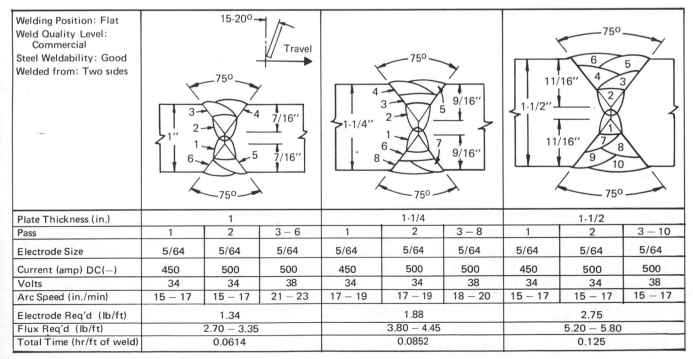

Plate Thickness (in.)	5/8		3/4	
Pass	1	2	1	2
Electrode Size	5/64	5/64	5/64	5/64
Current (amp) DC(+)	475	500	475	500
Volts	35	36	35	36
Arc Speed (in./min)	16 – 18	16 – 18	11 – 13	11 – 13
Electrode Req'd (lb/ft)	0.37		0.53	
Flux Req'd (lb/ft)	0.60 – 0.75		0.75 – 0.96	
Total Time (hr/ft of weld)	0.0235		0.0333	
Depth, A (in.)	7/32		9/32	
Depth, B (in.)	7/32		9/32	

SUBMERGED-ARC (SEMIAUTOMATIC) MANUAL

Welding Position: Flat
Weld Quality Level:
  Commercial
Steel Weldability: Good
Welded from: Two sides

Plate Thickness (in.)	1			1-1/4			1-1/2		
Pass	1	2	3 – 6	1	2	3 – 8	1	2	3 – 10
Electrode Size	5/64	5/64	5/64	5/64	5/64	5/64	5/64	5/64	5/64
Current (amp) DC(−)	450	500	500	450	500	500	450	500	500
Volts	34	34	38	34	34	38	34	34	38
Arc Speed (in./min)	15 – 17	15 – 17	21 – 23	17 – 19	17 – 19	18 – 20	15 – 17	15 – 17	15 – 17
Electrode Req'd (lb/ft)	1.34			1.88			2.75		
Flux Req'd (lb/ft)	2.70 – 3.35			3.80 – 4.45			5.20 – 5.80		
Total Time (hr/ft of weld)	0.0614			0.0852			0.125		

Seam must be tight. Seal all gaps with small bead on first-pass side.

SUBMERGED-ARC (SEMIAUTOMATIC) MANUAL

Welding Position: Flat
Weld Quality Level: Commercial
Steel Weldability: Good

Weld Size, L (in.)	3/32—	3/32	1/8—	5/32—	3/16
Plate Thickness (in.)	0.075 (14 ga)	0.105 (12 ga)	0.135 (10 ga)	3/16	1/4
Pass	1	1	1	1	1
Electrode Size	1/16	1/16	1/16	1/16	1/16
Current (amp) DC(+)	185	250	325	360	400
Volts	23	24.5	28	30	37
Arc Speed (in./min)	35 — 39	47 — 52	57 — 63	47 — 52	31 — 34
Electrode Req'd (lb/ft)	0.028	0.030	0.034	0.047	0.081
Flux Req'd (lb/ft)	0.07 — 0.09	0.08 — 0.10	0.10 — 0.12	0.10 — 0.13	0.11 — 0.14
Total Time (hr/ft of weld)	0.00540	0.00404	0.00333	0.00404	0.00615

SUBMERGED-ARC (SEMIAUTOMATIC) MANUAL

Welding Position: Flat
Weld Quality Level: Commercial
Steel Weldability: Good

Procedure for Conventional Fillets with 1-in. Electrical Stickout

Weld Size, L (in.)	3/16	1/4	5/16	3/8	1/2	5/8
Plate Thickness (in.)	1/4	5/16	3/8	1/2	5/8	3/4
Pass	1	1	1	1	1	1, 2 & 3
Electrode Size	5/64	5/64	5/64	5/64	5/64	5/64
Current (amp) DC(−)	375	400	425	425	425	450
Volts	36	37	38	39	39	40
Arc Speed (in./min)	31 — 32	22 — 24	17 — 19	13.5 — 14.5	7.5 — 8.5	14 — 15
Electrode Req'd (lb/ft)	0.08	0.13	0.19	0.26	0.45	0.74
Flux Req'd (lb/ft)	0.07 — 0.11	0.12 — 0.16	0.17 — 0.24	0.25 — 0.33	0.44 — 0.54	0.80 — 0.95
Total Time (hr/ft of weld)	0.00615	0.00870	0.0111	0.0143	0.0250	0.0404

SUBMERGED-ARC (SEMIAUTOMATIC) MANUAL

Welding Position: Flat
Weld Quality Level: Commercial
Steel Weldability: Good

Procedure for Long Stickout (2-1/4 in.)

Weld Size, L (in.)	1/4	5/16	3/8	1/2	5/8
Plate Thickness (in.)	5/16	3/8	1/2	5/8	3/4
Pass	1	1	1	1	1, 2 & 3
Electrode Size	5/64	5/64	5/64	5/64	5/64
Current (amp) DC(−)	425	450	450	450	450
Volts	45	47	47	47	47
Arc Speed (in./min)	28 − 31	22 − 24	17 − 19	9 − 11	17 − 19
Electrode Req'd (lb/ft)	0.14	0.22	0.30	0.52	0.81
Flux Req'd (lb/ft)	0.10 − 0.15	0.16 − 0.22	0.26 − 0.35	0.42 − 0.52	0.80 − 0.95
Total Time (hr/ft of weld)	0.00678	0.00870	0.0111	0.0200	0.0333
Electrical Stickout, 2-1/4 in.					

SUBMERGED-ARC (SEMIAUTOMATIC) MANUAL

Welding Position: Flat
Weld Quality Level: Strength only
Steel Weldability: Good

Procedure for Penetration Welds with 1-in. Electrical Stickout

Weld Size, L (in.)	5/32	3/16(−)	3/16	1/4	5/16	3/8
Plate Thickness, T (in.)	1/4	5/16	3/8	1/2	5/8	3/4
Pass	1	1	1	1	1	1
Electrode Size	5/64	5/64	5/64	5/64	5/64	5/64
Current (amp) DC(+)	350	400	410	425	425	425
Volts	30	33	34	35	35	36
Arc Speed (in./min)	36 − 40	33 − 36	24 − 27	16 − 18	11.5 − 12.5	8.5 − 9.5
Electrode Req'd (lb/ft)	0.046	0.061	0.084	0.13	0.19	0.25
Flux Req'd (lb/ft)	0.05 − 0.08	0.09 − 0.13	0.14 − 0.18	0.20 − 0.25	0.26 − 0.32	0.32 − 0.40
Total Time (hr/ft of weld)	0.00526	0.00580	0.00784	0.0118	0.0167	0.0222

SUBMERGED-ARC (SEMIAUTOMATIC) MANUAL

Welding Position: Horizontal
Weld Quality Level: Commercial
Steel Weldability: Good

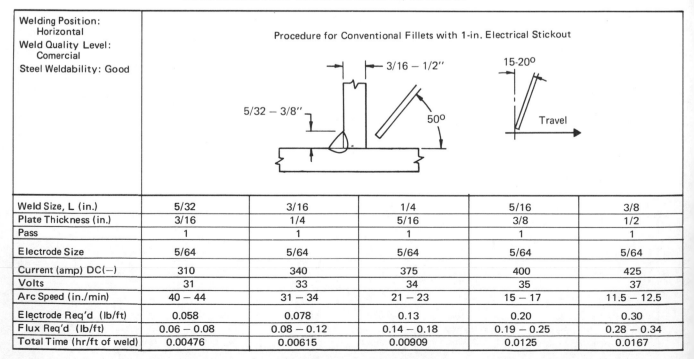

Weld Size, L (in.)	3/32—	3/32	1/8—	5/32—	3/16
Plate Thickness (in.)	0.075 (14 ga)	0.105 (12 ga)	0.135 (10 ga)	3/16	1/4
Pass	1	1	1	1	1
Electrode Size	1/16	1/16	1/16	1/16	1/16
Current (amp) DC(+)	185	250	325	350	375
Volts	23	24.5	28	30	34
Arc Speed (in./min)	35 — 39	47 — 52	52 — 58	43 — 47	27 — 30
Electrode Req'd (lb/ft)	0.029	0.030	0.037	0.050	0.078
Flux Req'd (lb/ft)	0.08 — 0.10	0.08 — 0.12	0.08 — 0.12	0.09 — 0.13	0.09 — 0.13
Total Time (hr/ft of weld)	0.00540	0.00404	0.00364	0.00444	0.00702

SUBMERGED-ARC (SEMIAUTOMATIC) MANUAL

Welding Position:
  Horizontal
Weld Quality Level:
  Comercial
Steel Weldability: Good

Procedure for Conventional Fillets with 1-in. Electrical Stickout

Weld Size, L (in.)	5/32	3/16	1/4	5/16	3/8
Plate Thickness (in.)	3/16	1/4	5/16	3/8	1/2
Pass	1	1	1	1	1
Electrode Size	5/64	5/64	5/64	5/64	5/64
Current (amp) DC(−)	310	340	375	400	425
Volts	31	33	34	35	37
Arc Speed (in./min)	40 — 44	31 — 34	21 — 23	15 — 17	11.5 — 12.5
Electrode Req'd (lb/ft)	0.058	0.078	0.13	0.20	0.30
Flux Req'd (lb/ft)	0.06 — 0.08	0.08 — 0.12	0.14 — 0.18	0.19 — 0.25	0.28 — 0.34
Total Time (hr/ft of weld)	0.00476	0.00615	0.00909	0.0125	0.0167

SUBMERGED-ARC (SEMIAUTOMATIC) MANUAL

Welding Position: Horizontal
Weld Quality Level: Commercial
Steel Weldability: Good

Procedure for Long Electrical Stickout (2-1/4'')

Weld Size, L (in.)	1/4	5/16	3/8	1/2
Plate Thickness (in.)	5/16	3/8	1/2	5/8
Pass	1	1	1	1, 2 & 3
Electrode Size	5/64	5/64	5/64	5/64
Current (amp) DC(−)	450	450	400	400
Volts	48	48	42	42
Arc Speed (in./min)	31 - 34	21 - 23	13 − 14	23 − 25*
Electrode Req'd (lb/ft)	0.16	0.23	0.32	0.56
Flux Req'd (lb/ft)	0.10 − 0.14	0.16 − 0.21	0.37 − 0.43	0.58 − 0.64
Total Time (hr/ft of weld)	0.00615	0.00909	0.0148	0.0250
Electrical Stickout, 2-1/4 in.				

* Each pass

SUBMERGED-ARC (SEMIAUTOMATIC) MANUAL

Welding Position: Horizontal
Weld Quality Level: Strength only
Steel Weldability: Good

Procedure for Penetration Fillets with 1-in. Electrical Stickout

Weld Size, L (in.)	5/32(−)	3/16	3/16(+)	1/4(−)	1/4(+)	5/16(+)
Plate Thickness, T (in.)	3/16	1/4	5/16	3/8	1/2	5/8
Pass	1	1	1	1	1	1
Electrode Size	5/64	5/64	5/64	5/64	5/64	5/64
Current (amp) DC(+)	325	325	350	380	400	400
Volts	26	26	28	31	32	32
Arc Speed (in./min)	37 − 41	32 − 35	25 − 28	21 − 23	13 − 14	8 − 9
Electrode Req'd (lb/ft)	0.038	0.044	0.064	0.081	0.15	0.21
Flux Req'd (lb/ft)	0.05 − 0.07	0.06 − 0.09	0.10 − 0.14	0.15 − 0.20	0.22 − 0.28	0.30 − 0.40
Total Time (hr/ft of weld)	0.00513	0.00597	0.00755	0.00909	0.0148	0.0235

SUBMERGED-ARC (SEMIAUTOMATIC) MANUAL

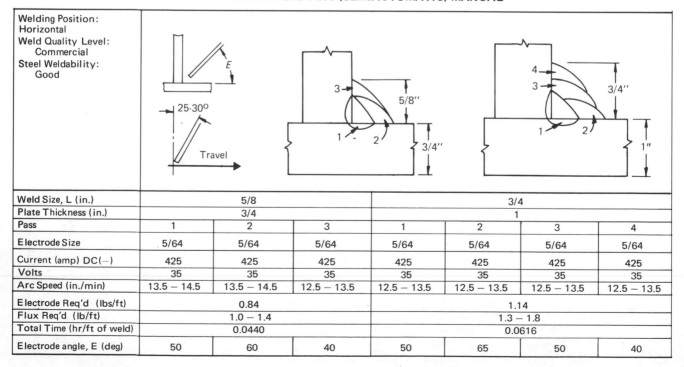

Welding Position: Horizontal					
Weld Quality Level: Commercial					
Steel Weldability: Good					
Weld Size, L (in.)	3/8		1/2		
Plate Thickness (in.)	1/2		5/8		
Pass	1	2	1	2	3
Electrode Size	5/64	5/64	5/64	5/64	5/64
Current (amp) DC(—)	425	425	425	425	425
Volts	35	35	35	35	35
Arc Speed (in./min)	23 — 25	23 — 25	20 — 22	20 — 22	20 — 22
Electrode Req'd (lb/ft)	0.31		0.53		
Flux Req'd (lb/ft)	0.32 — 0.50		0.55 — 0.80		
Total Time (hr/ft of weld)	0.0167		0.0286		
Electrode Angle, E (deg)	65	50	50	60	40

SUBMERGED-ARC (SEMIAUTOMATIC) MANUAL

Welding Position: Horizontal						
Weld Quality Level: Commercial						
Steel Weldability: Good						
Weld Size, L (in.)	5/8			3/4		
Plate Thickness (in.)	3/4			1		
Pass	1	2	3	1	2	3	4
Electrode Size	5/64	5/64	5/64	5/64	5/64	5/64	5/64
Current (amp) DC(—)	425	425	425	425	425	425	425
Volts	35	35	35	35	35	35	35
Arc Speed (in./min)	13.5 — 14.5	13.5 — 14.5	12.5 — 13.5	12.5 — 13.5	12.5 — 13.5	12.5 — 13.5	12.5 — 13.5
Electrode Req'd (lbs/ft)	0.84			1.14			
Flux Req'd (lb/ft)	1.0 — 1.4			1.3 — 1.8			
Total Time (hr/ft of weld)	0.0440			0.0616			
Electrode angle, E (deg)	50	60	40	50	65	50	40

SUBMERGED-ARC (SEMIAUTOMATIC) MANUAL

Welding Position: Horizontal Weld Quality Level: Commercial Steel Weldability: Good					
Weld Size, L (in.)	3/32(−)	3/32	1/8(−)	3/16	1/4
Plate Thickness (in.)	0.075 (14 ga)	0.105 (12 ga)	0.135 (10 ga)	3/16	1/4
Pass	1	1	1	1	1
Electrode Size	1/16	1/16	1/16	1/16	1/16
Current (amp) DC(+)	185	250	325	360	400
Volts	23	24.5	28.5	30.5	37
Arc Speed (in./min)	47 − 52	47 − 52	52 − 58	42 − 47	27 − 30
Electrode Req'd (lb/ft)	0.022	0.030	0.037	0.055	0.086
Flux Req'd (lb/ft)	0.09 − 0.13	0.11 − 0.15	0.11 − 0.15	0.12 − 0.16	0.13 − 0.17
Total Time (hr/ft of Weld)	0.00404	0.00404	0.00364	0.00449	0.00702

SUBMERGED-ARC (SEMIAUTOMATIC) MANUAL

Welding Position: Horizontal Weld Quality Level: Commercial Steel Weldability: Good				
Weld Size, L (in.)	3/16	1/4	5/16(−)	5/16(+)
Plate Thickness (in.)	3/16	1/4	5/16	3/8
Pass	1	1	1	1
Electrode Size	5/64	5/64	5/64	5/64
Current (amp) DC(−)	400	425	450	450
Volts	36	37	38	38
Arc Speed (in./min.)	40 − 44	31 − 34	22 − 24	16 − 18
Electrode Req'd (lb/ft)	0.080	0.12	0.17	0.22
Flux Req'd (lb/ft)	0.10 − 0.13	0.14 − 0.18	0.19 − 0.25	0.22 − 0.29
Total Time (hr/ft of weld)	0.00476	0.00615	0.00870	0.0118
Electrode angle, E (deg)	65	60	55	55

SUBMERGED-ARC (SEMIAUTOMATIC) MECHANIZED

Welding Position: Flat
Weld Quality Level: Commercial
Steel Weldability: Good

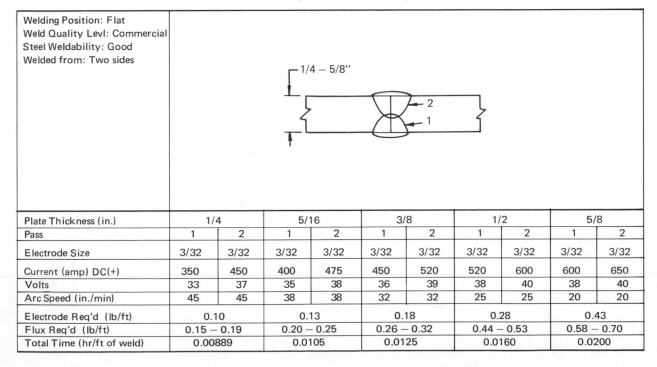

Plate Thickness (in.)	3/16	1/4	5/16	3/8
Pass	1	1	1	1
Electrode Size	3/32	3/32	3/32	3/32
Current (amp) DC(+)	500	550	575	600
Volts	32	34	35	36
Arc Speed (in./min)	26	20	18	14
Electrode Req'd (lb/ft)	0.12	0.18	0.22	0.32
Flux Req'd (lb/ft)	0.14 − 0.18	0.22 − 0.28	0.27 − 0.35	0.35 − 0.48
Total Time (hr/ft of weld)	0.00769	0.0100	0.0111	0.0143
Backing, minimum size (in.)	3/16 x 3/4	1/4 x 3/4	1/4 x 1	1/4 x 1
Gap (in.)	1/8	5/32	5/32	3/16

SUBMERGED-ARC (SEMIAUTOMATIC) MECHANIZED

Welding Position: Flat
Weld Quality Levl: Commercial
Steel Weldability: Good
Welded from: Two sides

Plate Thickness (in.)	1/4		5/16		3/8		1/2		5/8	
Pass	1	2	1	2	1	2	1	2	1	2
Electrode Size	3/32	3/32	3/32	3/32	3/32	3/32	3/32	3/32	3/32	3/32
Current (amp) DC(+)	350	450	400	475	450	520	520	600	600	650
Volts	33	37	35	38	36	39	38	40	38	40
Arc Speed (in./min)	45	45	38	38	32	32	25	25	20	20
Electrode Req'd (lb/ft)	0.10		0.13		0.18		0.28		0.43	
Flux Req'd (lb/ft)	0.15 − 0.19		0.20 − 0.25		0.26 − 0.32		0.44 − 0.53		0.58 − 0.70	
Total Time (hr/ft of weld)	0.00889		0.0105		0.0125		0.0160		0.0200	

SUBMERGED-ARC (SEMIAUTOMATIC) MECHANIZED

Welding Position: Flat
Weld Quality Level: Commercial
Steel Weldability: Good
Welded from: Two sides

Plate Thickness (in.)	5/8		3/4	
Pass	1	2	1	2
Electrode Size	3/32	3/32	3/32	3/32
Current (amp) DC(+)	500	525	500	525
Volts	34	35	34	35
Arc Speed (in./min)	17.0	18.0	12.0	12.5
Electrode Req'd (lb/ft)	0.37		0.56	
Flux Req'd (lb/ft)	0.64 — 0.71		0.81 — 0.90	
Total Time (hr/ft of weld)	0.0229		0.0327	
Depth, A (in.)	7/32		9/32	
Depth, B (in.)	7/32		9/32	

SUBMERGED-ARC (SEMIAUTOMATIC) MECHANIZED

Welding Position: Flat
Weld Quality Level: Commercial
Steel Weldability: Good
Welded from: Two sides

Plate Thickness (in.)	7/8			1		
Pass	1	2	3 — 6	1	2	3 — 8
Electrode Size	3/32	3/32	3/32	3/32	3/32	3/32
Current (amp) DC(−)	500	550	550	500	550	550
Volts	33	33	38	34	34	38
Arc Speed (in./min)	25	25	30	25	25	30
Electrode Req'd (lb/ft)	0.98			1.28		
Flux Req'd (lb/ft)	2.23 — 2.52			2.82 — 3.05		
Total Time (hr/ft of weld)	0.0427			0.0560		

SUBMERGED-ARC (SEMIAUTOMATIC) MECHANIZED

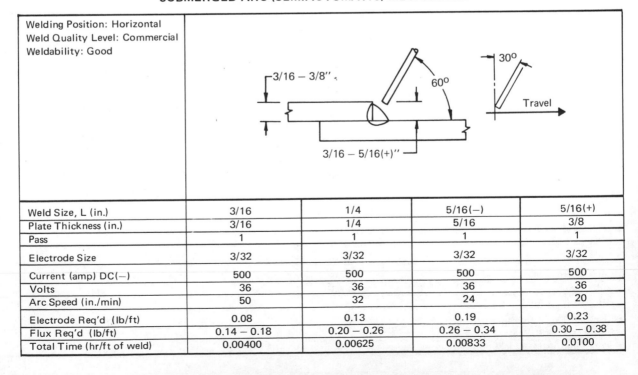

Welding Position: Flat
Weld Quality Level: Commercial
Steel Weldability: Good
Welded from: Two sides

Plate Thickness (in.)	1-1/4			1-1/2		
Pass	1	2	3 – 10	1	2	3 – 14
Electrode Size	3/32	3/32	3/32	3/32	3/32	3/32
Current (amp) DC(−)	500	550	550	500	550	550
Volts	34	34	39	34	34	39
Arc Speed (in.min)	23	23	24	21	21	25
Electrode Req'd (lb/ft)	1.90			2.58		
Flux Req'd (lb/ft)	4.00 – 4.25			5.42 – 5.75		
Total Time (hr/ft of weld)	0.0841			0.115		

SUBMERGED-ARC (SEMIAUTOMATIC) MECHANIZED

Welding Position: Horizontal
Weld Quality Level: Commercial
Weldability: Good

Weld Size, L (in.)	3/16	1/4	5/16(−)	5/16(+)
Plate Thickness (in.)	3/16	1/4	5/16	3/8
Pass	1	1	1	1
Electrode Size	3/32	3/32	3/32	3/32
Current (amp) DC(−)	500	500	500	500
Volts	36	36	36	36
Arc Speed (in./min)	50	32	24	20
Electrode Req'd (lb/ft)	0.08	0.13	0.19	0.23
Flux Req'd (lb/ft)	0.14 – 0.18	0.20 – 0.26	0.26 – 0.34	0.30 – 0.38
Total Time (hr/ft of weld)	0.00400	0.00625	0.00833	0.0100

SUBMERGED-ARC (SEMIAUTOMATIC) MECHANIZED

Welding Position: Flat Weld Quality Level: Commercial Steel Weldability: Good					
Weld Size, L (in.)	3/16	1/4	5/16	3/8	1/2
Plate Thickness (in.)	1/4	5/16	3/8	1/2	5/8
Pass	1	1	1	1	1
Electrode Size	3/32	3/32	3/32	3/32	3/32
Current (amp) DC(−)	475	550	600	600	600
Volts	37	40	42	42	42
Arc Speed (in./min)	50	36	28	19	11
Electrode Req'd (lb/ft)	0.08	0.13	0.18	0.26	0.46
Flux Req'd (lb/ft)	0.11 − 0.15	0.15 − 0.20	0.20 − 0.27	0.28 − 0.37	0.50 − 0.62
Total Time (hr/ft of weld)	0.00400	0.00556	0.00714	0.0105	0.0182

SUBMERGED-ARC (SEMIAUTOMATIC) MECHANIZED

Welding Position: Flat Weld Quality Level: Commercial Steel Weldability: Good		
Weld Size, L (in.)	5/8	3/4
Plate Thickness (in.)	3/4	1
Pass	1 − 3	1 − 3
Electrode Size	3/32	3/32
Current (amp) DC(−)	600	600
Volts	42	42
Arc Speed (in./min)	21	15
Electrode Req'd (lb/ft)	0.74	1.05
Flux Req'd (lb/ft)	1.0 − 1.2	1.3 − 1.6
Total Time (ft/ft of weld)	0.0286	0.0400

SUBMERGED-ARC (SEMIAUTOMATIC) MECHANIZED

Welding Position: Horizontal — Weld Quality Level: Commercial — Steel Weldability: Good

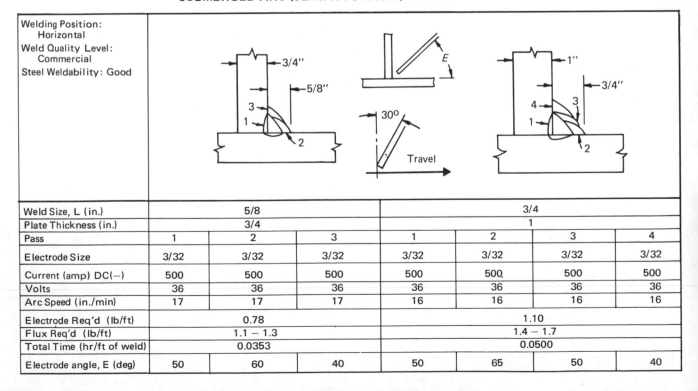

Weld Size, L (in.)	3/16	1/4	5/16	3/8		1/2	
Plate Thickness (in.)	1/4	5/16	3/8	1/2		5/8	
Pass	1	1	1	1	2	1	2
Electrode Size	3/32	3/32	3/32	3/32	3/32	3/32	3/32
Current (amp) DC(−)	450	500	550	500	500	500	500
Volts	34	36	38	36	36	36	36
Arc Speed (in./min)	45	32	24	28	28	16.5	16.5
Electrode Req'd (lb/ft)	0.08	0.13	0.20	0.29		0.49	
Flux Req'd (lb/ft)	0.13 − 0.17	0.18 − 0.23	0.24 − 0.30	0.35 − 0.45		0.60 − 0.75	
Total Time (hr/ft of weld)	0.00445	0.00625	0.00833	0.0143		0.0243	
Electrode Angle, E (deg)	50	50	50	65	40	65	40

SUBMERGED-ARC (SEMIAUTOMATIC) MECHANIZED

Welding Position: Horizontal — Weld Quality Level: Commercial — Steel Weldability: Good

Weld Size, L (in.)	5/8			3/4			
Plate Thickness (in.)	3/4			1			
Pass	1	2	3	1	2	3	4
Electrode Size	3/32	3/32	3/32	3/32	3/32	3/32	3/32
Current (amp) DC(−)	500	500	500	500	500	500	500
Volts	36	36	36	36	36	36	36
Arc Speed (in./min)	17	17	17	16	16	16	16
Electrode Req'd (lb/ft)	0.78			1.10			
Flux Req'd (lb/ft)	1.1 − 1.3			1.4 − 1.7			
Total Time (hr/ft of weld)	0.0353			0.0500			
Electrode angle, E (deg)	50	60	40	50	65	50	40

The Self-Shielded Flux-Cored Electrode Process

The self-shielded flux-cored arc-welding process is an outgrowth of shielded metal-arc welding. The versatility and maneuverability of stick electrodes in manual welding stimulated efforts to mechanize the shielded metal-arc process. The thought was that if some way could be found for putting an electrode with self-shielding characteristics in coil form and feeding it mechanically to the arc, welding time lost in changing electrodes and the material loss as electrode stubs would be eliminated. The result of these efforts was the development of the semiautomatic and full-automatic processes for welding with continuous flux-cored tubular electrode "wires". Such fabricated wires (Fig. 12-1) contain in their cores the ingredients for fluxing and deoxidizing molten metal and for generating shielding gases and vapors and slag coverings.

In essence, semiautomatic welding with flux-cored electrodes is manual shielded metal-arc welding with an electrode many feet long instead of just a few inches long. By the press of the trigger completing the welding circuit, the operator activates the mechanism that feeds the electrode to the arc (Fig. 12-2). He uses a gun instead of an electrode holder, but it is similarly light in weight and easy to maneuver. The only other major difference is that the weld metal of the electrode surrounds the shielding and fluxing chemicals, rather than being surrounded by them.

Full-automatic welding with self-shielded flux-cored electrodes is one step further in mechanization — the removal of direct manual manipulation in the utilization of the open-arc process.

ELECTRODE CONSTRUCTION AND DEPOSITION RATE

One reason for incorporating the flux inside a tubular wire is to make feasible the coiling of electrode; outside coverings such as used on stick electrodes are brittle and would not permit coiling. The "inside-out" construction of the fabricated electrodes also solved the probelm of how to make continuous electric contact at a point in the welding gun close to the arc.

One of the limitations of the stick electrode is the long and varying length of electrode between the point of electrical contact in the electrode holder and the electrode tip. This limits the current that can be used because of electrical resistance heating. High currents — capable of giving high deposition rates — in passing through an electrode length more than a few inches long would develop enough resistance heating to overheat and damage the covering. But when electrical contact can be made close to the arc, as with the inside-out construction of tubular electrodes, relatively high currents can be used even with small-diameter electrode wires.

The inside-out construction of self-shielded electrode, thus, brought to manually manipulated welding the possibility of using higher-amperage

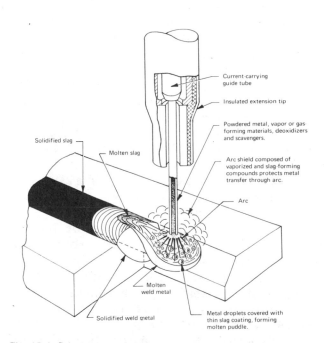

Fig. 12-1. Principles of the self-shielded flux-cored arc-welding process. The electrode may be viewed as an "inside-out" construction of the stick electrode used in shielded metal-arc welding. Putting the shield-generating materials inside the electrode allows the coiling of long, continuous lengths of electrode and gives an outside conductive sheath for carrying the welding current from a point close to the arc.

Fig. 12-2. The operator activates electrode feed when he presses the trigger completing the welding circuit. With the semiautomatic gun he can reach into areas that are inaccessible to the semiautomatic equipment of other processes.

currents than feasible with stick-electrode welding. As a result, much higher deposition rates are possible with the hand-held semiautomatic gun than with the hand-held stick-electrode holder.

Higher deposition rates, plus automatic electrode feed and elmination of lost time for changing electrodes, have resulted in substantial production economies wherever the semiautomatic process has been used to replace stick-electrode welding. Decreases in welding costs as great as 50% have been common, and in some production welding deposition rates have been increased as much as 400%

The intent behind the development of self-shielded flux-cored electrode welding was to mechanize and increase the efficiency of manual welding. The semiautomatic use of the process does just that — serves as a direct replacement for stick-electrode welding. The full-automatic use of the process, on the other hand, competes with other fully automatic processes and is used in production where it gives the desired performance characteristics and weld properties, while eliminating problems associated with flux or gas handling. Although the full-automatic process is important to a few industries, the semiautomatic version has the wider application possibilities. In fact, semiautomatic self-shielded flux-cored welding has potential for substantially reducing welding costs when working with steel wherever stick-electrode

welding is used to deposit other than minor volumes of weld metal. This has been proved to be true in maintenance and repair welding (Fig. 12-3), as well as in production work.

Although the AWS-accepted term for the process is self-shielded flux-cored arc welding, it is also referred to as vapor-shielded welding, or cored-electrode welding. The prefix "semiautomatic" or "full-automatic" is used to distinguish the degree of mechanization. In shop practice, the proprietary name for the electrode is often the term employed in referring to the process, with the semiautomatic version generally implied. Thus, in many shops the trade name "Innershield" is used to mean semiautomatic self-shielded flux-cored welding. Should the full-automatic method be employed in the same shop, it would likely be called "automatic Innershield."

The semiautomatic version of the process was developed as a replacement for the manual shielded metal-arc process in the welding of mild and low-alloy steels. Since the process is of recent origin, weldors are less experienced with it, and sometimes are apprehensive about their abilites to manually weld with a mechanized welding gun. Where the semiautomatic process has been introduced in welding shops, however, it has been found that an experienced weldor learns to handle the gun with a degree of proficiency after about a day of instruction and practice. In a week, he has mastered the art and is capable of bringing to the work the full cost-reduction benefits of semimechanization.

Fig. 12-3. The semiautomatic self-shielded flux-cored arc-welding process substantially reduces costs in repair, rebuilding, and maintenance work, as well as in manufacturing, fabrication, and structural steel erection. Here, the weldor is using the process to repair and rebuild shovel crawler pads.

SELF-SHIELDED FLUX-CORED ELECTRODES

Becuase the process is relatively new — and electrode composition and types were still under development when this book was published — data on the process are not so rigidly standardized as with other processes. This is especially true in respect to performance characteristics of the electrodes, which vary not only from classification to classification, but also from manufacturer to manufacturer within the same classification. For this reason, it is important that the manufacturer's performance data be consulted in making a selection of an electrode for a specific type of joint and welding position. Some electrodes can be used in the flat and horizontal positions only; other perform satisfactorily in all positions.

The AWS A5.20-69 classification system for flux-cored arc-welding electrodes of both the self-shielded and gas-shielded types follows the general pattern used in other AWS filler-metal classifications. Some variations are necessary, however, to accommodate the composite nature of the electrodes. The classification system is explained in Chapter 5, together with a description of the characteristics of the various electrodes and suggested areas of application. Required chemical composition of deposited weld metal from electrodes for mild and low-alloy steels are shown in Table 12-1 and mechanical-property requirements are listed in Table 5-12.

The welding-position capability of these electrodes is influenced by weld-puddle size, slag volume, electrode diameter, and current capacity. All self-shielded flux-cored electrodes are capable of flat-position performance. Those with high deposition rates usually produce flat-position welds most

economically. As with covered manual electrodes, the small-diameter flux-cored electrodes suitable for downhand welding can also be used to make vertical and overhead welds, but their performance and weld quality will not match that achieved with electrodes specifically designed for out-of-position work.

The composition of the core and current-carrying capacity of the mild-steel sheath influence deposition rates. The electrode's ability to tolerate extended electrical stickout while maintaining the required mechanical properties and quality of weld metal is also a factor that affects deposition rate.

The arc characteristics of the self-shielded flux-cored electrode are primarily responsible for penetration. Changing welding current and electrical stickout within the tolerance limits of the specific electrode will also affect penetration, but the effect is minimal compared to the difference in penetration of electrodes of different classifications. Electrodes that have a confined arc invariably give deep penetration, as compared to electrodes having the globular, soft-type arc. The need for penetration varies with joint design and precision in fitup.

Slag covering differs primarily in volume and type with the various flux-cored electrodes. Large slag volume is associated with limited-position operation. The type of slag produced by electrodes that give high volume is usually a "friable-porous" slag or a "dense-solid" slag. Both types perform the desired action of blanketing the molten weld metal, preventing atmospheric contamination as it solidifies, and protecting the solidified weld metal as it cools. Both types are easily removed from welds.

Self-shielded flux-cored electrodes producing low-volume slags are either those particularly suited to vertical and overhead welding or those designed for the high-speed joining of sheet materials. Electrodes designed for out-of-position performance produce a low volume of slag that sets up quickly and is easily removed. The slag produced by the electrodes designed for high-speed sheet--metal welding promotes good wetting action and uniform fusion between the deposit and the base material along the edges of the weld. Such slag has a very dense, glasslike appearance and structure and is difficult to remove.

Weld spatter volume and size vary with arc characteristics. The electrodes that have a confined arc usually have a smaller droplet transfer in the arc stream. The spatter from this type is finer than that produced by the electrodes that have a globular, soft-arc characteristic. Since the deposition efficiencies of flux-cored electrodes are very similar, the spatter volume, although differing consider-

TABLE 12-1. Composition Requirements* for Flux-Cored Electrodes

AWS Classification	Chemical Composition, Max. (%)						
	Mn	Si	Ni	Cr†	Mo†	V†	Al
E60T-7	1.50	0.90	0.50	0.20	0.30	0.08	1.8
E60T-8	1.50	0.90	0.50	0.20	0.30	0.08	1.0
E70T-1	1.75	0.90	0.30†	0.20	0.30	0.08	- -
E70T-2	No chemical requirements						
E70T-3	No chemical requirements						
E70T-4	1.50	0.90	0.50	0.20	0.30	0.08	1.8
E70T-5	1.50	0.90	0.30†	0.20	0.30	0.08	- -
E70T-6	1.50	0.90	0.80	0.20	0.30	0.08	- -
E70T-G	No chemical requirements						

* Chemical composition requirements are based on the analysis of deposited weld metal.
† These elements may be present, but are not intentionally added.

ably in appearance, can be assumed to be approximately the same.

As a group, the self-shielded flux-cored electrodes are practically immune to moisture pickup. No special storage facilities under normal usage are required — a factor that is especially important in field welding where jobsite control of the moisture content is a difficult task with low-hydrogen stick electrodes. Welds produced in the field with flux-cored electrode wire taken directly from the shipping carton are as low or lower in hydrogen as those produced with carefully stored low-hydrogen electrodes. If the electrode wire is rusty, however, the result is the same as if it had picked up moisture, and excessive spatter and weld porosity can occur. In addition, wire feeding becomes difficult and contact tips wear rapidly.

EQUIPMENT FOR FLUX-CORED ELECTRODE WELDING

The equipment required for self-shielded flux-cored arc welding consists of a power source, a wire-feeder mechanism, and a welding gun. See Figs. 4-13, 4-14, and 4-15 in Chapter 4.

Constant-voltage DC power sources — either transformer-rectifiers (Fig. 12-4) or generators — are used. The transformer-rectifier is preferably of the flat-slope type; the DC generator can be either electric-motor-driven or engine driven.

Fig. 12-5. Wire-feeder mechanism mounted on power source.

Fig. 12-4. A constant-voltage transformer-rectifier DC power source.

The wire feeder (Figs. 4-14 and 12-5) may be located either at a distance from the arc, as in semiautomatic welding, or just above the nozzle, as in full-automatic welding. In semiautomatic welding, by the use of a wire-feed extension (Fig. 4-14b), the feeder may be as much as 45 feet ahead of the coil of electrode and 15 feet behind the welding gun. In this arrangement, the feeder pulls electrode from the coil and pushes it another 15 feet to the gun. In standard operations, electrode is pushed to the semiautomatic gun and pulled to the full-automatic welding head. The wire-feed motor and rolls in a typical full-automatic head are directly above the nozzle, and the electrode is pulled from a reel that rides on the travel carriage with the welding head.

Welding guns for semiautomatic work (Fig. 4-15) are light and maneuverable to facilitate sustained high-speed work. They should be equipped with a small guide tip for reaching into deep grooves. Guns are made in light, medium, and heavy-duty models, with different ampere ratings and to accommodate different electrode diameters. Electrical contact is made within the nozzle of the gun, and the electrode is electrically "cold" until the trigger is pressed. A shield protects the operator's hand from excessive heat and sparks on medium and heavy-duty guns.

Nozzles for full-automatic self-shielded arc welding are also available in light, medium, and heavy-duty types, with optional water-cooling attachments for heavy work.

The procedures for self-shielded flux-cored arc welding specify electrical stickout along with electrode type and diameter and current and voltage ranges. Thus, the procedures for a typical 1/8-in. E70T-4 electrode wire may prescribe a current range of 325 to 600 amp at 28 to 35 volts with a 2-3/4-in. electrical stickout, or a current range of 400 to 600 amp at 34 to 37 volts with 3-3/4-in. electrical stickout. Amount of electrical stickout must, therefore, be selected in advance of the welding, along with the type and size of electrode.

A long electrical stickout (Fig. 12-6; also see Chapter 11) — the distance from the arc to the

point of electrical contact — increases deposition rate by preheating the wire before it is melted at the arc. Effects on welding costs can be significant; deposition rates can increase by as much as 50%. With the various flux-cored electrodes, the electrical stickouts prescribed in procedures range from 3/4 to 3-3/4 in. Use of the 3-3/4-in. stickout is generally limited to 5/16-in. and larger leg-size flat fillets, multiple-pass flat fillets, and flat deep-groove butt welds.

The specified electrical stickouts are obtained by using the proper guide tip and visible stickout on the welding gun. Thus, a medium-length guide tip and a 1-3/8-in. visible stickout provide a 2-3/4-in. electrical stickout, and a long (3-3/8-in.) guide tip and a 1-3/8-in. visible stickout provide a 3-3/4-in. stickout. When changing from a medium guide tip to a long guide tip for a 3-3/4-in. stickout with E70T-4 electrode, the voltage must be increased two to three volts to obtain a good flat bead, along with an increase in the current setting, which increases the wire-feed speed. The need for increases in current and voltage is shown by the higher ranges specified in the procedures.

A guide tip is not usually used with fill-freeze and fast-freeze electrodes, and electrical stickout is limited. The normal stickout with these electrodes is 3/4 to 1 in., although sound welds can be made with the fill-freeze types with stickouts from 5/8 to 1-1/2 in. The longer stickouts are used for making horizontal butt welds and for handling poor fitup.

SEMIAUTOMATIC WELDING TECHNIQUES

In semiautomatic welding with the self-shielded flux-cored electrode, the control settings should be within the range specified by procedures and adjusted according to past experience with the specific joint. Drive rolls and wire guide tubes should be correct for the wire size, and drive-roll pressure should be adjusted according to the manufacturer's instruction. The wire feeder and power source should be set for constant-voltage output. The gun, cable, and nozzle contact tip should be correct for the wire size and for the stickout.

Starting the Arc: To start the arc, the electrode is "inched" out beyond the nozzle to the visible stickout recommended for the electrode size and guide tip. The tip of the electrode is positioned just off, or lightly touching, the work, and the trigger is pressed to start the arc. The electrode should not be pushed into the joint as it burns away, as in stick-electrode welding, since the mechanical feed will take care of advancing the electrode. Welding is stopped by releasing the trigger or quickly pulling the gun from the work. The instruction manual

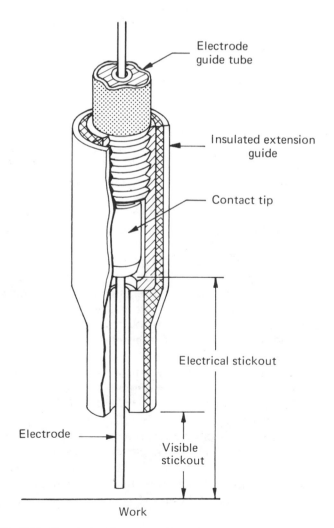

Fig. 12-6. Electrical stickout is the length of electrode wire between the point of electrical contact in a gun or welding head and the arc.

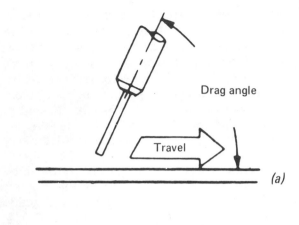

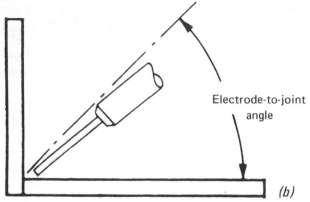

Fig. 12-7. The drag angle (a) and the electrode-to-joint angle (b) are variables that affect performance and weld appearance.

with the specific wire feeder usually gives specific recommendations on setting feed speed and open-circuit voltage to facilitate starting.

When a long electrical stickout is to be used, it is best to start with a visible stickout of about 1/2 in., and increase the visible stickout to the specified amount after the arc has been established.

Accommodating Poor Fitup: One of the advantages of flux-cored electrode welding is the ability to handle poor fitup. With a fast-fill electrode, poor fitup can be accommodated by increasing the visible stickout to as much as 3 in. Pulling the gun away from the work to increase the visible stickout reduces the current, and thus the penetration, and helps to avoid burnthrough. After a poor fitup area has been traversed, normal stickout should be used for the remainder of the joint. This method of controlling penetration should be used only with the short guide tip.

With the fill-freeze electrodes, poor fitup can be handled by reducing the welding current to the minimum value specified in the procedures. Increasing the stickout to 1-1/2 in. also helps to reduce penetration and burnthrough.

Removing Slag: Slag removal is easy in most self-shielded flux-cored electrode welding. In heavy

fast-fill work, the slag often curls up and peels off behind the welding gun. Otherwise, a light scrape with a chipping hammer or wire brush is usually all that is needed to dislodge the slag.

Slag is occasionally trapped on 90° vertical welds or in a downhand convex bead. Entrapment can be avoided by proper bead location and drag angle and by using a smooth, even travel speed to insure good bead shape.

Electrode Position: The drag angle is the angle between the electrode center line and the seam center line in the direction of travel, as illustrated in Fig. 12-7(a). The desired drag angle is approximately the same as in stick-electrode welding. If slag tends to run ahead of the arc, the drag angle should be decreased.

For best bead shape on most 5/16-in. and larger horizontal fillets, the electrode should point at the bottom plate, as illustrated in Fig. 12-7(b), and the angle between the electrode and bottom plate should be less than 45°. With this arrangement, the molten metal washes up onto the vertical plate. Pointing the electrode directly into the joint and using a 45 to 55° angle will decrease root-porosity problems, if they occur, but may produce spatter and a convex bead.

For 1/4-in. and smaller fillets the wire should be pointed directly into the joint and the electrode angle held at about 40°.

When a flow-freeze electrode is used on sheet or thin plate, arc striking is best accomplished by starting with a 1/2-in. visible stickout and increasing it slowly to 1 in. Welding should be done with a stringer bead technique in all positions, with a steady travel speed. A steady speed is important; hesitation is likely to cause burnthrough, with metal sag developing on the underside of the joint and porosity in the weld.

Fitup with light material should be tight, although a small gap on 12-gage to 3/16-in. steel can be handled by reducing the current and voltage about 10%. A steady whip or weave may help, but these motions should not be overdone.

The light slag on thin-gage material adheres tightly, but does not have to be removed. A wipe with a weak acid solution before painting will neutralize the weld area and remove smoke deposits.

For out-of-position welding with E70T-G electrode, best results are obtained by positioning the work downhill or vertical-down. Stringer beads should be used, with the current settings in the middle to high portion of the range. The gun should be tipped in the direction of travel so that the arc force helps hold the molten metal in the joint.

In vertical-up and overhead welding with fill-freeze electrodes, low-hydrogen techniques, as

Butt Welds, Including Pipe First Two Passes with Stick Electrode

1. Make a distinct hesitation at the outer edges of bevel.

2. Minimize each upward step. Do not step up at the edges; come straight out from the hesitation point, and move up across the weld.

Fillet and Lap Welds 5/16-in. and Larger

1. FIRST PASS: Use a triangular weave with a hesitation at the outer edges.

2. SECOND PASS: Use a side-to-side weave similar to that used for butt welds. The previous bead should have a face width of 5/16 to 3/8-in. before weave is started.

3. Make welds smaller than 5/16-in. with vertical-down techniques.

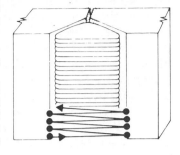
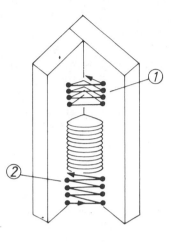

Fig. 12-8. Techniques for vertical-up and overhead welding with E70T-G electrodes.

opposed to E6010 techniques, should be used. Whipping, breaking the arc, moving out of the puddle, or moving too fast in any direction should be avoided. Currents should be in the low portion of the range. Fig. 12-8 shows general techniques for vertical-up and overhead work.

OPERATING VARIABLES WITH FLUX-CORED ELECTRODES

Four major variables affect welding performance with flux-cored electrodes: arc voltage, current, travel speed, and electrical stickout. These variables are interdependent, and, if one is changed, one or more of the other three usually require adjustment.

Arc voltage variations, with current, travel speed, and electrical stickout held constant, produce these effects:

1. A high arc voltage produces a wider and flatter bead.

2. An excessive arc voltage may produce a porous weld.

3. A low voltage tends to cause a convex, ropey bead.

4. Extremely low voltage may produce a tendency for the wire to stub on the plate. The wire may dive through the molten metal and strike the joint bottom, pushing the gun up.

In most applications, a good bead shape is obtained by using the highest voltage possible without causing porosity. With higher currents, higher voltages can be used without causing porosity.

Current variations, when arc voltage, travel speed, and electrical stickout are held constant, have the following effects:

1. Increasing current increases melt-off and deposition rates.

2. Excessive current produces convex beads, resulting in poor appearance and wasted weld metal.

3. Too low current gives a droplet transfer, with reduced penetration.

As current is increased, arc voltage must also be increased to maintain good bead shape. Increased current also increases the maximum voltage that can be used without porosity occurring.

Travel speed, assuming the other variables are held constant, can have the following effects:

1. Excessive travel speed increases the convexity of the bead and causes uneven edges.

2. Too slow a travel speed results in slag interference and inclusions and a rough, uneven bead.

Travel speed is always faster with self-shielded flux-cored electrodes than with stick electrodes — to accommodate the higher deposition rates. The beginning operator with the semiautomatic process will tend to move to slow because of his experience with stick-electrode welding. As in all other welding processes, travel speed should be that necessary to handle the molten metal and slag and produce the desired weld size.

Uniformity in travel speed is important. It is accomplished by maintaining a unifrom distance between the wire and the molten slag behind the wire.

Electrical stickout variations, with the other variables held constant, have the following effects:

1. Increasing the stickout decreases the welding current and vice versa.

2. Increasing the stickout lowers the actual voltage across the arc. Lower arc voltage increases the convexity of the bead and reduces the tendency for porosity.

3. Short stickout gives greater penetration than long stickout.

FULL-AUTOMATIC OPERATING TECHNIQUES

The self-shielded flux-cored electrode process is used in high-production industries with full-automatic equipment where it provides special production economies. The student or beginning weldor cannot expect to have opportunities for practice or work with such specialized equipment. However, should the student find himself in a position where knowledge of full-automatic operational techniques with the self-shielded flux-cored electrode would be helpful, reference to the Lincoln *Procedure Handbook of Arc Welding,* Section 6.4, is recommended.

ADVANTAGES OF THE PROCESS

Some of the advantages of the self-shielded flux-cored electrode process have already been mentioned. However, the impact of a mechanized, all-position, manually maneuvered arc-welding process on weldment production and structural steel fabrication and erection is not always obvious and merits further discussion.

Since the semiautomatic process can be used any place stick-electrode can be used, it makes possible one-process welding in the erection of structural steel in building framing. As proved on major

Fig. 12-9. Before all-position electrodes for self-shielded flux-cored arc welding were developed, beam web-to-column connections in building erection were made with stick electrodes. If the flange-to-column joints were made with semiautomatic equipment, the operator had to change to the stick electrode for the vertical joint, or the connection had to be made by bolting the web to an angle welded to the column. The all-position electrode wires were the development that made possible one-process mechanized welding in building erection, with all of its incidental benefits in the scheduling of erection operations.

highrise projects, this factor is possibly as important as the higher deposition rates of semiautomatic welding in reducing erection costs. One process substantially reduces the amount of equipment needed on the job and allows every welding operator to be qualified for every joint. This, in turn, permits the more systematic deployment of men, equipment, and materials and reduces delays and minimizes equipment handling. One-process welding — from tack welding to column-splice and beam-to-column welding — gives erectors the opportunity to take a "systems approach" to erection logistics, with the result that cost savings above those attributable to the speed of the semiautomatic process are realizable.

Fig. 12-9 shows the welding of a beam web-to-column connection in the erection of a major highrise building. When this weld was made possible by the development of an all-position electrode, one-process mechanized erection welding became feasible.

The tolerance of the semiautomatic process to poor fitup is also a decisive benefit to steel fabricators. Although every reasonable effort should be made to guard against poor fitup, its avoidance is economically impractical with some weldments, especially those made from heavy material and pieces of complex configuration where appearance or perfection in detail has little or no value in the end product. In manufacturing where fitup has been a major problem, use of semiautomatic self-shielded flux-cored arc welding has reduced rework and repair without affecting final product quality. This factor has been of cost-saving value as important to the company as the cost savings resulting from the increased welding speeds when changing from manual shielded metal-arc welding. The tolerance of the semiautomatic process to poor fitup has expanded the use of tubular steel members in structures by making possible sound connections where perfect fitup would be extremely difficult or too costly to achieve.

The advantages of the self-shielded flux-cored arc-welding process may be summarized as follows:

1. When compared with stick-electrode welding, gives deposition rates up to four times as great, often decreasing welding costs by as much as 50 to 70%.

2. Eliminates the need for flux-handling and recovery equipment, as in submerged-arc welding, or for gas and gas storage, piping, and metering equipment, as in gas-shielded mechanized welding. The semiautomatic process is applicable where other mechanized processes would be too unwieldy.

3. Has tolerance for elements in steel that normal-

ly cause weld cracking when stick-electrode or one of the other mechanized welding processes are used. Produces crack-free welds in medium-carbon steel, using normal welding procedures.

4. Under normal conditions, eliminates the problems of moisture pickup and storage that occur with low-hydrogen electrodes.

5. Eliminates stub losses and the time that would be required for changing electrodes with the stick-electrode process.

6. Eliminates the need for wind shelters required with gas-shielded welding in field erection; permits fans and fast air-flow ventilation systems to be used for worker comfort in the shop.

7. Enables "one-process," and even "one-process, one-electrode," operation in some shop and field applications. This, in turn, simplifies operator training, qualification, and supervision; equipment selection and maintenance; and the logistics of applying men, materials, and equipment to the job efficiently.

8. Enables the application of the long-stickout principle to enhance deposition rates, while allowing easy operator control of penetration.

9. Permits more seams to be welded in one pass, saving welding time and the time that otherwise would be consumed in between-pass cleaning.

10. Is adaptable to a variety of products; permits continuous operation at one welding station, even though a variety of assemblies with widely different joint requirements are run through it.

11. Provides the fast filling of gouged-out voids often required when making repairs to weldments or steel castings.

12. Gives the speed of mechanized welding in close quarters; reaches into spots inaccessible by other semiautomatic processes.

13. Provides mechanized welding where mechanized welding was formerly impossible, such as in the joining of a beam web to a column in building erection (Fig. 12-9).

14. Enables the bridging of gaps in fitup by operator control of the penetration without reducing quality of the weld. Minimizes repair, rework, and rejects.

SEMIAUTOMATIC PROCEDURES WITH THE SELF-SHIELDED FLUX-CORED PROCESS

Procedures for the semiautomatic welding of carbon and low-alloy steels by the self-shielded flux-cored electrode process are given on the following pages. For definition of terms and other general information about welding procedures, the student should refer to Chapter 9.

FLUX-CORED ARC WELDING (SEMIAUTOMATIC) SELF-SHIELDED

Welding Position: Flat
Weld Quality Level: Commercial
Steel Weldability: Good or fair

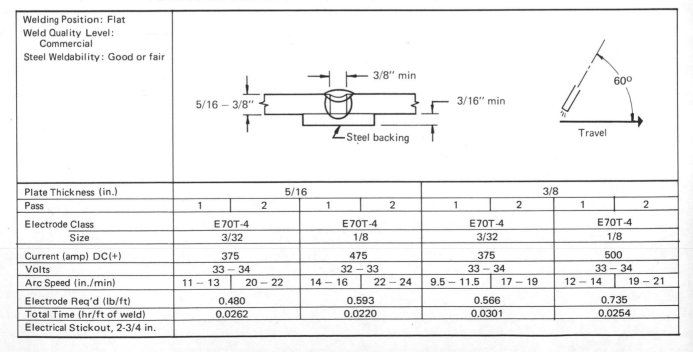

Plate Thickness (in.)	0.135 (10 ga)	3/16	1/4
Pass	1	1	1
Electrode Class	E70T-4	E70T-4	E70T-4
Size	3/32	3/32	3/32
Current (amp) DC(+)	350	400	400
Volts	29 − 30	30 − 31	30 − 31
Arc Speed (in./min.)	21 − 23	16 − 18	12.5 − 13.5
Electrode Req'd (lb/ft)	0.16	0.24	0.32
Total Time (hr/ft of weld)	0.00909	0.0118	0.0154
Backing, minimum thickness (in.)	10 ga	3/16	3/16
Gap (in.)	5/32	3/16	7/32
Electrical Stickout, 2-3/4 in.			

FLUX-CORED ARC WELDING (SEMIAUTOMATIC) SELF-SHIELDED

Welding Position: Flat
Weld Quality Level: Commercial
Steel Weldability: Good or fair

Plate Thickness (in.)	5/16				3/8			
Pass	1	2	1	2	1	2	1	2
Electrode Class	E70T-4		E70T-4		E70T-4		E70T-4	
Size	3/32		1/8		3/32		1/8	
Current (amp) DC(+)	375		475		375		500	
Volts	33 − 34		32 − 33		33 − 34		33 − 34	
Arc Speed (in./min)	11 − 13	20 − 22	14 − 16	22 − 24	9.5 − 11.5	17 − 19	12 − 14	19 − 21
Electrode Req'd (lb/ft)	0.480		0.593		0.566		0.735	
Total Time (hr/ft of weld)	0.0262		0.0220		0.0301		0.0254	
Electrical Stickout, 2-3/4 in.								

FLUX-CORED ARC WELDING (SEMIAUTOMATIC) SELF-SHIELDED

Welding Position: Flat
Weld Quality Level: Commercial
Steel Weldability: Good or fair

Plate Thickness (in.)	1/2	5/8	3/4	1
Pass	1 – 3	1 – 4	1 – 6	1 – 8
Electrode Class	E70T-4	E70T-4	E70T-4	E70T-4
Size	3/32	3/32	3/32	3/32
Current (amp) DC(+)	350	350	350	350
Volts	30 – 31	30 – 31	30 – 31	30 – 31
Arc Speed (in./min)	11.5 – 13.5	11.0 – 13.0	12.5 – 14.5	11.0 – 13.0
Electrode Req'd (lb/ft)	0.830	1.16	1.53	2.29
Total Time (hr/ft of weld)	0.0480	0.0668	0.0888	0.134
Electrical Stickout, 2-3/4 in.				

FLUX-CORED ARC WELDING (SEMIAUTOMATIC) SELF-SHIELDED

Welding Position: Flat
Weld Quality Level:
   Commercial
Steel Weldability:
   Good or fair

Plate Thickness (in.)	1/2	5/8	3/4	1	
Pass	1 – 3	1 – 4	1 – 5	1	2 – 6*
Electrode Class	E70T-4	E70T-4	E70T-4	E70T-4	E70T-4
Size	1/8	1/8	1/8	1/8	1/8
Current (amp) DC(+)	500	500	500	500	550
Volts	31 – 32	31 – 32	31 – 32	31 – 32	35 – 36
Arc Speed (in./min)	13.5 – 16.5	13.5 – 15.5	13.0 – 15.0	14.5 – 17.5	14.5 – 17.5
Electrode Req'd (lb/ft)	1.14	1.56	2.02	3.03	
Total Time (hr/ft of weld)	0.0400	0.0552	0.0715	0.0750	
Electrical Stickout (in.)	2-3/4	2-3/4	2-3/4	2-3/4	3-3/4

* Change to 3-3/4 in. stickout after first pass.

FLUX-CORED ARC WELDING (SEMIAUTOMATIC) SELF-SHIELDED

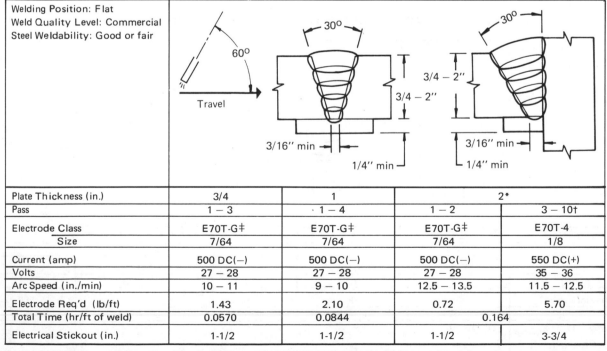

Welding Position: Flat
Weld Quality Level: Commercial
Steel Weldability: Good or fair
Welded from: One side

Plate Thickness (in.)	1/2		5/8		
Pass	1	2	1	2	3
Electrode Class *	E70T-G		E70T-G		
Size	7/64		7/64		
Current (amp) DC(−)	425		450		
Volts	25 − 26		26 − 27		
Arc Speed (in./min)	12 − 13	8 − 9	13 − 14	12 − 13	11 − 12
Electrode Req'd (lb/ft)	0.75		1.00		
Total Time (hr/ft of weld)	0.0395		0.0482		
Electrical Stickout, 1-1/2 in.					

* A fast-follow type E70T-G with penetration capability. See introductory notes.
This joint is similar to some of the prequalified joints in the AWS Structural Codes.

FLUX-CORED ARC WELDING (SEMIAUTOMATIC) SELF-SHIELDED

Welding Position: Flat
Weld Quality Level: Commercial
Steel Weldability: Good or fair

Plate Thickness (in.)	3/4	1	2*	
Pass	1 − 3	1 − 4	1 − 2	3 − 10†
Electrode Class	E70T-G‡	E70T-G‡	E70T-G‡	E70T-4
Size	7/64	7/64	7/64	1/8
Current (amp)	500 DC(−)	500 DC(−)	500 DC(−)	550 DC(+)
Volts	27 − 28	27 − 28	27 − 28	35 − 36
Arc Speed (in./min)	10 − 11	9 − 10	12.5 − 13.5	11.5 − 12.5
Electrode Req'd (lb/ft)	1.43	2.10	0.72	5.70
Total Time (hr/ft of weld)	0.0570	0.0844	0.164	
Electrical Stickout (in.)	1-1/2	1-1/2	1-1/2	3-3/4

* Typical two electrode procedure. Can be finished with 7/64 E70T-G but with an increase in total arc time.

† Layers should be split when the previous bead face is 3/4-in. wide. This occurs after pass 4.

‡ A fast-follow type E70T-G with penetration capability. See introductory notes.

This joint is similar to some of the prequalified joints in the AWS Structural Codes.

FLUX-CORED ARC WELDING (SEMIAUTOMATIC) SELF-SHIELDED

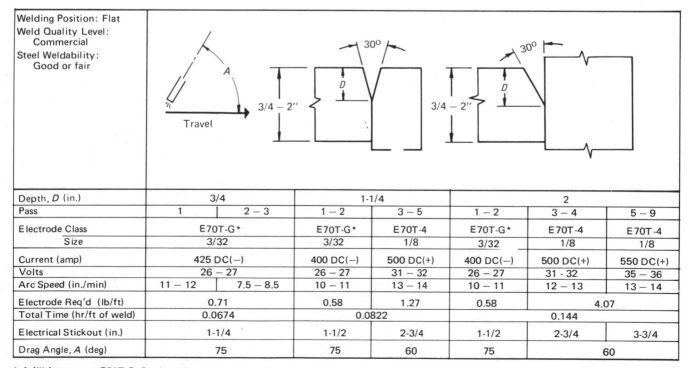

Weld Position: Flat
Weld Quality Level: Commercial
Steel Weldability: Good or fair
Welded from: One side

Plate Thickness (in.)	1-1/2			
Pass	1	2 – 14	1	2 – 8*
Electrode Class	E70T-4	E70T-4	E70T-4	E70T-4
Size	3/32	3/32	1/8	1/8
Current (amp) DC(+)	350	350	500	550
Volts	30 – 31	30 – 31	31 – 32	35 – 36
Arc Speed (in./min)	7.0 – 8.5	11.0 – 13.5	11.0 – 13.0	13.0 – 16.0
Electrode Req'd (lb/ft)	4.48		4.59	
Total Time (hr/ft of weld)	0.239		0.114	
Electrical Stickout, 2-3/4 in.				

* Change to 3-3/4 in. stickout after first pass.

FLUX-CORED ARC WELDING (SEMIAUTOMATIC) SELF-SHIELDED

Welding Position: Flat
Weld Quality Level: Commercial
Steel Weldability: Good or fair

Depth, D (in.)	3/4		1-1/4		2		
Pass	1	2 – 3	1 – 2	3 – 5	1 – 2	3 – 4	5 – 9
Electrode Class	E70T-G*		E70T-G*	E70T-4	E70T-G*	E70T-4	E70T-4
Size	3/32		3/32	1/8	3/32	1/8	1/8
Current (amp)	425 DC(–)		400 DC(–)	500 DC(+)	400 DC(–)	500 DC(+)	550 DC(+)
Volts	26 – 27		26 – 27	31 – 32	26 – 27	31 - 32	35 – 36
Arc Speed (in./min)	11 – 12	7.5 – 8.5	10 – 11	13 – 14	10 – 11	12 – 13	13 – 14
Electrode Req'd (lb/ft)	0.71		0.58	1.27	0.58	4.07	
Total Time (hr/ft of weld)	0.0674		0.0822		0.144		
Electrical Stickout (in.)	1-1/4		1-1/2	2-3/4	1-1/2	2-3/4	3-3/4
Drag Angle, A (deg)	75		75	60	75	60	

* A fill-freeze type E70T-G. See introductory notes.
This joint is similar to some of the prequalified joints in the AWS Structural Codes.

FLUX-CORED ARC WELDING (SEMIAUTOMATIC) SELF-SHIELDED

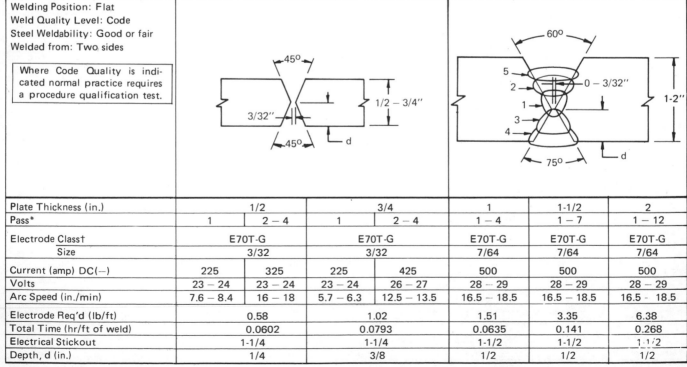

Welding Position: Flat
Weld Quality Level: Commercial
Steel Weldability: Good or fair
Welded from: Two sides

Plate Thickness (in.)	1/4	5/16		3/8		1/2
Pass	1,2	1,2	1,2	1,2	1,2	1,2
Electrode Class	E70T-4	E70T-4	E70T-4	E70T-4	E70T-4	E70T-4
Size	3/32	3/32	1/8	3/32	1/8	1/8
Current (amp) DC(+)	350	350	500	350	500	500
Volts	30 − 31	30 − 31	31 − 32	30 − 31	31 − 32	31 − 32
Arc Speed (in./min)	19 − 22	14 − 16	23 − 27	11 − 13	19 − 22	13 − 15
Electrode Req'd (lb/ft)	0.338	0.480	0.490	0.595	0.613	0.912
Total Time (hr/ft of weld)*	0.0195	0.0266	0.0160	0.0334	0.0195	0.0286
Depth, A minimum (in.)	1/8	5/32	5/32	3/16	3/16	1/4
Width, W minimum (in.)	5/16	3/8	3/8	7/16	7/16	1/2
Electrical Stickout, 2-3/4 in.						

*Gouging time not included.

FLUX-CORED ARC WELDING (SEMIAUTOMATIC) SELF-SHIELDED

Welding Position: Flat
Weld Quality Level: Code
Steel Weldability: Good or fair
Welded from: Two sides

Where Code Quality is indicated normal practice requires a procedure qualification test.

Plate Thickness (in.)	1/2		3/4		1	1-1/2	2
Pass*	1	2 − 4	1	2 − 4	1 − 4	1 − 7	1 − 12
Electrode Class†	E70T-G		E70T-G		E70T-G	E70T-G	E70T-G
Size	3/32		3/32		7/64	7/64	7/64
Current (amp) DC(−)	225	325	225	425	500	500	500
Volts	23 − 24	23 − 24	23 − 24	26 − 27	28 − 29	28 − 29	28 − 29
Arc Speed (in./min)	7.6 − 8.4	16 − 18	5.7 − 6.3	12.5 − 13.5	16.5 − 18.5	16.5 − 18.5	16.5 - 18.5
Electrode Req'd (lb/ft)	0.58		1.02		1.51	3.35	6.38
Total Time (hr/ft of weld)	0.0602		0.0793		0.0635	0.141	0.268
Electrical Stickout	1-1/4		1-1/4		1-1/2	1-1/2	1-1/2
Depth, d (in.)	1/4		3/8		1/2	1/2	1/2

* Layers are split when bead face width exceeds 3/4 in.

† A fast-follow type E70T-G with penetration capabilities. See introductory notes.

FLUX-CORED ARC WELDING (SEMIAUTOMATIC) SELF-SHIELDED

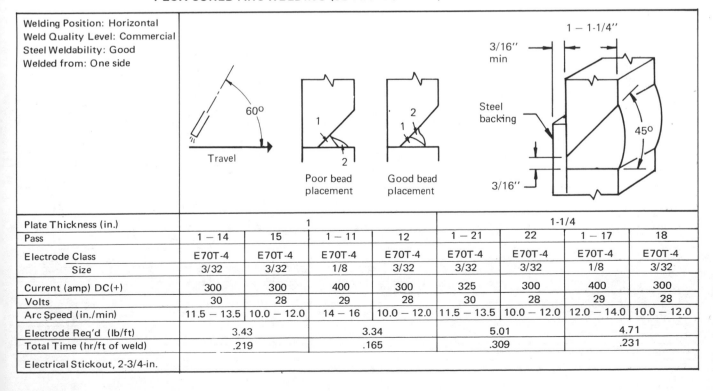

Welding Position: Horizontal
Weld Quality Level: Commercial
Steel Weldability: Good
Welded from: One side

Plate Thickness (in.)	3/8		1/2		3/4			
Pass	1 — 3	4	1 — 4	5	1 — 9	10	1 — 7	8
Electrode Class	E70T-4	E70T-4	E70T-4	E70T-4	E70T-4	E70T-4	E70T-4	E70T-4
Size	3/32	3/32	3/32	3/32	3/32	3/32	1/8	3/32
Current (amp) DC(+)	300	250	300	250	300	250	400	250
Volts	28	25	28	26	28	26	28	26
Arc Speed (in./min)	12.5-14.5	12.5-14.5	11.0-13.0	10.0-12.0	12.0-14.0	10.0-12.0	12.5-14.5	10.0-12.0
Electrode Req'd (lb/ft)	0.746		1.11		2.11		2.39	
Total Time (hr/ft of weld)	0.0592		0.0840		0.157		0.122	
Drag angle, *A* (deg)	60		60		60		60	
Electrical Stickout, 2-3/4 in.								

FLUX-CORED ARC WELDING (SEMIAUTOMATIC) SELF-SHIELDED

Welding Position: Horizontal
Weld Quality Level: Commercial
Steel Weldability: Good
Welded from: One side

Plate Thickness (in.)	1				1-1/4			
Pass	1 — 14	15	1 — 11	12	1 — 21	22	1 — 17	18
Electrode Class	E70T-4	E70T-4	E70T-4	E70T-4	E70T-4	E70T-4	E70T-4	E70T-4
Size	3/32	3/32	1/8	3/32	3/32	3/32	1/8	3/32
Current (amp) DC(+)	300	300	400	300	325	300	400	300
Volts	30	28	29	28	30	28	29	28
Arc Speed (in./min)	11.5 — 13.5	10.0 — 12.0	14 — 16	10.0 — 12.0	11.5 — 13.5	10.0 — 12.0	12.0 — 14.0	10.0 — 12.0
Electrode Req'd (lb/ft)	3.43		3.34		5.01		4.71	
Total Time (hr/ft of weld)	.219		.165		.309		.231	
Electrical Stickout, 2-3/4-in.								

FLUX-CORED ARC WELDING (SEMIAUTOMATIC) SELF-SHIELDED

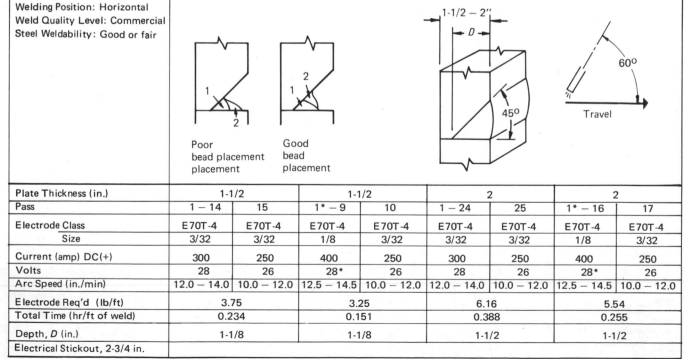

Welding Position: Horizontal
Weld Quality Level: Commercial
Steel Weldability: Good or fair
Welded from: One side

3/32 electrode   1/8" electrode

1"
3/4"
60°
Travel
45°

Plate Thickness (in.)	1				1			
Pass	1	2 − 3	4 − 6	7	1*	2	3 − 4	5**
Electrode Class	E70T-4	E70T-4	E70T-4	E70T-4	E70T-4	E70T-4	E70T-4	E70T-4
Size	3/32	3/32	3/32	3/32	1/8	1/8	1/8	3/32**
Current (amp) DC(+)	325	325	325	275	400	400	400	275
Volts	28	28	28	26	28*	28	28	26
Arc Speed (in./min)	11.0 − 13.0	12.5 - 14.5	13.0 − 15.0	10.0 − 12.0	11.5 − 13.5	13.5 − 16.5	13.0 − 15.0	10.0 − 12.0
Electrode Req'd (lb/ft)	1.44				1.56			
Total Time (hr/ft of weld)	0.108				0.0762			
Electrical Stickout, 2-3/4 in.								

* With tight fitup use 30-32 v or 7/32 in. E7018 stick electrode for the first pass.

** An alternate to changing electrode size is to run the final pass with 3/16 E7018 stick electrode.

FLUX-CORED ARC WELDING (SEMIAUTOMATIC) SELF-SHIELDING

Welding Position: Horizontal
Weld Quality Level: Commercial
Steel Weldability: Good or fair

Poor
bead placement
placement

Good
bead
placement

1-1/2 − 2"
D
60°
Travel
45°

Plate Thickness (in.)	1-1/2		1-1/2		2		2	
Pass	1 − 14	15	1* − 9	10	1 − 24	25	1* − 16	17
Electrode Class	E70T-4	E70T-4	E70T-4	E70T-4	E70T-4	E70T-4	E70T-4	E70T-4
Size	3/32	3/32	1/8	3/32	3/32	3/32	1/8	3/32
Current (amp) DC(+)	300	250	400	250	300	250	400	250
Volts	28	26	28*	26	28	26	28*	26
Arc Speed (in./min)	12.0 − 14.0	10.0 − 12.0	12.5 − 14.5	10.0 − 12.0	12.0 − 14.0	10.0 − 12.0	12.5 − 14.5	10.0 − 12.0
Electrode Req'd (lb/ft)	3.75		3.25		6.16		5.54	
Total Time (hr/ft of weld)	0.234		0.151		0.388		0.255	
Depth, D (in.)	1-1/8		1-1/8		1-1/2		1-1/2	
Electrical Stickout, 2-3/4 in.								

* With tight fitup use 30-32v on the first pass or 7/32 E7018 stick electrode.

FLUX-CORED ARC WELDING (SEMIAUTOMATIC) SELF-SHIELDING

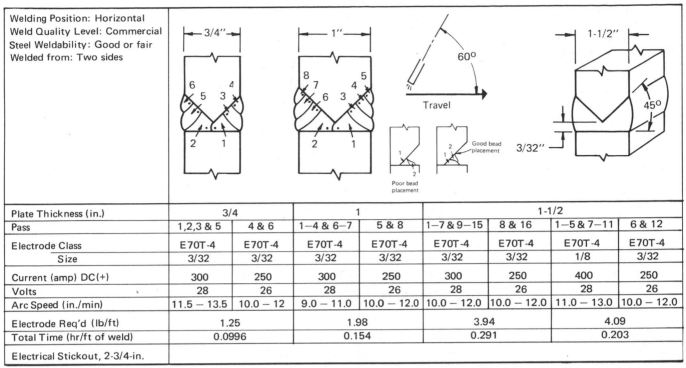

Welding Position: Horizontal
Weld Quality Level: Commercial
Steel Weldability: Good or fair
Welded from: Two sides

Plate Thickness (in.)	3/4		1		1-1/2			
Pass	1,2,3 & 5	4 & 6	1–4 & 6–7	5 & 8	1–7 & 9–15	8 & 16	1–5 & 7–11	6 & 12
Electrode Class	E70T-4	E70T-4	E70T-4	E70T-4	E70T-4	E70T-4	E70T-4	E70T-4
Size	3/32	3/32	3/32	3/32	3/32	3/32	1/8	3/32
Current (amp) DC(+)	300	250	300	250	300	250	400	250
Volts	28	26	28	26	28	26	28	26
Arc Speed (in./min)	11.5 – 13.5	10.0 – 12	9.0 – 11.0	10.0 – 12.0	10.0 – 12.0	10.0 – 12.0	11.0 – 13.0	10.0 – 12.0
Electrode Req'd (lb/ft)	1.25		1.98		3.94		4.09	
Total Time (hr/ft of weld)	0.0996		0.154		0.291		0.203	
Electrical Stickout, 2-3/4-in.								

First pass should be back-gouged or ground. Using 5/32 E7018 for the first pass reduces the amount of gouging required.

FLUX-CORED ARC WELDING (SEMIAUTOMATIC) SELF-SHIELDED

Welding Position: Horizontal
Weld Quality Level: Code
Steel Weldability: Good or fair
Welded from: Two sides

> Where Code Quality is indicated normal practice requires a procedure qualification test.

Back weld
3/32 – 1/8″
0 – 1/16″
60°

Plate Thickness (in.)	All	3/8	1/2		3/4	
Pass	1	2 – 4	2 – 3	4 – 6	2 – 6	7 – 9
Electrode Class	E60T-7	E60T-7	E60T-7		E60T-7	
Size	5/64	5/64	5/64		5/64	
Current (amp) DC(–)	175	175	250	185	250	185
Volts	18 – 19	18 – 19	19 – 20	18 – 19	19 – 20	18 – 19
Arc Speed (in./min)	5.0 – 5.5	5.1 – 5.6	6.4 – 7.1	5.4 – 6.0	4.9 – 5.4	4.0 – 4.4
Electrode Req'd (lb/ft) *		0.53	0.88		1.83	
Total Time (hr/ft of weld) *		0.150	0.203		0.375	
Electrical Stickout, 7/8 in.						

* Does not include electrode or time to gouge and weld the back weld.

  Back weld may be made by stick electrode or semiautomatic welding.

FLUX-CORED ARC WELDING (SEMIAUTOMATIC) SELF-SHIELDED

Welding Position: Horizontal
Weld Quality Level: Code
Steel Weldability: Good or fair
Welded from: Two sides

Where Code Quality is indicated normal practice requires a procedure qualification test.

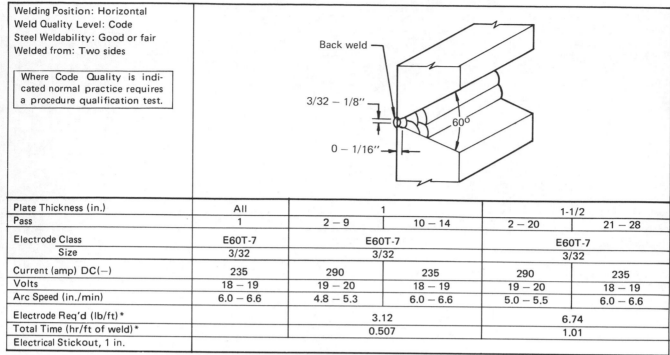

Plate Thickness (in.)	All	1		1-1/2	
Pass	1	2 – 9	10 – 14	2 – 20	21 – 28
Electrode Class	E60T-7	E60T-7		E60T-7	
Size	3/32	3/32		3/32	
Current (amp) DC(−)	235	290	235	290	235
Volts	18 – 19	19 – 20	18 – 19	19 – 20	18 – 19
Arc Speed (in./min)	6.0 – 6.6	4.8 – 5.3	6.0 – 6.6	5.0 – 5.5	6.0 – 6.6
Electrode Req'd (lb/ft)*		3.12		6.74	
Total Time (hr/ft of weld)*		0.507		1.01	
Electrical Stickout, 1 in.					

* Does not include electrode or time to gouge and weld the back weld.
  Back weld may be made by stick electrode or semiautomatic welding.

FLUX-CORED ARC WELDING (SEMIAUTOMATIC) SELF-SHIELDED

Welding Position: Vertical
Weld Quality Level: Commercial
Steel Weldability: Good or fair
Welded from: One side

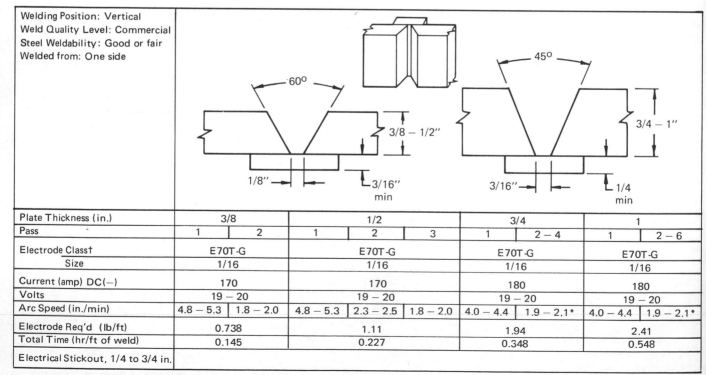

Plate Thickness (in.)	3/8		1/2			3/4		1	
Pass	1	2	1	2	3	1	2 – 4	1	2 – 6
Electrode Class†	E70T-G		E70T-G			E70T-G		E70T-G	
Size	1/16		1/16			1/16		1/16	
Current (amp) DC(−)	170		170			180		180	
Volts	19 – 20		19 – 20			19 – 20		19 – 20	
Arc Speed (in./min)	4.8 – 5.3	1.8 – 2.0	4.8 – 5.3	2.3 – 2.5	1.8 – 2.0	4.0 – 4.4	1.9 – 2.1*	4.0 – 4.4	1.9 – 2.1*
Electrode Req'd (lb/ft)	0.738		1.11			1.94		2.41	
Total Time (hr/ft of weld)	0.145		0.227			0.348		0.548	
Electrical Stickout, 1/4 to 3/4 in.									

* Average speed for all passes after first.

† A fast-freeze type E70T-G. See introductory notes.

FLUX-CORED ARC WELDING (SEMIAUTOMATIC) SELF-SHIELDED

Welding Position: Vertical up
Weld Quality Level: Commercial
Steel Weldability: Good or fair
Welded from: One side

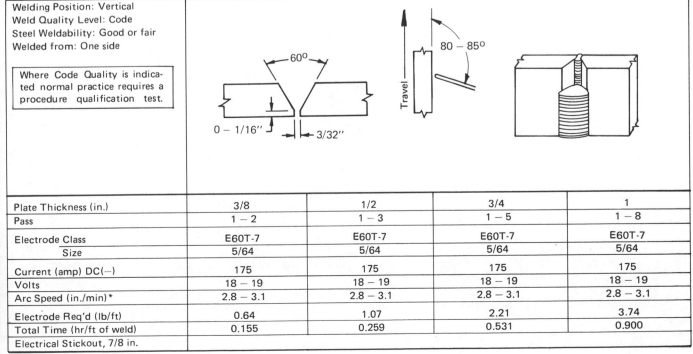

Plate Thickness (in.)	3/8-1/2-5/8	3/8	1/2	5/8	3/4 – 1	3/4		1	
Pass	1	2	2	2	1 & 2	3	4	3	4
Electrode Class	E6010 E6011	E70T-G†	E70T-G†	E70T-G†	E6010 E6011	E70T-G†		E70T-G†	
Size	1/8	1/16	1/16	1/16	1/8	1/16		1/16	
Current (amp) DC	80 (+)	160 (−)	160 (−)	160 (−)	80 (+)	180 (−)		195 (−)	
Volts		19 – 20	19 – 20	19 – 20		20 – 21		20.5 – 21.5	
Arc Speed (in./min)	3.3 – 3.7	2.4 – 2.6	1.3 – 1.4	0.8 – 0.9	3.3 – 3.7	1.5 – 1.7	1.3 – 1.4	1.2 – 1.3	0.7 – 0.8
Electrode Req'd (lb/ft) *	0.227	0.342	0.625	1.02	0.454	1.37		2.49	
Total Time (hr/ft of weld) *	0.0571	0.0800	0.147	0.235	0.114	0.273		0.427	
Electrical Stickout, 1/2-1 in.									

* Add stick electrode to semiautomatic passes.

† A fast-freeze type E70T-G. See introductory notes.

FLUX-CORED ARD WELDING (SEMIAUTOMATIC) SELF-SHIELDED

Welding Position: Vertical
Weld Quality Level: Code
Steel Weldability: Good or fair
Welded from: One side

Where Code Quality is indicated normal practice requires a procedure qualification test.

Plate Thickness (in.)	3/8	1/2	3/4	1
Pass	1 – 2	1 – 3	1 – 5	1 – 8
Electrode Class	E60T-7	E60T-7	E60T-7	E60T-7
Size	5/64	5/64	5/64	5/64
Current (amp) DC (−)	175	175	175	175
Volts	18 – 19	18 – 19	18 – 19	18 – 19
Arc Speed (in./min) *	2.8 – 3.1	2.8 – 3.1	2.8 – 3.1	2.8 – 3.1
Electrode Req'd (lb/ft)	0.64	1.07	2.21	3.74
Total Time (hr/ft of weld)	0.155	0.259	0.531	0.900
Electrical Stickout, 7/8 in.				

* For first pass only. Subsequent full weave passes are slower.

FLUX-CORED ARC WELDING (SEMIAUTOMATIC) SELF-SHIELDED

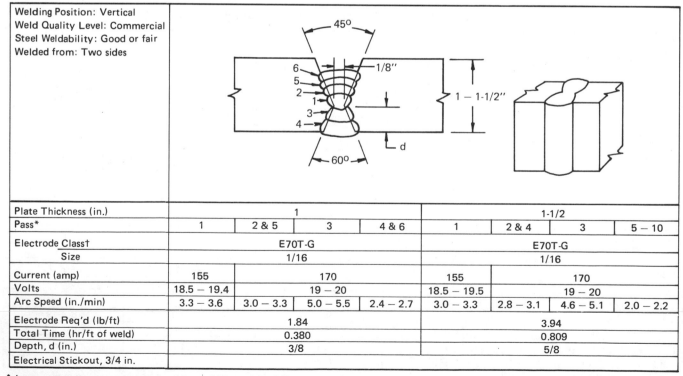

| Welding Position: Vertical up
Weld Quality Level: Commercial
Steel Weldability: Good or fair
Welded from: Two sides | | | | | | | | | |

Plate Thickness (in.)	1/2			5/8			3/4		
Pass	1	2	3	1 – 2	3	4	1	2 & 4	3
Electrode Class*	E70T-G			E70T-G			E70T-G		
Size	1/16			1/16			1/16		
Current (amp) DC(−)	155			155			155		
Volts	18.5 – 19.5			18.5 – 19.5			18.5 – 19.5		
Arc Speed (in./min)	3.6 – 4.0	3.6 – 4.0	2.9 – 3.2	3.4 – 3.8	5.0 – 5.5	3.0 – 3.3	3.0 – 3.3	2.0 – 2.2	4.3 – 4.8
Electrode Req'd (lb/ft)	0.685			0.852			1.21		
Total Time (hr/ft of weld)	0.171			0.213			0.299		
Depth, d (in.)	1/4			5/16			3/8		
Electrical Stickout, 3/4 in.									

* A fast-freeze type E70T-G. See introductory notes.

FLUX-CORED ARC WELDING (SEMIAUTOMATIC) SELF-SHIELDED

| Welding Position: Vertical
Weld Quality Level: Commercial
Steel Weldability: Good or fair
Welded from: Two sides | | | | | | | | |

Plate Thickness (in.)	1				1-1/2			
Pass*	1	2 & 5	3	4 & 6	1	2 & 4	3	5 – 10
Electrode Class†	E70T-G				E70T-G			
Size	1/16				1/16			
Current (amp)	155	170			155	170		
Volts	18.5 – 19.4	19 – 20			18.5 – 19.5	19 – 20		
Arc Speed (in./min)	3.3 – 3.6	3.0 – 3.3	5.0 – 5.5	2.4 – 2.7	3.0 – 3.3	2.8 – 3.1	4.6 – 5.1	2.0 – 2.2
Electrode Req'd (lb/ft)	1.84				3.94			
Total Time (hr/ft of weld)	0.380				0.809			
Depth, d (in.)	3/8				5/8			
Electrical Stickout, 3/4 in.								

* Layers are split when previous bead face width exceeds 5/8 in.

† A fast-freeze type E70T-G. See introductory notes.

FLUX-CORED ARC WELDING (SEMIAUTOMATIC) SELF-SHIELDED

Welding Position: Overhead Weld Quality Level: Commercial Steel Weldability: Good or fair Welded from: two sides

Plate Thickness (in.)	1/2		3/4		1		1-1/2	
Pass	1 – 2	3	1 – 2	3 – 4	1 – 2	3 – 5	1 – 3	4 – 10
Electrode Class	E70T-G*	E70T-G†	E70T-G*	E70T-G†	E70T-G*	E70T-G†	E70T-G*	E70T-G†
Size	1/16	7/64	1/16	7/64	1/16	7/64	1/16	7/64
Current (amp) DC(–)	130	500	140	500	150	500	150	500
Volts	17.5 – 18.5	27 – 28	18 – 19	27 – 28	18.5 – 19.5	27 – 28	18.5 – 19.5	27 – 28
Arc Speed (in./min)	4.5 – 5.0	9.5 – 10.5	4.2 – 4.6	10.5 – 11.5	3.5 – 3.9	9.5 – 10.5	3.9 – 4.4	9.5 – 10.5
Electrode Req'd (lb/ft)	0.29	0.41	0.34	0.76	0.45	1.24	0.60	2.92
Total Time (hr/ft of weld)	0.0842	0.0200	0.0910	0.0364	0.108	0.0600	0.147	0.140
Electrical Stickout (in.)	3/4	1-1/2	3/4	1-1/2	3/4	1-1/2	3/4	1-1/2
Angle, A (deg)	60		45		45		45	
Depth, d (in.)	3/16		1/4		5/16		3/8	

* A fast-freeze type E70T-G.

† A fast-follow type E70T-G with good penetration capability.

See introductory notes.

FLUX-CORED ARC WELDING (SEMIAUTOMATIC) SELF-SHIELDED

Welding Position: Overhead Weld Quality Level: Commercial Steel Weldability: Good

Plate Thickness (in.)	3/8		1/2		5/8		3/4		1	
Pass	1	2	1	2 – 3	1	2 – 4	1	2 – 5	1	2 – 7
Electrode Class*	E70T-G		E70T-G		E70T-G		E70T-G		E70T-G	
Size	1/16		1/16		1/16		1/16		1/16	
Current (amp) DC(–)	155		165		165		170		170	
Volts	18.5 – 19.5		19 – 20		19 – 20		19 – 20		19 – 20	
Arc Speed (in./min)†	3.5 – 3.9	1.6 – 1.8	3.5 – 3.9	2.3 – 2.5	3.5 – 3.9	2.3 – 2.5	3.3 – 3.7	2.3 – 2.5	3.1 – 3.4	2.1 – 2.3
Electrode Req'd (lb/ft)	0.729		1.05		1.45		1.94		3.01	
Total Time (hr/ft of weld)	0.172		0.221		0.354		0.391		0.607	
Electrical Stickout, 3/4 in.										

  * A fast-freeze type E70T-G. See introductory notes.

  † Arc speeds are average for all passes after the first. Normally speeds decrease on subsequent passes.

  Use split layers when bead face width exceeds 3/4 in.

FLUX-CORED ARC WELDING (SEMIAUTOMATIC) SELF-SHIELDED

Welding Position: Overhead
Weld Quality Level: Code
Steel Weldability: Good or fair

Where Code Quality is indicated normal practice requires a procedure qualification test.

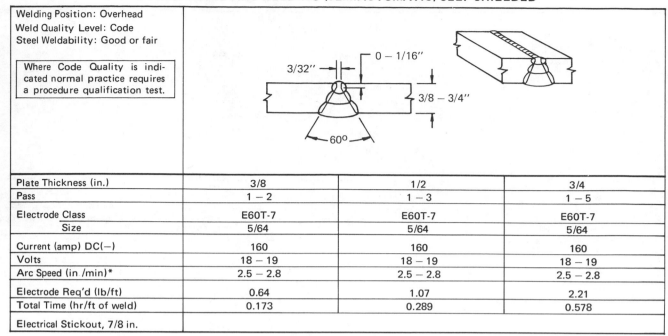

Plate Thickness (in.)	3/8	1/2	3/4
Pass	1 – 2	1 – 3	1 – 5
Electrode Class	E60T-7	E60T-7	E60T-7
Size	5/64	5/64	5/64
Current (amp) DC(−)	160	160	160
Volts	18 – 19	18 – 19	18 – 19
Arc Speed (in /min)*	2.5 – 2.8	2.5 – 2.8	2.5 – 2.8
Electrode Req'd (lb/ft)	0.64	1.07	2.21
Total Time (hr/ft of weld)	0.173	0.289	0.578
Electrical Stickout, 7/8 in.			

* For the first pass only. Subsequent passes are slower.
The root pass may be made with stick electrode. See Section 6.2 procedures.

FLUX-CORED ARC WELDING (SEMIAUTOMATIC) SELF-SHIELDED

Welding Position: Flat
Weld Quality Level: Strength only
Steel Weldability: Good

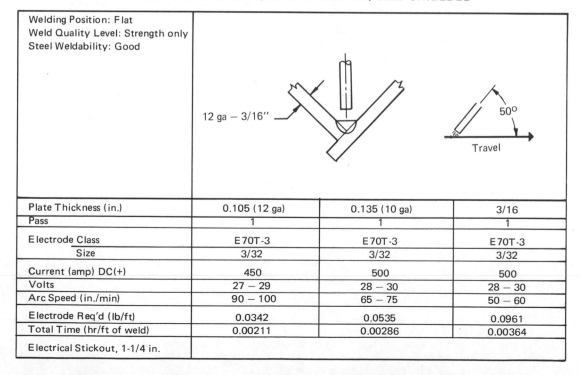

Plate Thickness (in.)	0.105 (12 ga)	0.135 (10 ga)	3/16
Pass	1	1	1
Electrode Class	E70T-3	E70T-3	E70T-3
Size	3/32	3/32	3/32
Current (amp) DC(+)	450	500	500
Volts	27 – 29	28 – 30	28 – 30
Arc Speed (in./min)	90 – 100	65 – 75	50 – 60
Electrode Req'd (lb/ft)	0.0342	0.0535	0.0961
Total Time (hr/ft of weld)	0.00211	0.00286	0.00364
Electrical Stickout, 1-1/4 in.			

FLUX-CORED ARC WELDING (SEMIAUTOMATIC) SELF-SHIELDED

Welding Position:
  Flat and horizontal
Weld Quality Level:
  Commercial
Steel Weldability: Good or fair

Weld Size, L (in.)			3/16	3/16+	1/4
Plate Thickness (in.)	0.105 (12 ga)	0.135 (10 ga)	3/16	1/4	5/16
Pass	1	1	1	1	1
Electrode Class	E70T-G*	E70T-G*	E70T-G†	E70T-G†	E70T-G†
Size	5/64	5/64	3/32	3/32	3/32
Current (amp) DC(−)	235	260	315	325	350
Volts	19 − 20	20 − 21	23 − 24	24 − 25	25 − 26
Arc Speed (in./min)	25 − 28	23 − 25	20 − 22	17 − 19	15 − 17
Electrode Req'd (lb/ft)	0.053	0.070	0.11	0.13	0.17
Total Time (hr/ft of weld)	0.00755	0.00833	0.00953	0.0111	0.0125
Electrical Stickout (in.)	3/4	3/4	1-1/4	1-1/4	1-1/4

* A fast-freeze type E70T-G.

† A fast-follow type E70T-G.

See introductory notes.

FLUX-CORED ARC WELDING (SEMIAUTOMATIC) SELF-SHIELDED

Welding Position: Flat
Weld Quality Level:
  Commercial
Steel Weldability:
  Good or fair

Weld Size, L (in.)	1/4 (−)	1/4	5/16	3/8	1/2
Plate Thickness (in.)	1/4	5/16	3/8	1/2	5/8
Pass	1	1	1	1	1*
Electrode Class	E70T-4	E70T-4	E70T-4	E70T-4	E70T-4
Size	3/32	3/32	3/32	3/32	3/32
Current (amp) DC(+)	360	375	375	375	375
Volts	29 − 30	30 − 31	30 − 31	30 − 31	30 − 31
Arc Speed (in./min)	21 − 23	18 − 20	13 − 15	10 − 11	5.2 − 5.8
Electrode Req'd (lb/ft)	0.17	0.21	0.28	0.39	0.67
Total Time (hr/ft of weld)	0.00909	0.0105	0.0143	0.0190	0.0364
Electrical Stickout, 2-3/4 in.					

* For better penetration use two passes. Overall speed is the same.

FLUX-CORED ARC WELDING (SEMIAUTOMATIC) SELF-SHIELDED

Welding Position: Flat
Weld Quality Level: Commercial
Steel Weldability: Good or fair

Weld Size, L (in.)	5/16	3/8	1/2	5/8		3/4	
Plate Thickness (in.)	3/8	1/2	5/8	3/4		1	
Pass	1	1	1	1	2	1,3 & 4	2
Electrode Class	E70T-4	E70T-4	E70T-4	E70T-4	E70T-4	E70T-4	E70T-4
Size	1/8	1/8	1/8	1/8	1/8	1/8	1/8
Current (amp) DC(+)	525	565	580	580	580	580	580
Volts	35 − 36	36 − 37	37 − 38	37 − 38	37 − 38	37 − 38	37 − 38
Arc Speed (in./min)	23 − 25	20 − 22	13 − 15	21 − 23	16 − 18	26 − 28	17 − 19
Electrode Req'd (lb/ft)	0.313	0.404	0.617	1.02		1.47	
Total Time (hr/ft of weld)	0.00833	0.00952	0.0143	0.0209		0.0333	
Electrical Stickout, 3-3/4 in.							

FLUX-CORED ARC WELDING (SEMIAUTOMATIC) SELF-SHIELDED

Welding Position: Flat
Weld Quality Level: Commercial*
Steel Weldability: Good or fair

Weld Size, L (in.)	3/16	3/16 (+)	1/4	5/16	3/8	1/2
Plate Thickness (in.)	1/4	5/16	3/8	1/2	5/8	3/4
Pass	1	1	1	1	1	1 − 2
Electrode Class *†	E70T-G	E70T-G	E70T-G	E70T-G	E70T-G	E70T-G
Size	7/64	7/64	7/64	7/64	7/64	7/64
Current (amp) DC(−)	450	500	500	525	525	525
Volts	27 − 28	28 − 29	28 − 29	29 − 30	29 − 30	29 − 30
Arc Speed (in./min)	32 − 35	26 − 29	22 − 24	18 − 20	13 − 14	15 − 17
Electrode Req'd (lb/ft)	0.12	0.17	0.21	0.27	0.38	0.64
Total Time (hr/ft of weld)	0.00597	0.00727	0.00870	0.0105	0.0148	0.0250
Electrical Stickout, 1-1/2 in.						

* Classified "Commercial" because the fillets are smaller than required by most codes. The welds have strength in excess of requirements if an E70T-G electrode is used which has penetration capabilities.

† A fast-follow type E70T-G with penetration capability. See introductory notes.

FLUX-CORED ARC WELDING (SEMIAUTOMATIC) SELF-SHIELDED

Welding Position: Horizontal
Weld Quality Level: Strength only
Steel Weldability: Good or fair

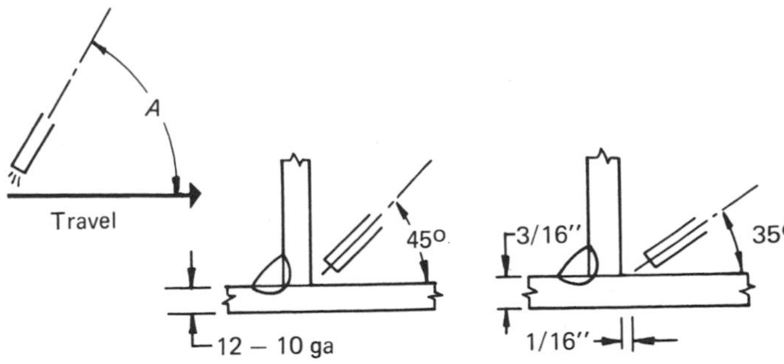

Plate Thickness (in.)	0.105 (12 ga)	0.135 (10 ga)	3/16
Pass	1	1	1
Electrode Class	E70T-3	E70T-3	E70T-3
Size	3/32	3/32	3/32
Current (amp) DC(+)	450	500	500
Volts	27 − 29	28 − 30	28 − 30
Arc Speed (in./min)	85 − 95	55 − 65	30 − 34
Electrode Req'd (lb/ft)	0.0370	0.0627	0.118
Total Time (hr/ft of weld)	0.00222	0.00333	0.00625
Drag Angle, A (deg)	45	50	55
Electrical Stickout, 1-1/4 in.			

FLUX-CORED ARC WELDING (SEMIAUTOMATIC) SELF-SHIELDED

Welding Position: Horizontal
Weld Quality Level:
  Commercial
Steel Weldability:
  Good or fair

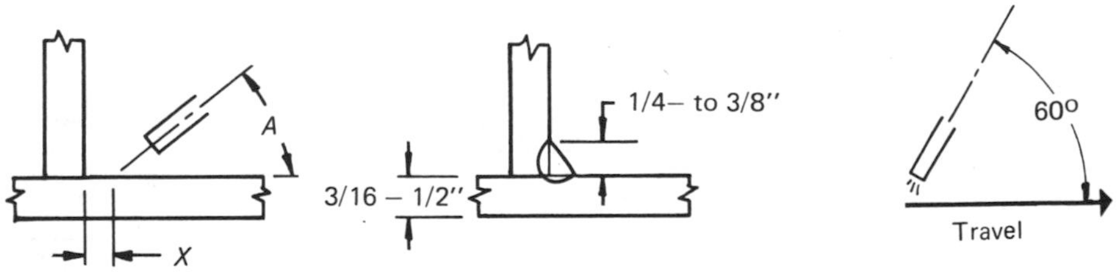

Weld Size, L (in.)	1/4 (−)	1/4 (−)	1/4		5/16		3/8
Plate Thickness (in.)	3/16	1/4	5/16		3/8		1/2
Pass	1	1	1	1	1	1	1
Electrode Class	E70T-4	E70T-4	E70T-4	E70T-4	E70T-4	E70T-4	E70T-4
Size	3/32	3/32	3/32	1/8	3/32	1/8	1/8
Current (amp) DC(+)	325	350	375	425	375	425	450
Volts	28 − 29	29 − 30	30 − 31	27 − 30	30 − 31	27 − 30	28 − 31
Arc Speed (in./min)	18 − 20	17 − 19	15 − 17	18 − 20	14 − 16	16 − 18	12 − 13
Electrode Req'd (lb/ft)	0.17	0.20	0.25	0.25	0.27	0.27	0.39
Total Time (hr/ft of weld)	0.0105	0.0111	0.0125	0.0105	0.0133	0.0118	0.0154
Electrode location, X (in.)	0	1/16	3/32	1/8	1/8	5/32	5/32
Electrode angle, A (deg)	40	35	35	30	30	25	25
Electrical Stickout, 2-3/4 in.							

FLUX-CORED ARC WELDING (SEMIAUTOMATIC) SELF-SHIELDED

Welding Position: Horizontal
Weld Quality Level: Commercial
Steel Weldability: Good or fair

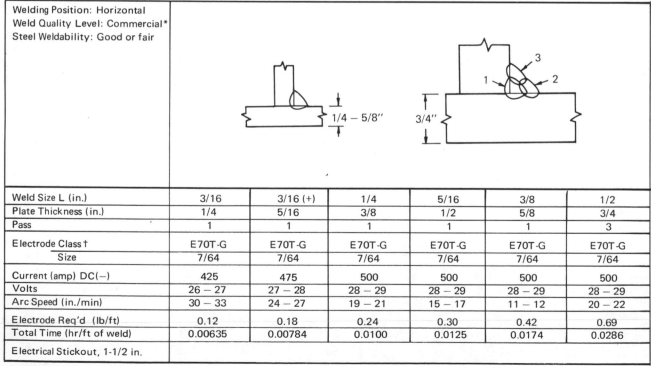

Weld Size, L (in.)	1/2		5/8			3/4		
Plate Thickness (in.)	5/8		3/4			1		
Pass	1	2	1	2	3	1 & 5	2	3 & 4
Electrode Class	E70T-4	E70T-4	E70T-4	E70T-4	E70T-4	E70T-4	E70T-4	E70T-4
Size	1/8	1/8	1/8	1/8	1/8	1/8	1/8	1/8
Current (amp) DC(+)	450	450	450	450	450	450	450	450
Volts	28 – 31	28 – 31	28 – 31	28 – 31	28 – 31	28 – 31	28 – 31	28 – 31
Arc Speed (in./min)	13 – 15	16 – 18	15 – 17	16 – 18	13 – 15	15 – 17	14 – 16	18 – 20
Electrode Req'd (lb/ft)	0.670		0.962			1.42		
Total Time (hr/ft of weld)	0.0259		0.0386			0.0593		
Electrical Stickout, 2-3/4 in.								

FLUX-CORED ARC WELDING (SEMIAUTOMATIC) SELF-SHIELDED

Welding Position: Horizontal
Weld Quality Level: Commercial*
Steel Weldability: Good or fair

Weld Size L (in.)	3/16	3/16 (+)	1/4	5/16	3/8	1/2
Plate Thickness (in.)	1/4	5/16	3/8	1/2	5/8	3/4
Pass	1	1	1	1	1	3
Electrode Class †	E70T-G	E70T-G	E70T-G	E70T-G	E70T-G	E70T-G
Size	7/64	7/64	7/64	7/64	7/64	7/64
Current (amp) DC(−)	425	475	500	500	500	500
Volts	26 – 27	27 – 28	28 – 29	28 – 29	28 – 29	28 – 29
Arc Speed (in./min)	30 – 33	24 – 27	19 – 21	15 – 17	11 – 12	20 – 22
Electrode Req'd (lb/ft)	0.12	0.18	0.24	0.30	0.42	0.69
Total Time (hr/ft of weld)	0.00635	0.00784	0.0100	0.0125	0.0174	0.0286
Electrical Stickout, 1-1/2 in.						

* Classified "Commercial" because the fillets are smaller than required by most codes. The welds have strength in excess of requirements if an E70T-G electrode is used which has penetration capabilities.

† A fast-follow type E70T-G with penetration capability. See introductory notes.

FLUX-CORED ARC WELDING (SEMIAUTOMATIC) SELF-SHIELDED

Welding Position: Vertical down
Weld Quality Level: Commercial
Steel Weldability: Good or fair

12 ga — 1/4''

Weld Size, L (in.)			3/16	3/16+
Plate Thickness (in.)	0.105 (12 ga)	0.135 (10 ga)	3/16	1/4
Pass	1	1	1	1
Electrode Class*	E70T-G	E70T-G	E70T-G	E70T-G
Size	5/64	5/64	3/32	3/32
Current (amp) DC(—)	235	260	300	300
Volts	19 — 20	20 — 21	21 — 22	21 — 22
Arc Speed (in./min)	30 — 33	26 — 29	25 — 28	22 — 24
Electrode Req'd (lb/ft)	0.045	0.061	0.082	0.10
Total Time (hr/ft of weld)	0.00635	0.00727	0.00755	0.00870
Electrical Stickout, 3/4 in.				

* A fast-freeze type E70T-G.

See introductory notes.

FLUX-CORED ARC WELDING (SEMIAUTOMATIC) SELF-SHIELDED

Welding Position: Vertical up
Weld Quality Level: Commercial
Steel Weldability: Good

Weld Size, L (in.)	1/4(+)	5/16(—)	5/16	3/8	7/16	1/2	5/8		3/4	
Plate Thickness (in.)	1/4	5/16	3/8	1/2	9/16	5/8	3/4		1	
Pass	1	1	1	1	1	1	1	2	1	2
Electrode Class*	E70T-G	E70T-G	E70T-G	E70T-G	E70T-G	E70T-G	E70T-G		E70T-G	
Size	1/16	1/16	1/16	1/16	1/16	1/16	1/16		1/16	
Current (amp) DC(—)	130	140	155	155	155	185	185		185	
Volts	19.0	19.5	20.0	20.0	20.0	21.5	21.5		21.5	
Arc Speed (in./min)	3.8 — 4.2	3.5 — 3.9	3.2 — 3.4	2.3 — 2.5	1.9 — 2.1	1.7 — 1.9	2.3 — 2.5	2.4 -- 2.8	2.2 — 2.6	1.4 — 1.6
Electrode Req'd (lb/ft)	0.180	0.210	0.285	0.345	0.468	0.662	0.967		1.35	
Total Time (hr/ft of weld)	0.0500	0.0542	0.0607	0.0833	0.100	0.111	0.161		0.217	
Electrical Stickout, 1 in., ± 1/4 in.										

* A fast-freeze type E70T-G. See introductory notes.

FLUX-CORED ARC WELDING (SEMIAUTOMATIC) SELF-SHIELDED

Welding Position: Vertical up
Weld Quality Level: Code
Steel Weldability: Good or fair

> Where Code Quality is indicated normal practice requires a procedure qualification test.

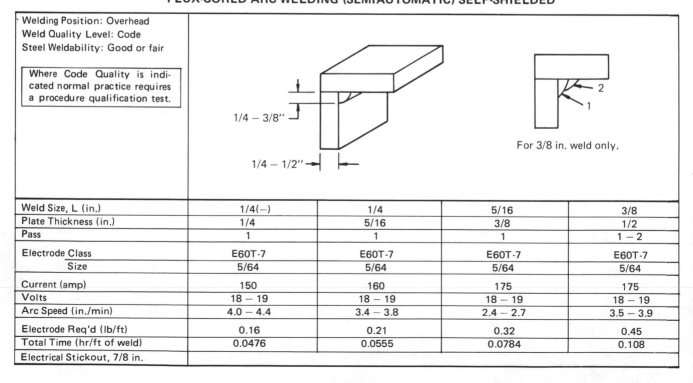

Weld Size, L (in.)	1/4	5/16	3/8	1/2	5/8	3/4
Plate Thickness (in.)	5/16	3/8	1/2	5/8	3/4	1
Pass	1	1	1	1	1	1
Electrode Class	E60T-7	E60T-7	E60T-7	E60T-7	E60T-7	E60T-7
Size	5/64	5/64	5/64	5/64	5/64	5/64
Current (amp) DC(−)	150	160	170	180	190	200
Volts	18 − 19	18 − 19	18 − 19	19 − 20	19 − 20	19 − 20
Arc Speed (in./min)	3.0 − 3.3	2.1 − 2.3	1.6 − 1.8	1.0 − 1.1	0.70 − 0.75	0.65 − 0.60
Electrode Req'd (lb/ft)	0.22	0.34	0.47	0.92	1.27	1.74
Total Time (hr/ft of weld)	0.0635	0.0909	0.118	0.190	0.276	0.348
Electrical Stickout, 7/8 in.						

FLUX-CORED ARC WELDING (SEMIAUTOMATIC) SELF-SHIELDED

Welding Position: Overhead
Weld Quality Level: Code
Steel Weldability: Good or fair

> Where Code Quality is indicated normal practice requires a procedure qualification test.

Weld Size, L (in.)	1/4(−)	1/4	5/16	3/8
Plate Thickness (in.)	1/4	5/16	3/8	1/2
Pass	1	1	1	1 − 2
Electrode Class	E60T-7	E60T-7	E60T-7	E60T-7
Size	5/64	5/64	5/64	5/64
Current (amp)	150	160	175	175
Volts	18 − 19	18 − 19	18 − 19	18 − 19
Arc Speed (in./min)	4.0 − 4.4	3.4 − 3.8	2.4 − 2.7	3.5 − 3.9
Electrode Req'd (lb/ft)	0.16	0.21	0.32	0.45
Total Time (hr/ft of weld)	0.0476	0.0555	0.0784	0.108
Electrical Stickout, 7/8 in.				

FLUX-CORED ARC WELDING (SEMIAUTOMATIC) SELF-SHIELDED

Welding Position: Flat
Weld Quality Level: Strength only
Steel Weldability: Good

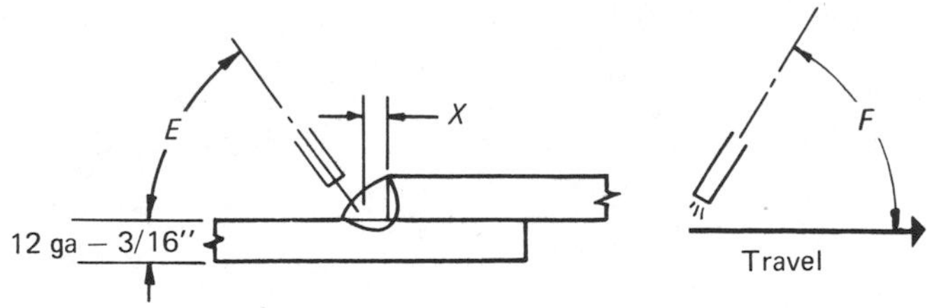

12 ga — 3/16"

Plate Thickness (in.)	0.105 (12 ga)	0.135 (10 ga)	3/16
Pass	1	1	1
Electrode Class	E70T-3	E70T-3	E70T-3
Size	3/32	3/32	3/32
Current (amp) DC(+)	450	500	500
Volts	27 — 29	28 — 30	28 — 30
Arc Speed (in./min)	85 — 95	65 — 75	38 — 42
Electrode Req'd (lb/ft)	0.0370	0.0502	0.0940
Total Time (hr/ft of weld)	0.00222	0.00286	0.00500
Angle, E (deg)	55	50	45
Angle, F (deg)	45	50	55
Electrode location, X (in.)	3/64	1/16	5/64
Electrical Stickout, 1-1/4 in.			

FLUX-CORED ARC WELDING (SEMIAUTOMATIC) SELF-SHIELDED

Welding Position: Horizontal
Weld Quality Level:
   Commercial
Steel Weldability:
   Good or fair

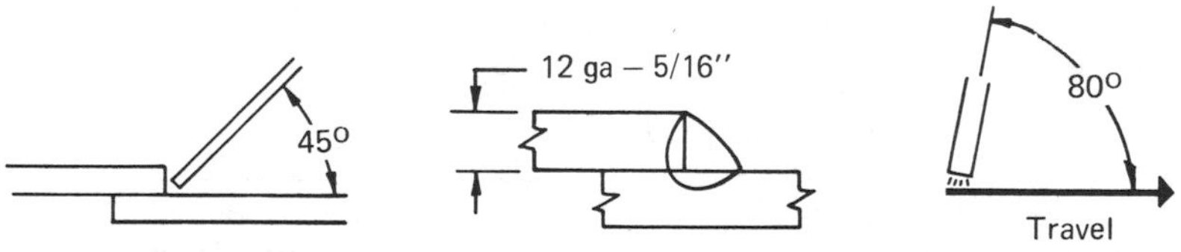

45°   12 ga — 5/16"   80°   Travel

Weld Size, L (in.)			3/16 (−)	3/16 (+)	1/4
Plate Thickness (in.)	0.105 (12 ga)	0.135 (10 ga)	3/16	1/4	5/16
Pass	1	1	1	1	1
Electrode Class*	E70T-G	E70T-G	E70T-G	E70T-G	E70T-G
Size	5/64	5/64	3/32	3/32	3/32
Current (amp) DC(−)	260	275	315	340	350
Volts	20.5	20.5	23.5	25.5	25.5
Arc Speed (in./min)	28 — 31	26 — 28	20 — 22	17 — 19	14 — 16
Electrode Req'd (lb/ft)	0.057	0.067	0.11	0.14	0.18
Total Time (hr/ft of weld)	0.00678	0.00741	0.00952	0.0111	0.0133
Electrical Stickout (in.)	3/4	3/4	1-1/4	1-1/4	1-1/4

* A fast-freeze type E70T-G. See introductory notes.

FLUX-CORED ARC WELDING (SEMIAUTOMATIC) SELF-SHIELDED

Welding Position: Horizontal
Weld Quality Level: Commercial
Steel Weldability: Good or fair

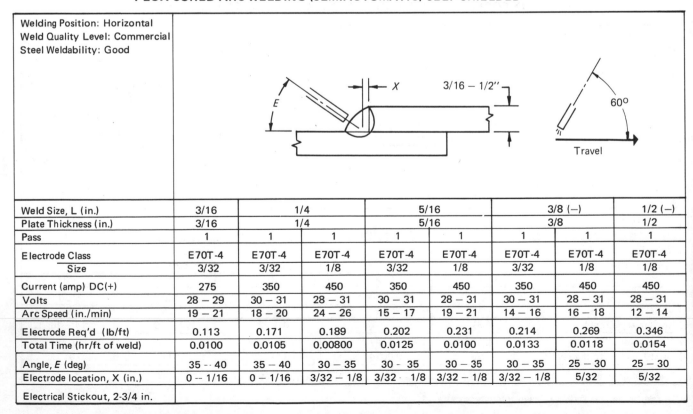

Weld Size, L (in.)	3/16	1/4 (−)	1/4 (+)	5/16	3/8
Plate Thickness (in.)	3/16	1/4	5/16	3/8	1/2
Pass	1	1	1	1	1
Electrode Class*	E70T-G	E70T-G	E70T-G	E70T-G	E70T-G
Size	7/64	7/64	7/64	7/64	7/64
Current (amp) DC(−)	350	400	425	450	475
Volts	25 − 26	26 − 27	27 − 28	28 − 29	29 − 30
Arc Speed (in./min)	21 − 23	20 − 22	19 − 21	15 − 17	11 − 12
Electrode Req'd (lb/ft)	0.13	0.16	0.19	0.26	0.39
Total Time (hr/ft of weld)	0.00909	0.00952	0.0100	0.0125	0.0174
Electrical Stickout, 1-1/2 in.					

* A fast-follow type E70T-G.

See introductory notes.

FLUX-CORED ARC WELDING (SEMIAUTOMATIC) SELF-SHIELDED

Welding Position: Horizontal
Weld Quality Level: Commercial
Steel Weldability: Good

Weld Size, L (in.)	3/16	1/4		5/16		3/8 (−)		1/2 (−)
Plate Thickness (in.)	3/16	1/4		5/16		3/8		1/2
Pass	1	1	1	1	1	1	1	1
Electrode Class	E70T-4	E70T-4	E70T-4	E70T-4	E70T-4	E70T-4	E70T-4	E70T-4
Size	3/32	3/32	1/8	3/32	1/8	3/32	1/8	1/8
Current (amp) DC(+)	275	350	450	350	450	350	450	450
Volts	28 − 29	30 − 31	28 − 31	30 − 31	28 − 31	30 − 31	28 − 31	28 − 31
Arc Speed (in./min)	19 − 21	18 − 20	24 − 26	15 − 17	19 − 21	14 − 16	16 − 18	12 − 14
Electrode Req'd (lb/ft)	0.113	0.171	0.189	0.202	0.231	0.214	0.269	0.346
Total Time (hr/ft of weld)	0.0100	0.0105	0.00800	0.0125	0.0100	0.0133	0.0118	0.0154
Angle, E (deg)	35 − 40	35 − 40	30 − 35	30 − 35	30 − 35	30 − 35	25 − 30	25 − 30
Electrode location, X (in.)	0 − 1/16	0 − 1/16	3/32 − 1/8	3/32 − 1/8	3/32 − 1/8	3/32 − 1/8	5/32	5/32
Electrical Stickout, 2-3/4 in.								

FLUX-CORED ARC WELDING (SEMIAUTOMATIC) SELF-SHIELDED

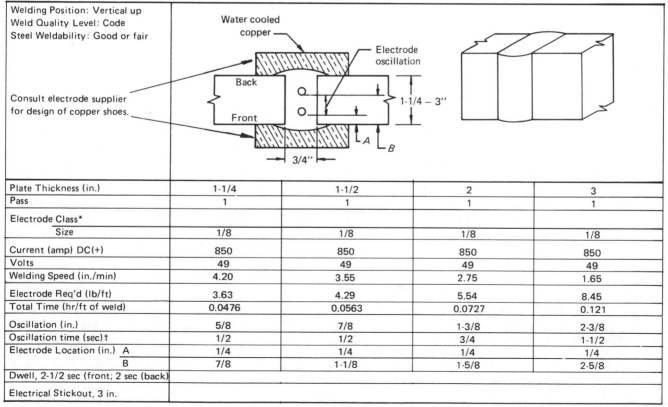

Welding Position: Horizontal			
Weld Quality Level: Strength only			
Steel Weldability: Good			

Plate Thickness (in.)	0.105 (12 ga)	0.135 (10 ga)	3/16
Pass	1	1	1
Electrode Class	E70T-3	E70T-3	E70T-3
Size	3/32	3/32	3/32
Current (amp) DC(+)	450	500	500
Volts	27 — 29	28 — 30	28 — 30
Arc Speed (in./min)	85 — 95	70 — 80	40 — 46
Electrode Req'd (lb/ft)	0.0370	0.0502	0.0874
Total Time (hr/ft of weld)	0.00222	0.00267	0.00465
Drag Angle, A (deg)	45	45	50
Electrode location, X (in.)	3/64	1/16	5/64
Electrical Stickout, 1-1/4 in.			

FLUX-CORED ARC WELDING (SEMIAUTOMATIC) SELF-SHIELDED

Welding Position: Vertical up				
Weld Quality Level: Code				
Steel Weldability: Good or fair				
Consult electrode supplier for design of copper shoes.				

Plate Thickness (in.)	1-1/4	1-1/2	2	3
Pass	1	1	1	1
Electrode Class*				
Size	1/8	1/8	1/8	1/8
Current (amp) DC(+)	850	850	850	850
Volts	49	49	49	49
Welding Speed (in./min)	4.20	3.55	2.75	1.65
Electrode Req'd (lb/ft)	3.63	4.29	5.54	8.45
Total Time (hr/ft of weld)	0.0476	0.0563	0.0727	0.121
Oscillation (in.)	5/8	7/8	1-3/8	2-3/8
Oscillation time (sec)†	1/2	1/2	3/4	1-1/2
Electrode Location (in.) A	1/4	1/4	1/4	1/4
B	7/8	1-1/8	1-5/8	2-5/8
Dwell, 2-1/2 sec (front; 2 sec (back)				
Electrical Stickout, 3 in.				

* Electrode not classified. Consult the supplier.

† Time for one direction only.

The Gas-Shielded Electrode Process

As noted in the preceding chapters, the shielded metal-arc process and the self-shielded flux-cored electrode process depend in part on gases generated by the heat of the arc to provide arc and puddle shielding. In contrast, the gas-shielded arc-welding processes use either bare of flux-cored filler metal and gas from an external source for shielding. The gas is impinged upon the work from a nozzle that surrounds the electrode. It may be an inert gas — such as argon or helium — or carbon dioxide (CO_2), a much cheaper gas that is suitable for use in the welding of steels. Mixtures of the inert gases, oxygen, and carbon dioxide also are used to produce special arc characteristics.

There are three basic gas-shielded arc-welding processes that have broad application in industry. They are the gas-shielded flux-cored process, the gas tunsten-arc (TIG) process, and the gas metal-arc (MIG) process.

THE GAS-SHIELDED FLUX-CORED PROCESS

The gas-shielded flux-cored process may be looked upon as a hybrid between self-shielded flux-cored arc welding and gas metal-arc welding. Tubular electrode wire is used (Fig. 13-1), as in the self-shielded process, but the ingredients in its core are for fluxing, deoxidizing, scavenging, and sometimes alloying additions, rather than for these functions plus the generation of protective vapors. In this respect, the process has similarities to the self-shielded flux-cored electrode process, and the tubular electrodes used are classified by the AWS along with electrodes used in the self-shielded process. On the other hand, the process is similar to gas metal-arc welding in that a gas is separately applied to act as an arc shield.

The guns and welding heads for semiautomatic and full-automatic welding with the gas-shielded process are of necessity more complex than those used in self-shielded flux-cored welding. Passages must be included for the flow of gases. If the gun is water-cooled, additional passages are required for this purpose. Fig. 13-2 shows typical guns for semiautomatic gas-shielded flux-cored arc welding, and Fig. 13-3 typical nozzle assemblies for full-automatic operation. The wire feeder is similar to the wire feeder used with the self-shielded flux-cored electrode process. Fig. 13-4 shows a schematic for a full-automatic welding facility with either self-shielded or gas-shielded flux-cored electrode; the dotted line indicates the addition required with the gas-shielded version when using CO_2 as the shielding gas.

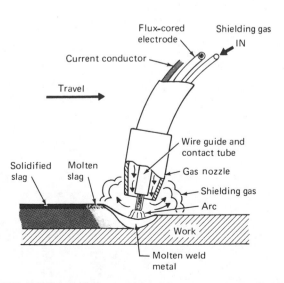

Fig. 13-1. Principles of the gas-shielded flux-cored process. Gas from an external source is used for the shielding; the core ingredients are for fluxing and metal-conditioning purposes.

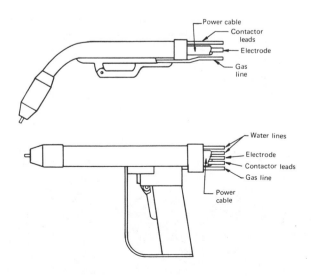

Fig. 13-2. Typical guns for semiautomatic gas-shielded flux-cored arc welding.

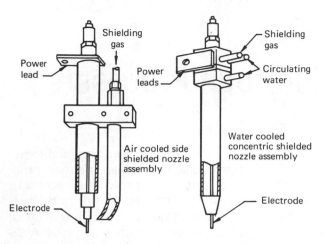

Fig. 13-3. Typical nozzle assemblies for full-automatic welding with gas-shielded flux-cored electrode or with solid-wire electrode (MIG welding).

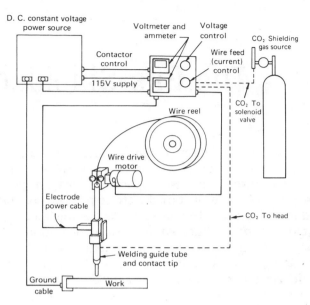

Fig. 13-4. Schematic for a full-automatic welding facility with either self-shielded or gas-shielded flux-cored electrode. The dotted line indicates the additions required with the gas-shielded version when using CO_2 as the shielding gas.

The gas-shielded flux-cored process is used for welding mild and low-alloy steels. It gives high deposition rates, high deposition efficiencies, and high operating factors. Radiographic-quality welds are easily produced, and the weld metal with mild and low-alloy steels has good ductility and toughness. The process is adaptable to a wide variety of joints and gives the capability for all-position welding.

ELECTRODES FOR THE GAS-SHIELDED FLUX-CORED PROCESS

The tubular electrodes for the process are specified in AWS A5.20-69 (see Table 5-12). The AWS

TABLE 13-1. Typical Mechanical Properties of Weld Metal Deposited with CO_2-Shielded Flux-Cored Electrodes

Alloy Type or AWS Class	AW (As Welded) or SR (Stress Relieved)	Yield Strength (1000 psi)	Tensile Strength (1000 psi)	Elongation in 2 in. (%)	Impact Strength (ft-lb) Charpy V-Notch				
					Test Temperature (°F)				
					+72	−25	−50	−60	−75
E70T-1	AW	77.5	85	30	98	41	25	21	....
	SR(1150°F)	62	74	34	86	42	25	19	....
E70T-2*	AW	81	86	30	....	....	....	....	....
1-1/2% Mn-1/2% Mo	AW	97	108.5	16.5	50	30	24	....	....
	SR(1150°F)	96.5	107.8	17	....	....	....	....	....
1% Cr-1/2% Mo	SR(1275°F)	78.5	88	25	....	....	....	....	....
1-1/4% Cr-1/2% Mo	AW	94	106	14	....	....	....	....	....
	SR(1275°F)	75	88	22	....	....	....	....	....
	SR(1350°F)	71	85	22	....	....	....	....	....
2-1/4% Cr-1% Mo	AW	109.5	128	12	....	....	....	....	....
	SR(1275°F)	82.5	96	20	....	....	....	....	....
	SR(1350°F)	77.6	92	20	....	....	....	....	....
1% Ni	AW	79.3	88.6	24	64	....	....	32	26
	SR(1150°F)	76.7	85.8	29	74	....	....	29	25
Q and T	AW	107.5	119	20	47	....	....	27	24
	SR(1050°F)	109	121	20	40	....	....	22	19

* Single-pass weld.

TABLE 13-2. Typical Current Ranges for CO₂-Shielded Flux-Cored Electrodes

Electrode Diameter (in.)	Current Range (amp)
1/16, 5/64	150 to 450
3/32	300 to 550
7/64, 1/8	400 to 650

specification covers only mild-steel electrodes; there is no specification for low-alloy steel electrodes, even though such electrodes are available (see Table 13-1). Typical mechanical properties of mild-steel and low-alloy steel weld deposits are shown in Table 13-1. Typical current ranges are listed in Table 13-2.

Electrode sizes generally range from 0.045 in. to 1/8 in., with 5/32-in. and larger diameters available on special order. Electrodes 3/32-in. and larger are usually limited to flat welding; electrodes 5/64 in. and smaller may be used to weld out-of-position by operating at the low end of the welding-current range.

Fig. 13-5 shows deposition rates for typical current ranges for various diameters of E70T1 electrode with CO₂ shielding. Deposition efficiencies of gas-shielded flux-cored electrodes generally range from 85 to 90%.

The shielding gas is usually CO₂ (dew point should be at least -45°F), and, for most applications, the gas flow is 25 to 45 cfh. Higher flow rates may be necessary when welding in drafts. Mixtures of argon with oxygen and argon with CO₂ reduce spatter and penetration and are sometimes preferred for welding thin material.

Wire-feeding equipment is essentially the same for the cored electrode as for solid electrode. However, since the diameter of cored wire is larger than a solid electrode for a comparable application, the feeding equipment must be able to feed larger wire. Power sources are the constant-voltage type — the same as used with self-shielded flux-cored welding.

WELDING VARIABLES

The appearance and quality of welds are affected by such variables as arc voltage, travel rate, electrode angle, electrical stickout, nozzle-to-work distance, gas-flow rate, and drafts or winds.

Arc Voltage: If the arc voltage is too high, the bead tends to widen in an irregular manner, with excessive spatter. Too low arc voltage results in a narrow, high bead with excessive spatter and reduced penetration.

Travel Rate: As with other mechanized processes, travel rate affects the build-up of molten metal and penetration into the base material. Slow travel increases penetration, but excessively slow travel

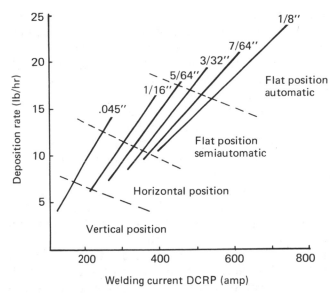

Fig. 13-5. Deposition rate versus current — for various diameters of E70T-1 electrode with CO₂ shielding.

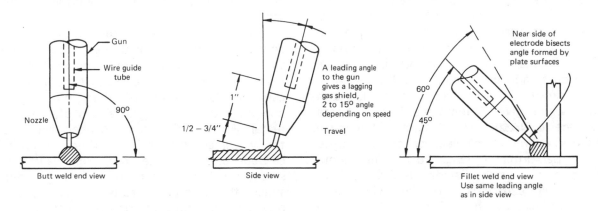

Fig. 13-6. Correct positions for gas-shielded flux-cored arc welding.

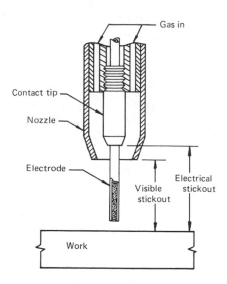

Fig. 13-7. The nozzle-to-work distance influences performance characteristics when welding with flux-cored electrodes.

can lead to excessive build-up of molten metal, overheating of the weld area, and a rough-appearing bead. Too high travel rates may result in inadequate penetration and a ropy, irregular bead. Travel rates between 12 and 30 inches per minute usually give satisfactory results.

Electrode Angle: Fig. 13-6 shows the correct gun positions when welding with gas-shielded flux-cored electrodes. With a butt weld, the electrode should be perpendicular to the sides of the joint and slanted from 2 to 15° in the direction of travel. The leading angle results in a "lagging" gas shield, with much of the gas flowing back over the newly deposited weld metal. With a fillet weld, the electrode is dropped offcenter of the joint approximately half the diameter of the electrode, as shown in Fig. 13-6, and a leading angle of 2 to 15° used.

Electrical Stickout: Varying the electrical stickout — as with self-shielded flux-cored welding and submerged-arc welding — offers a method of controlling deposition rate and penetration. At a given rate of wire feed, a short stickout results in deeper penetration than a long stickout. With gas-shielded flux-cored electrodes, an electrical stickout of 3/4 to 1-1/4 in. is usually recommended, depending on the type of nozzle. If the stickout is excessive, spatter occurs, and arc shielding is lost. With increased stickout, the wire feed rate should be increased — which gives an increased deposition rate.

Distance to Nozzle: The distance of the nozzle to the work, as well as the electrical stickout, influences the performance (Fig. 13-7). The recommended nozzle-to-work distance is 3/4 to 1 in., which, with concentric-type nozzles, will give an electrical stickout of about 1 to 1-1/4 in. If the nozzle-to-work distance is too short, spatter may

rapidly build up on the nozzle and contact tube. With side-shielded nozzles, electrical stickout is normally set at 3/4 to 1-1/4 in.

Gas Flow: The gas flow will depend on the diameter of the nozzle, distance of nozzle from the work, and air movements in the welding region. Inadequate flow will result in poor shielding of the arc and molten metal, leading to weld porosity. Excessive gas flow can cause turbulence at the arc, resulting in porosity and irregular beads. Most welding with gas-shielded flux-cored electrodes is done with the gas flow in the range of 35 to 45 cubic feet per hour. When welding in moving air or when the stickout is longer than normal, flow rates up to 55 cubic feet per hour may be required. To maintain desired flow rates, it is necessary to keep the nozzle opening free from adhering spatter.

PROCEDURES

On pages 13-5 and 13-6 are typical procedures for welding carbon and low-alloy steel. In these representative procedures, E70T-1 electrode is used with CO_2 gas.

GAS METAL-ARC WELDING

Gas metal-arc welding, popularly known as MIG welding, uses a continuous electrode for filler metal and an externally supplied gas or gas mixture for shielding. The shielding gas — helium, argon, carbon dioxide, or mixtures thereof — protects the molten metal from reacting with constituents of the atmosphere. Although the gas shield is effective in shielding the molten metal from the air, deoxidizers are usually added as alloys in the electrode. Sometimes light coatings are applied to the electrode for arc stabilizing or other purposes. Lubricating films may also be applied to increase the electrode feeding efficiency in semiautomatic welding equipment. Reactive gases may be included in the gas mixture for arc-conditioning functions. Fig. 13-8 illustrates the method by which shielding gas and continuous electrode are supplied to the welding arc.

MIG welding may be used with all of the major commercial metals, including carbon, alloy, and stainless steels and aluminum, magnesium, copper, iron, titanium, and zirconium. It is a preferred process for the welding of aluminum, magnesium, copper, and many of the alloys of these reactive metals. Most of the irons and steels can be satisfactorily joined by MIG welding, including the carbon-free irons, the low-carbon and low-alloy steels, the high-strength quenched and tempered steels, the chromium irons and steels, the high-nickel steels, and some of the so-called superalloy steels. With these various materials, the welding

**Typical Procedures for Semiautomatic Gas-Shielded Flux-Cored Arc Welding
With AWS E70T-1 Electrode and CO_2 Gas**

Plate Thickness (in.)	Root Opening (in.)	Passes	Electrode Size (in.)	Current DC+ (amp)	Volts	Average Arc Speed (in./min)	Total Time (hr/ft) of weld	Joint Design
1/8	1/16	1	5/64	325	28	40	0.0050	
1/2	1/4	2	3/32	450	32	12	0.0333	
1/2	0	2	3/32	480	30	14	0.0286	
1	0	6	7/64	525	32	11	0.108	
5/8	3/16	3	7/64	525	32	14	0.0428	
1	3/16	6	7/64	525	32	14	0.0855	
5/8	1/8	3	7/64	525	32	16	0.0374	
1	1/8	6	7/64	525	32	14	0.0855	
1	0	6	7/64	525	32	31	0.0385	
2	0	20	7/64	525	32	26	0.154	
1	0	4	7/64	500	32	17	0.0471	
2	0	12	7/64	500	32	13	0.185	
1/2	1/8	6	5/64	350	28	20	0.0599	
1	1/8	18	5/64	350	28	18	0.200	

Typical Procedures for Semiautomatic Gas-Shielded Flux-Cored Arc Welding With AWS E70T-1 Electrode and CO_2 Gas

Plate Thickness (in.)	Root Opening (in.)	Passes	Electrode Size (in.)	Current DC+ (amp)	Volts	Average Arc Speed (in./min)	Total Time (hr/ft) of weld	Joint Design
3/8	0	2	.045	180	22	8	0.0500	
1/2	0	3	.045	180	22	8	0.0750	
1/2	3/32	4	0.045	180	22	8	0.100	
1	3/32	9	0.045	180	22	5	0.356	
1	1/16	6	0.045	180	22	8	0.149	
2	1/16	16	0.045	180	2	5	0.627	
1/8	0	1	0.045	180	21	36	0.00555	
1/2	0	2	0.045	180	21	5	0.0834	
3/16	0	1	5/64	350	28	36	0.00555	
1/2	0	3	7/64	450	20	18	0.0333	

* Vertical

Adapted from AWS Handbook, Section 3B

techniques and procedures may vary widely. Thus, carbon dioxide or argon-oxygen mixtures are suitable for arc shielding when welding the low-carbon and low-alloy steels, whereas pure inert gas may be essential when welding highly alloyed steels. Copper and many of its alloys and the stainless steels are successfully welded by the process.

Welding is either semiautomatic, using a hand-held gun to which electrode is fed automatically, or full-automatic equipment is used. The welding guns or heads are similar to those used with gas-shielded flux-cored welding (Figs. 13-2 and 13-3). When the term "manual" gas metal-arc welding is

used, the semiautomatic process with its hand-held gun is implied.

Metal transfer with the MIG process is by one of two methods: "spray-arc" or short circuiting. With spray-arc, drops of molten metal detach from the electrode and move through the arc column to the work. With the short-circuiting technique — often referred to as short-arc welding — metal is transferred to the work when the molten tip of the electrode contacts the molten puddle.

The latter, short-arc welding, uses low currents, low voltages, and small-diameter wires. The molten drop short-circuits the arc an average of 100 times

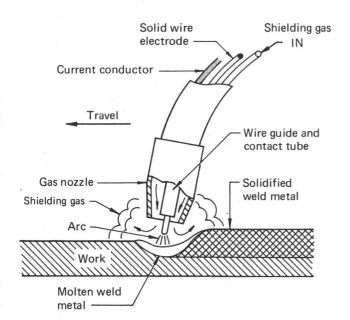

Fig. 13-8. Principle of the gas metal-arc process. Continuous solid-wire electrode is fed to the gas-shielded arc.

a second and at rates lower and much higher than this average. Metal is transferred with each short circuit, rather than across the arc as in spray-arc welding.

Fig. 13-9 illustrates a complete short-arc cycle, starting with (A), the beginning of the short circuit, progressing through arc reignition and arcing period, and ending with arc extinction immediately prior to the beginning of metal transfer. The technique results in low heat input, which minimizes distortion. It is useful for welding thin-gage materials in all positions and for vertical and overhead welding of heavy sections. Short-arc welding toler-

ates poor fitup and permits the bridging of wide gaps.

To use short-arc welding efficiently, special power sources with adjustable slope, voltage, and inductance characteristics are required. These power sources produce the predictable and controllable current surges needed for successful use of the short-arc technique.

Spray-arc transfer may be subdivided into two different types. When the shielding gas is argon or argon-oxygen mixture, the droplets in the spray are very fine and never short-circuit the arc. When carbon dioxide or argon-carbon dioxide mixture is used, a molten ball tends to form on the end of the electrode and may grow in size until its diameter is greater than the diameter of the electrode. These droplets, larger in size, may cause short circuits and this mode is known as globular transfer. Under conditions that cause the short circuits to occur very rapidly, the mode becomes short-circuiting transfer.

Spray-arc MIG welding produces an intensely hot, higher voltage arc, and, thus, gives a higher deposition rate than short-arc welding. A high current density is required for metal transfer through the arc. The spray-arc technique is recommended for 1/8-in. and thicker sections, requiring heavy single or multipass welds, or for any filler-pass application where high deposition rate is advantageous.

MIG welding is a DC weld process; AC current is seldom, if ever, used. Most MIG welding is done with reverse polarity (DCRP). Weld penetration is deeper with reverse polarity than it is with straight polarity. MIG welding is seldom done with straight polarity, because of arc-instability and spatter

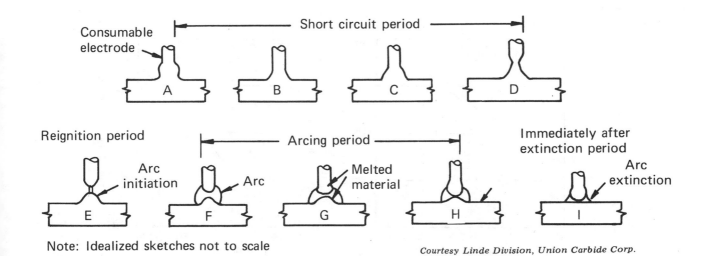

Note: Idealized sketches not to scale

Courtesy Linde Division, Union Carbide Corp.

Fig. 13-9. The short-arc cycle in MIG welding. Short-circuiting starts with (A); the arc is reignited at (E); and is extinguished when the molten metal on the electrode tip touches the molten puddle at (H). Metal is transferred during the short circuit.

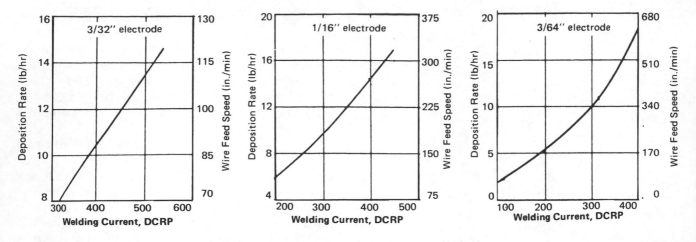

Fig. 13-10. Deposition rates of 3/32, 1/16, and 3/64-in. E70S-2 electrodes with argon-5% oxygen shielding.

problems that make straight polarity undesirable for most applications.

The gas metal-arc process can be used for spot welding to replace either riveting, electrical resistance, or TIG spot welding. It has proved applicable for spot welding where TIG spot welding is not suitable, such as in the joining of aluminum and rimmed steel. Fitup and cleanliness requirements are not as exacting as with TIG spot welding, and the MIG process may be applied to thicker materials.

ELECTRODES FOR MIG WELDING OF STEEL

AWS specification AWS A5.18-69, *Mild Steel Electrodes for Gas Metal-Arc Welding,* classes electrodes on the bases of chemical composition of the wire (Table 5-17) and mechanical properties of the deposited weld metal (Tables 5-15 and 5-16). This specification also gives recommendations for use of the electrode.

The AWS specification covers only mild-steel electrodes, but the chemical requirements of the electrodes in Group B do not fall strictly within the requirements of mild steel. The alloy additions to electrodes in Group B are for deoxidization and usability improvement and not for upgrading the strength of the weld deposit.

In general, electrodes with lower amounts of deoxidizer are intended for welding killed steels with argon-oxygen gas, but they can be used with other steels and CO_2 gas if quality requirements of the weld metal in regard to porosity are not critical. Those electrodes with higher amounts of deoxidizers produce quality welds on semikilled and rimmed steels as well as on killed steels. Electrodes (not listed in the specification) are also available for welding high-strength low-alloy steels and quenched-and-tempered steels.

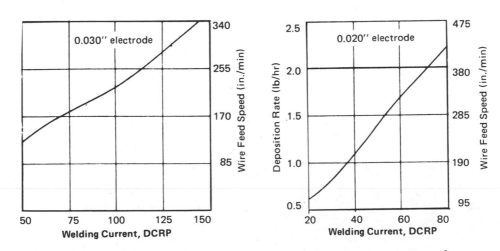

Fig. 13-11. Deposition rates of 0.030 and 0.020-in. E70S-2 electrodes with argon-25% CO_2 shielding gas, short-circuiting-type transfer.

WELDING VARIABLES

Porosity: In order to avoid porosity, the proper electrode must be used. (For further information about electrodes, see the appendix of AWS A5.18 or consult the supplier.) Other ways to minimize porosity in welding carbon steel are:

1. Avoid excessive current densities. Change to a larger wire or lower the current.

2. Check the welding speed with recommended welding procedures. Too high a speed sometimes causes porosity.

3. Maintain a flow of shielding gas of 40 to 60 cfh when argon with 5% oxygen is used with spray transfer, and 10 to 15 cfh with short-circuiting transfer.

4. Keep the electrode centered in the gas flow from the gun.

5. When welding from both sides of the plate, be sure the first pass on the second side penetrates well into the weld on the first side. Back-chip if necessary.

Deposition Rates: Weld-metal deposition rates for three different wire sizes are indicated in Fig. 13-10. These rates are for a triple-deoxidized wire (E70S-2) used with a mixture of argon with 5% oxygen and spray-type transfer. Fig. 13-11 shows similar information for E70S-2 wire used with a mixture of argon and 25% CO_2 and a short-circuiting-type transfer. These figures, along with the procedures, can be used for estimating the amount of wire required and welding costs.

Equipment: The wire-feeding equipment for solid electrode is essentially the same as that used for flux-cored electrode. The electrode is fed at a constant speed, and the current (DCRP) is supplied by a constant-voltage power source. The current is adjusted by changing the electrode feed, and the voltage is adjusted at the power source.

Conventional constant-voltage power sources are discussed in Chapter 4. More sophisticated power sources have been developed especially for gas metal-arc welding. These have adjustable slope control and adjustable inductance control. When a short circuit occurs in short-circuiting-type transfer, the slope determines the maximum short-circuit current, and the inductance determines the rate at which the current rises to the maximum. The proper combination of slope and inductance provides the optimum welding conditions for gas metal-arc welding. Fig. 13-12 illustrates the slope and voltage ranges that are typical with such power supplies.

JOINT REQUIREMENTS

Plate 1/8-in. thick and thinner (down to .035-in.) may be butt-welded with square edges, if an opening of zero to 1/16 in. is used. The short-circuiting technique should be used for wider openings. Short circuiting bridges relatively wide gaps and eliminates excessive penetration.

Plate thicknesses of 3/16-in. may be welded with square edges with a 1/16 to 3/32 in. opening. Two passes are usually necessary — one from each side. A bead overlap greater than the original root spacing is desired to prevent centerline porosity and cold laps. Maximum overlap is attainable if the backhand technique is used on the second side.

For the best quality welds, some bevel should be provided. A 60° single or double-V joint is recommended. A root opening of zero to 1/16 in. should be maintained. Double-V welds can tolerate wider openings than single-V welds. In single-V grooves, a sealing pass from the reverse side will generally be required unless the fitup is uniform.

Plates 1/4-in. thick and thicker generally require single or double-V grooves with 60° included angles. It is generally advantageous to employ a double V. Less metal is needed to fill the joint and less distortion results when welding from alternate sides.

For both types of joints, zero root face is recommended. This assures overlap of the root passes. A root face should not be considered unless an opening larger than normal can be maintained to insure penetration. Uniform penetration is obtainable in joints having no root face if the opening is held less than 3/32 in.

Poor fitup and root overlap should be avoided. Where variations in spacing greater than 1/16 in. are encountered, copper backup strips will prevent excessive penetration.

U grooves should be employed on plate thicker than 1 in. They require considerably less weld metal. Root spacings should be maintained

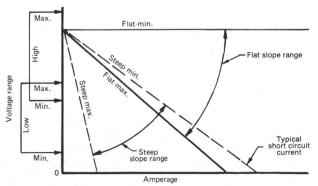

Courtesy Linde Division, Union Carbide Corp.

Fig. 13-12. Slope and voltage ranges typical of power supplies that give control over slope, voltage, and inductance.

between 1/32 and 3/32 in. to assure adequate penetration.

PROCEDURES

The following are typical procedures for gas metal-arc welding of butt and fillet welds in carbon-steel plate.

PROCEDURES FOR GAS METAL-ARC WELDING CARBON-STEEL BUTTS BY SPRAY TRANSFER

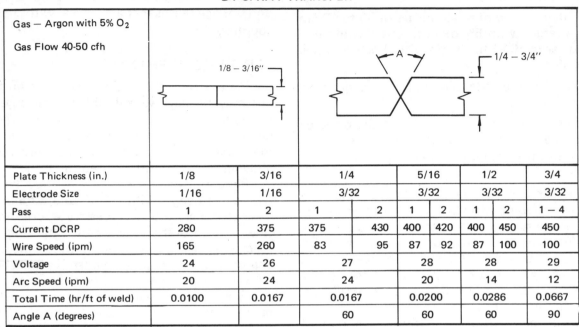

Gas — Argon with 5% O_2
Gas Flow 40-50 cfh

Plate Thickness (in.)	1/8	3/16	1/4		5/16		1/2		3/4
Electrode Size	1/16	1/16	3/32		3/32		3/32		3/32
Pass	1	2	1	2	1	2	1	2	1 — 4
Current DCRP	280	375	375	430	400	420	400	450	450
Wire Speed (ipm)	165	260	83	95	87	92	87	100	100
Voltage	24	26	27		28		28		29
Arc Speed (ipm)	20	24	24		20		14		12
Total Time (hr/ft of weld)	0.0100	0.0167	0.0167		0.0200		0.0286		0.0667
Angle A (degrees)			60		60		60		90

PROCEDURES FOR GAS METAL-ARC WELDING CARBON-STEEL BUTTS BY SHORT-CIRCUITING TRANSFER

Gas — Argon with 25% CO_2
Gas Flow 10-15 cfh
Electrode Size 0.030 in.

0.035 — 0.125"

Plate Thickness (in.)	0.035	0.047	0.063	0.078	0.100	0.125
Current DCRP	55	65	85	105	110	130
Wire Speed (ipm)	117	140	170	225	235	300
Voltage	16	17	17	18	18	19
Arc Speed (ipm)	13	15	15	15	15	16
Total Time (hr/ft of weld)	0.0154	0.0133	0.0133	0.0133	0.0133	0.0125

PROCEDURES FOR GAS METAL-ARC WELDING OF CARBON-STEEL FILLETS BY SPRAY TRANSFER

Gas — Argon with 5% O_2 Gas Flow 40 — 50 cfh Electrode Size 3/32 in.				
Weld Size, (in.)	1/4	5/16	3/4	3/8
Plate Thickness, (in.)	5/16	1/2	1	3/4
Pass	1	1	4	1
Current (DCRP)	400	450	450	475
Wire Feed Speed (ipm)	87	100	100	110
Voltage	27	28	28	30
Arc Speed (ipm)	16	12	7	9
Total Time (hr/ft of weld)	0.0125	0.0167	0.114	0.0222

GAS TUNGSTEN-ARC WELDING

The AWS definition of gas tungsten-arc (TIG) welding is "an arc welding process wherein coalescence is produced by heating with an arc between a tungsten electrode and the work." A filler metal may or may not be used. Shielding is obtained with a gas or a gas mixture.

Essentially, the nonconsumable tungsten electrode is a "torch" — a heating device. Under the protective gas shield, metals to be joined may be heated above their melting points so that material from one part coalesces with material from the other part. Upon solidification of the molten area, unification occurs. Pressure may be used when the edges to be joined are approaching the molten state to assist coalescence. Welding in this manner requires no filler metal.

If the work is too heavy for the mere fusing of abutting edges, and if groove joints or reinforcements, such as fillets, are required, filler metal must be added. This is supplied by a filler rod, manually or mechanically fed into the weld puddle. Both the tip of the nonconsumable tungsten electrode and the tip of the filler rod are kept under the protective gas shield as welding progresses.

Fig. 13-13 illustrates the TIG torch, and Fig. 13-14 a schematic for manual TIG welding. The mode of manually feeding filler rod into the weld puddle is illustrated in Fig. 13-15. In automatic welding, filler wire is fed mechanically through a guide into the weld puddle. When running heavy joints manually, a variation in the mode of feeding is to lay or press the filler rod in or along the joint and melt it along with the joint edges. All of the standard types of joints can be welded with the TIG process and filler metal.

Usually the arc is started by a high-frequency, high-voltage device that causes a spark to jump from the electrode to the work and initiate the welding current. Once the arc is started, the electrode is moved in small circles to develop a pool of molten metal and is positioned about 75° to the surface of the puddle formed. The filler rod, held

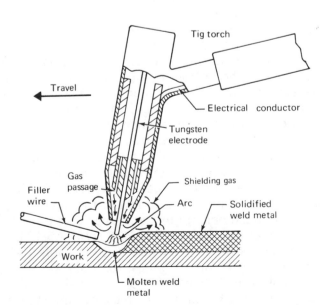

Fig. 13-13. Principles of the gas tungsten-arc process. If filler metal is required, it is fed into the pool from a separate filler rod.

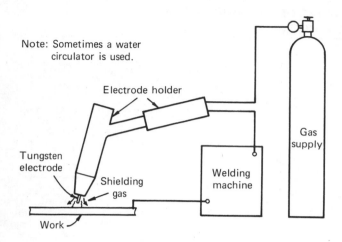

Note: Sometimes a water circulator is used.

Fig. 13-14. Schematic of manual TIG welding.

at an angle of about 15° to the surface of the work, is advanced into the weld puddle. When adequate filler metal has been added to the pool, the rod is withdrawn and the torch moved forward. The cycle is then repeated. At all times, however, the filler rod is kept within the protective gas shield. For carbon steel, low-alloy steel, and copper, the touch and withdraw method can be used to establish the arc but seldom if ever is this method satisfactory for the reactive metals.

Materials weldable by the TIG process are most grades of carbon, alloy, and stainless steels; aluminum and most of its alloys; magnesium and most of its alloys; copper and various brasses and bronzes; high-temperature alloys of various types; numerous hard-surfacing alloys; and such metals as titanium, zirconium, gold and silver. The process is especially adapted for welding thin materials where the requirements for quality and finish are exacting. It is one of the few processes that are satisfac-

tory for welding such tiny and thin-walled objects as transistor cases, instrument diaphragms, and delicate expansion bellows.

The gases employed in the TIG process are argon and helium and mixtures of the two (see Chapter 5). Filler metals are available for a wide variety of metals and alloys, and these are often similar although not necessarily identical to the metals being joined.

TIG WITH CARBON AND LOW-ALLOY STEELS

Gas tungsten-arc welding is not widely used in mass production for welding carbon and low-alloy steel. Some applications, however, require the unique characteristics of the process and, in those applications, the process is the most economical method of welding. Porosity can be a problem but, if this can be resolved, the process is good for thin sheets and the first pass on multiple-pass butts welded from one side.

Killed steel is fully deoxidized during the refining process and little difficulty from porosity is experienced in welding this material with the gas tungsten-arc process. Rimmed steel is not fully deoxidized and can be a cause of porosity unless filler metal of the proper composition is added. A filler rod containing deoxidizers similar to Class E70S-2 (AWS Specification A5.18-69) is satisfactory, (see Table 5-17). If filler metal cannot be added, a fluxing material can be used to minimize porosity.

Low-alloy steels such as the chromium-molybdenum alloys (ASTM A387 and A335) are fully deoxidized and can be welded using a rod with a composition similar to the base metal. Alloy losses due to welding are negligible.

One important characteristic of gas tungsten-arc welding is its ability to weld thin sheets or the first pass in the bottom of a groove with complete penetration and a uniform, continuous bead on the underside. For example, the first bead in the bottom of a circumferential pipe joint can be fully penetrated, and a continuous small bead is laid on the inside of the pipe. This method has considerable advantage over using a backup ring.

Electrodes used for gas tungsten-arc welding are of three types; pure tungsten, thoriated tungsten, and zirconium-tungsten. Specifications for tungsten electrodes are listed in AWS A5.12-69, and chemical requirements are given in Table 13-3. Recommended current range for each electrode size is given in Table 13-4. For mild and low-alloy steels, argon is the preferred shielding gas. Typical welding conditions for butt joints are given in Table 13-5.

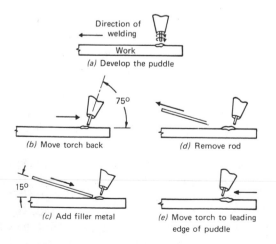

Fig. 13-15. Mode of manually feeding filler metal into the weld puddle when TIG welding.

Welding torches are available in several sizes. Those used up to about 200 amp are air-cooled; water cooling is necessary for operation at high currents.

For mild and low-alloy steels, DCSP is used, supplied by a variable-voltage-type power source. This equipment is described in Chapter 4.

TABLE 13-3. AWS 5.12-69 Chemical Requirements for Tungsten Electrodes

AWS Electrode Class	Composition (%)			
	Tungsten*	Thoria†	Zirconia	Other+
EWP	99.5	—	—	0.5
EWTh-1	98.5	0.8 to 1.2	—	0.5
EWTh-2	97.5	1.7 to 2.2	—	0.5
EWTh-3	98.95	0.35 to 0.55	—	0.5
EWZr	99.2	—	0.15 to 0.40	0.5

* Minimum, by difference.
† Chemical analysis may be made by any method agreed upon by supplier and purchaser. If there is a dispute regarding thoria content, the procedure described in Specification F288, ASTM Standards, Part 8, shall be used.
+ Total of other elements, maximum.

TABLE 13-4. Typical Current Ranges for Tungsten Electrodes (DCSP, Argon Shielding Gas)

Current Range (amp)	Electrode Diameter (in.)
To 15	0.010
5 — 20	0.020
15 — 80	0.040
70 — 150	1/16
150 — 250	3/32
250 — 400	1/8
350 — 500	5/32
500 — 750	3/16
750 — 1000	1/4

TABLE 13-5. Typical Conditions for Butt-Welding Mild and Low-Alloy Steels with Gas Tungsten-Arc Process

Thickness (in.)	Current, DCSP (amp)	Suggested Rod Size (in.)	Average Welding Speed (ipm)	Argon Flow (cfh)
0.035	100	1/16	12 — 15	8 — 10
0.049	100 — 125	1/16	12 — 18	8 — 10
0.060	100 — 140	1/16	12 — 18	8 — 10
0.089	140 — 170	3/32	12 — 18	8 — 10
0.125	150 — 200	1/8	10 — 12	8 — 10

Oxyacetylene Welding

So-called "oxyacetylene" welding is the most popular of the gas welding techniques. Oxyacetylene welding involves the combustion of acetylene gas in a mixture with oxygen, thereby producing a temperature high enough to melt most metals, including steel. Other gases, such as "Mapp" gas (stabilized methylacetylene-propadiene), hydrogen, propane, and natural gas are used in gas welding, but acetylene is the most widely used fuel gas, and the oxyacetylene process is the most representative of commercial gas welding with the major metals.

Gas welding is fundamentally simpler than electric-arc welding. Two pieces of metal are brought together, and their edges are melted with a flame and allowed to flow together, with or without supplementary molten metal from a welding rod. The flame is, thus, a "tool" by which fusion and coalesence are accomplished. Since the flame results from a careful mixturing of the combustible element — acetylene or other fuel gases — and the oxidizing agent (oxygen gas), by varying the mixture the chemical environment around the molten metal can be controlled. Inadequate oxygen for complete oxidation of the fuel gas will give a "reducing" flame; an excess of oxygen will give an "oxidizing" flame.

The equipment used for oxyacetylene welding is likewise simpler than that used for arc welding. It consists of compressed-gas cylinders, gas regulators, hoses, and the welding torch. The gas regulators on the acetylene and oxygen cylinders control the pressures of the gases as they exit into the flexible rubber hoses that are attached to the inlets of the welding torch. Fig. 14-1 illustrates a typical oxyacetylene torch. At the torch, the gases pass through an inlet control valve and into a mixing chamber. The mixed gases exit through a tip, where, upon ignition, they produce a long, elliptical-shaped flame. The tip temperature of the flame may range up to and surpassing 6000°, depending on the ratio of oxygen to acetylene used.

APPLICATIONS FOR OXYACETYLENE WELDING

Oxyacetylene welding has certain advantages over arc welding — notably its portability. With the equipment mounted on a hand truck, welding can be done anywhere. The cylinders and torch can be carried to the field to repair a broken piece of machinery or used anyplace out of reach of an AC power outlet. An additional advantage of the equipment is that it can be quickly converted to a metal-cutting tool by substituting a cutting torch for the welding torch. (See Fig. 14-2). In out-of-the-way places, cutting frequently precedes welding in repair jobs. The heat of the flame can also be

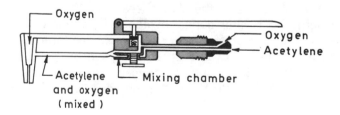

Fig. 14-2. The cutting-torch attachment that can be substituted for a welding torch on an oxyacetylene system.

used for brazing and preheating and postheating on weldments. Because of this flexibility and utility, the oxyacetylene torch is preferred for maintenance welding — field and shop repairs — and sometimes for very short production runs.

Gas welding also has other advantages. The weldor has excellent control of the temperature of

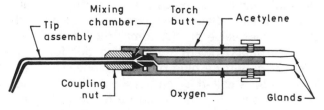

Fig. 14-1. A typical oxyacetylene welding torch.

the welding zone, merely by his manipulation. When the rate of heat input from the flame is coordinated with the speed of welding, the size of the weld can be controlled, permitting the pressure of the flame to be used in shaping and positioning the rolled bead. Also, the weldor has complete control of filler-metal deposition; he can add more or reduce according to his observation of the need. This flexibility in control makes gas welding suited for joining thin metals, small pipe, and assemblies with poor fitup and for smoothing or repairing rough arc welds. With heavy sections, however, gas welding becomes uneconomical.

Oxyacetylene welding can be used with most ferrous and nonferrous metals, providing the appropriate flame characteristic is employed. Oxyacetylene supplies the heat intensity and flame atmosphere necessary for welding carbon steels; cast iron; alloys of iron, copper, and nickel; and alloys of aluminum and zinc. Gas welding of steel is done exclusively with the oxygen-acetylene flame.

CHEMISTRY OF THE OXYACETYLENE FLAME

The chemistry of the oxyacetylene flame is partially responsible for the versatility of this welding process. When acetylene (C_2H_2) is burned with approximately an equal volume of oxygen (O_2), the flame produces a temperature in the range of 5500° to 6000°F. This is called a neutral flame; combustion is complete — there is no noticeable excess of oxygen, or of carbon or hydrogen from disassociation of the fuel gas. (Whereas a 1 to 1 ratio of oxygen to acetylene is considered to give a neutral flame, more precisely the ratio is 1.1 to 1.) At this ratio, the flame (see Fig. 14-3) has a bright short inner cone, enveloped by a long transparent and reddish-blue outer cone. The temperature of the tip of the inner cone, where combustion results from supply oxygen, is in the range from 5500 to 6000°. In the long envelope, where

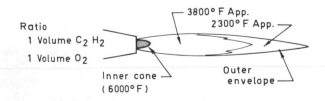

Fig. 14-3. The neutral oxyacetylene flame, produced by equal volumes of acetylene and oxygen, gives a flame with a temperature of 5500 to 6000°F at the tip of the inner cone and a long outer envelope that is essentially neither oxidizing nor reducing.

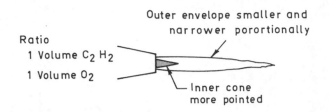

Fig. 14-4. An oxidizing flame — never used in the welding of steel.

atmospheric oxygen oxidizes carbon monoxide and hydrogen resulting from the breakdown of acetylene, the temperature of the flame diminishes. The long outer cone requires about 1-1/2 times as much atmospheric oxygen as the supply oxygen fed to the inner cone. The chemical equations involved are:

Primary combustion producing the inner cone —

$$C_2H_2 + O_2 \rightarrow 2CO\uparrow + H_2\uparrow + heat$$

Secondary combustion in the outer cone —

$$4CO + 2O_2 \rightarrow 4CO_2 + heat$$
$$2H_2 + O_2 \rightarrow 2H_2O + heat$$

When this neutral flame is used in welding steel, the tip of the inner cone is held near, but not touching, the metal. Its extremely high heat melts the areas on which the inner cone is directed. The molten metal is protected against oxidation or carburization by the neutral characteristic of the flame. The neutral flame is ideal for welding steel and is mandatory for good results with stainless steels.

With an excess of supply oxygen, an oxidizing flame is produced. As Fig. 14-4 shows, the inner cone becomes more pointed, and the outer envelope becomes smaller and narrower. With considerable excess, the hissing sound characteristic of oxyacetylene cutting develops. Oxidizing flames are never used in the welding of steel, and the weldor should always be careful in adjusting his torch valves to avoid a flame that might oxidize or "burn" the molten metal. The only use for an oxidizing flame in welding is in the welding of copper and certain copper-base alloys. Here, the flame should be just sufficiently rich in oxygen to insure that a film of slag will form over the molten pool.

A deficiency of oxygen in the flame results in a reducing flame. As oxygen is added to the shapeless acetylene flame by gradually opening the oxygen inlet valve on the torch, the luminous portion contracts toward the welding tip, forming a bright zone with a blue outer envelope. This flame (Fig. 14-5) is called a "carburizing" flame. It has a lower temperature than a neutral flame at its bright luminous inner-cone tip and is useful for silver brazing and soldering and in the welding of lead.

As more oxygen is introduced, the bright inner cone contracts, becomes more regularly shaped, and has a pale-green feather extending from its tip. This feather, which disappears as ratios approach 1:1, indicates that a slight excess of acetylene exists. At this ratio, the flame is reducing enough to insure the absence of oxidizing conditions at the weld; it is not reducing enough, however, to carburize metals. Such a flame is used when welding with low-alloy steel rods.

EQUIPMENT FOR OXYACETYLENE WELDING

As noted in the introduction to this chapter, the equipment for oxyacetylene welding is relatively simple: a cylinder of oxygen, a cylinder of acetylene, two regulators, two flexible hoses, and a torch with the necessary tips. This equipment may be mounted on a hand cart for portability or it may be stationary. When stationary, the two gases may flow from central gas stations through piping and manifolds, in which case additional equipment may be required such as flashback arrestors downstream from the gas cylinders.

The Welding Torch: The function of the welding torch (Fig. 14-1) is to act as the mixing and control device for the gases and as the manipulating tool for directing the oxyacetylene flame. The torch consists of a butt or handle suitable for holding in the hand. It has two inlet connections for attaching the oxygen and acetylene hoses. Each inlet has a valve that adjusts the volume of gas passing through it. With these valves, the proportions of oxygen and acetylene flowing into a mixing chamber in the torch-tip assembly are controlled.

The Tip Assembly: The welding tip and (in some cases) the mixing head make up the tip assembly. This assembly is attached to the torch with a coupling nut (Fig. 14-1). The seat between the mixing head and torch handle is usually sealed with a Neoprene ring, making it unnecessary to use a wrench when changing tips. Orifices in the mixing head meet with gas passages in the torch handle and provide mixing of the gases in the proportions set by the inlet valve adjustments. The tip, itself, is

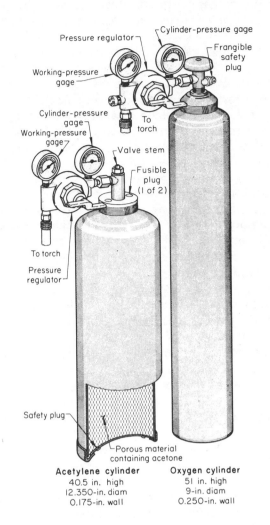

Fig. 14-6. Portable gas cylinders and regulators used in gas welding.

usually a hard-copper tube, bent at the forward end as shown in Fig. 14-1. It may be made integrally with the mixer head or may be a separate unit that screws into the head. Tips of various orifice diameters are available for a particular make of welding torch.

Tips with small orifice diameters produce small flames for welding thin sections; tips with larger diameters are required for heavier work. Manufacturers of welding tips supply information on the proper size tip to be used in relation to gas pressure and the thickness of material. The bore configuration at the exit of the tip influences the shape of the inner flame cone; the tip of the inner cone may be bulbous, sharply pointed, or of a shape between these extremes, according to tip selected.

Pressure Regulators: The function of the regulator on each gas cylinder is to reduce cylinder pressure to working pressure and maintain the latter at a constant value. Fig. 14-6 shows pressure

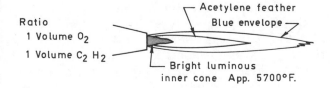

Fig. 14-5. A carburizing flame, which has a considerable excess of acetylene.

regulators on gas cylinders. Regulators are designed for specific gases and are not generally interchangeable.

The oxygen pressure in a full cylinder usually ranges from 2200 to 2700 psi. Acetylene is supplied as a gas dissolved in liquid acetone with the cylinder pressurized to about 250 psi. (It is necessary to dissolve acetylene in acetone to get an appreciable volume of the gas in a cylinder. Acetylene cannot be compressed by a pressure beyond 29.4 psi. At or above 29.4 psi, it is chemically unstable and will explode at the slightest shock. For welding, pressures have to be reduced to about 1 to 12 psi and maintained without fluctuation. For cutting, the oxygen pressure is maintained at a range of approximately 20 to 60 psi, depending on the job requirements, while acetylene remains about the same as for welding.

The regulator must be more than a simple pressure-reducing valve, because cylinder pressure is constantly changing as the contents are used. Thus, a regulator is a precision instrument to reduce high cylinder pressure to working pressure, to maintain these pressures without fluctuation, and to perform these functions automatically. It must be constructed so that the rough handling it will receive in ordinary shop practice will not easily cause damage.

Regulators are mechanical devices and may be either single or two-stage. They must be selected for the application: an acetylene regulator should not be used on an oxygen line, and vice versa. Also, a regulator designed for a pipeline should not be used on a cylinder.

Oxygen regulators are usually painted green. Their union nuts are right-hand and have thread sizes to fit oxygen cylinders. They are designed to withstand the very high pressures of oxygen cylinders. It is customary to provide a 3000-psi pressure gage on oxygen regulators, thus providing a safety factor to prevent damage to the gage mechanism. The pressure gage usually has a second scale indicating the contents of the cylinder in terms of cubic feet of gas at 70°F. Regulators are provided with safety devices to vent the gas in the working-pressure stage, should a faulty valve allow pressure build-up.

Acetylene regulators are usually painted red. They may have either union nuts with right-hand threads or male cylinder connectors with left-hand threads. Cylinder pressures may be graduated to 400 psi and working pressures to 30 psi. Newer gages indicate anything above 15 psi in the working side with a broad red line, since acetylene should *never* be used at a working pressure above 15 psi.

Flashback Arrestors: Safe practice requires that a flashback arrestor be attached forward of the pressure regulator in both acetylene and oxygen outlets. The flashback arrestor may be mounted directly downstream from the regulators on the gas cylinders or downstream from the outlets on a piping and manifold gas-distribution system. When a flashback fire occurs in the hoses carrying acetylene or oxygen to the welding or cutting torch, the arrestor extinguishes the flame and acts as a reverse-flow check valve. The gas supply is, thus, protected from flashback fire.

Flexible Hoses: Flexible hoses permit the gas cylinders and regulators to be kept a safe distance from the working area and allow the weldor freedom of movement. Only hose designed for welding and cutting should be used. The standard color for acetylene hose is red and oxygen hose green. The word "OXYGEN" is usually molded into the surface of 1/4 in. and larger oxygen hoses at regular intervals. Acetylene hose is marked "ACETYLENE" in a similar manner. The internal construction of the hoses is such that they have good flexibility yet resistance to kinking and entanglement. The standard sizes for oxygen and acetylene hoses are 3/16 in. and 1/4 in. inside diameter.

The connecting nuts on oxygen hose lines have right-hand threads and on acetylene hose lines, left-hand threads. This makes errors in line connection impossible. For easy recognition, the left-hand acetylene nuts are marked with a groove cut around their centers. Often oxygen nuts are marked "STD. OXY" and acetylene nuts "STD. ACET".

Hoses are attached to the welding torch by pushing over and clamping onto the provided glands (see Fig. 14-1), or hose connections may be made with ferrules. After fitting the hose to the torch, the connection should be tested for leaks with soap suds or by immersing in water. Any hose leak at the coupling should be repaired by cutting the hose and remaking the connection. Leaks in a hose at other locations may be repaired by cutting out the damaged section and inserting a splice coupling fitted with ferrules. Repairs to hoses should never be made with tape.

Lighters: Spark lighters are necessary with oxyacetylene welding and cutting equipment. Matches or cigarette lighters should not be used, since holding the hand close to the torch can lead to serious burns. The torch should never be lighted by allowing acetylene to flow onto hot metal.

Oxygen Supply: Oxygen is the chemical element that supports combustion. When it is compressed to high pressures in nearly pure form in storage cylinders, it is dangerous for two reasons — the possible sudden release of that pressure and the violent oxidation reactions that could occur should concentrated oxygen come into contact with easily ignitable materials. Oxygen itself can't burn; it is the element that does the burning. And pressurized oxygen won't explode, as unstabilized acetylene pressurized to 29.4 psi might do, unless the cylinder containing it, or the cylinder fittings, fail. Assuming all safety precautions are followed in using oxygen, it is not a threat to property, life, or limb. However, the slightest misuse of this reactive gas can be deadly. Anything other than use with the welding and cutting equipment designed for it can lead to fires and explosion. Cylinder oxygen should never be used:

- For powering pneumatic tools or paint spraying.
- To blow out pipe lines.
- To dust clothing or wash.
- For pressure tests of any kind.
- To start internal combustion engines.
- In oil preheating burners.

A stream of high-purity oxygen directed onto a greasy surface can cause a violent fire or explosion. There have been instances of weldors being killed by directing a stream of oxygen onto grease. *NEVER, NEVER* use oxygen for other than its prescribed purpose in welding or cutting.

Most commercial oxygen is supplied in standard-size steel cylinders (Fig. 14-6), holding what would amount to 244 cubic feet of the gas at 70°F and atmospheric pressure. The cylinder is usually under a pressure of 2200 psi when the ambient temperature is 70°F. The weight of the gas in a standard 51" x 9" O.D. cylinder is apprximately 20 pounds. Smaller-size tanks are also available for use in handling where small volumes are required.

The construction, distribution, handling, and use of oxygen cylinders are covered by safety laws and regulations. The cylinders are made from a high-grade steel, deep drawn from a single plate. Cylinder valves are specially designed to handle high pressures and are equipped with safety devices that will melt or burst to release pressure should the cylinder be accidentally exposed to high heat. A metal cap that screws on the neck ring protects the valve from damage during shipment and handling.

The following safety precautions are recommended by the Linde Division, Union Carbide Corporation, a major supplier of welding gases:

1. Use only cylinders carrying ICC markings. These markings indicate that the cylinders comply with the regulations of the Interstate Commerce Commission. Cylinders meeting such specifications and regulations are manufactured under close inspection, are provided with proper safety devices, and must pass severe tests. It is illegal to tamper with numbers and markings on cylinders.

2. Cylinders should be stored only in approved, safe places. Store cylinders in definitely assigned places where they will not be knocked over or damaged by passing or falling objects. Cylinders should be kept away from stoves, radiators, furnaces, or other hot places. They should be stored well away from highly combustible material, such as grease, oil, or excelsior.

   Inside buildings, cylinders of oxygen should not be stored close to cylinders of acetylene or other fuel gas. Unless they are well separated, there should be a fire-resistant partition between the oxygen and fuel-gas cylinders.

   Where cylinders are stored in the open, they should be protected against accumulations of ice and snow and from the direct rays of the sun in locations where high temperatures prevail. Cylinders containing oxygen should be placed well away from cylinders containing combustible gases.

   Regulations of the National Board of Fire Underwriters and any local, state, or municipal regulations regarding cylinder storage should be followed carefully. While cylinders are being moved, keep them from being knocked over or from falling. When moving cylinders by crane or derrick, use a suitable cradle or platform. Never use slings or an electric magnet. Whenever practical, suitable trucks should be provided for conveying and handling cylinders. Unless cylinders are on a suitable truck, regulators should be removed and valve-protection caps should be in place hand-tight when cylinders are moved. Always close cylinder valves before moving cylinders.

3. Never use valve-protection caps for lifting cylinders from one vertical position to another. Valve-protection caps are designed to protect valves from damage. Before raising oxygen cylinders from a horizontal to a vertical position, be sure that the cap is properly in place and hand-tight; then raise the cylinder by grasping the cap firmly in hand. It is not good practice to allow acetylene cylinders to lie in a horizontal position.

4. Never use cylinders as rollers or supports even if they are considered to be empty.

5. Keep cylinders from being knocked over while in use. Use a suitable truck, chain, or steadying device. It doesn't take much of a shock to

break off an oxygen cylinder valve. Should this happen the force from the high pressure inside the cylinder is capable of driving it through a reinforced concrete wall or most any obstacle that might be in its way.

6. Never allow cylinders to come in contact with live wires, third rails, or ground wires from electrical equipment.

7. Keep cylinders far enough away from welding and cutting work so that sparks, hot slag, or flame will not reach them.

8. Always close cylinder valves when work is finished, and always close vales of empty cylinders while in storage prior to return to supplier.

9. Never use oxygen from a cylinder except through an oxygen regulator. When an oxygen regulator is attached, do not open the valve abruptly. The valve should be "cracked" slightly until the regulator has become filled with oxygen. Then open the valve all the way. If the valve is suddenly opened, the pressure may damage the regulator and cylinder gage. Stand to one side of the regulator when opening the cylinder valve.

10. Never tamper with or attempt to repair oxygen cylinder valves. If trouble is experienced, tag the cylinder and promptly send the supplier a full report of the trouble, giving the serial number stamped on the cylinder.

Acetylene Supply: Acetylene is a colorless gas with a garlic-like odor. It is made up of two atoms of carbon and two atoms of hydrogen (CH:CH), a constituency suggesting both ease in decomposition and oxidation. It is, in fact, an explosive; it readily forms explosive mixtures with air; and it disassociates with explosive force when pressurized at about 29.4 psi — or roughly about twice atmospheric pressure. Dissociation means that the molecule CH:CH breaks up into carbon and hydrogen with the release of much heat. At the heat of dissociation — if air or oxygen is present — carbon and hydrogen are oxidized (burned), releasing more heat and adding to the violences of the explosion. Acetylene when not pressurized will also explode (disassociate) at a temperature of 635°F. Oxyacetylene welding and cutting equipment is designed so that *acetylene gas* is never subjected to more than 15 psi pressure and its ambient temperature is never allowed to get above room temperature except under controlled combustion conditions.

The cylinder that acetylene comes in, however, will have a gage reading of about 250 psi — or about 17 times atmospheric pressure. The paradox between the explosive nature of acetylene at 29.4

psi and its availability in cylinders at 250 psi is explained by the fact that cylinder acetylene is in a dissolved, rather than free, form. It is dissolved in acetone, which organic liquid will dissolve 25 times its volume of acetylene for each atmosphere of pressure. The gage reading on the gas cylinder is, thus, not the reading for acetylene pressure, but the pressure of acetone.

A fully charged acetylene cylinder contains 425 times as much acetylene as the volume of liquid acetone in it. On release of pressure — opening of the cylinder valve — acetylene "boils" out of the acetone-acetylene solution. The acetone in the cylinder is "contained" in a porous, absorbent material, such as asbestos or diatomaceous earth. When using a cylinder of acetylene, acetone vapors will also be released, especially if the discharge rate is excessive. "Acetone blowing" — as it is called — is shown by the green color imparted to the torch flame. Storage of an acetylene cylinder in a horizontal position, as well as excessive discharge rate, will lead to acetone blowing, which not only gives an undesirable flame for welding but results in a hazardous situation to exist within the cylinder.

Acetylene is supplied in cylinders of 10, 40, 60, 100, 225, and 300-cubic feet. Fig. 14-6 shows a typical cylinder. Acetylene cylinders are fitted with fusible safety plugs that melt at 212°F. Plugs are located in both the top and bottom of all but the smallest cylinders, so that excessive heat at any location can be readily conducted to the plug.

Acetylene cylinders *must* be handled with precaution. The weldor should always bear in mind that he is handling an explosive — one that is subject to complete control with proper handling, but one that can cause devastation with the slightest abuse. The following are accepted storage and handling safety rules:

1. Cylinders must be protected against excessive rise in temperature. Cylinders may be stored in the open, but should be protected against extremes of weather.

2. Cylinders permitted inside of a building should be stored in a well protected, ventilated, dry location, well away from highly combustible material, such as oil or excelsior, and away from stoves, radiators, or furnaces.

3. Acetylene cylinders should be stored and used with valve-end up and *NOT BE ALLOWED TO LIE ON THEIR SIDES.*

4. Acetylene cylinders should be handled carefully. Rough handling, knocks, or falls could damage the cylinder, valve, or fuse plugs and cause leakage.

5. When the valve on the acetylene cylinder is

opened and a leak of acetylene is found around the valve stem, close the valve and tighten the gland nut. If this does not stop the leak, discontinue the use of the cylinder and move it outdoors. Attach a tag to it and advise the supplier.

6. Never tamper with fuse plugs.

7. Never use acetylene from a cylinder or cylinder manifold without reducing the pressure through an approved pressure-reducing regulator.

8. Always open the cylinder valve slowly.

9. Do not open an acetylene cylinder valve more than *ONE AND ONE-HALF TURNS* of the spindle.

10. Always use the special wrench provided for the acetylene cylinder valve when a wrench is required.

11. Leave this special wrench in position on the stem of the acetylene valve while the cylinder is in use, so that the acetylene can be quickly turned off in case of emergency.

12. Never under any circumstances attempt to transfer acetylene from one cylinder to another, nor to refill an acetylene cylinder, nor to mix any other gas with acetylene in the cylinder.

Acetylene for welding and cutting can also be made available by the use of acetylene generators. With these, acetylene gas is obtained by the reaction of calcium carbide and water (the old miner's-cap principle). Such generators are designed so the gas will not be given off at pressure in excess of 15 psi. The convenience of acetylene in cylinders has made acetylene generators outmoded to a large extent except in special circumstances, and the student of welding is not likely to encounter them. Acetylene in quantity is usually more economical when generated in-plant, but when the welding operations are of such a magnitude that large quantities of acetylene are required the trend is to go to electric arc welding.

FILLER METAL FOR OXYACETYLENE WELDING

Filler metal for gas welding low-carbon steels is supplied in the form of cold-drawn steel rods 36" long and 1/16" to 1/4" in diameter. Rods for other metals are also available and supplied in various diameters and sizes. Rods for gas welding are bare — no flux covering — and out-of-position work depends solely on the weldor's manipulative skill. Steel welding rods are standardized in AWS

specifications A5.2. There are three classifications, based on minimum tensile strength of all-weld metal and transverse-weld test specimens:

RG 65 . . . . 67,000 psi minimum
RG 60 . . . . 60,000 psi minimum
RG 45 . . . . 45,000 psi minimum

The mechanical properties specified for these rods are obtained by welding with a neutral to slightly reducing oxyacetylene flame. Forehand and backhand techniques can be used with these rods. Choice of rod influences weld strength to considerable extent, as does the weldor's ability to control the properties of the weld by how he mixes molten base and filler metal. Thus, reinforced welds in thin-wall tubes of 4130 steel welded with RG 45 rod often shows tensile strengths up to 100,000 psi. When such welds are made with RG 60, weld strength may go up to 125,000 psi — or more than twice the specified strength for the metal from the 60,000-psi welding rod. Controlled agitation in the weld puddle brings about the mixing of base and filler metal to give desired weld-metal properties.

Class RG 65 welding rods have a low-alloy steel composition and are used with low-alloy sheet, plate, tube, and pipe with strengths in the range of 65,000 to 75,000 psi. They give the highest strengths when the rod and flame are manipulated to mix base and filler metal.

Class RG 60 welding rods are probably most widely used. They are low-alloy and are preferred in the gas welding of carbon and low-alloy steels in the tensile-strength range of 50,000 to 65,000 psi.

Class RG 45 rods are low-carbon steel and are used in gas-welding of various carbon and low-alloy steels.

No fluxes are used in the oxyacetylene welding of steel. Fluxes are used in the gas welding of cast iron, stainless steel, and most commercial nonferrous metals and alloys.

TECHNIQUES IN OXYACETYLENE WELDING

It is assumed in this text that the student preparing himself to be a weldor will in his professional work use oxyacetylene welding primarily in practice work or repair jobs. Therefore, the details of how oxyacetylene welding might be used in high-production work is slighted and only the fundamental principles explained in the following text. This is believed to be justified since arc welding has taken over most of the productive functions once supplied by oxyacetylene welding. Yet, oxyacetylene welding is vital in repair work and, for this reason, the student should have knowledge of how to apply and, especially, should be knowledgeable of how to set up and operate oxyacetylene equipment.

There are two primary techniques used in manipulating the oxyacetylene flame — forehand welding and backhand welding. With these, the usual welding positions — flat, horizontal, vertical, and overhead — are employed. Techniques vary for joint thicknesses, welding position, and weldor preference.

In forehand welding, the flame is positioned about 45° to the work and directed along the joint away from the completed weld, as shown in Fig. 14-7(a). The welding rod, if used, is held at 30° to 40° to the work, with the tip of the rod in the joint slightly in advance of the weld. The inner cone of the flame is close to but not touching the work. The flame is oscillated sideways so both sides of the joint are properly heated.

The background technique [Fig. 14-7(b)] points the flame in the direction of the completed weld, and the rod is fed in from the welded side of the joint. The angle of the flame is about 50°, and the rod is about 40° to the work.

Backhand welding is usually preferred on steel over 1/8", because the welding can be done faster and smaller bevel angles can be used. Forehand welding is used on thin sheet since it gives better control of a small weld puddle and there is less heat build-up in the work to cause distortion.

Lighting and Adjusting the Torch: The welding procedure begins with lighting and adjusting the torch. The tip or nozzle size should have been selected for the job, with reference to the tip manufacturer's recommendation. The tip should be secured in the torch with firm hand pressure; never use a wrench. The steps are as follows:

1. Adjust the acetylene and oxygen pressure regulators to correct working pressures. (On some manifold systems, regulators may be present.)

2. Hold the torch in one hand and the spark lighter in the other unless a pilot light is available.

3. Partially open the acetylene valve on the torch (1/4 turn or less) and ignite the gas.

4. Point the flame away from persons, the cylinders, or any inflammable materials.

5. Keep opening the torch valve until the flame stops excessive smoking, but not far enough to cause the flame to leave the end of the tip.

6. Open the oxygen valve on the torch until a bright inner cone appears on the flame. The point at which the feathery edges of the flame disappears and a sharp inner cone is visible is the neutral flame (Fig. 14-3). Keep adjusting the torch oxygen valve back and forth until you are sure what a neutral flame looks like. An oxidizing flame (Fig. 14-4) is the flame that has an excessive amount of oxygen beyond the neutral flame. It is a pale blue color without the clearly defined inner cone that the neutral flame has. It is somewhat more pointed than the neutral flame and tends to hiss more. A carburizing flame (Fig. 14-5) is the flame you have before the neutral flame is reached. It is distinguished by the long carburizing feather called the acetylene feather.

The neutral or slightly reducing flame is usually the one wanted in welding steel.

Soft and Harsh Flames: When the weldor has learned to adjust his flame so that the proportions of oxygen and acetylene are correct, he must then learn how to obtain a soft flame. This is a flame produced when the gases flow to the welding tip at a comparatively low speed. If the gases flow to the welding tip at a comparatively high speed, under too much pressure, they produce a harsh flame that is easily recognized because it is noisy. A harsh flame destroys the weld puddle and causes the metal to splash around the edges of the puddle. It is very difficult to get the metal parts to fuse properly with a flame of this kind.

If there is any fluctuation in the flow of the gases from the regulators, the mixture will change, regardless of other conditions; hence a good weldor watches his flame constantly and makes any necessary adjustments to keep it neutral and soft. If he hears a popping noise, he knows that insufficient gas is reaching the tip and immediately delivers a little more oxygen and acetylene by opening both

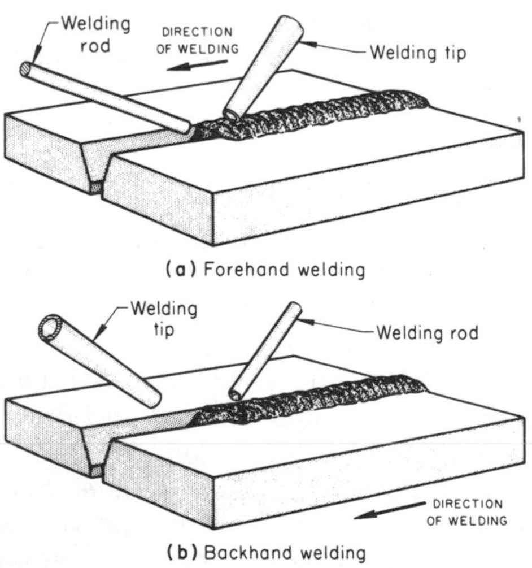

(a) Forehand welding

(b) Backhand welding

Fig. 14-7. Two basic techniques for manipulating the welding tip and welding rod in oxyacetylene welding.

needle valves slightly more.

Obstructed Tips: Should the flame adjustment and operating pressures be correct and still a soft flame can not be produced, a dirty or obstructed welding tip is probably the reason. An obstructed welding tip does not permit the gas mixture to flow evenly. It restricts the source of heat required to melt the metal, and, thus, creates welding difficulties.

If the orifice in the tip becomes clogged, it should be cleaned with the proper size "tip cleaner". *Do not force a cleaner that is too large into the orifice.* This will cause enough damage to require the discarding of the tip, or the attempted removal may cause the cleaner to break off and thus render the tip useless. Likewise, one should not use a cleaner that is too small. This will cause the orifice to become out of round, which will, in turn, make proper flame adjustment impossible. The tip is made of soft copper, so excessive cleaning should be avoided.

PROBLEMS IN OXYACETYLENE WELDING

Backfire and flashback are problems encountered when operating the torch. The two terms are used interchangeably in industry, although there is a well defined difference that should be understood. Backfire is a minor malfunction, while flashback is a serious phenomenon that could cause a fire or explosion.

Backfire: Backfire — or popping of the torch — is a localized explosion in the tip of the torch forward of the mixing chamber. It occurs when the flame recedes momentarily into the tip and is characterized by a loud popping noise. The flame usually reappears immediately, but sometimes is completely extinguished.

The causes of backfire can be varied. One is insufficient gas velocity. Inexperienced operators concerned with "burning through" often attempt to gain control by turning the flame so low that the burning rate of gases exceeds the velocity of the gases leaving the tip. Under normal conditions, the flame cannot enter the tip because the gases are coming out faster than the flame can travel against them. When this situation is reversed a backfire occurs.

If the point of "no smoke" is used as a means for determining the normal valve opening for acetylene with a tip, the problem of torch backfire will be minimized. When the proper heat cannot be obtained except by turning the flame too low, a smaller tip is needed.

When fillet welds are made or when welding is done in a confined space, such as a corner, there is often sufficient heat reflected to overheat the tip.

When this happens the temperature inside the tip exceeds the ignition point of the gas and a backfire occurs. Holding the tip too close to the work, touching the work, or any means of overheating will have the same result.

Sparks entering the orifice of the tip may also ignite the gases before they get outside, and, thus, cause a backfire. If the torch is properly adjusted, this seldom happens, but if there is excess sparking because of an oxidizing flame, if the distance of the inner cone from the weld puddle is greater than 1/3 of the length of the inner cone, or if there is just too much heat, excessive sparking will occur. The odds that a spark will enter the orifice are usually low when the torch is properly adjusted and manipulated, but if sparking is profuse, a backfire can happen.

Flying sparks from the molten weld puddle are deposited as bits of metal that adhere to the face of the tip or the inner surface of the orifice. If the deposit on the face of the tip builds up sufficiently high, or if a single piece adheres to the outer edge of the orifice, a turbulence may be induced that will cause the gases to burn back into the tip, thus causing a backfire and malformation of the inner cone.

Defects in the torch and tip assembly can lead to both backfire and flashback. If the connecting nut that holds the tip assembly in place is loose, there will be an external leak as well as an internal leak. Sparks from the weld puddle will usually ignite an external leak with the possibility of inflicting a hand burn. This connection should always be tight before lighting the torch.

The seal rings that prevent gas mixture between the torch butt and the mixing chamber on the tip assembly are sometimes damaged or worn. Should this be the case, improper mixing of the gases will occur and lead to backfire. If the seal happens to be of the metal-to-metal type, any dirt or extraneous material under the seal would have the same effect.

In the event of a backfire, it may be necessary to relight and readjust the torch for the desired flame. The force of the explosion will take up valve thread slack and may slightly alter the resilience of the regulator diaphragm. Either of these will change the character of the flame, necessitating readjustment.

Flashback: Flashback may be defined as an explosion occurring in or behind the mixing chamber. It is possible for this to involve the hoses, regulators, or even the manifolding system and cylinders. In any event, this is an indication of something radically wrong with the equipment. Damage to the torch, regulators, and hoses and injury to the weldor are possible results.

When a flashback occurs, the flame goes out with a snap or pop louder than with a backfire. Black smoke and sparks issue from the tip, accompanied by a loud squeaking or hissing noise.

At the first indication of a flashback, the weldor should work fast to prevent a serious accident. He should immediately turn off both the oxygen and acetylene torch valves if the torch has not become too hot to hold. Even if he must drop the torch, he should try to turn off these valves. If this is impossible, he should turn off the pressure regulators immediately.

After a fire has been extinguished, the equipment should be inspected and either replaced or repaired to new standards before use. Burn damage inside a hose can lead to continuous clogging of the welding tip in subsequent work.

Common causes for flashback are clogged tips and improper gas mixtures. A tip may become clogged by the weldor accidentally dipping it into the molten puddle. Should a plug of hot metal get inside the tip, internal ignition is instantaneous. The same may happen to a cutting torch when it is held too close to the work or if slag is thrown back into the tip.

Loose nuts, kinked hoses, overheated torches or tips, improper gas pressures, and failure to purge lines before lighting the torch after making changes in equipment are other causes of flashback. When the pressure of one gas is very high and the other very low with a small welding tip, the high-pressure gas may feed back into the low-pressure line, forming an explosive mixture within the line and leading to a flashback and bursted hose. As a rule, the equipment and the condition must be such that mixturing occurs only in the mixing chamber of the torch. Backflow valves used on both inlets to the torch are safety devices designed to stop backflow of opposing gases into hose lines. When used in conjunction with flame arrestors, flashback fires and explosions are minimized.

Thermal Metal-Cutting Processes

Before metals can be weld-joined into assemblies, the parts must be cut from mill materials to desired shapes and dimensions and weld grooves, if any, must be prepared. Cutting may be done by machining, which is costly with thick materials, or it may be done with one of the thermal metal-cutting processes. Thermal cutting includes the gas (usually acetylene) and various arc-cutting processes.

OXACETYLENE CUTTING

Oxyacetylene cutting, often called flame cutting or oxygen cutting, is the most widely used process for the thermal cutting of carbon steels. The oxyacetylene cutting torch is to the steel fabricator as the saw is to the carpenter.

With this process, cutting is accomplished by preheating the metal to be cut to its "ignition" or "kindling" temperature — about 1500°F for steel — followed by introducing a stream of high-purity oxygen under pressure, thus oxidizing or burning

the metal to produce a cut or "kerf" along the direction of travel. See Fig. 15-1.

The ability of oxygen to cut steel is based upon reactions whereby iron is oxidized to its oxides with the evolution of considerable heat. When steel is heated to a temperature of 1500°F, the iron content combines vigorously with introduced oxygen, giving off enough heat to bring adjacent metal to kindling temperature and sustain the chemical reactions. Once started, "burning" continues as long as the oxygen stream is maintained in the heated area.

The chemistry of the reactions are believed to be as follows:

$$Fe + O \rightarrow FeO + heat$$
$$3Fe + 2O_2 \rightarrow Fe_3O_4 + heat$$
$$4Fe + 3O_2 \rightarrow 2Fe_2O_3 + heat$$

The second reaction produces the greatest amount of heat in the cutting operation. Some of the iron, however, is removed from the kerf by the kinetic energy of the gas stream and is not oxidized or only partially oxidized. Analysis of the material blown from the kerf may show as much as 30% unoxidized iron. To make good cuts, it is necessary to use high-purity oxygen, which is readily available commercially.

The metallurgical effect of cutting with an oxygen jet, in general, is not severe on low-carbon steels (under 0.25%), but may cause adverse effects when applied to high-carbon and low-alloy steels. Studies have shown that a slightly higher carbon content is present on the cut surface of carbon steels. In low-alloy steels containing nickel, the cut surface may show an increase in nickel. One theory is the increases are due to selective oxidation; the carbon and nickel do not oxidize as readily as iron.

In the higher-carbon steels and low-alloy steels, the cut surface has a higher hardness than the base metal due to the quench effect. The heat at the cut surface is conducted very rapidly to the cold base metal, causing a quench at the cut surface. The increase in hardness may be great enough to cause surface cracks.

Theoretically there is no limit to the thickness

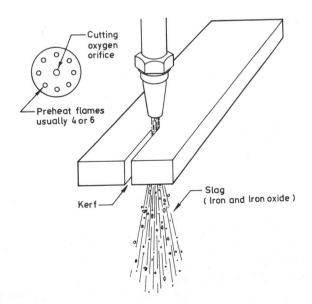

Fig. 15-1. After the steel has been preheated to kindling temperature with an oxyacetylene flame, a high-purity oxygen jet brings about and sustains the reactions whereby iron is oxidized to iron oxides. The iron oxide particles formed are "blasted" through the developing kerf by the pressure of the oxygen stream.

TABLE 15-1.
Cutability of Metals With The
Oxyacetylene Torch

Carbon Steel	Up to 0.25% carbon — good. Higher carbon steels may have to be preheated to prevent hardening and cracking. Cast iron (4% carbon) can be cut by special techniques with difficulty.
Manganese	Steels to about 14% manganese and 1.5% carbon can be cut with difficulty. Preheat is necessary.
Silicon	Usual amounts of silicon in steel have no effect. Transformer iron (4% silicon) is being cut.
Chromium	Up to 5% chromium — good when surface is clean. Five to 10% chromium requires special techniques. Use flux-injection or iron-powder processes.
Nickel	Up to 3% nickel — good if carbon is low. Up to 7% is fair. Stainless steels 18-8 to 35-15 can be cut with the flux-injection or iron-powder processes.
Molybdenum	About the same as nickel.
Copper	Cannot be cut. Copper in steel up to 2%, same as carbon steel.
Aluminum	Cannot be cut. Amounts usually found in steel have no effect.

*Adapted from the American Welding Society Handbook, Sixth Edition, Section 3A.

of steel that can be cut. Cuts have been made through thicknesses of seven to eight feet. However, it must be remembered that due to the oxidation principle of operation not all metals lend themselves to cutting by this process. See Table 15-1 for the cutability of metals.

Stack cutting, where several sheets of steel are cut simultaneously, can reduce cutting costs. In this method, pieces are stacked, one on the other, allowing the oxygen stream to cut through the entire thickness in one operation. The important thing here is to make certain that the surfaces of the various sheets are clean and free from rust, paint, or scale, and — most importantly — that the parts are always tight together. The usual practice is to either clamp or weld the sheets together before starting the cut. Any space between sheets may cause a loss of cutting action at that point, plus severe burning of the metal next to the cut edge. Total thicknesses up to six inches have been cut quite successfully. It is important to have the equipment in good condition and the work carefully prepared, since a malfunction could scrap the whole stack.

FUEL GASES FOR OXYGEN CUTTING

Several fuel gases are commercially available for oxygen cutting. These gases include acetylene, propane, MAPP gas, natural gas, butane, and hydrogen. Acetylene is the most widely used fuel gas, but other gases have advantageous features.

MAPP is manufactured and distributed by the Dow Chemical Company. It is a stabilized methylacetylene-propadiene mixture. It is not dangerous at any required operating pressure, and with oxygen will produce a flame temperature of 5300° F. One cylinder of MAPP gas weighing 120 pounds is said to replace up to five 240-pound acetylene cylinders. At the time of writing, it was being used mostly as a fuel gas in oxygen-cutting and for various heating requirements.

EQUIPMENT FOR OXYGEN CUTTING

Manual cutting torches are used where portable equipment is required or on cutting operations that do not need a high degree of accuracy. Typically, there are two types of cutting torches. In the tip-mixing type, the fuel gas and oxygen for the preheating flame are mixed in the tip. In the premixed type, the mixing takes place in the torch upstream from the tip. Fig. 15-2 shows a typical torch used when both gases are under appreciable pressure. However, if the fuel gas is at a very low pressure the injector type is used, as shown in Fig. 15-3.

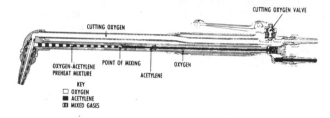

Fig. 15-2. Elements of the oxygen cutting torch.

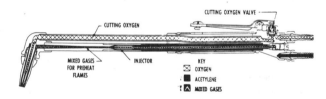

Fig. 15-3. The injector-type cutting torch, used when the fuel gas is at very low pressure.

Attachments are available to convert the standard welding torch to a cutting torch. Such a conversion is shown in Fig. 14-2.

The cutting tip or nozzle (Figs. 15-1 and 15-4) is a copper-alloy attachment that fits into the head of the cutting torch or cutting attachment. It has one large central orifice surrounded by either four or six preheat orifices. The central cutting orifice carries pure oxygen, which does the cutting. The thickness of the metal governs the size of the cutting orifice; the thicker the metal, the bigger the cutting orifice.

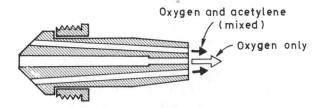

Oxygen and acetylene (mixed)

Oxygen only

Fig. 15-4. Cross section through a typical cutting tip.

Cutting tips carry size numbers, but, as with welding tips, there is no standardization among manufacturers. A tip-size chart can be obtained from the manufacturer to show the relationship between tip size, metal thickness, and pressure. Most often, however, the operator doing a variety of jobs learns to use a medium-size tip and manipulates the torch and pressure to obtain the best results. In production cutting, however, best results are obtained by following the manufacturer's recommended tip size and pressure for each metal thickness. Special cutting tips are available for gouging, sheet metal cutting, and other applications. These are especially shaped or bent for the particular needs of the job.

HOW TO OPERATE AN OXYACETYLENE CUTTING TORCH

Gas-cutting and gas-welding processes are similar in that they both use the same or similar gases, cylinders, pressure regulators, gages, hoses, and torches. It follows that all of the hazards present in gas welding are also present in gas cutting. In addition, in gas cutting there is a greater fire hazard due to falling sparks and hot metal. Therefore, it is mandatory that all of the safety precautions used with oxyacetylene welding be observed in gas cutting.

The first step is to select a tip or nozzle that is suitable for the job. The tip should be screwed into the torch securely but not with excessive force. The manufacturer's chart may be referred to for cutting data, or in the absence of such a chart Table 15-2 may provide useful information. With the oxygen and acetylene pressure regulators set according to the manufacturer's recommendations, the next step is to partially open the acetylene valve (about 1/4 turn) and ignite the gas with a spark lighter or a pilot light, if available. Point the flame away from persons, gas cylinders, or any flammable material.

The next step is to open the acetylene valve until the flame "feathers" on the end and the point of "no smoke" is reached. Then slowly open the oxygen needle valve until a neutral flame is established.

After the neutral flame has been established, depress the oxygen lever. The individual preheat flames around the oxygen orifice may then change from neutral to slightly carburizing. With the cutting lever in the depressed position, readjust the torch oxygen valve until the preheat flames are again neutral. After releasing the oxygen lever, the torch is ready to apply the preheat to the metal being cut, preferably at an edge.

When the point of preheat becomes red hot, the oxygen cutting can begin. This is initiated by depressing the oxygen lever, which sends a jet of oxygen onto the red-hot metal, igniting the metal at this point. The torch should be held steady until the cut is through the metal. Then (see Fig. 15-1), the torch is moved along the line to be cut, forming a kerf.

The kerf is the space that was occupied by the material removed during cutting. The kerf width is important, since it determines the accuracy with which material can be cut to dimension. Uniform kerf width from top to bottom is required if the cut piece is to have a square edge. Kerf width is a function of the type and size of the nozzle, cutting speed, and flow rate of the gases.

When the cut is finished, the oxygen lever is released, acetylene valve closed, and the oxygen valve closed — in that order.

The cut surface should be nearly smooth, and the drag lines should be at right angles to the plate surface and barely visible. Drag lines are indentations on the cut surface inherent with oxygen cutting (see Fig. 15-5). Deep irregular drag lines

TABLE 15-2. Data for Manual and Machine Cutting of Clean Mild Steel (Not Preheated)

Thickness of Steel, In.	Diameter of Cutting Orifice, In.	Cutting Speed, In. per Min.	Gas Consumptions, Cu. Ft. per Hour			
			Cutting Oxygen	Acetylene	Natural Gas	Propane
1/8	0.020-0.040	16-32	15-45	3-9	9-25	3-10
1/4	0.030-0.060	16-26	30-55	3-9	9-25	5-12
3/8	0.030-0.060	15-24	40-70	6-12	10-25	5-15
1/2	0.040-0.060	12-23	55-85	6-12	15-30	5-15
3/4	0.045-0.060	12-21	100-150	7-14	15-30	6-18
1	0.045-0.060	9-18	110-160	7-14	18-35	6-18
1-1/2	0.060-0.080	6-14	110-175	8-16	18-35	8-20
2	0.060-0.080	6-13	130-190	8-16	20-40	8-20
3	0.065-0.085	4-11	190-300	9-20	20-40	9-22
4	0.080-0.090	4-10	240-360	9-20	20-40	9-24
5	0.080-0.095	4-8	270-360	10-24	25-50	10-25
6	0.095-0.105	3-7	260-500	10-24	25-50	10-30
8	0.095-0.110	3-5	460-620	15-30	30-55	15-32
10	0.095-0.110	2-4	580-700	15-35	35-70	15-35
12	0.110-0.130	2-4	720-850	20-40	45-95	20-45

Preheat Oxygen Consumptions: Preheat oxygen for acetylene = 1.1 to 1.25 x acetylene flow (cu ft per hr); preheat oxygen for natural gas = 1.5 to 2.5 x natural gas flow (cu ft per hr); preheat oxygen for propane = 3.5 to 5 x propane flow (cu ft per hr).

Operating Notes: Higher gas flows and lower speeds are generally associated with manual cutting, whereas lower gas flows and higher speeds apply to machine cutting. When cutting heavily scaled or rusted plates, use high gas flows and low speeds. Maximum indicated speeds apply to straight-line cutting; for intricate shape cutting and best quality, lower speeds will be required.

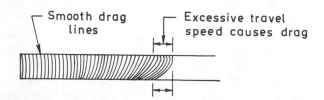

Fig. 15-5. Drag lines on a cut surface should be at right angles to the plate surface.

indicate an improper procedure, impure oxygen, segregations in the steel, or a correction required in the equipment.

The methods used to guide the torch across the work are varied. In addition to hand guidance, there are available:

- Electric-driven variable-speed guidance machines traveling on straight or curved tracks.

- Tracing devices operated by magnetic tracers following a steel pattern.

- Stationary track guidance machines that either span the work or use cantilevered arms to reach over the material.

- Electronic tracers that follow a black line against a white background. In this case, a master drawing is used to guide the torches.

- Numerically controlled or tape-operated guidance machines.

In many cases, more than one torch is used simultaneously, thus lowering the total cost by cutting several parts in one operation.

UNDERWATER GAS CUTTING

Oxygen cutting may be done underwater, using hydrogen or natural gas as the fuel gas and a special cutting torch that ejects compressed air around the flames. Fig. 15-6 illustrates such a tip torch. The

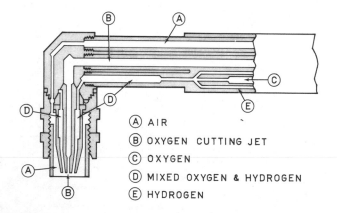

Ⓐ AIR
Ⓑ OXYGEN CUTTING JET
Ⓒ OXYGEN
Ⓓ MIXED OXYGEN & HYDROGEN
Ⓔ HYDROGEN

Fig. 15-6. The tip of an underwater cutting torch. Compressed air provides an envelope of air around the preheat and cutting flames.

compressed air envelope, in essence, provides an air atmosphere in which cutting is done. The operation is conducted with the fuel gas at higher pressures than would be feasible with pressure-sensitive acetylene. Although the quality of underwater cuts is poor compared to the smooth cuts in industrial shop work, the technique is valuable in salvage work and for work with piers, docks, and other underwater structures.

ELECTRIC-ARC CUTTING

The electric arc is used in several processes as the heat source for cutting metals. These processes include:

- Shielded metal-arc cutting
- Carbon-arc cutting
- Oxygen-arc cutting
- Bare metal-arc cutting
- Air carbon-arc cutting
- Plasma-arc cutting

Shielded metal-arc cutting involves the use of a special covered electrode with electric welding equipment. Although very little cutting is done commercially by this method, it permits the arc weldor to make cuts in metals without the need for gas-cutting equipment. Since shielded metal-arc cutting does not depend on oxidation to propagate cutting, it can be used to cut many metals other than those containing iron. Thus, it is useful in cutting nickel, Monel, Inconel, copper, brass, bronze, aluminum, and the stainless steels.

Electrodes for the process are designed to give a slow burn-off rate, so that the maximum length of cut can be achieved with each electrode. The coverings are formulated to react exothermically with the metal and to concentrate the heat and force of the arc on the cut. They may be used with AC or DC current.

In cutting, the operator sets his amperage to the proper level, strikes the arc, and then moves the electrode in a sawing motion over the point to be cut. The force of the arc "blows" the molten metal out of the cut as he proceeds. Cutting speed is enhanced by pushing the tip of the electrode against the metal, which is possible without sticking the electrode or extinguishing the arc.

The technique is also useful for piercing metals. After striking, the electrode is pushed into the point where a hole is to be made. The metal melts rapidly, and a hole can be "drilled" in one-inch steel plate in a little over two seconds by this method. By holding the electrode at low angle and pushing it back and forth, a type of gouging can be accomplished.

Fig. 15-7. Butt joint that has been partially beveled by arc gouging.

Carbon-arc cutting uses a carbon electrode, direct current, and straight polarity (electrode negative) to create the heat needed to melt metal at the point of cut. It is used very little today, since anyone wishing to use welding equipment for cutting would be disposed to turn to the more sophisticated shielded metal-arc process.

Oxygen-arc cutting is a term that may be applied to two methods of using oxygen as an aid in cutting with the electric arc. In one method, gaseous oxygen is introduced to the arc through a hollow, mineral-covered electrode. In the other method, a cored steel electrode containing oxidizing chemicals is used. Oxygen-arc cutting has had limited acceptance in industry.

Bare metal-arc cutting employs a bare metal electrode in conjuction with an argon-oxygen gas mixture. Useable with either ferrous or nonferrous metals, it is an outgrowth of gas metal-arc (MIG) welding, just as shielded metal-arc cutting is an outgrowth of stick-electrode welding. New and better

processes have taken over much of the cutting done by this method.

Air carbon-arc cutting — most widely used as a gouging process — was developed as a method for removing risers and defective areas from iron and steel castings. It was later found to be an effective and economical method for back-gouging or scarfing the root side of weld and for beveling butt-weld grooves (see Fig. 15-7).

In arc gouging, as the process is commonly called, a carbon electrode is used to form the arc. The electrode is held by a special, fully insulated torch through which air is ducted and directed against the arc by a nozzle. The air blasts the molten metal from the puddle, leaving an indentation, or gouge, in the metal. The torch can be operated manually or by mechanized equipment. (See Figs. 15-8 and 15-9.)

The arc is powered by an arc-welding machine, but for a given diameter of electrode the power requirements are normally higher for arc gouging than for arc welding. Compressed air commonly used to power air tools is suitable.

The process does not depend upon oxidation, and therefore works well with all metals regardless of how rapidly they oxidize. Material can be removed approximately five times faster by arc gouging than by chipping. A 3/8-in. groove, for example, can be gouged at a speed of more than 2 fpm. Depth of cut can be controlled closely, and welding slag does not deflect or hamper the cutting action as it would with cutting tools. The cost of operating gouging equipment is generally less than for chipping hammers or gas-cutting torches, and the arc-gouging equipment also requires less space. An arc-gouged surface is clean and smooth and can usually be welded without further preparation.

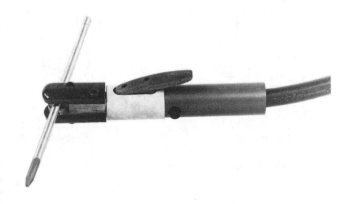

Fig. 15-8. Typical torch for manual arc gouging.

Fig. 15-9. Mechanized torch for arc gouging, providing automatic travel along the seam.

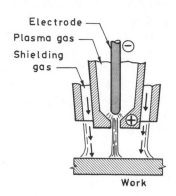

Fig. 15-10. Diagrammatic sketch of the plasma-arc torch.

The process has several drawbacks, however,. It is not as good as other processes for through-cutting, and large volumes of compressed air are required. Improper operation of the torch may result in carbon pickup (and undesirable metallurgical changes) in some materials. Increased hardness produced on cast iron and air-hardenable materials may be objectionable.

Several types of electrodes are used for arc-gouging. The most commonly used electrode is a copper-coated composition of graphite, manufactured for DC operation and available in sizes from 5/32 to 1 inch. The type of electrodes and current recommended for arc gouging various metals are summarized in Table 15-3.

TABLE 15-3. Electrode Type and Current Recommended for Arc Gouging

Material	Electrode	Power
Steel	DC	DCRP
	AC	AC
Stainless Steel	DC	DCRP
	AC	AC
Iron (cast iron, ductile iron, malleable iron)	AC	AC or DCSP
	DC	DCRP (high-amperage)
Copper Alloys	AC	AC or DCSP
	DC	DCRP
Nickel Alloys	AC	AC or DCSP

From AWS Handbook, Sixth Edition, Section 3A.

PLASMA-ARC CUTTING

The plasma-arc cutting process was introduced to the metals industries in 1958, when plasma-arc torches capable of producing and sustaining temperature of 60,000°F and higher were developed. Such torches provide an excellent heat source for cutting, welding, machining, and surfacing metal.

A plasma is the ionized column of gas that carries an electric current between two electrodes, creating the phenomenon known as the electric arc. (See Chapter 3.) When this column of ionized gas is not permitted to diffuse, but is constricted by being forced through a small orifice, as illustrated in Fig. 15-10, an extremely hot jet results. This jet will melt or gasify any material at which it is directed. The plasma gas may or may not be shielded by another gas supplied through an outer concentric ring (Fig. 15-10 shows use of a torch with a shielding-gas ring.)

The workpiece may or may not be a part of the electric circuit. In the "transferred-arc" arrangement (Fig. 15-11), the workpiece is part of the circuit. In the "nontransferred-arc" arrangement, the constricting nozzle surrounding the tungsten electrode acts as an electrical terminal, and the arc is struck between it and the electrode tip; the plasma gas then carries the heat to the workpiece.

The high heat of the plasma torch makes it an extremely fast cutting tool. One-inch-thick carbon-steel plate can be cut at the rate of 50 inches per minute; 3" aluminum plate, at 15 inches per minute. The variables that control the operation of the torch are size of the nozzle orifice, amperage and voltage, composition of the introduced plasma gas, and rate of gas flow. Mixtures of argon and hydrogen, or nitrogen and hydrogen, are used for cutting nonferrous metals and stainless steels. Specific gas mixtures should follow the recommendations of the manufacturer of the plasma torch — as should the procedures for operation.

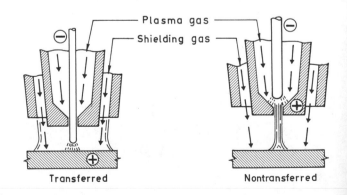

Fig. 15-11. The two types of plasma-arc torch tips.

Braze Welding, Brazing and Soldering

As mentioned in Chapter 1, brazing and soldering are methods of metal joining in which molten filler metals act as the liquid in a solid-liquid-solid bonding scheme. When the temperature is lowered below the melting point of the filler metal, it solidifies — with the result that a solid-solid-solid system exists in which molecular attraction and possible intermetallic compound and alloy formation provide the joining. Brazing and soldering differ from welding in that there is no coalesence or admixture of filler metal with base metal. There may be some intermetallic compounds formed or interchange of ions in the crystal lattices at the interface, but this is not coalescence in the sense that weld metal mixes with base metal.

The difference between brazing and soldering is an arbitraty one depending on temperature. The joining process is called brazing if solidification of the filler metal occurs above 800°F; soldering, if below 800°F.

Brazing can be of two types — "braze welding" (Fig. 16-1) and simple "brazing" (Fig. 16-2). With braze welding, joint preparations similar to the joints for fusion welding are used, and the strength of the joint depends on the strength of the filler metal. In simple brazing, the filler metal is distributed between closely fitted surfaces by capillary attraction. The closeness of the fit brings molecular forces into play, so that the strength of the joint may exceed by far the strength of the filler metal and be equal to the strength of the base metal.

BRAZE WELDING

Braze welding is done with the oxyacetylene torch and is probably an outgrowth of the old blacksmith process known as "brassing". In "brassing", a thin sheet of brass placed between the joint surfaces was fluxed and heated in the forge to produce the bond. With the advent of the oxyacetylene process, the brass rod was developed as a filler material.

Braze welding is widely used in repairing broken cast-iron parts and in joining dissimilar metals in production. Since the process is similar to oxyacetylene fusion welding, a minimum of special equipment is required.

Filler metal is supplied by alloy rods made of approximately 60% copper and 40% zinc. Small percentages of manganese, tin, and iron may be used also, as the requirements for joining different metals dictate. A few hundredths of a percent of silicon is usually added as a deoxidizer to remove the oxides of copper, zinc, and whatever other metals may be present. The silicon forms silicon dioxide, which floats to the top of the molten pool. In doing so, it cuts down fuming and forms a protective layer against atmospheric oxidation.

Flux is necessary in braze welding to remove oxides from the base and filler metals, cut down fuming, and prevent oxidation by the atmosphere. When gray cast iron is being braze-welded, the flux also removes graphite from the joint surfaces.

Brazing flux is made up of such materials as borax, boric acid, borates, fluorides, chlorides, and wetting agents. Melting begins at about 1,000°F and is complete at about 1350°F. The powder form is most widely used. It is applied by dipping a heated rod into the flux can and allowing the powder to adhere to it. It is now possible to purchase rods coated with the correct amount of flux. This speeds the operation considerably, but often the added expense may offset the advantage. In a few cases, it is desirable to use a paste flux. Brazing

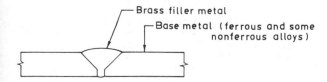

Fig. 16-1 Typical braze-welded joint. The strength of the joint is dependent on the strength of the filler metal.

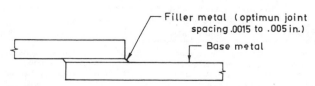

Fig. 16-2 Typical braze joint. The joint strength may be equal to the strength of the base metal. It is possible to produce joint strengths as high as 160,000 psi from filler materials under 60,000 psi.

fluxes are proprietary items, and at the time of writing there was no standard specification or classification of fluxes. Table 16-1 indicates the general types of brazing fluxes for various base metals. This is not, however, a specification.

BRAZE WELDING PROCEDURES

Joint preparation for a braze butt weld consists of beveling the edges in the form of a V if the metal to be welded is more than 1/8" in thickness. Each side of the joint should be beveled from 30° to 45°. See Fig. 16-1.

If the material is cast iron, beveling by grinding should be avoided whenever possible. Some other method, such as hacksawing, should be used. Grinding tends to smear the graphite over the surface and make bonding difficult or impossible. If graphite smearing is unavoidable because grinding is the only practical method of beveling, the graphite smear can often be removed by heating the surface with an oxidizing flame until it is dull red in color, followed by wire brushing after the metal has cooled. If there is rust, scale, paint, oil, grease, or any other substance on surfaces to be braze welded, they must be cleaned by whatever method is feasible.

Preheating and controlled cooling may be necessary if an intricate casting is to be braze welded, but the need is less than required by most fusion welding processes.

METALS ADAPTABLE TO BRAZE WELDING

The repair of worn or broken cast-iron parts probably constitutes the greatest use of braze welding. Since the peak temperature of the base metal can be low enough to avoid, or cause very little, transformation during the heating cycle, brittle transformation products in the heat-affected zone are largely prevented. Malleable as well as gray iron can be successfully braze welded.

Braze welding of steel is faster than gas welding because less heat is required. One advantage with thin steels is the reduction of the burn-through problems that might be encountered with arc welding and the minimization of distortion — both because of the lower peak temperature. However, proper arc-welding procedures are likely to be more economical.

Copper conducts heat away from the welding zone so rapidly that it is cheaper to join copper to

TABLE 16-1. General Data on Applications for Commercially Available Brazing Fluxes*

AWS Brazing Flux Type No.	Metal Combinations for Which Various Fluxes Are Suitable		Effective Temperature Range of Flux, °F	Major Constituents of Flux	Physical Form	Methods of Application†
	Base Metals	Filler Metals				
1	Aluminum and aluminum alloys.	BAlSi	700-1190	Fluorides; Chlorides	Powder	1,2,3,4
2	Magnesium alloys.	BMg	900-1200	Fluorides; Chlorides	Powder	3,4
3A	Copper and copper-base alloys (except those with aluminum) iron-base alloys; cast iron; carbon and alloy steel; nickel and nickel-base alloys; stainless steels; precious metals (gold, silver, palladium, etc.)+	BCuP BAg	1050-1600	Boric Acid, Borates, Fluorides, Fluoborate, Wetting Agent	Powder Paste Liquid	1,2,3
3B	Copper and copper-base alloys (except those with aluminum); iron-base alloys; cast iron; carbon and alloy steel; nickel and nickel-base alloys; stainless steels; precious metals (gold, silver, palladium, etc.)	BCu BCuP BAg BAu RBCuZn BNi	1350-2100	Boric Acid Borates Fluorides Fluoborate Wetting Agent	Powder Paste Liquid	1,2,3
4	Aluminum-bronze; aluminum-brass §	BAg, BCuZn, BCuP	1050-1600	Borates Fluorides Chlorides	Powder Paste	1,2,3
5	Copper and copper-base alloys (except those with aluminum); nickel and nickel-base alloys; stainless steels; carbon and alloy steels; cast iron and miscellaneous iron-base alloys; precious metals (except gold and silver).	BCu, BCuP BAg-(8-19) BAu, BCuZn BNi	1400-2200	Borax Boric Acid Borates	Powder Paste Liquid	1,2,3

* This table provides a guide for classification of most of the proprietary fluxes available commercially.
   For additional data consult AWS specification for brazing filler metal A5.8; consult also AWS Brazing Manual, 1963 Ed.
† 1 — Sprinkle dry powder on joint; 2 — Dip heated filler metal rod in powder or paste; 3 — Mix to paste consistency with water, alcohol, monochlorobenzene, etc; 4 — Molten flux bath.
+ Some Type 3A fluxes are specifically recommended for base metals listed under Type 4.
§ In some cases Type 1 flux may be used on base metals listed under Type 4.
From AWS Handbook, Sixth Edition, Section 3B

copper, and copper to other metals, by this process than it is by fusion welding, since the bonding temperature is about 400°F lower.

Brasses and bronzes can be joined by braze welding if their melting temperatures are high enough. Usually, however, in practice it is difficult to control the temperature sufficiently to prevent melting of the parent metal. If this happens, porosity may result from fuming.

Most other commercial metals and alloys can be joined by braze welding with possibly the exception of high-nickel alloys and some low-carbon steels that are subject to intergranular corrosion.

The advantages and disadvantages of braze welding are as follows:

Advantages

1. The lower bonding temperatures, compared to fusion welding, result in less damage to the base metal.

2. Shrinkage occurs above 500°F in most ferrous alloys, and brass has little strength above that point; therefore the probability of locked-up stresses is lessened.

3. The mechanical properties, such as ductility and tensile strength, are favorable. Tensile strengths up to about 55,000 psi may be obtained.

Disadvantages

1. Braze welded joints are not very successful where large fluctuations in service temperatures occur because of the difference in the coefficient of expansion between the base and filler metals. The bond tends to break when expansion differentials are significant.

2. Any joints that come into contact with elevated service temperatures would obiously be weakened, especially above 500°F.

3. The difference in the electrochemical potential of brass and other metals in the presence of salt water is occasionally a limiting factor.

4. In contact with some metals, the filler metal produces intergranular corrosion

5. The color differences between the filler metal and base metal may detract from the appearance of the joint.

CAPILLARITY BRAZING

As noted in the introduction to this chapter, the difference between braze welding and brazing per se is the joint. In the former, it is a prepared bevel; in brazing, the metals to be joined are fitted so closely that the molten filler metal is fed to the joint by capillary action. The strength characteristics are of diverse magnitudes, since in braze welding the strength of the filler metal is controlling, while in a joint of capillary size molecular attraction becomes significant — and the strength of the base metals may sometimes be achieved.

Brazing may be applied to practically all of the ferrous and nonferrous metals and alloys, with the exceptions of those that have melting temperatures below that of the brazing filler metals. This versatility accounts for the fact that brazing is one of the most widely used bonding processes.

Silver brazing, with some 15 alloys with bonding temperatures upwards of 1150°F, is one of the most favored brazing methods. It is used extensively in the manufacture of equipment for the dairy industry because of the resistance of the brazed joint to corrosion and the ideally smooth joints that minimize cleaning and the harboring of bacteria. It is used extensively with refrigeration equipment in joining copper tubing and other assemblies because of the high resistance of the brazed joint to fatigue failure. In electronic equipment, it produces the tight, strong, and electrically conductive joints that are vital to good performance.

Copper brazing is probably next in importance and is used extensively for the joining of small parts in mass production, using a furnace to supply the needed temperatures. Copper brazing is used extensively in the automobile and aircraft industries.

Capillary brazing is accomplished by various heating methods, the most widely used of which are:

- Torch brazing
- Twin carbon-arc brazing
- Furnace brazing
- Induction brazing
- Dip brazing
- Resistance brazing

Whatever heating method is employed, the joint characteristics as illustrated in Fig. 16-2 prevail, and the brazing temperature is always above 800°F. Also, capillarity is always the means of transporting the molten filler metal to the joint surfaces.

Torch brazing may be done either manually or by machine. The manual operation may use single or multi-flame torch tips. Hand torch heating is preferred on repair and fabrications where conditions vary widely. Where a high rate of production is demanded, machines with multiple torches and single or multiple tips are used.

The gas used determines the degree of heat de-

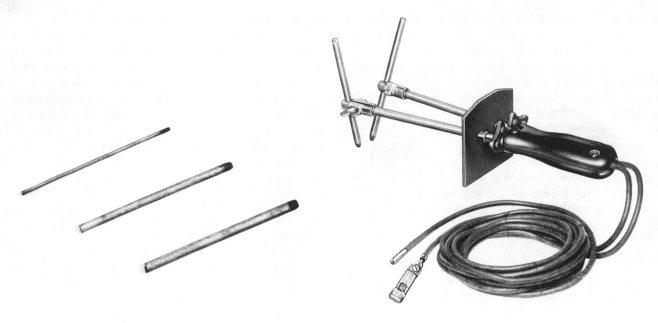

Fig. 16-3. The twin arc torch, a tool for welding, brazing, soldering, and heating for bending, straightening, and shrinking.

veloped. The gas mixtures commonly used, together with the approximate temperatures achieved, are as follows:

- Oxyacetylene .... 6000°F
- Oxyhydrogen .... 4600°F
- Methane — Air .... 4400°F
- Natural Gas — Air .... 4000°F
- Acetylene — Air .... 3230°F

The filler metal may be applied with a hand-held rod or by preplaced shapes in the form of rings, washers, strip, powder, or slugs. Proper cleaning and fluxing must precede the application of the torch.

Twin carbon-arc brazing is mainly a manual operation and is not used extensively. The intense heat of the electric arc requires such careful manipulation to avoid overheating that machine operation has not been developed.

The equipment consists of an AC or DC welding machine as power source and a holder for two carbon or graphite electrodes. The holder is designed so that the electrodes can be held at an angle and the distance between the tips varied as is needed. The electrode holder is manipulated in much the same manner as a hand torch and has the advantage of producing the desired heat very rapidly. See Fig. 16-3.

Furnace brazing is used extensively in the brazing of small parts in quantity production. The parts must be adaptable to the preplacement of brazing filler metals, which may be in such forms

as powder, wire, sheet foil, or slugs. Fluxing is necessary unless an inert atmosphere is introduced into the furnace to avoid reactions with oxygen and nitrogen.

Four types of furnaces are used. They are the box type, conveyor type, retort type, and the bell type.

Induction brazing uses the heat of a high-frequency AC current induced into the parts to be brazed by an induction coil. The heat from induction heating is localized and develops so fast that a small joint in a massive part can be self-quenched or water-quenced without superficial oxidation.

Induction coils for brazing are produced in a variety of shapes and sizes. Their design must provide for the production of magnetic field in the area of the joint to be brazed. An important advantage of this process is that no special atmosphere is required, although flux must be used.

Dip brazing is done by dipping the assembly into a salt (flux) bath or a molten metal bath. Preplaced filler metal similar to the shapes and types for furnace and induction brazing are used with the salt-bath method. When the assemblies with filler metal are dipped into the molten salt bath, both the heating and fluxing actions are accomplished.

In the molten-metal bath, no preplacement of filler metals are necessary — only fluxing. The molten filler metal heats the parts to be brazed and runs into the joint. The main limitation of this method is the wastage of filler metal, since a film is likely to adhere to the assembly. Its use is prohibitive when the parts are large.

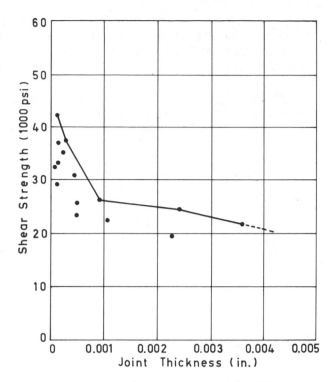

Fig. 16-4. Relationship of shear strength to joint thickness, pure silver joints in 0.5-in. dia. drill rod. Induction brazed in a dry atmosphere of $10\%H_2$, 90% N_2 (no mineral flux used). The joint was measured in four places on the diameter of the bar after machining to the 0.50-in. diameter. The two bars were butt-brazed together and shear texted in a guillotine-type fixture.

Resistance brazing uses a conventional resistance welder or resistance brazing tongs as the heat source. Instead of the conventional electrodes, large carbon, graphite, or copper-alloy blocks clamp the assemblies to be brazed.

One advantage of this process is the close temperature control possible. Another is the fact that joints are cooled under electrode pressure, which produces superior joint properties and minimizes filler metal usage. Brazing tongs have the advantage of being portable.

BRAZE JOINT DESIGN

The strength of any braze joint depends largely on its design. Close fitting is the key to good

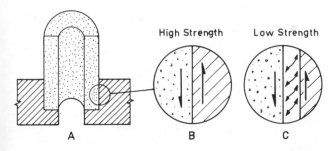

Fig. 16-5. The metal is so confined in B that it is unable to deform as in C. When deforming is decreased, shear strength is increased. This is also true with tensile strength.

strength. Most brazing alloys have relatively low strength by themselves, yet produce joints with as much as two and a half times their tensile strength. Fig. 16-4 shows the relationship of shear strength and joint fit in a silver-brazed drill rod. The shear strength drops rapidly as joint clearance increases. Optimum spacing varies from approximately .0002" to approximately .006" in most cases. Some conditions warrant deviation on either side of this figure.

Although it is probable that molecular bonding is the explanation for the exceptional strength of extremely close fits, mechanical principles may be used to explain why the joint continues to decrease in strength as the clearance increases. This is illustrated in Fig. 16-5. In (b) of this figure the bond line is so narrow that a shear force is unable to deform it. In (c), however, the bond line is broad enough for the shear force to deform the filler metal.

Another reason for using close fits is that they promote capillary attraction and thus the flow of molten filler metal to all surfaces of the joint. Capillary attraction can be demonstrated by placing two pieces of glass together and dipping the lower edges of the assembly into a pan of water. The water will rise between the plates of glass against the forces of gravity. If the spacing is increased beyond a critical point, the water will no longer rise. The same principle functions with the braze joint. Molten silver alloys spread exceptionally well because of their low surface tension and wetting characteristics.

The water and glass illustration also points out the need for clean brazing joint surfaces. If grease is present on the plates of glass, wetting and capillarity will not occur; voids will be left wherever grease is present.

Joint Types: The basic joint types in capillarity brazing are lap, scarf, and butt, as illustrated in Fig. 16-6. They may be used with any of the common shapes, such as flat, round, square, tubular, and irregular cross sections.

Brazed joints in shear tend to be stronger than those in tension. For this reason, lap joints are often preferable. They have the added advantage that the strength can be controlled by increasing the lap or joint area. It has been shown that when joining flat sheets a lap equal to two times the thickness of the metal is usually enough to produce joint strength of as much or more than that of the

Fig. 16-6. Basic joint types.

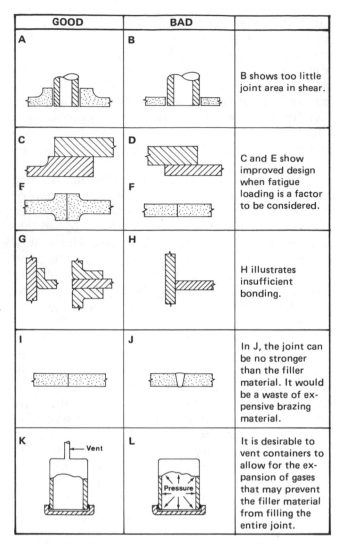

GOOD	BAD	
A	B	B shows too little joint area in shear.
C E	D F	C and E show improved design when fatigue loading is a factor to be considered.
G	H	H illustrates insufficient bonding.
I	J	In J, the joint can be no stronger than the filler material. It would be a waste of expensive brazing material.
K	L	It is desirable to vent containers to allow for the expansion of gases that may prevent the filler material from filling the entire joint.

Fig. 16-7. Some examples of good and bad joint designs.

base metal. In practice, a lap three times the flat sheet thickness usually will yield the maximum joint efficiency. With tubular members, lap joints help in jigging and supporting the parts to be brazed.

Scarf joints are a modified type of butt joint used where it is desirable to have a thickness equal to that of the base metal and yet more bonding area than a butt joint. Silver brazing alloys are usually used. Whenever possible the length of the scarf joint is made two or three times that of the thickness of the base metal.   Butt joints can be made that will have the mechanical properties necessary provided that care is taken to stay within the tolerances of .001" to .003" in joint clearance. Figures 16-7 and 16-8 illustrate some good and poor joints and some typical joints used in manufactured products.

Cleaning and Fluxing: It is absolutely necessary that braze joints be free from foreign substances, such as dirt, grease, and oil. Chemical and mechanical methods are employed, both of which tend to remove oxides as well as foreign matter. Cleaning is followed by fluxing, which further removes oxides and performs other functions.

Wire brushing, filing, scraping, and "sanding" with emery cloth are mechanical means of surface cleaning. If much oil or grease is present, washing with hydrocarbon solvents or with chemicals such as trisodium phosphate or triclorethylene may be necessary. Care should be taken to see that all cleaning agents are removed before beginning the brazing operation.

Insofar as feasible, oxides — particularly scale — should be removed by the cleaning procedures. Fluxing will then remove residual oxides and those formed in the interim between cleaning and brazing. Fluxing also protects the joint surfaces from oxidation during bonding and helps to relieve the surface tension of the filler metal (promotes "wetting"). To be effective the flux must be chemically active through the range of brazing temperatures and active on the metals being joined (see Table 16-1).

Removal of flux after cooling of the brazed assembly is usually of importance, since corrosion from active chemicals may result. Often, this is done by washing in water. In some instances, chemical solvents or mechanical means may be required.

Controlled Atmospheres: Controlled atmospheres are used for the same purposes as flux. They have the advantage that application is easy and no cleaning is necessary after the brazing operation. Controlled atmosheres are most commonly used in furnace brazing and sometimes with induction and resistance brazing. In applications such as electronic-component manufacture, the elimination of chemical fluxes by the use of inert atmospheres is of great importance.

Table 16-2 lists ten recommended atmosphere types. Approximate compositions are listed for the first seven.

BRAZING FILLER METAL

There are over forty different brazing filler metals classified in *Specification for Brazing Filler Metal,* AWS 5.8-69. They are grouped into seven general classes:

Silver
Copper-Phosphorus
Nickel
Copper and Copper-Zinc
Magnesium
Precious Metals (Gold)
Aluminum-Silicon

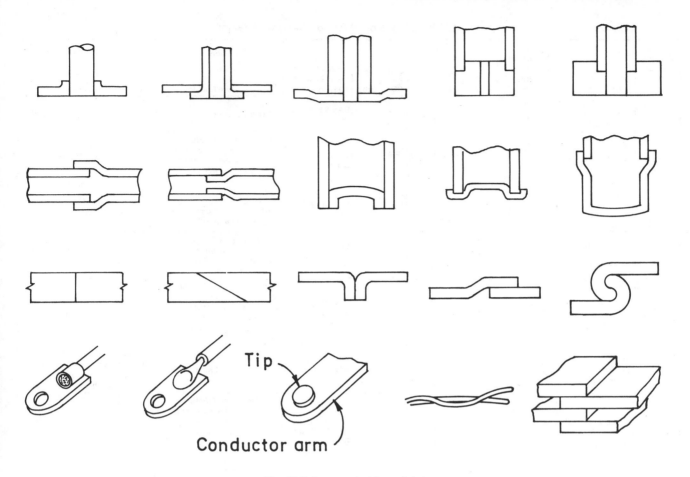

Fig. 16-8. Some typical braze joints.

The brazing temperature range for these metals is given in Table 16-3. Filler metal is used in various forms, including wire, sheet, filings, rings, and shapes specially prepared for preplacing on individual assemblies. The chemical compositions of AWS-classified filler metals are given in Table 16-4.

Operating Characteristics and Use of Brazing Filler Metals: Following the AWS classification as given in Table 16-3 (from aluminum-silicon to nickel), the uses for the filler-metal types may be summarized:

BAlSi (Aluminum-Silicon) — Brazing filler metals of this classification are used for joining the following grades of aluminum and aluminum alloys: 1060, EC, 1100, 3003, 3004, 5005, 5050, 6053, 6061, 6062, 6063, 6951, and cast alloys A612 and C612. All clasified filler metals are suitable for the furnace and dip-brazing processes. The *BAlSi-3, -4, and -5* filler metals are suitable for the manual and automatic torch-brazing processes. These filler metals are also used to a limited extent with the other brazing processes. They are generally used with lap or tee joints rather than butt joints.

BCuP (Copper-Phosphorus) — Brazing filler metals of this classification are used primarily for joining copper and copper alloys with limited use on silver, tungsten, and molydenum. These should not be used on ferrous or nickel-base alloys. The filler metals are self-fluxing when used on copper, but a flux is necessary when used on other metals, including copper alloys.

BAg (Silver) — Filler metals in this classification are used for joining most ferrous and nonferrous metals except aluminum and magnesium. These filler metals have good brazing properties and are suitable for placement in the joint or for manual feeding.

BAu (Precious Metals) — These filler metals contain an appreciable amount of gold and are used for brazing iron, nickel, and cobalt-base alloys. They resist oxidation and corrosion. Usually they are used with induction, furnace, or resistance-heating in a reducing atmosphere or vacuum.

BCu (Copper) — Filler metals are useful for brazing ferrous and nonferrous metals with various brazing heat sources.

TABLE 16-2. Controlled Atmospheres for Brazing

AWS Brazing Atmosphere No.	Type Atmosphere	Maximum Dew Point At Entry, °F	Approximate Composition, %					Brazing Application		Remarks
			H_2	N_2	CO	CO_2	Other	Filler Metals (AWS-ASTM Designations)	Base Metals	
1	Combusted fuel gas (low-hydrogen, exothermic)	Ambient temperatures	0.5-1	87	0.5-1	11-12	—	BAg,* BCuZn,* BCuP, § BNi-6	Copper; brasses*	
2	Combusted fuel gas (exothermic)	Ambient temperatures	14-15	70-71	9-10	5-6	—	BCu, BAg, BCuZn, BCuP, § BNi-6	Deoxidized or OFHC‡ copper; brass;* low- and medium-carbon steels; nickel; nickel-copper (Monel); cupronickels.	Decarburizing atmosphere.
3	Combusted fuel gas (CO_2 removed and gas dried, exothermic.)	−40	15-16	73-75	10-11	—	—	BCu, BAg, BCuZn, BCuP, § BNi-6	Deoxidized or OFHC copper; brass; low-, medium- and high-carbon steels; cupronickels; high-nickel alloys.	Nondecarburizing atmosphere.
4	Reacted fuel gas (high-hydrogen, endothermic)	−20 to +10	38-40	41-45	17-19	0-1	—	BCu, BAg, BCuZn, BCuP, § BNi-6	Deoxidized or OFHC copper; brass; low-, medium- and high-carbon steels; nickel; nickel-copper (Monel).	Carburizing to decarburizing atmosphere.
5	Dissociated (cracked) ammonia	−50 to −65	75	25	—	—	—	BAg, BCuZn, BCu, BCuP, § BNi	Deoxidized or OFHC copper; brass; low-, medium- and carbon steels, nickel and high-nickel alloys; cupronickels; stainless steel and other alloys containing Cr.	Add fluxes if titanium aluminum, silicon or beryllium are present.
6	High-purity cylinder hydrogen	Ambient to −40	97-100	—	—	—	—	BCu, BAg, BCuZn, BCuP, § BNi	Deoxidized or OFHC copper; brass; low- and medium-carbon steels; high-nickel alloys.	Add fluxes if titanium, aluminum, silicon or beryllium are present; nondecarburizing atmosphere.
7	Deoxidized and dried high-purity hydrogen	−75 to −100	100	—	—	—	—	BCu, BAg, BCuZn, BCuP, § BNi, BAu	Deoxidized or OFHC copper; brass; low-, medium- and high-carbon steels; nickel and high-nickel alloys; cupronickels; stainless steel; carbides and other alloys with cobalt, chromium and tungsten.	Nondecarburizing atmosphere.
8	Heated volatile materials	Inorganic vapors (i.e., zinc, cadmium, lithium, volatile fluorides).						BAg	Brasses and other special purpose applications.	Special purpose may be used in conjunction with atmosphere 1 thru 7 to avoid use of flux.
9	Purified inert gas	(Inert gas, dried argon and helium, etc.)						BCu, BAg, BCuZn, BCuP, § BNi	Deoxidized or OFHC copper; brass; low-, medium- and high-carbon steels; nickel and high-nickel alloys; cupronickels; stainless and other chromium alloys; titanium; zirconium; hafnium, refractory metals.	Highest-purity gases and complete cleaning of parts important for optimum results.
10	Vacuum	Range from 0.001 to above 500 microns, depending upon base and filler metals.						BCu, BAg, BAu, BNi (other higher-temperature brazing alloys)† any metal which does not vaporize.	Deoxidized or OFHC copper; low-, medium- and high-carbon steels; nickel and high-nickel alloys; cupronickels; stainless steel and other chromium and cobalt alloys; titanium; zirconium; refractory metals.	Degree of vacuum required depends on filler and base metals. Good cleaning of parts recommended, although high vacuum has the effect of removing impurities, foreign materials and some types of oxides at brazing temperature.

* Fluxes required to supplement controlled atmosphere when brazing alloys of base metals containing volatile components. Not suitable in pure dry hydrogen and vacuum atmospheres.
† BCu and BCuP will show vaporization at high temperatures except when special brazing techniques are employed because of low-pressure effects.
‡ Oxygen-free, high-conductivity.
§ BCuP filler metals are not recommended for furnace brazing when the heating rate is low.

From AWS Handbook, Sixth Edition, Section 3B.

BCuZn (Copper-Zinc) — These alloy filler metals can be used for the same materials and with the same processes as BCu filler metals. Due to the zinc, more control must be used to avoid overheating.

BMg (Magnesium) — These filler metals are used for joining magnesium alloys AZ10A, K1A, M1A, AZ31B, and ZE10A. They can be used with the torch, dip, or furnace brazing processes.

BNi (Nickel) — The filler metals are mostly used when corrosion and heat-resistant properties are required. Base metals commonly brazed are the AISI 300 and 400 series stainless steels and nickel and cobalt-base alloys. BNi alloys are particularly suited to vacuum systems and vacuum-tube applications.

APPLICATION COMMENTS

The student who wishes to delve into the subject of capillarity brazing more deeply should refer to *Specification for Brazing Filler Metal*, AWS A5.8-69, and American Society for Metals' *Metals Handbook, Vol. 6, Welding and Brazing*, 8th edition. The following are random comments on the applications of brazing considered to be of general interest:

• Aluminum alloys are brazed in ways similar to the brazing of ferrous alloys. The main difference is that the brazing temperature of the filler material is closer to the melting temperature of the base metal. Consequently, greater skill in heat control is required if the operation is done manually either with a hand or carbon-arc torch. Less trouble is experienced with automatically controlled furnaces. Lap and fillet joints are more desirable than butt joints.

• Magnesium is similar to aluminum in its brazing characteristics. The BMg filler contains beryllium to avoid possible ignition of the magnesium.

• Aside from the difficulties involved in the heating of highly conductive materials, copper and its alloys are brazed with success by almost all brazing methods.

• The low-carbon and low-alloy steels are brazed with about the same ease as the copper alloys. The stainless steels require more exacting controls, but brazing is neither difficult nor unusual.

• The successful brazing of high-carbon and high-speed tool steels is dependent upon the particular steel. The important factors to consider are close joint tolerance for high strength and a filler alloy with high enough melting temperature. Copper is often used since it has a melting temperature of approximately 2000°F. The brazing and heat-treating operation should be combined whenever possible. Brazing is probably the most used method for tool repair.

• Malleable and ductile irons are easily wet with filler alloys, but care must be exercised not to remove the heat treatment they have received. Any temperature above 1400°F may damage the structure.

• Nickel and high-nickel alloys can be brazed by most of the brazing processes. Special treatment, however, is usually required.

TABLE 16-3. Solidus, Liquidus, and Brazing Temperature Ranges*

AWS Classification	Solidus, °F	Liquidus, °F	Brazing Temperature Range, °F
Aluminum-silicon:			
BAlSi-2	1070	1135	1110 — 1150
BAlSi-3	970	1085	1060 — 1120
BAlSi-4	1070	1080	1080 — 1120
BAlSi-5	1070	1095	1090 — 1120
Copper-phosphorus:			
BCuP-1	1310	1695	1450 — 1700
BCuP-2	1310	1460	1350 — 1550
BCuP-3	1190	1485	1300 — 1500
BCuP-4	1190	1335	1300 — 1450
BCuP-5	1190	1475	1300 — 1500
Silver:			
BAg-1	1125	1145	1145 — 1400
BAg-1a	1160	1175	1175 — 1400
BAg-2	1125	1295	1295 — 1550
BAg-2a	1125	1310	1310 — 1550
BAg-3	1170	1270	1270 — 1500
BAg-4	1240	1435	1435 — 1650
BAg-5	1250	1370	1370 — 1550
BAg-6	1270	1425	1425 — 1600
BAg-7	1145	1205	1205 — 1400
BAg-8	1435	1435	1435 — 1650
BAg-8a	1410	1410	1410 — 1600
BAg-13	1325	1575	1575 — 1775
BAg-13a	1420	1640	1600 — 1800
BAg-18	1115	1325	1325 — 1550
BAg-19	1435	1635	1610 — 1800
Precious metals:			
BAu-1	1815	1860	1860 — 2000
BAu-2	1635	1635	1635 — 1850
BAu-3	1785	1885	1885 — 1995
BAu-4	1740	1740	1740 — 1840
Copper and Copper-Zinc:			
BCu-1	1980	1980	2000 — 2100
BCu-1a	1980	1980	2000 — 2100
BCu-2	1980	1980	2000 — 2100
RBCuZn-A	1630	1650	1670 — 1750
RBCuZn-D	1690	1715	1720 — 1800
Magnesium:			
BMg-1	830	1110	1120 — 1160
BMg-2a	770	1050	1080 — 1130
Nickel:			
BNi-1	1790	1900	1950 — 2200
BNi-2	1780	1830	1850 — 2150
BNi-3	1800	1900	1850 — 2150
BNi-4	1800	1950	1850 — 2150
BNi-5	1975	2075	2100 — 2200
BNi-6	1610	1610	1700 — 1875
BNi-7	1630	1630	1700 — 1900

*Solidus and liquidus shown are for the nominal composition in each classification.

• Precious metal contacts are almost always joined to contact arms by brazing. Practically all types of electrical apparatus require some type of contact for opening and closing circuits. Silver, gold, and platinum are used separately or in alloy form. The parts to be assembled are small, so to avoid difficulty in preplacing alloys the brazing filler metal is usually alloyed to the side of the part. Resistance and furnace brazing are the most commonly used methods. Tungsten, molybdenum, tantalum, and other refractory metals are used as electrical contacts and as electron tube compon-

TABLE 16-4. Chemical Requirements of Brazing Filler Metal

NOTE 1: Analysis shall be made for the elements for which specific values are shown in this table. If, however, the presence of other elements is indicated in the course of routine analysis, further analysis shall be made to determine that the total of these other elements is not present in excess of the limits specified for "other elements-total" in the last column in the table.

NOTE 2: Single values shown are maximum percentages, except where otherwise specified.

SILVER

AWS Classification	Silver, %	Copper, %	Zinc, %	Cadmium, %	Nickel, %	Tin, %	Lithium, %	Phosphorus, %	Other Elements, Total, %
BAg-1	44 – 46	14 – 16	14 – 18	23 – 25	–	–	–	–	0.15
BAg-1a	49 – 51	14.5 – 16.5	14.5 – 18.5	17 – 19	–	–	–	–	0.15
BAg-2	34 – 36	25 – 27	19 – 23	17 – 19	–	–	–	–	0.15
BAg-2a	29 – 31	26 – 28	21 – 25	19 – 21	–	–	–	–	0.15
BAg-3	49 – 51	14.5 – 16.5	13.5 – 17.5	15 – 17	2.5 – 3.5	–	–	–	0.15
BAg-4	39 – 41	29 – 31	26 – 30	–	1.5 – 2.5	–	–	–	0.15
BAg-5	44 – 46	29 – 31	23 – 27	–	–	–	–	–	0.15
BAg-6	49 – 51	33 – 35	14 – 18	–	–	–	–	–	0.15
BAg-7	55 – 57	21 – 23	15 – 19	–	–	4.5 – 5.5	–	–	0.15
BAg-8	71 – 73	remainder	–	–	–	–	–	–	0.15
BAg-8a	71 – 73	remainder	–	–	–	–	0.15 – 0.3	–	0.15
BAg-13	53 – 55	remainder	4.0 – 6.0	–	0.5 – 1.5	–	–	–	0.15
BAg-13a	55 – 57	remainder	–	–	1.5 – 2.5	–	–	–	0.15
BAg-18	59 – 61	remainder	–	–	–	9.5 – 10.5	–	0.025	0.15
BAg-19	92 – 93	remainder	–	–	–	–	0.15 – 0.3	–	0.15

COPPER-PHOSPHORUS

AWS Classification	Phosphorus, %	Silver, %	Copper, %	Other Elements, Total, %
BCuP-1	4.8 – 5.2	–	remainder	0.15
BCuP-2	7.0 – 7.5	–	remainder	0.15
BCuP-3	5.8 – 6.2	4.8 – 5.2	remainder	0.15
BCuP-4	7.0 – 7.5	5.8 – 6.2	remainder	0.15
BCuP-5	4.8 – 5.2	14.5 – 15.5	remainder	0.15

NICKEL

AWS Classification	Nickel,* %	Chromium, %	Boron, %	Silicon, %	Iron, %	Carbon, %	Phosphorus, %	Other Elements, Total, %
BNi-1	remainder	13.0 – 15.0	2.75 – 4.00	3.0 – 5.0	4.0 – 5.0	0.6 – 0.9	–	0.50
BNi-2	remainder	6.0 – 8.0	2.75 – 3.5	4.0 – 5.0	2.0 – 4.0	0.15	–	0.50
BNi-3	remainder	–	2.75 – 3.5	4.0 – 5.0	1.5	0.06	–	0.50
BNi-4	remainder	–	1.0 – 2.2	3.0 – 4.0	1.5	0.06	–	0.50
BNi-5	remainder	18.0 – 20.0	–	9.75 – 10.5	–	0.15	–	0.50
BNi-6	remainder	–	–	–	–	0.15	10.0 – 12.0	0.50
BNi-7	remainder	11.0 – 15.0	–	–	–	–	9.0 – 11.0	0.50

*Cobalt 1.0 max., per cent (unless otherwise specified) if determined.

COPPER AND COPPER-ZINC

AWS Classification	Copper, %	Zinc, %	Tin, %	Iron, %	Manganese, %	Nickel, %	Phosphorus, %	Lead, %	Aluminum, %	Silicon, %	Other Elements, Total, %
BCu-1	99.90 min.	–	–	–	–	–	0.075	0.02	0.01	–	0.10
BCu-1a	99.0 min.	–	–	–	–	–	–	–	–	–	0.30a
BCu-2b	86.5 min.	–	–	–	–	–	–	–	–	–	0.50c
RBCuZn-Ae	57 – 61	remainder	0.25 – 1.00	*	*	–	–	0.05*	0.01*	*	0.50d
RBCuZn-Dc	46 – 50	remainder	–	–	–	9.0 – 11.0	0.25	0.05*	0.01*	0.04 – 0.25	0.50d

a Total other elements requirements pertains only to the metallic elements for this filler metal.
b These chemical requirements pertain only to the copper oxide and do not include requirements for the organic vehicle in which the copper oxide is suspended.
c Total other elements requirement pertains only to metallic elements for this filler metal. The following limitations are placed on the non-metallic elements:

Constituent	per cent (max)	Constituent	per cent (max)
Chlorides	0.4	Nitric acid insoluble	0.3
Sulfates	0.1	Acetone soluble matter	0.5
Oxygen	remainder		

d Total other elements, including the elements marked with an asterisk (*), shall not exceed the value specified.
e This AWS classification in intended to be identical with the same classification that appears in the Specification for Copper and Copper-Alloy Welding Rods (AWS Designation A5.7).

TABLE 16-4. Chemical Requirements of Brazing Filler Metal (Continued)

MAGNESIUM

AWS Classification	Aluminum, %	Manganese, %	Zinc, %	Silicon, %	Copper, %	Nickel, %	Iron, %	Beryllium, %	Magnesium, %	Other Elements, Total, %
BMg-1	8.3 — 9.7	0.15 min.	1.7 — 2.3	0.05	0.05	0.005	0.005	0.0002 — 0.0008	balance	0.30
BMg-2a*a*	11.0 — 13.0	--	4.5 — 5.5	—	—	—	—	0.0002 — 0.0008	balance	0.30

a See paragraph A1.18.2 in the Appendix to the specification.

PRECIOUS METALS

AWS Classification	Gold, %	Copper, %	Nickel, %	Other Elements, Total, %
BAu-1	37.0 $^{+1}_{-0}$	remainder	—	0.15
BAu-2	79.5 $^{+1}_{-0}$	remainder	—	0.15
BAu-3	34.5 $^{+1}_{-0}$	remainder	2.5 — 3.5	0.15
BAu-4	81.5 $^{+1}_{-0}$	—	remainder	0.15

ALUMINUM-SILICON

AWS Classification	Silicon, %	Copper, %	Iron, %	Zinc, %	Magnesium, %	Manganese, %	Chromium, %	Titanium, %	Aluminum, %	Other Elements, Total, % Each	Other Elements, Total, % Total
BAlSi-2	6.8 — 8.2	0.25	0.8	0.20	—	0.10	—	—	remainder	0.05	0.15
BAlSi-3	9.3 — 10.7	3.3 — 4.7	0.8	0.20	0.15	0.15	0.15	—	remainder	0.05	0.15
BAlSi-4	11.0 — 13.0	0.30	0.8	0.20	0.10	0.15	—	—	remainder	0.05	0.15
BAlSi-5	9.0 — 11.0	0.30	0.8	0.10	0.05	0.05	—	0.20	remainder	0.05	0.15

ents. Some of these are also joined to structural elements by brazing.

ADVANTAGES AND DISADVANTAGES OF BRAZING

The advantages of capillarity brazing include:

- Good and controlled corrosion resistance at the joint.
- High resistance of the brazed joint to fatigue failure.
- Low bonding temperatures make possible the joining of metals without destroying their heat-treated characteristics.
- Joints have good electrical conductivity, especially those made with silver alloys.
- Brazing is one of the best methods for joining dissimilar metals where high strengths are desired.
- Most of the common metals can be joined by this process.

The disadvantages or limitations when joining by brazing include:

- The precision types of joints may be expensive to prepare.
- The relatively high cost of filler metal.
- Massive parts do not lend themselves readily to a precision joint.
- Color differences may sometimes make brazing undesirable.

- Brazed assemblies could be ruined if subjected accidentally to temperatures above the melting point of the filler metal.

SOLDERING

Soldering, as noted in the introduction to this chapter, amounts to low-temperature brazing — joining with molten filler metal below 800°F. The most common soldering temperatures are in the range from 360°F to 475°F.

The soldered joint, as the brazed joint, depends on molecular attraction, intermetallic compound formation, and possibly a type of alloying for its bond. Also, as with a brazed joint, the closer the fit, the stronger the bond. Since solder materials are weaker than brazing materials, the filler material in the bond line is more easily deformed, and, thus, the joint is weaker than a similar brazed joint. In tension, as opposed to shear, a solder joint is no stronger than the filler metal. For this reason, butt joints are rarely made with solder. In critical work, a solder joint would be fashioned for shear stresses with precision preparation. Generally, however, soldering is used where the service demands are not severe and little attention is given to precision fitting. In many applications, even in electrical-equipment soldering, the parts are interlocked mechanically before soldering. The only function of the solder is then to make a tight joint — one that doesn't leak or that will conduct electrical current without undue resistance.

PREPARATION OF PARTS FOR SOLDERING

Parts to be soldered must be free from all foreign matter — dirt, oil, grease, paint, crayon marks, rust, and oxide films. The need for clean surfaces cannot be overemphasized. Cleaning is accomplished mechanically or chemically.

Mechanical cleaning may be done by grinding or filing if the shape of the parts permit. Shot or grit-blasting are frequently used and are preferred over sand-blasting, which may leave small particles of sand embedded in the surface of a soft material. Perhaps, the most common method is simply abrading the surface with steel wool or sandpaper.

Chemical methods include solvent degreasing, such as with trichlorethylene, which leaves little or no residue on the work. Immersion in detergent or hot alkali solutions is suitable, but all cleaning solutions must be thoroughly removed with hot water or steam. Even the residue from hard water may be detrimental. Acid cleaning is done by the usual pickling methods. Following acid cleaning, parts should be rinsed in hot water, quickly dried, and "wetted" as soon as possible to avoid oxidation on the cleaned surface.

Wetting, or "tinning" as it is more commonly called, involves melting a continuous thin film of solder on the joint surface. A flux is used when tinning and may also be used when the tinned parts are joined with a heat source.

If the fit is close, pretinning may not be feasible. Thus, in joining copper water pipe to fittings, pretinning would require a loose fit to accommodate the solder film or films. Instead, the surfaces are cleaned with steel wool to a bright shiny condition, after which a flux (usually a paste flux) is spread on the male surface and the parts immediately joined. The flux acts as a lubricant, facilitating assembly of the tight-fitting parts. The joint is then heated and solder touched to it. By capillary action, the surfaces of the tight joint are coated with the solder. Excess molten solder and any flux that has " boiled out" is wiped from the exterior of the joint before the solder freezes with a cloth. When water is run into the piping system, any corrosive residues from the flux within the pipe are flushed out of the system.

Noncorrosive fluxes, such as rosin, are used when soldering electrical equipment. On heating, such a flux becomes mildly active, but its function is largely protective against the oxidation of the metal. The residue is noncorrosive and nonconductive.

Mildly corrosive fluxes are composed of organic materials (acids or bases) that are active at soldering temperatures but short-lived because of thermal decomposition. They are used where only

a small amount of flux is needed and where heat will be sufficient to decompose any excess. The residue is mildly corrosive, but can be removed with water.

The active agents in corrosive fluxes are inorganic acids or salts. These give rapid and positive cleaning, but unless completely removed after soldering can cause severe corrosion.

Torches and heating irons are commonly used to apply heat when soldering. Any source of heat that will not contaminate the joint may be used. All the methods of heating used with capillarity brazing, discussed earlier in this chapter, can be applied to soldering.

TYPE OF SOLDERS

Solders of the **tin-lead alloy system** constitute the largest portion of all solders in use. They are used for joining most metals and have good corrosion resistance to most media. All cleaning and soldering processes may be used with the tin-lead solders. Fluxes of all types can also be used; the choice depends on the metals to be joined.

Soft solder is an alloy of tin and lead. In describing solders it is customary to give the tin content first. A 40/60 solder, for example, is understood to be 40% tin and 60% lead. The 50/50 composition is most common. Wiping solder for plumbing and cable sheathing is 38% tin and 62% lead. The 60% tin, 40% lead solders find limited use because of the high price of tin. Soft solders can be obtained commercially in wire, bar, powder, and ingot forms. The wire solder is available with or without a flux core.

The behavior of the various tin-lead alloys can best be illustrated by their consitutional diagram in Fig. 16-9. In order to understand the diagram more fully, the terms used are defined as follows:

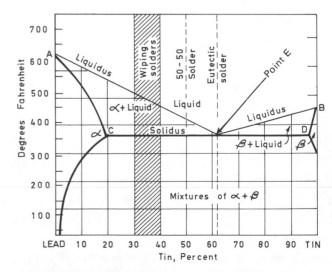

Fig. 16-9. Constitutional diagram for the tin-lead alloy system.

TABLE 16-5. Tin-lead Solders

ASTM* Solder Classification	Composition, Weight %		Temperature, °F/°C		
	Tin	Lead	Solidus	Liquidus	Pasty Range
5	5	95	572/300	596/314	24/13
10	10	90	514/268	573/301	59/33
15	15	85	437/225	553/290	116/65
20	20	80	361/183	535/280	174/97
25	25	75	361/183	511/267	150/84
30	30	70	361/183	491/255	130/72
35	35	65	361/183	477/247	116/64
40	40	60	361/183	455/235	94/52
45	45	50	361/183	441/228	80/45
50	50	50	361/183	421/217	60/34
60	60	40	361/183	374/190	13/7
70	70	30	361/183	378/192	17/9

* ASTM solders Grade A are considered high-purity solders and contain 0.12% antimony, maximum.
ASTM solders Grade B contain 0.2% antimony, minimum; 0.5% maximum.

Solidus temperature is the highest temperature at which a metal or alloy is completely solid, curve ACEDB.

Liquidus temperature is the lowest temperature at which a metal or alloy is completely liquid, curve AEB.

Eutectic alloy is an alloy that behaves like a pure metal in that it melts at one temperature and not over a range, point E.

Pasty range is the temperature differential between solidus and liquidus in which the solder is partially melted, curve ACEDBEA.

As shown in the diagram, 100% lead melts at 621°F, point A, and 100% tin melts at 450°F, point B. Solders containing 19.5% (point C) to 97.5% (point D) tin have the same solidus temperature, which is 361°F. Any composition other than a eutectic composition will not become completely liquid until a higher temperature is reached. For example, 50/50 lead solder has a solidus temperature of 361°F, and a liquidus temperature of 417°F, or a pasty range of 56°F, the difference between the solidus and liquidus.

Melting characteristics of the tin-lead solders are shown in Table 16-5.

The 5-grade solder is a relatively high melting-temperature solder with a short pasty range. Its wetting and flow characteristics are poorer than the higher-tin solders, necessitating extra care in surface preparation. This high-lead solder has better strength properties at 300°F than solders containing more tin. The high soldering temperature limits the use of organic fluxes, such as rosin. This solder is particularly adaptable to torch, dip, induction, or oven soldering. It is used for sealing precoated containers, coating, and joining metals and for moderately elevated temperature uses.

The 10, 15 and 20-grade solders have lower liquidus and solidus temperatures but wider pasty ranges than the 5-grade solder. The wetting and flow characteristics are also better. Extreme care must be taken, however, to avoid movement of the solder during solidification to prevent hot tearing. Fluxes of all types and all soldering methods are applicable. These solders are used for sealing cellular automobile radiators, filling joints and dents in automobile bodies, and for the coating and joining of metals.

The 25 and 30-grade solders have lower liquidus temperatures than all previously mentioned alloys, but have the same solidus temperature as the 20-grade solder. Therefore, the pasty range is narrower. All standard cleaning, fluxing, and soldering techniques can be used with these solders. Machine and torch soldering are widely used.

The 35, 40 and 50-grade solders have liquidus temperatures low enough to be easily worked. The solidus temperature is the same as the 20 to 30-grade solders and the pasty ranges are narrower. Solders of this group have the best combination of wetting properties, strength, and economy, and for these reasons are widely used. They are the general-purpose solders used extensively on sheet metal work. They are used as a rosin-cored wire for radio and television applications.

The 60-grade solder is used wherever temperature requirements are critical, such as in delicate instruments. The composition is close enough to that of the eutectic tin-lead alloy to have an extremely narrow pasty range. All methods of cleaning, fluxing, and heating may be used with this solder.

Up to 6% antimony may be added to the tin-lead solders to increase the mechanical properties with only a slight loss of soldering characteristics. Such solders should not be used on aluminum, zinc, or zinc-coated metals.

Tin-zinc solders have come into use for soldering aluminum. Alloys of 70% to 80% tin, with the remainder zinc, are recommended.

Lead-silver solders have a relatively high solidus temperature, which makes them useful where strength is required at moderately elevated temperatures.

Cadmium-silver solders can be used for higher than normal service temperatures for solders. A tensile strength of 2600 psi at 425°F can be obtained in a butt joint in copper. (Caution: cadmium may cause a health hazard. See Chapter 2.)

Zinc-aluminum solders are specifically for aluminum. Joints have high strength and good corrosion resistance. High solidus temperature requires higher than normal soldering temperature.

Welding, Brazing And Soldering Aluminum

Aluminum and aluminum alloys are the lightest commercial metals used in quantity. Light weight, plus good tensile strength in the alloys, ease of fabrication, and availability in many forms make the metal and its alloys desirable materials in fabrication and construction.

Commercially annealed aluminum has an ultimate tensile strength of approximately 13,000 psi. Cold working easily doubles this strength. The addition of alloying elements, together with utilization of certain thermal treatments, materially increases the strength of aluminum so that it competes with steel structurally. Ultimate tensile strengths as high as 78,000 psi may be obtained, or as much as six times that of pure aluminum and above that of some steels. The ultimate tensile strength of many of the more common structural steels averages in the vicinity of 60,000 psi.

In addition to light weight and strength, many other factors have contributed to the popularity of aluminum. It stands third on the scale of malleability, fifth in ductility, and is exceeded only by copper and silver with regard to electrical conductivity. Its thermal conductivity is high, and, while a surface film of the oxide forms on aluminum metal, corrosion does not advance beyond a few mils into the metal in normal industrial atmospheres. Aluminum, however, reacts chemically with both acids and alkalis.

Various aluminum alloys are available in the form of sheet or plate with a cladding on one or both sides. The cladding can be pure aluminum or an aluminum-base alloy up to 15% of the base metal thickness. The reason for cladding is to improve corrosion resistance to hostile atmospheres, prevent chemcial reactions in certain fluids, or obtain better finishing characteristics.

Aluminum alloys are identified by their composition, thermal treatment, and work-hardening characteristics. For wrought aluminum and aluminum alloys, the numbering system now in use was originated by the Aluminum Association. This is a four-digit system that indicates the chemical composition of the alloy, as shown in Table 17-1. Aluminum castings are referred to by either a popular "commercial" system of identification, an ASTM system, or by proprietary designations.

High-purity aluminum is soft and ductile and has uses in modern industry where these properties are useful or not damaging. However, for many commercial and most structural applications, aluminum of greater strength and hardness is required. Greater strengths and hardnesses are obtained by

TABLE 17-1. Designations for Wrought Aluminum Alloys According to the System of the Aluminum Association

Number	Alloying Elements
1XXX	Aluminum — 99.00% or more pure aluminum.
2XXX	Copper is the main alloying element.
3XXX	Manganese is the main alloying element.
4XXX	Silicon is the main alloying element.
5XXX	Magnesium is the main alloying element.
6XXX	Magnesium and silicon are the main alloys.
7XXX	Zinc is the main alloying element.
8XXX	Special element alloys.
9XXX	Unused series.

TABLE 17-2. Wrought Aluminum Alloys Grouped by Basic Method of Obtaining Optimum Mechanical Properties

Nonheat-Treatable (alloys normally cold-worked)	Heat-Treatable (alloys normally heat-treated)
1060	2011
1100	2014
3003	2017
3004	2018
4043	2024
5005	2025
5050	2117
5052	2218
5056	2618
5083	4032
5086	6053
5184	6061
5252	6063
5257	6066
5357	6101
5454	6151
5456	7039
5557	7075
5657	7079
	7178

TABLE 17-3. Basic Temper Designations Applicable to the Nonheat-Treatable Aluminum Alloys

Designation	Description	Application
—0	Annealed, recrystallized	Softest temper of wrought products.
—F	As fabricated	Applies to products that acquire some temper from shaping processes not having special control over the amount of strain hardening or thermal treatment.
—H1	Strain hardened only	Applies to those products that have some temper from shaping processes without special control over the amount of strain hardening or thermal treatment. The number following this designation indicates the degree of strain hardening.
—H2	Strain hardened and then partially annealed	Applies to products that are strain hardened more than the desired final amount and then reduced in strength to the desired level by partial annealing.
—H3	Strain hardened and then stabilized	Applies to products that are strain hardened and then stabilized by a low temperature heating to slightly lower their strength and increase ductility. This designation applies only to the magnesium containing alloys which, unless stabilized, gradually age-soften at room temperature.

NOTE: The degree of strain hardening is indicated by the number following either the —H1, —H2 or —H3 designations shown above. The hardest commercially practical temper is designated by the numeral 8 (full hard). Tempers between —0 (annealed) and 8 (full hard) are designated by numerals 1 through 7. Thus numeral 2 designates "quarter hard," numeral 4 "half hard," and numeral 6 "three-quarter hard." Numeral 9 designates extra hard tempers. Reference should be made to ASTM B296 and ASA H35.1 for full description of temperature designations.

the addition of alloying elements. The alloys thus produced are roughly classified into two categories, nonheat-treatable and heat-treatable (see Table 17-2).

Initial, or "as-cast", strengths of nonheat-treatable alloys are increased over pure aluminum by the addition of the alloying elements. Further strength is gained as they undergo cold work. Cold working, or strain hardening, is accomplished by rolling, drawing through dies, stretching, or similar operations that reduce the cross-sectional area. Material that has been strain-hardened can be given an elevated temperature treatment, called "stabilizing", to insure retention of properties if no further work or heat treatment is applied. See Table 17-3 for temper designations for nonheat-treatable aluminum alloys.

Initial strengths of heat-treatable alloys are pro-

TABLE 17-4. Basic Temper Designations Applicable to the Heat-Treatable Aluminum Alloys

Designation	Description	Application
—0	Annealed, recrystallized.	Softest temper of wrought products.
—F	As fabricated.	
—W	Solution heat-treated.	An unstable temper applicable only to alloys that spontaneously age at room temperature after solution heat-treatment. This designation is specific only when the period of natural aging is indicated (for example, —W 1/2 hour.)
—W5	Solution heat-treated and stress relieved.	
—T1	Modified solution heat-treated and then cold worked.	Applies to certain extruded material.
—T2	Annealed (cast products only).	
—T3	Solution heat-treated and then cold worked.	
—T4	Solution heat-treated and naturally aged to a substantially stable condition.	
—T5	Artificially aged after a modified solution heat-treatment.	Applies to certain extruded products.
—T6	Solution heat-treated and then artificially aged.	
—T7	Solution heat-treated and then stabilized.	
—T8	Solution heat-treated, cold worked and then artificially aged.	
—T9	Solution heat-treated, artificially aged and then cold worked.	
—T10	Artificially aged and then cold worked.	Applies to products that are artificially aged after an elevated-temperature rapid-cool fabrication process, such as casting or extrusion and then cold worked to improve strength.

*Reference should be made to ASTM B296 and ASA H35.1 for full description of temper designations.

duced by the addition of other elements to pure aluminum. These include copper, magnesium, zinc and silicon. When present in a given alloy singly or in various combinations, these metals exhibit increasing solid solubility in aluminum as the temperature increases. It is possible therefore to impart pronounced additional strengthening to heat-treatable alloys by subjecting them to various degrees of thermal treatment, quenching, and aging. The principal methods of heat treatment for this group of aluminum alloys are *solution heat treatment* and *precipitation heat treatment.* See Table 17-4 for temper designations for heat-treatable aluminum alloys.

WELDABILITY OF ALUMINUM AND ITS ALLOYS

To understand the weldability of aluminum and aluminum alloys, one should be aware of some of the differences in physical characteristics between aluminum and steel. (See Table 17-5). The aluminum oxide that forms a coating on aluminum is more difficult to cope with than the iron oxide that forms on steel. The thermal conductivity of aluminum is higher than steel and therefore requires a greater rate of heat input for fusion welding. Below the melting point, aluminum shows no temperature colors, which makes it more difficult to judge when the metal is approaching the melting point.

Aluminum has a great affinity for oxygen. In fact, aluminum is so active chemically that it reacts almost instantly with the oxygen in the air to produce a thin, hard, refractory film of aluminum oxide on the surface of the metal. It has been said that no one has ever seen aluminum, because what one is actually looking at is the thin transparent oxide film that covers the metal as rapidly as a new surface is exposed. The presence of this oxide film complicates the weld-joining of aluminum. Before welding, as much film as possible must be removed by mechanical abrading or chemical treatment.

During welding, an atmosphere must be maintained that prevents oxidation.

A second factor that makes the joining of aluminum different from the joining of steel is its high thermal conductivity. Aluminum conducts heat from three to five times faster than iron or steel, depending upon the alloy. In welding, brazing, and soldering, this means that considerable heat must be put into aluminum during a given period of time in order to bring it up to working temperature, since heat is being rapidly conducted away from the joint.

This is why attempting to solder aluminum with a soldering iron is not practical, as most irons simply do not have enough heat output. Thus, a torch is needed as a heat source for soldering aluminum. Similarly, in torch brazing and torch welding, provision must be made for the greater heat input requirement — usually obtained by using a slightly larger tip orifice. The high conductivity of aluminum is also the reason why the intense heat of the electric arc is so well adapted to welding the metal. Again, the high thermal conductivity explains why procedures for welding, brazing and soldering emphasize the rapid completion of the joint; speed reduces the amount of heat that is conducted into the area surrounding the joint — and reduced total heat input minimizes warping and distortion.

HEAT EFFECTS WHEN WELDING ALUMINUM

Welding heat adversely affects weld-zone mechanical properties of all aluminum alloys. Strength of the weld area is less than that of the unaffected base metal. Although welds in sections that are in the annealed condition do not change the temper, the cast-structure of the weld metal usually has lower strength than the base metal. However, upgrading the weld metal with a suitable filler alloy, increasing the welding speed, and bead reinforcement usually strengthen the welded joint.

Some heat-treatable alloys in the T6 temper (solution heat-treated, then artifically aged) are used in welded structural applications, where it is customary to proportion members on the basis of yield strength. The minimum tensile and compressive yield strength of 6061-T6 alloy sheet and plate in the weld-heat zone adjacent to a butt weld is 20,000 psi with 5356 or 5556 filler alloy. This compares favorably with weld-heat-zone yield strengths of other high-strength aluminum alloys.

Hot cracking is caused by stresses induced by metal contraction as the weld pool cools. Cracking of this type usually develops in the weld metal itself, but a similar type of cracking sometimes occurs in the heat-affected zone adjacent to the weld.

TABLE 17-5. Comparison of Certain Properties of Aluminum and Steel*

| Material | Plastic Range (°F) | Conductivity | | Specific Heat (cal/g) | Tensile Strength (psi) | Linear Coefficient of Expansion (cm/°C) | Density gr./cm³ |
		Electrical % (Cu)	Thermal (CGS)				
Aluminum 1100-0	1125-1190	59	0.53	0.23	13000	25.6 x 10⁶	2.71
Aluminum 5052-H38	1100-1200	35	0.33	0.23	41000	25.8 x 10⁶	
Aluminum 7075-T6	890-1190	30	0.29	0.22	72000	26.0 x 10⁶	
Steel 1010	1700-2700	10	0.10	0.11	72000	13.0 x 10⁶	7.83

*Adapted from table in *Resistance Welding of Aluminum Alloys* by J.F. Detfenbaugh of Federal Welding Co.

Cracking of welds during arc-welding operations can also be caused by a hot-short characteristic of some resultant weld compositions, as illustrated in Fig. 17-1. Hot-short compositions are weak at elevated temperatures. Hot cracking is a function of contraction stress and of the hot-short tendency of the alloy. Hot cracking can also be caused by restraint of the joint during welding. Hot cracking does not normally occur in pure aluminum or in deposits of eutectic composition.

Other factors that affect the amount of hot cracking that occurs in the weld include the solidification temperature range of the alloy, the coefficient of expansion, the thermal gradient, the ratio of the volume of liquid remaining to the volume of solidified material, and the amount of restraint across the weld joint.

Hot-short cracking can be reduced by several methods:

Use Higher Welding Speed. As welding speed is increased, the heat input in the weld zone is decreased. Thus, the stresses created by temperature differentials between the hot and room-temperature metal are less severe. Also, at high welding speeds shorter lengths of weld are within the hot-short range at any one time, and the already solidified metal takes a portion of the load that would otherwise be imposed upon the hot-short weld metal. The same effect is also advantageous in welding aluminum alloys that are not hot-short. In addition, the faster cooling rate that occurs with higher welding speeds results in a finer dendritic structure, which is less susceptible to cracking.

Use Preheat. Preheating reduces the stress on the solidifying weld metal by reducing the temperature gradient across the weld zone and by permitting faster joining rates. Preheating should not be used, however, unless the joint is unrestrained. The mechanical properties of the parent alloy are decreased by excessive preheating, except where the material is already in the annealed condition. This is particularly true of heat-treatable alloys such as 6061.

Changing the Joint Design. The chemical composition of an aluminum alloy affects its hot-short characteristics. The chemical composition of the weld metal is the product of a mixture of the base alloy and the filler metal, and this mixture may be highly susceptible to hot-short cracking. To reduce this susceptibility, the joint design can be changed to either increase or decrease the amount of parent alloy in the final weld metal.

Selection of the proper joint design usually requires that sample weldments be prepared to evaluate crack susceptibility in cases where data on comparable welds are not available.

Select A More Compatible Filler Alloy. A filler alloy that will minimize hot-short cracking is one that, when dilution is considered, will give a resultant weld composition having an individual alloy content above or below known hot-short ranges. A proper aluminum filler selection or recommendation, using hot-short cracking tendency as a criterion, requires consideration of the relative cracking tendencies of various weld-metal compositions. For example, in binary alloys of aluminum, maximum cracking occurs in these composition ranges:

Alloying Element	Amount (%)
Silicon	0.5 to 1.2
Copper	2.0 to 4.0
Manganese	1.5 to 2.5
Magnesium	2.0 to 5.0
Zinc	4.0 to 5.0
Iron	1.0 to 1.5

FILLER METALS FOR WELDING ALUMINUM ALLOYS

The metal produced in the weld pool is a combination of metals that must have the strength, ductility, freedom from cracking, and the cor-

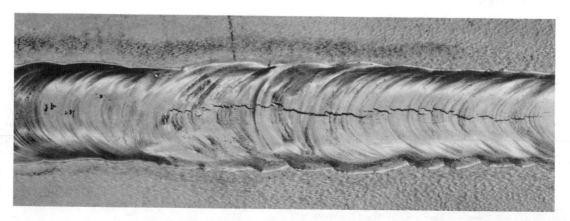

Fig. 17-1. Hot-short crack in aluminum weld metal.

rosion resistance required by the application. Correct choice of a filler alloy minimizes the presence of intermetallic compounds and brittleness in aluminum fusion welds.

Strength: Some filler metals commonly used for inert-gas welding, arranged in decreasing order of as-welded strength, reading left to right, are:

5039, 5556, 5183, 5356, 5654, 5554, 4043, and 1100.

This order of strength is generally true for these fillers when used to weld any alloy of the 5000, 3000, or 1100 series. This sequence does not necessarily apply to some combinations of dissimilar alloys or to assemblies subjected to post-weld heat treatment.

Ductility: An arrangement of the same filler metals in decreasing order of ductility is almost the reverse of the arrangement by strength:

1100, 4043, 5654, 5356, 5183, 5554, 5556, and 5039.

Up to 50% elongation can be expected with 1100 filler, whereas 15% to 20% is normal for 5183 or 5356 filler. Ductility of the weld is often affected by dilution of the filler metal with the base material. For example, 4043 can vary from 5 to 17% elongation, depending on type and quantity of alloy with which it is diluted. Table 17-6 lists

recommended filler metals for various aluminum alloys, both for maximum strength and for maximum elongation.

Availability of Filler Wire: A relatively small number of filler alloys can be used to weld a wide range of aluminum alloys. Certain filler alloys — 5356 or 5183 for example — can be used for practically all aluminum fusion-welding applications.

Filler wire of alloys EC, 1100, 4043, 5039, 5654, 5356, 5183, 5554, and 5556 is available on 1 or 12-1/2-lb spools for use with the MIG and automatic TIG processes. Wire of 0.030, 3/64, 1/16, 3/32, and 1/8-in. is also available. For certain alloys, welding wire of 3/16, 7/32 and 1/4-in. is also available. Wire of alloys other than these is available upon request.

Straight lengths of bare aluminum wire in EC, 1100, 4043, 5039, 5654, 5183, 5356 and 5556 alloys are available in diameters of 1/16, 3/32, 1/8, 5/32, 3/16, and 1/4-in. This bare rod stock is used primarily for TIG welding.

Maximum rate of deposition is obtained with filler wire or rod of the largest practical diameter while welding at the maximum practical welding current. Wire diameter best suited for a specific application depends upon the current that can be used to make the weld. The current, in turn, is governed by the available power supply, joint design, alloy type and thickness, and the welding position. For detailed information on filler sizes, refer to the discussions on TIG and MIG welding.

Quality of Weld Deposit: Good weld quality is obtained only if the filler wire is clean and of high quality. If the wire is not clean, a large amount of contaminant may be introduced into the weld pool, particularly in MIG welding, because of the relatively large surface area of the filler wire with respect to the amount of weld metal being deposited.

Contaminants on the filler wire are most often an oil or a hydrated oxide. The heat of welding releases the hydrogen from these sources, causing porosity in the weld. High-quality aluminum welding wire is manufactured under rigorous control to exacting standards and is packaged to prevent contamination during storage. Since filler wire is alloyed, or diluted, with base metal in the weld pool, the compositions of both the filler wire and the base metal affect the quality of the weld.

Care of Filler Wire and Rod: The best quality welds are obtained by using welding wire as soon as possible after it is removed from the package. Even a high-quality wire can produce welds of inferior quality if the wire surface is contaminated by oil, dust, or other foreign material. Consequently, spools of wire should be protected by a cover

TABLE 17-6. Recommended Filler Metals for Various Aluminum Alloys

Base Metal	Recommended Filler Metal[1]	
	For Maximum As-Welded Strength	For Maximum Elongation
EC	1100	EC, 1260
1100	1100, 4043	1100, 4043
2219	2319	(2)
3003	5183, 5356	1100, 4043
3004	5554, 5356	5183, 4043
5005	5183, 4043, 5356	5183, 4043
5050	5356	5183, 4043
5052	5356, 5183	5183, 4043, 5356
5083	5183, 5356	5183, 5356
5086	5183, 5356	5183, 5356
5154	5356, 5183	5183, 5356, 5654
5357	5554, 5356	5356
5454	5356, 5554	5554, 5356
5456	5556	5183, 5356
6061	4043, 5183	5356[3]
6063	4043, 5183	5356[3]
7005	5039	5183, 5356
7039	5039	5183, 5356

Notes:
1. Recommendations are for plate of "0" temper.
2. Ductility of weldments of these base metals is not appreciably affected by filler metal. Elongation of these base metals is generally lower than that of other alloys listed.
3. For welded joints in 6061 and 6063 requiring maximum electrical conductivity, use 4043 filler metal. However, if both strength and conductivity are required, use 5356 filler metal and increase the weld reinforcement to compensate for the lower conductivity of 5356.

during use. Components of a wire-drive system (drive rolls, guides, and liners) can also contaminate the wire if they are not clean. Welding wire packages with desiccant in plastic bags should remain unopened until the wire is to be used.

When maximum weld quality is essential or the cost of repairing welds is prohibitive, questionable spools should be pretested before use in fabrication. Several test methods may be used, all of which involve making a sample weld that is checked by radiography or by examination of the weld fracture. A triple-pass horizontal fillet weld is the simplest for evaluation. A radiograph from a multipass flat-position butt weld is a valid check, provided that at least three passes are used. Such a test may save costly repair cutouts, particularly in welds that require radiographic inspection.

SURFACE PREPARATION FOR WELDING

Aluminum sheet and plate that is to be welded should be carefully stored and handled. Clean dry storage is preferred. If outdoor storage is necessary, the plate should be covered or stored on edge with interspacing to prevent staining. Aluminum should not be primed or painted before welding.

Pieces to be welded are usually formed, sheared, sawed, or machined prior to the welding operation. Complete removal of all lubricants from these operations is a prerequisite for high-quality welds. Particular care must be taken to remove all oil, other hydrocarbons, and loose particles from sawed or sheared edges prior to welding. Sheared edges should be clean and smooth, not ragged. For ease of cleaning, lubricants used in fabrication should be promptly removed.

To reduce the possibility of porosity and dross in welds, cleanliness of the welding surfaces cannot be overemphasized. Hydrogen can cause porosity, and oxygen can cause dross in welds. Oxides, greases, and oil films contain oxygen and hydrogen if left on the edges to be welded, will cause unsound welds with poor mechanical and electrical properties. Cleaning should be done just prior to welding. A summary of general cleaning procedures is given in Table 17-7.

Oil or grease films are usually removed chemically by dipping, spraying, or wiping the aluminum sheet or plate with a solvent. Mildly alkaline solutions and commercial degreasers that do not emit toxic fumes during welding may be used.

All welding surfaces should be dried before welding. Cloth or absorbent paper is usually effective. Drying with compressed dry air is often used in difficult-to-reach areas. Some cleaning solutions — especially those containing alcohol or acetone — evaporate much faster than others.

Aluminum and its alloys rapidly develop a self-limiting oxide surface film upon exposure to air. The melting point of this oxide is above 3600°F, or about 2400°F above the melting point of pure aluminum. This oxide film can prevent fusion between the filler metal and base plate, or flakes of

TABLE 17-7. Common Methods for Cleaning Aluminum Surfaces for Welding

Compounds Removed	Type of Cleaning	
	Welding Surfaces Only	Complete Piece
Oil, grease, moisture, and dust (Use any method listed.)	Wipe with mild alkaline solution. Wipe with hydrocarbon solvent, such as acetone or alcohol. Wipe with proprietary solvents. Dip edges, using any of above.	Vapor degrease. Spray degrease. Steam degrease. Immerse in alkaline solvent. Immerse in proprietary solvents.
Oxides (Use any method listed.)	Dip edges in strong alkaline solution, then water, then nitric acid. Finish with water rinse. Wipe with proprietary deoxidizers. Remove mechanically, such as by wire-brushing, filing, or grinding. For critical applications, scrape all joint and adjacent surfaces immediately prior to welding, using no lubricant. Remove about one mil of metal.	Immerse in strong alkaline solution, then water, then nitric acid. Finish with water rinse. Immerse in proprietary solutions.

oxide or dross may become entrapped within the weld metal, reducing the ductility of the weld.

It is usually necessary to remove surface oxides mechanically just prior to welding. Chemically deoxidized parts may also require mechanical removal of oxide if more than a day has elapsed since deoxidation was performed. Welding should be done as soon as practical after oxide removal or cleaning operations, usually within 24 hours when resistance welding. When fusion welding, two or three days may be allowed to elapse after oxide removal, providing the joint area is wire-brushed immediately before welding. Excessively black or dirty-appearing inert gas welds may be an indication of excessive plate oxide.

Wire brushing, scraping, filing, and grinding are common mechanical cleaning methods used on aluminum plates. In wire brushing, stainless-steel bristles are preferred, but are not mandatory. The main disadvantage of using carbon-steel brushes is that iron deposits left by the bristles may rust if moisture is present. Large amounts of iron oxide may result in weld-metal inclusions. Carbon-steel brushes are satisfactory if they are grease-free, and both they and the work are kept dry. A moisture film that would rule out the use of carbon-steel brushes would also require recleaning the aluminum plate.

WELDING ALUMINUM AND ITS ALLOYS WITH THE GAS METAL-ARC PROCESS

Most arc welding of aluminum alloys is done with the inert-gas metal-arc (MIG) process. Weld properties generally are at least equal to those of the base metal at zero temper. Welding speeds are higher than those obtainable with any other arc or gas process. Heat-affected zones are narrower than those with oxyacetylene or covered-electrode arc welding A DCRP (reverse-polarity) electric arc, established in an envelope of inert gas between a consumable electrode and the workpiece, is used for welding aluminum by the MIG process.

MIG and another inert-gas, shielded-arc process, gas tungsten-arc (TIG), are the principal methods for welding aluminum. The two processes are similar in that an inert gas is used to shield the arc and the weld pool, making flux unnecessary. The chief differences are in the electrodes and the characteristics of the power used.

In MIG welding, the electrode is aluminum filler fed continuously from a reel into the weld pool. TIG welding uses a nonconsumable tungsten electrode, with aluminum alloy filler material added separately, either from a hand-held rod or from a reel.

The equipment required for MIG welding con-

sists of a drive system that pulls the electrode from a reel and pushes it through the welding gun. In the gun, it becomes energized by passing through a contact tube connected to the power supply. While simple in principle, accurate controls are required to initiate and stop the shielding gas, cooling water, and electrode and to operate the contactor in the welding circuit.

The MIG process is used for either semiautomatic or automatic welding. It is referred to as "semiautomatic" when the gun is operated manually. Once the gun is started and the arc struck, the welding conditions are automatically controlled (on constant-voltage equipment, particularly) by the machine settings. This leaves the operator free to concentrate on placement of the weld bead.

With a direct-current, reverse-polarity (DCRP) arc, used for MIG welding aluminum, the electrode is positive, the work negative. Both the consumable filler metal and weld zone of the workpiece are melted.

With argon shielding, the DCRP arc also breaks up the surface oxide on the base metal ahead of the weld pool. This cleaning action is believed to be caused by the electrons leaving the base plate or the inert-gas ions striking the plate, or a combination of the two phenomena.

The DCRP action propels the filler metal across the arc to the workpiece in line with the axis of the electrode, regardless of the orientation of the electrode. Because of this and aluminum's density, surface tension, and cooling rate, horizontal, vertical, and overhead welds are made with relative ease. High deposition rates are practical, producing less distortion, greater weld strength, and lower welding costs for a given job than other fusion-welding processes.

The efficient use of energy, characteristic of the MIG process, makes preheating of aluminum workpieces unnecessary in most cases. Consequently, the process is widely accepted for welding heavy sections of aluminum. MIG welding is also applicable to joining sheet thicknesses of aluminum at high speeds. It is practical to MIG-weld aluminum as thin as 0.062-in. in regular production.

MAINTAINING WELD QUALITY

While a limited amount of porosity and dross can be tolerated in some welded joints, ductility, fatigue strength, and tensile strength are adversely affected by porosity, and weld metal — just as base metal — should be sound in all respects.

The main cause of porosity in aluminum welds is entrapped gas in the weld puddle. Porosity occurs when metal freezes before the gas has a chance to escape. Gases may originate from con-

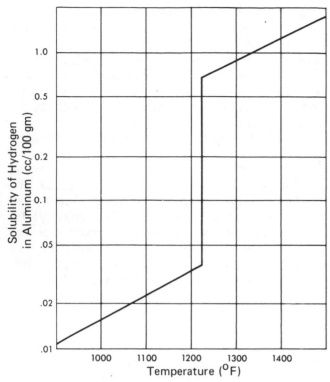

Fig. 17-2. Solubility of hydrogen in aluminum at various temperatures.

dirty base or filler metal, from too long an arc, or as a result of violent arc action. The amount of gas that remains in the weld pool is a function of the cooling rate of the weld puddle. Various causes of porosity and some corrective measures are listed in Table 17-8.

Entrapment: Shielding gas, air, or gaseous contaminants can be entrapped in the weld puddle as a result of the violent arc action. Weld porosity is similar to the air bubbles that are entrapped in a rapidly frozen ice cube.

Turbulence in a weld pool is related to droplet transfer. If too low a welding current is used, so that large globules of metal transfer across the arc, more turbulent puddle reaction occurs than if small, well-formed droplets transfer in a fine-spray pattern.

Excessive welding currents can entrap gas by depositing metal over a gas bubble in the weld pool. Such metal freezes before the entire bubble has escaped. This type of porosity is generally irregular in shape.

Hydrogen: In addition to air entrapment, the generation of hydrogen from contaminants in the weld is another cause of gas porosity in aluminum. Molten aluminum has a high affinity for atomic hydrogen (see Fig. 17-2). On the other hand, solid aluminum can contain very little hydrogen. Therefore, hydrogen gas is emitted as the weld puddle

taminants in the shielding gas, from air and water, from contaminants that get into the puddle from

TABLE 17-18. Causes and Cures for Porosity in Mig Welds

Cause	Contributing Factors	Corrective Measures
Gas entrapment	Turbulence of weld pool. Excessive current entrains gas.	Use adequate welding current to stabilize droplet transfer, but avoid excessive current. Reduce travel speed.
Hydrogen	Oil or other contaminants on electrode. Hydrated oxide film on electrode. Oily drive rolls or liner in MIG gun. Wet shielding gas. Water leaks in MIG gun. Oily workpiece. Spatter particles ahead of puddle.	Change to clean, high-quality electrode. Keep electrode supply covered. Do not open desicated plastic packaging until ready to use. Do not use electrode that has been kept for any length of time outside of desicated storage. Clean rolls with solvent; change liner. Check dewpoint of gas; reject bottles above minus 40°F dewpoint. Repair guns that have been overheated due to water failure. Clean plate. Adjust welding conditions to minimize spatter.
Rapid cooling rate of weld pool	Low rate of heat input into the weld. Too rapid a rate of heat extraction from the weld. Low temperature of backup bar, if used. Groove configuration of backup bar.	Use higher welding current or a slower speed. Preheat sometimes helps. Hot backup bars reduce root porosity. Shallow, wide grooves are better than deep, narrow grooves in backup bars.
Erratic wire feeding	Drive-roll slip. Excessive bending of guide liner. Bent contact tube puts kink in electrode. Galling in contact tube. Electronic "hunting." Wrong size liner.	Increase pressure on rolls, change to knurled roll; change to V-groove roll rather than U-groove. Change position of MIG unit to reduce necessity of bending cable to gun. Replace thyratron tube or bias (balance) battery.
Other	Partial-penetration joint. Multiple-pass welds.	Use full-penetration joint. Increase fillet size to compensate for line of root porosity in critical applications. Use high-current-density, single-pass-per-side technique.

freezes. If the cooling rate of the weld puddle is too fast, the gas cannot rise to the surface, but remains within the metal, causing porosity.

Any compound containing hydrogen and contaminating the filler wire or work surface can be the source of hydrogen gas. For example, if a film of drawing compound (containing hydrocarbons) or hydrated aluminum oxide remains on the filler wire, extreme porosity will occur in the welds made with that wire.

Other possible sources of hydrogen-forming contaminants include the base material and the shielding gas. A bottle of wet gas will cause contaminated welds, as will mositure leaks in the welding torch or hose line. Gas having a dewpoint higher than minus 40°F is unsuitable for MIG welding of aluminum.

Poor welds can also result from using electrode that has been stored under humid conditions, where atmospheric moisture can combine chemically or be absorbed by the aluminum oxide film.

Cooling System: Before welding, the MIG torch should be checked in regard to the following points:

Are all O-rings seated properly?

Are all fittings drawn up tight?

Are all solder joints tight?
   (Torches that have been overheated may have developed leaks in soldered joints.)

Are all ceramic parts in good condition?
   (Broken or distorted ceramics should be replaced.)

Is the gas hose clean and in good condition?
   (Do not use leaky or deteriorated hose. Do not use hose that previously has carried water, or liquids or gases containing compounds such as hydrocarbons, which will cause weld porosity. A vinyl or other suitable plastic hose is recommended.)

Most MIG equipment can be adjusted for either "continuous" or "weld-only" cooling-water flow. In humid weather, water flow should not be continuous. Water vapor from the atmosphere may condense on the gas cup and internal parts of the gun if the cold water flows during idle periods. When welding is resumed, the water condensate will vaporize and be carried to the weld area by the shielding gas, causing weld porosity. Therefore, particularly in humid weather, cooling-water flow should be stopped when welding is stopped. Residual heat in the gun will keep the gas cup and other critical parts warm, preventing condensation.

Cooling Rate of Weld Pool: The amount of gas remaining in the weld pool is a function of how fast the weld pool solidifies. If most of the gas has

time to escape before the molten metal solidifies, the weld will have minimal porosity and be of generally good radiographic quality. The length of time that the aluminum weld pool is molten is determined by the heat input into the weld, the rate of heat extraction from the weld, the freezing range (solidification temperature) of the alloy, and the temperature and mass of the surrounding material. The temperature and groove configuration of the backup bar (if used) also affect the rate of heat loss.

To retard the cooling rate of the weld puddle, the heat input generally must be increased, since the factors affecting heat loss are usually fixed. This can be done by increasing the current, decreasing the travel speed, or both. Changes in either of these must always be regulated, however, within operating limits conducive to proper bead deposition and contour and to the thickness limitations of the base material.

Use of higher arc voltage also increases the heat input. Helium may be added to argon in amounts greater than 10% to increase arc voltage and reduce porosity.

The rate of heat extracted from the weld is generally high, due to the high thermal conductivity of aluminum. Obviously, heavier or large sections can contain more than thinner sections. Thus, heavy or large sections act as better heat sinks than light sections and extract or conduct heat from the weld faster than thin materials.

When welding speed is reduced to retard the cooling rate, the effect is to allow more heat to be lost to the heat sink, thus warming the assembly

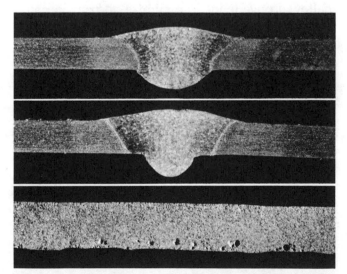

Fig. 17-3. Effects of backup bar groove configuration on porosity in welds in aluminum sheet. The wide, shallow groove (top) minimizes porosity because it produces a large mass of metal at the root. The deep, narrow groove (center) promotes root porosity. The lower specimen shows root porosity in a MIG weld, resulting from a narrow backup-bar groove. Magnification. 3X.

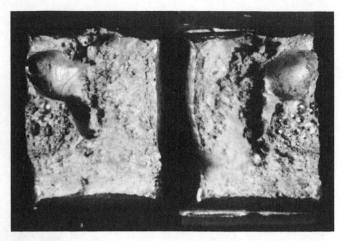

Fig. 17-4. Fractured surface of a tensile test bar showing "worm hole" porosity in a MIG weld, caused by spongy cast base metal.

being welded. Consideration must be given to the fact that such heating may decrease the mechanical properties in the metal outside the weld zone, which, itself, is annealed by the arc.

Weld metal cools from the outer edges toward the center of the weld nugget. One frequent condition is that in which a wide weld bead, having a thin edge at its width extremities, has a line of porosity at the edges due to the faster freezing of the thin section of weld metal in those areas. This shows as line porosity in a radiograph and generally is associated with multiple-pass welding.

Root porosity, which is similar to fusion-line porosity, occurs particularly in welds made on a backup bar having an unsuitable groove configuration. A deep, narrow groove in a backup bar is conducive to root porosity, whereas a wide, shallow groove tends to minimize porosity, because of the larger mass of weld metal at the root (see

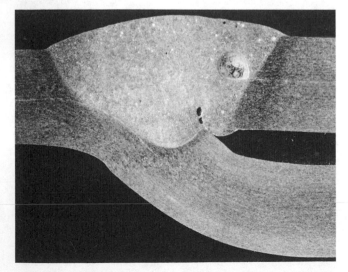

Fig. 17-5. A MIG weld in aluminum sheet showing porosity caused by lamination.

Fig. 17-3). Preheating of the backup bar has been found to reduce further the tendency to form root porosity.

Electrode Feeding: Erratic electrode feeding can cause porosity in weld metal, due to increased turbulence of the weld pool. Erratic feeding can be caused by a number of things. The electrode may slip in the drive rolls because of insufficient pressure, excessive bending in the electrode transport tube, excessive bending in the guide tube of the gun, or excessive bending of the cable between the drive unit and the welding gun. Kinks in the electrode will jam in the gun and cause a burn-back. If the kinks manage to feed through, they usually produce a momentary slowing of the electrode. Improperly wound spools with crossovers or edge-bound strands also cause erratic wire feeding.

Aluminum electrode can seize and gall inside the contact tube, causing an erratic or stitching arc action. Replacing the contact tube corrects the

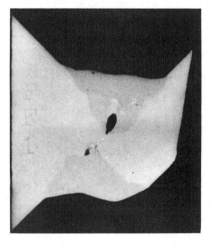

Fig. 17-6. Radiograph showing root porosity in a transverse wafer cut from a lap weld.

situation.

Quality of Base Material: Weld porosity is also dependent on the quality of the base material, particularly in castings. The presence of large pores in cast base material can cause an elongated type of porosity in the weld, as shown in Fig. 17-4. In the case illustrated, a "boiler effect" occurred where the weld metal heated a volume of gas from the pore in the base material. The gas expanded along a channel in the molten metal to form a long tube, until the diminishing gas pressure was equalized by the weight of the weld metal. A similar effect can occur when the base metal sheet is laminated, as shown in Fig. 17-5.

Welding partial-penetration joints (as in making a welded lap joint) can also cause a boiler effect, as shown by the radiograph in Fig. 17-6. In this case, the source of gas was the line at the root, where sufficient pressure was built up from the heat of welding (on the second side to be welded) to cause porosity to form in the molten metal.

Multiple-Pass Welding: Porosity is more prevalent in multiple-pass welds than in single-pass welds. Thus, in welds where porosity exists, top passes in heavy plate have been observed generally to contain more porosity than root passes. Wherever practical, welds with a minimum number of passes should be used. With high current-density techniques, MIG butt welding with a single pass per side can be done in aluminum plate as thick as 1-1/4 in.

Effect of Porosity on Properties: Just what effect does weld porosity have on the properties of aluminum welds? As shown in Fig. 17-7, some porosity can be tolerated in a weld before mechanical properties are reduced, but tensile properties are reduced appreciably when the amount of porosity is high. Data shown are for MIG weldments in 5083 plate; different porosity levels were obtained by contaminant additions to the welding arc. Data are not available on the effect of porosity on fatigue properties of weld metal.

Dross in MIG Welds: Most dross consists of broken particles of aluminum oxide or aluminum nitride films, which can be scattered throughout the weld bead. The presence of oxygen in the shielding gas or on the surface of the solidifying weld pool causes dross. Dross has the appearance of pepper on the fractured metal surface.

Dross also may be present as a film in "cold shut" areas, where the arc length was too long, producing temperatures too low to fuse the weld bead into the underlying metal. Dross, unlike gas porosity, has a markedly adverse effect upon the mechanical properties of aluminum welds.

Shielding: Oxygen may enter the weld pool from several sources. The primary cause of oxygen entry from the atmosphere is poor shielding. Drafts in the welding area can cause a momentary loss of shielding, allowing air to contaminate the surface of the molten metal. Also, if the gas flow is too low, inadequate shielding of the weld pool results. Entrained air entering the contact tube may also cause dross to form. Use of too small a gas cup for wire diameter, current, and size of puddle can result in inefficient shielding, thus allowing excessive air to get to the weld puddle.

Electrode Surface: Just as it can be a source of porosity-causing hydrogen, the electrode can also be a source of dross-causing oxygen. If an electrode has more than a minimal oxide coating, it is a potential source of oxygen and is unsuitable for MIG welding of aluminum. Oxygen may also be present in organic substances on the electrode, particularly if the spools of filler metal have been exposed to the shop atmosphere without protective covers. Unused spools should be kept in their packages; partly used spools on welding machines should be covered between jobs.

Base Metal and Weld Oxide: Welding over base metal surfaces that have not been deoxidized or properly wire-brushed prior to welding can result in oxygen pickup, particularly with sheet material. Preceding weld beads, if not cleaned or brushed. also are a source of oxygen, as well as of hydrogen. All beads must be properly wire-brushed before subsequent beads are deposited.

The underside of root beads in joints that are to be welded from both sides should be chipped or milled to remove the dross prior to depositing weld metal on the second side. No back-chipping is required on welds made by high current-density techniques in properly prepared square butt or heavy-

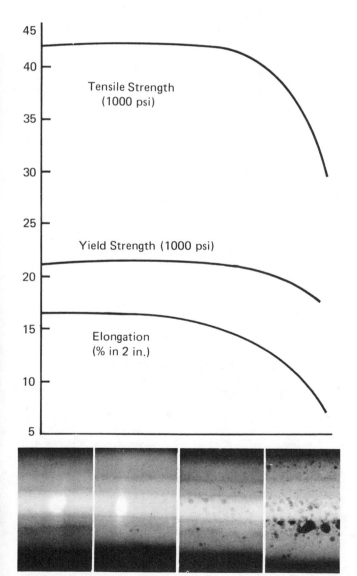

Fig. 17-7. Effect of porosity on MIG weld properties of 5083 plate, welded with 5356 filler.

TABLE 17-9. Causes and Cures for Dross in Mig Welds

Cause	Contributing Factors	Corrective Measures
Poor shielding	Drafts, causing loss of shielding. Gas flow too low. Entrained air in contact tube. Gas cup too small.	Provide protection against drafts in welding area. Increase shielding-gas flow rate. Pressurize contact tube with shielding gas. Use a larger gas cup.
Contaminated electrode surface	Oxygen from excessive oxide or from hydrocarbon contaminant.	Use electrode with clean surface and minimum oxide film. Protect electrode in shop with plastic covers.
Contaminated base-metal surface	Heavy oxide film. Spatter particles.	Wire-brush or chemically remove oxide. Adjust welding conditions so spatter does not occur ahead of puddle.
Contaminated weld	Oxide film on preceding beads. Dross on underside of root passes.	Wire-brush each bead before depositing next bead. Chip or mill underside to sound metal.

root-face butt joints. A summary of causes and cures for dross in MIG weld metal is given in Table 17-9.

INERT GASES FOR MIG WELDING

The inert gas has three primary functions. First, it provides a controlled ionized path, which aids in the smooth transfer of current. Second, it surrounds the arc and weld pool with an atmosphere that is nonreactive with molten aluminum. Third, it has a cleaning action, which partially removes aluminum oxide from the plate during DCRP welding. (Only argon shielding produces such cleaning action in DCRP welding, however.) It is not known whether this cleaning action is a result of gas ions striking the surface, or electrons leaving the base plate, or a combination of each.

In addition to the inert gases commonly used — argon and helium — neon or krypton could probably be used with the MIG process for shielding purposes. However, argon and helium are the gases generally used because they are more readily available and less expensive.

Shielding Efficiency: Any disturbance of the inert gas shield around the arc and the weld pool reduces its shielding efficiency. If insufficient gas is used or if the flow of gas is disturbed, poor quality welding will result. Such disturbances may be caused by improper gas flow, drafts, erratic arcs, gas stoppage, or turbulence due to spatter in the nozzle.

The flow of inert gas necessary for good-quality MIG welding depends upon a number of

TABLE 17-10. Factors that Affect Flow Rate of Shielding Gas in Mig Welding

Factor or Condition	Higher Flow Required	Lower Flow Required
Draft: No draft Increasing draft	 X	 X
Gas: Argon Helium	 X	 X
Torch lead angle: 10° Lead 0° 10° Lag (not recom.)	 X 	 X
Welding current: High Low	 X 	 X
Diameter of nozzle: Large Small	 X 	 X
Joint design: Flat surface In a groove or fillet	 X 	 X
Welding speed: Fast Slow	 X 	 X
Position Flat, overhead Vertical, horizontal	 X	 X

TABLE 17-11. Suggested Flow Rates for Mig Welding of Aluminum Butt Joints in Various Positions

Position	Shielding Gas Flow (cfh)		
	Argon	Helium	75% He, 25% A
Flat	$50^1 - 70^2$	70 — 90	60 — 80
Horizontal	50 — 70	70 — 90	60 — 80
Vertical	50 — 70	70 — 90	60 — 80
Overhead	70 — 90	80 — 100	70 — 90

Values are for 1/32 to 1/16-in. electrode size and 5/8 or 3/4-in. cup size.

1. With 0.030-in. and 3/64-in. electrode flow can be reduced by 25% under normal conditions.

2. Highest flow rates indicated apply to thicker base materials and to alloys containing greater amounts of magnesium.

factors, including type of gas used, welding current, diameter of gun nozzle, joint design, welding position, speed of welding, torch lead angle, and the amount of draft in the welding area (see Table 17-10).

Drafts can affect gas usage and weld quality considerably. It is important that the welding area be essentially draft-free. In field welding, suitable shielding with tarpaulins or other types of windbreaks should be provided to prevent air currents from interfering with the gas shield.

Overhead welding usually requires higher gas flow rates than flat-position welding, regardless of gas used. As a basis for determining correct gas flow for a given welding job, the gas flow rates in Table 17-11 are suggested as starting points. Lower gas flows can frequently be used. The correct flow for any job is determined by gradually reducing the flow rate used in making sample weldments until the weld quality is adversely affected. The gas flow should then be increased to provide a safety margin.

Only high-purity, dry inert gas ("welding grade") should be used in MIG welding. Impure or wet gas will degrade weld quality.

Argon Shielding: Argon is preferred for flat, vertical, and horizontal-position manual MIG welding by most operators, because argon produces a more stable arc then helium. Less argon is required than helium for shielding in MIG welding because

its density is greater (argon, 1.4; helium, 0.14; air, 1.0).

Argon is produced by fractionating air and is readily available. Argon is sold in compressed gas form in a variety of cylinder sizes. Where large volumes are consumed, liquid argon installations may be economical.

Helium Shielding: At any given (DCRP) arc length, a helium-shielded arc has a higher voltage than an argon arc. This results in a deeper penetration with helium, which, in turn, can be used to increase welding speed. However, the arc is slightly more erratic in helium than in argon, and, since helium shielding provides no cleaning action, the resultant weld bead appearance is usually inferior.

Helium is usually preferred for welding very heavy material because it provides deeper weld penetration. The lightness of helium makes it preferable for overhead welding. The high welding speed obtainable with a helium arc make it attractive for automatic welding, where arc length can be controlled precisely. Helium, however, produces more spatter and requires more frequent nozzle cleaning than does argon — deterrent to the use of helium in certain automatic MIG operations.

Argon-Helium Mixtures: Mixtures of argon and helium are used to obtain advantages not obtained with either gas alone. Blends of 75% helium and 25% argon are commercially available. Other ratios can be mixed by combining flows from separate

TABLE 17-12. Procedures for Gas Metal-Arc Welding of Aluminum (Semiautomatic)

Plate Thickness, T (in.)	1/8	3/16	1/4	3/8	1/2	1/2	5/8	3/4
Pass Face	1	1	1	1	1	1	1	1
Pass Back		1	1	1	1	1	1	1
Electrode Size (in.)	3/64	3/64 or 1/16	1/16	1/16	1/16	1/16	1/16	1/16
Current (amp)	90 – 120	120 – 150	180 – 220	220 – 260	240 – 280	260 – 320	260 – 320	300 – 400
Volts	19 – 21	22 – 24	27 – 29	28 – 30	28 – 30	29 – 31	29 – 31	33 – 37
Arc Speed (ipm)	30 – 34	25 – 29	20 – 24	16 – 20	14 – 18	12 – 16	10 – 14	10 – 14
Argon Gas (cfh)	30 – 40	30 – 40	30 – 40	40 – 60	40 – 60	40 – 60	60 – 80	60 – 80
Gas Cup Opening (in.)	1/2	1/2	1/2	1/2	1/2	1/2	1/2	1/2
Total Time (hr/ft. of weld)	0.00625	0.0148	0.0182	0.0222	0.0250	0.0286	0.0333	0.0333

TABLE 17-13. Procedures for Gas Metal-Arc Welding of Aluminum (Semiautomatic)

Process: GasMetal-Arc Type of Joint: Butt Plate Thickness: 1/2 — 1-1/2 Position: Flat Welded from: Two sides Polarity: DCRP								
Plate Thickness (in.)	1/2	3/4	1	1/2	3/4	1	1-1/4	1-1/2
Pass Face	4	5	7	1	2	3	3	4
Pass Back*	1	1	1	1	2	3	3	4
Electrode Size (in.)	1/16	3/32	3/32	1/16	1/16	1/16	1/16	1/16
Current (amp)	200 — 230	260 — 280	260 — 300	220 — 250	240 — 280	240 — 280	240 — 280	240 — 280
Volts	27 — 29	27 — 29	27 — 29	28 — 30	28 — 30	28 — 30	28 — 30	28 — 30
Arc Speed (ipm)	16 — 20	12 — 16	10 — 14	16 — 20	16 — 20	14 — 20	14 — 20	14 — 20
Argon Gas (cfh)	40 — 60	40 - 60	40 — 60	40 — 60	40 — 60	60 — 80	60 — 80	60 — 80
Gas Cup Opening (in.)	1/2	5/8	5/8	5/8	5/8	5/8	5/8	5/8
Total Time (hr/ft. of weld)	0.0555	0.0858	0.133	0.0222	0.0444	0.0708	0.0708	0.0944

*Back chip before first pass
on back side optional.

TABLE 17-14. Procedures for Gas Metal-Arc Welding of Aluminum (Semiautomatic)

Process: Gas Metal-Arc Type of Joint: Butt Plate Thickness: 1/8 — 1 Position: Horizontal Welded from: Two sides Polarity: DCRP							
Plate Thickness (in.)	1/8	3/16	1/4	3/8	1/2	3/4	1
Pass Face	1	1	1	2	2	3	5
Pass Back*	1	1	1	2	2	3	5
Electrode Size (in.)	3/64	3/64	3/64	1/16	1/16	1/16	1/16
Current (amp)	100 — 120	120 — 140	160 — 200	180 — 200	200 — 220	220 — 260	240 — 280
Volts	19 — 22	20 — 23	26 — 28	27 — 29	27 — 29	28 — 30	28 — 30
Arc Speed (ipm)	24 — 30	24 — 30	22 — 26	24 — 30	20 — 24	20 — 24	16 — 20
Argon Gas (cfh)	30 — 40	30 — 40	30 — 40	40 — 60	40 — 60	60 — 80	60 — 80
Gas Cup Opening (in.)	1/2	1/2	1/2	1/2	5/8	5/8	5/8
Total Time (hr/ft. of weld)	0.0148	0.0148	0.0167	0.0296	0.0364	0.0545	0.111

*Back chip before first pass
on back side optional.

TABLE 17-15 Procedures for Gas Metal-Arc Welding of Aluminum (Semiautomatic)

Process: Gas Metal-Arc Type of Joint: Butt Plate Thickness: 1/8 — 1 Positions: Vertical Welded from: Two sides Polarity: DCRP							
Plate Thickness (in.)	1/8	3/16	1/4	1/4	3/8	1/2	3/4	1
Pass Face	1	1	1	1	1	2	4	6
Pass Back*	1	1	1	1	1	2	4	6
Electrode Size (in.)	3/64	1/16	1/16	1/16	1/16	1/16	1/16	1/16
Current (amp)	90 — 120	100 — 140	140 — 190	160 — 180	180 — 200	200 — 220	220 — 240	220 — 240
Volts	19 — 22	20 — 23	26 — 28	23 — 25	27 — 29	27 — 29	28 — 30	28 — 30
Arc Speed (ipm)	30 — 36	28 — 32	24 — 30	24 — 30	20 — 24	14 — 18	12 — 16	8 — 12
Argon gas (cfh)	30 — 40	30 — 40	30 — 40	30 — 40	40 — 60	40 — 60	60 — 80	60 — 80
Gas Cup Opening (in.)	1/2	1/2	1/2	1/2	1/2	5/8	5/8	5/8
Total Time (hr/ft. of weld)	0.0121	0.0133	0.0148	0.0148	0.0182	0.0500	0.114	0.240

TABLE 17-16. Procedures for Gas Metal-Arc Welding of Aluminum (Semiautomatic)

Process: Gas Metal-Arc Weld Size (in.): 1/4 — 1/2 Type of Joint: Fillet Positions: Horizontal, Vertical, and Overhead Polarity: DCRP								
Fillet Size, L (in.)	1/4	3/8	1/2	1/4	3/8	1/2	1/4	3/8	1/2
Pass	1	1	3	1	2	3	1	2	3
Electrode Size (in.)	1/16	1/16	3/32	1/16	1/16	1/16	1/16	1/16	1/16
Current (amp)	160 — 180	200 — 230	240 — 280	160 — 180	180 — 200	180 — 220	160 — 180	180 — 200	180 — 220
Volts	24 — 26	27 — 29	26 — 28	24 — 26	27 — 29	27 — 29	23 — 25	27 — 29	27 — 29
Arc Speed (ipm)	24 — 28	20 — 24	16 — 20	16 — 20	14 — 18	12 — 16	18 — 22	18 — 22	16 — 20
Argon Gas (cfh)	30 — 40	30 — 40	40 — 60	30 — 40	40 — 60	40 — 60	40 — 60	40 — 60	60 — 80
Gas Cup Opening (in.)	1/2	1/2	5/8	1/2	1/2	5/8	1/2	1/2	5/8
Total Time (hr/ft. of weld)	0.00769	0.00909	0.0333	0.0111	0.0250	0.0429	0.0100	0.0200	0.0333

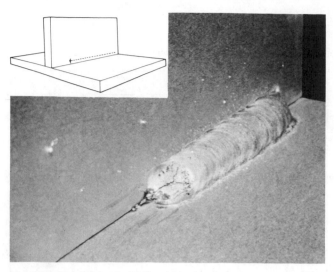

Fig. 17-8. The finish of a MIG weld in aluminum leaves a crater that is very susceptible to cracking.

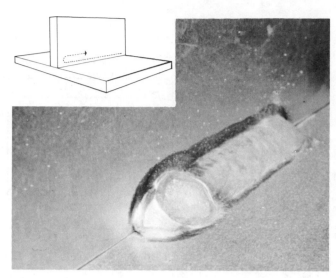

Fig. 17-9. Doubling back at the end of a MIG weld eliminates the crater and the cracking problems that usually accompany it.

tanks of helium and argon. Helium additions of over 10% to argon change the arc characteristics markedly. With increasing helium, arc voltage, spatter, and penetration increase.

PROCEDURES FOR MIG WELDING

Principal factors for consideration in the MIG welding of aluminum are thickness of plate, alloy, and type of equipment available. Typical procedures for conventional MIG welding of various joint designs in aluminum sheet and plate are given in Tables 17-12 through 17-16. These data are approximate and are intended to serve only as starting points. For each application, an optimum set of

TABLE 17-17. Characteristics of the Tig Welding Processes for Aluminum (at Same Current)

Process Characteristic	TIG Welding Process		
	AC	DC Straight Polarity (electrode -, work +)	DC Reverse Polarity (electrode +, work -)
Current	Alternate	Flows from electrode to work.	Flows from work to electrode.
Arc Heat Concentration	50% at each cycle (with balanced power source)	70% at work; 30% at electrode.	30% at work; 70% at electrode.
Effects of Heat Concentration	1. Electrode current capacity only slightly less than for DCSP (for AC about 0.001 in.-diam for each 1.25 amp welding current). 2. Medium penetration, greater than DCRP and somewhat less than DCSP. 3. Midrange welding speeds (5 ipm to 30 fpm is typical range). Note: Helium increases penetration and welding speeds as compared to argon; argon gives best cleaning action with AC.	1. Higher currents with smaller electrodes. 2. Narrow and deep penetration of arc heat into base metal. 3. Welding speed: 5 ipm to 120 fpm is typical range.	1. Larger electrode required. 2. Wide and shallow penetration. 3. Much slower welding speeds than DCSP.
Arc Stability	Stable (balanced AC, or AC with continuous high frequency — ACHF).	Stable	Stable
Cleaning Action of Arc and/or Gas	Good, with argon, on positive (reverse polarity) portion of cycle. (Satisfactory welds also can be made with pure helium or a mixture of argon and helium.)	None; however, satisfactory DCSP welds can be made with helium (maximum current about 600 amp; although with special techniques that help eliminate weld-pool turbulence, this current can be exceeded.) Argon is sometimes used in automatic DCSP TIG.	Continuous — excellent, with argon; DCRP has best cleaning action of the three, but penetration is poorest.
Size of Tungsten Electrode	Medium (3/32 in. at 125 amp)	Small (1/16 in. at 125 amp)	Large (1/4 in. at 125 amp)
Applications	General-purpose automatic and manual welding.	Automatic.	Thin sheet welding; also root pass in pipe.
Maximum Work Thickness	1/8 in. (full-penetration)	1/4 to 3/4 in. (full-penetration)	Very thin — below 0.050 in.

TABLE 17-18. Characteristics of Tig Welding Arcs

Arc Characteristic	TIG Welding Process		
	ACHF or Balanced AC	DCSP	DCRP
Arc Starting and Operation	With high frequency, arc starts without touching work. Strike on starting block; when electrode is thoroughly heated, re-ignite arc in the joint. This reduces tungsten inclusions at start of weld. Hold at starting point until weld pool is established. Add filler at leading edge of pool, but to one side of centerline.	Hot arc forms puddle immediately. Strike arc on work within weld width to avoid marking work. Runout tabs or striking plates are often desirable. Use of high frequency to strike arc is recommended.	Same as AC, but touch electrode to work.
Stability	Smooth arcing; no snapping or cracking sounds (argon).	Stable in helium.	Stable (argon).
Instability: Electrode contamination	Oxides resulting from contact of hot electrode with air or from contact with oxides or metal in weld pool cause arc instability. Dress or cut off tip or replace electrode.	Same as AC.	Same as AC.
Electrode too large	May result in unstable arc and excessive bead width. Use smallest electrode that will carry current.	Same as AC.	Same as AC
Excessive arc length	Unstable arc results; shorten arc length.	Same as AC.	Same as AC.
Narrow joints	May cause arc to jump from side to side. Widen groove where possible or bring electrode closer to work.	—	—
Length	Maintain short arc (about equal to electrode diameter; approximately 1/8 in.). If arc is too long, root penetration will not be complete, particularly in fillet welding; possible undercutting, excessive bead width, and poor weld contour also may result.	Short, about 1/16 in.	Long, 3/16 to 1/4 in.
Breaking the arc	Gradually reduce arc length or current to minimize weld craters. Continue adding filler at the same time where applicable. Snap torch to horizontal position to break arc.	Same as AC.	Same as AC.

welding conditions can be established from these procedures.

It is considered good practice to prepare prototype weldments in advance of the actual production so that welding conditions can be determined on the prototype. It is further recommended that weldors practice beforehand under simulated production conditions. This helps avoid mistakes caused by lack of experience.

Where intermittent welding is to be used, a deviation from the regular pattern of torch travel is recommended. MIG welding of aluminum normally leaves a crater at the end of the weld, as illustrated in Fig. 17-8. This crater is prone to cracking which, in turn, could initiate fracture in the intermittent weld.

One method of avoiding this problem is to reverse the direction of welding at the end of each tack or intermittent weld, so that the crater is filled, as shown in Fig. 17-9. Other techniques for eliminating problems of cracking of the crater area are:

1. Use run-on and run-off tabs.
2. Break the arc and restrike it to fill the crater.
3. Use special circuitry and power source control to produce a specific rate of arc decay.

WELDING ALUMINUM AND ITS ALLOY WITH THE GAS TUNGSTEN-ARC PROCESS

Aluminum can be welded by the tungsten inert-gas (TIG) method using direct-current straight polarity (DCSP), direct-current reverse polarity (DCRP), or alternating current (AC). Generally, DCRP is used for very thin sheet; DCSP for relatively thick sections with mechanized torch travel and controls; and AC for thin sheet and light plate. Typical characteristics of each process are listed in Table 17-17. TIG welding is faster than manual metal-arc welding, but slower than MIG welding.

TIG welding is accomplished with the heat of an electric arc operating between a tungsten elec-

TABLE 17-19. Appearance of Tig Weld Beads

| Characteristic | TIG Process and Gas | | | | | |
| | AC | | DCSP | | DCRP | |
	Argon	Helium	Argon	Helium	Argon	Helium
Typical Surface Appearance	Medium-width bead, medium rippling, light gray (etched) surface, shiny when brushed.	Medium-width bead, medium rippling, medium to dark gray surface, bright to dull when brushed.	Usually limited to automatic welding. Very narrow bead with finely rippled, bright appearance; smoky at edges.	Narrow bead; smoky film usually dulls surface but is easily brushed off. This is only surface oxide, not porosity, inclusions, or lack of fusion. Surface is shiny and smooth after brushing.	Wide, flat bead; shiny with slightly dull edges when brushed; very slight rippling.	Dirty beads, dull rippled surface.
Bead Faults Stitching	–	–	Very dirty surface. Bead consists of row of alternate deep holes and rough-rippled sections. Reduce current, improve arc-length control.	Turbulent-appearing, uneven bead. Same corrective measures as with argon.	–	–
Cratering	Shrink craters at end of weld bead may contain stress-raiser cracks and are also generally undersirable corrosion crevices. Craters can be eliminated by gradually reducing current, or gradually lengthening the arc, while backtracking (overlapping on circumferential welds) over weld bead.					

trode and the work in a shield of inert gas. The inert atmosphere prevents oxidation of the molten aluminum so no flux is required. The gas is usually argon for AC and DCRP TIG, and helium for DCSP TIG welding.

In the inert atmosphere, the tungsten electrode is practically nonconsumable. Actually, it is dissipated slowly by the arc and requires occasional dressing to maintain a hemispherical tip contour. For all practical purposes, however, the tungsten electrode imparts no metal to the weld pool under normal operating conditions.

Each of the three types of power produces different arc characteristics in TIG welding (Table 17-18) and has different penetration characteristics (Fig. 17-10). Appearance of welds made by the three methods is described in Table 17-19. Suggestions for correcting conditions that cause poros-

ity or cracking in TIG welds are given in Table 17-20.

Weldable aluminum in thin gages can be manually TIG-welded without filler metal, although cracking may occur in some of the heat-treatable alloys such as 6061-T6. With groove joints and the addition of filler metal, aluminum plate to 1 in. thick can be efficiently welded manually with the TIG process. With DCSP automatic equipment, sections to 1-1/4 in. thick can be welded without the addition of filler metal. Thicker sections that require edge preparation are usually welded by the MIG process, because larger grooves can be filled more efficiently by MIG than TIG.

Pure tungsten electrodes are usually used for AC TIG welding. Advantages claimed for zirconiated tungsten electrodes for AC TIG welding are that they can carry slightly higher currents and have a longer life than pure tungsten electrodes of equal size. Also, zirconiated tungsten retains the balled tip well, is less susceptible to contamination by molten aluminum, and is a lesser source of tungsten contamination in the weld than is pure tungsten.

Thoriated tungsten does not produce as stable an arc with AC TIG as pure tungsten when welding aluminum. Thoriated tungsten is usually preferred for automatic TIG welding with DCSP.

ALTERNATING-CURRENT TIG WELDING

Alternating current is preferred by many users for both manual and automatic TIG welding of aluminum. This is because AC TIG achieves an efficient balance between penetration and cleaning action, which are the chief advantages, respective-

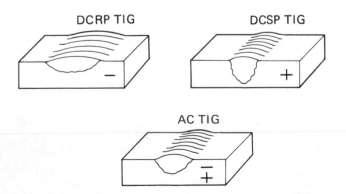

Fig. 17-10. Penetration characteristics of the three types of TIG welding processes.

TABLE 17-20. Causes and Cures for Porosity and Cracking in Tig Welds

Cause	Contributing Factors	Corrective Measures
Hydrogen	Dirt containing oils or other hydrocarbons; moisture in atmosphere or on metal, or a hydrated oxide film on metal; moisture in gas or gas lines. Base metal may be source of entrapped hydrogen (the thicker the metal, the greater the possibility for hydrogen). Spatter.	Degrease and mechanically or chemically remove oxide from weld area. Avoid humidity; use dry metal or wipe dry. Reduce moisture content of gas. Check gas and water lines for leaks. Increase gas flow to compensate for increased hydrogen in thicker sections. To minimize spatter, adjust welding conditions.
Impurities	Cleaning or other compounds, especially those containing calcium.	Use recommended cleaning compounds; keep work free of contaminants.
Incomplete Root Penetration	Incomplete penetration in heavy sections increases porosity in the weld.	Preheat; use higher welding current, or redesign joint geometry.
Temperature	Running too cool tends to increase porosity due to premature solidification of molten metal.	Maintain proper current, arc-length and torch-travel speed relationship.
Welding Speed	Too great a welding speed may increase porosity.	Decrease welding speed and establish and maintain proper arc-length and current relationship.
Solidification Time	Quick freezing of weld pool entraps any gases present, causing porosity.	Establish correct welding current and speed. If work is appreciably below room temperature, use supplemental heating.
Chemical Composition of Weld Metal	Pure aluminum weld metal is more susceptible to porosity than is an aluminum alloy.	If porosity is excessive, try an alloy filler material.
Cracking	Such causes of porosity as temperature, welding time, and solidification may also be contributing causes of cracking. Other causes may be discontinuous welds, welds that intersect, repair welds, cold-working either before or after welding, and weld-metal composition. In general, crack-sensitive alloys include those containing 0.4 to 0.6% Si, or 1.5 to 3.0% Mg, or 1.0% Cu.	Lower current and faster speeds often prevent cracking. However, a change to a filler alloy that brings weld-metal composition out of cracking range is recommended where possible.

ly, of straight and reverse polarity direct-current TIG welding.

Depth of penetration results from the heat produced by the heavy current flow into the work during the straight-polarity portion of the AC cycle. Because cleaning action is inherent in reverse-polarity welding, any oxide film on the work is broken up during the reverse polarity portion of the AC cycle. This balance between penetration and cleaning action is particularly important in tack welding and in making the first pass of pipe welds.

AC TIG can produce excellent quality aluminum welds in all positions. The process achieves complete single-pass weld penetration in thicknesses to 1/2-in. with properly prepared joints and recommended techniques. Particular care should be taken in TIG welding to avoid "bridging" of the molten pool at the root of the joint. Such bridging consists of a blanket of molten metal that barricades the arc at the root opening, preventing full root penetration. Full root penetration can be achieved by maintaining a short arc, assuming other conditions are normal for the job.

AC TIG is used for welding relatively thin aluminum sections. Material from 0.001 to 0.375 in. thick can be welded without filler metal and without preheat; heavier gages require preheat. Of the three types of TIG welding, DCSP is most effective at the heavy end of the thickness range, AC in the middle, and DCRP at the light end.

For efficient AC TIG welding, balanced power that produces a stable arc is required. It is not difficult to recognize an arc where a large amount of undesirable rectification is present. The arc will have an erratic, snapping sound, not the smooth buzzing or humming sound of a stable AC arc. In addition, the cleaning action of the arc and the

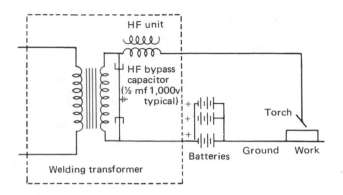

Fig. 17-11. Battery method for obtaining balanced AC power for TIG welding.

wetting action of the molten weld metal are reduced if the arc is not stable.

Power Supplies: Alternating-current welding transformers, delivering a balanced wave and incorporating high-frequency stabilization, are designed specifically for AC TIG aluminum welding. This equipment is recommended for high-quality work. Power supplies intended for AC TIG welding should be smoothly adjustable through the entire range of current required for various gages.

A conventional AC transformer can be adapted to serve as a power supply. One addition should be a high-frequency unit. A wave-balancing component is also desirable for certain aluminum welding work, but is not always necessary.

A balanced AC wave is one which has equal amplitude in both the positive and negative portion of the cycle. Aluminum will sometimes cause a partial rectification of the welding current and thus cause an unbalanced wave. An additional DC source is often used to boost the lower amplitude caused by rectification and thus create a "balanced wave".

There are several ways to obtain balanced AC power for TIG welding aluminum. A method commonly used is to connect automobile batteries (one 6-v battery per 50 to 75 amp of welding current) in the welding circuit, as shown in Fig. 17-11.

In another system for obtaining balanced current, the output from the secondary windings of the transformer is fed into two half-wave rectifiers of opposite polarity. This output is then combined to give balanced-wave AC power.

When AC transformers are adapted for TIG welding of aluminum, care must be taken to install the high-frequency units according to the manufacturer's instructions. Welding torch and ground cables should be kept as short as possible. This helps avoid radio interference and aids in complying with the regulations of the Federal Communications Commission (see current issues of FCC regulations, Part 18, Industrial, Scientific and Med-

ical Service). In addition, power companies may require installation of capacitors for power-factor correction. Most modern AC welding power supplies have these built in as standard equipment.

TIG Welding Torches: Light-duty electrode holders (called "torches") for TIG welding are air-cooled, (Fig. 17-12); other are water-cooled. The TIG torch carries the welding current to the work through the tungsten electrode and directs the inert gas to the weld area. Commercial torches are insulated for maximum welding current ranges to ensure operational safety. They are available in a range of sizes to suit light, medium, and heavy-duty operating conditions. TIG torches should not be used over their rated capacities.

The gas cup or nozzle of the torch can be either ceramic or metal. A ceramic cup is satisfactory for light-duty welding, but for welding at high-current levels ceramic cups are generally unsatisfactory since the nozzle may melt at the tip, partially closing the opening. On the other hand, metal nozzles of too small a diameter will short out the high-frequency current if the work is touched by the nozzle. Torch manufacturers usually recommend a specific type and size of nozzle for different current ranges. Generally, the diameter of the nozzle should be equal to or slightly greater than that of the molten weld pool.

For currents above 200 amp, water-cooling of the torch is necessary to dissipate excess heat generated by the arc and by the current. In addition, water-cooling the power cable permits use of a more flexible, lighter-weight electrical conductor.

Cooling water should be clean to prevent restricting the flow or clogging the water line or

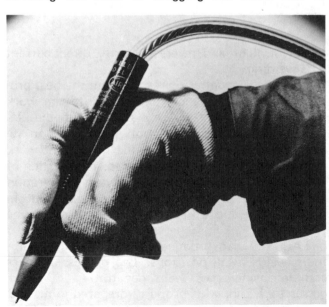

Courtesy Airco Welding Products Division

Fig. 17-12. Light-duty, pencil-type, 100-amp electrode holder for TIG welding.

TABLE 17-21. Typical Current Ranges for Tungsten Electrodes[a]

Electrode Diam (in.)	DCSP Pure and Thoriated Tungsten	DCRP Pure and Thoriated Tungsten	AC With High Frequency			
			Balanced Wave		Unbalanced Wave	
			Pure Tungsten	Thoriated Tungsten[b]	Pure Tungsten	Thoriated Tungsten[b]
0.010	up to 15	c	up to 15	up to 15	up to 15	up to 15
0.020	5 — 20	c	10 — 20	5 — 20	5 — 15	5 — 20
0.040	15 — 80	c	20 — 30	20 — 60	10 — 60	15 — 80
1/16	70 — 150	10 — 20	30 — 80	60 — 120	50 — 100	70 — 150
3/32	150 — 250	15 — 30	60 — 130	100 — 180	100 — 160	140 — 235
1/8	250 — 400	25 — 40	100 — 180	160 — 250	150 — 210	225 — 325
5/32	400 — 500	40 — 55	160 — 240	200 — 320	200 — 275	300 — 400
5/16	500 — 750	55 — 80	190 — 300	290 — 390	250 — 350	400 — 500
1/4	750 — 1000	80 — 125	250 — 400	340 — 525	325 — 450	500 — 630

a   With argon gas.
b   This range may be lowered when using electrodes with high-thoria cores.
c   DCRP is not commonly used in these sizes.

valves. A filter should be installed in the water system ahead of the welding equipment to remove any foreign material. The water-supply pressure should not be higher than that recommended by the torch manufacturer. If necessary, a reducing valve should be used to lower the pressure sufficiently so that it will not damage the torch.

Overheating a TIG torch can melt the silver-brazed metal joints in the torch handle or melt the plastic tube that sheaths the power cable. A control device is available that does not allow the welding current to start unless the water is flowing.

Water flow should be shut off when welding is stopped to prevent excessive cooling and resultant moisture condensation inside the torch. Moisture can contaminate the tungsten electrode and, being a source of hydrogen, can also cause porosity in the weld metal. The most obvious effect of the presence of water is the loss of the cleaning action of the arc (AC or DCRP). This condition continues until the torch is dry.

Electrodes: The size, tip condition, and position in the torch of the tungsten electrode are important factors that determine the quality of TIG welding. Size of electrode is chosen so that the tip is maintained at a temperature near its melting point when welding is done in any given AC range. The maximum electrode extension beyond the end of the gas cup should be about equal to the diameter of the cup for butt welding, and slightly greater for fillet welding. However, extension of the electrode somewhat less than these maximums is always preferable, where pratical, because it helps improve weld shielding.

Electrodes for AC TIG welding aluminum are available in sizes ranging from 0.010 to 1/4 in. Selecting the right size of electrode for each job is important to preventing poor welds and electrode damage caused by using too high or too low a current for the size electrode used. When electrode size is matched with the correct current, the tip will become a molten hemisphere. Recommended electrode sizes for various ranges of welding current are shown in Table 17-21.

Electrode Spitting: Particles of the electrode being ejected across the arc (electrode "spitting") cannot be tolerated. One result of spitting is that the electrode particles contaminate the weld metal and reduce the mechanical properties of the weld. Another is unnecessary and wasteful consumption of the electrode. Also. the time required to reset the electrode tip and eventually to replace it adds unnecessarily to welding time.

In AC TIG welding, the transfer of electrode particles into the weld pool can be caused by partial rectification of the welding current. The use of batteries in the circuit as a means of reducing partial rectification was discussed earlier.

In all three methods of TIG welding, the transfer of electrode particles can be caused by using too small an electrode for the welding current. This overheats the molten hemisphere at the electrode tip, causing it to drop off.

Spitting of electrode particles across the arc can also occur if too large an electrode is used. In this case, the path of the current or focal point of the arc wanders over the tip of the electrode, and particles of tungsten fly off. It is easy to detect whether the tungsten particles are flying off or whether the tip is becoming overheated and dropping off.

Electrode Care: The electrode should have a clean, silvery appearance. A dirty, rough electrode usually means the inert gas was shut off before the electrode cooled, that there was air leakage in the gas-supply system of the torch, or that the elec-

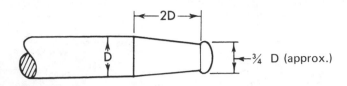

Fig. 17-13. Recommended shape for tip of electrode for AC TIG welding.

trode tip was contaminated by touching metal.

A dirty tungsten electrode can sometimes be cleaned satisfactorily with a fine emery cloth. The contamination can also be removed by using a high current while welding on scrap material until the tip has a sizable molten section; then quickly twisting the torch to flip off a drop of molten metal. If severely contaminated, the electrode should be replaced or the tip broken off and dressed.

In AC TIG welding, the tip should be hemispherical in shape. Needle-point tips are used only for tungsten electrodes when DC TIG welding. In general, tips should be tapered to a blunt end (Fig. 17-13) for AC TIG welding of aluminum.

A grinding wheel is a good tool to make the taper. Some authorities feel that grinding the tip to a sharp point to facilitate arc starting is worthwhile, but others no longer deem this necessary or advisable.

AC TIG Welding Techniques: Before welding is started, electrode size, current settings, and gas flow, as detailed in Table 17-22, should be selected to suit the metal thickness and the welding position.

Cleaning the Welding Surfaces: For routine TIG jobs, cleanliness is not so critical as in MIG welding, but, for high-quality TIG welding maximum cleanliness is necessary.

Manual AC TIG welding is slower than MIG; consequently, the weld pool is molten longer and porosity-causing elements have more time to rise to the surface of the aluminum and escape into the air. However, cleaning before welding is always excellent practice because the possibility of weld porosity is reduced when weld areas are clean. Water or oils usually found in entrapped dirt, hydrated oxide deposits, or hydrogen from any source are potential causes of poor weld quality.

Striking the Arc: In AC TIG welding, the high frequency or the high welding voltage (depending upon type of power supply) establishes an ionized path through the shielding gas for the welding current. When the electrode is brought within 1/8 to 1/16 in. of the plate, the welding arc is initiated. The arc is then adjusted to the desired length.

After the arc has been established, it is held stationary until a molten pool is formed. The area of the pool is determined by electrode size and welding current. Extent of the pool can be increased by rotating the arc with a slight circular motion of the torch. The proper way to hold the TIG torch during welding is shown in Fig. 17-14.

If desired, the arc can be started on a separate plate of aluminum, copper, or steel and then car-

TABLE 17-22. Recommended Practices for Manual AC Tig Welding of Aluminum

Plate Thickness (in.)	Welding Position[a]	Joint Type	Alternating Current (amp)	Electrode[b] Diameter (in.)	Argon Gas Flow[c] (cfh)	Filler Rod Diameter (in.)	Number of Passes
1/16	F	Square butt	70 − 100	1/16	20	3/32	1
	H, V	Square butt	70 − 100	1/16	20	3/32	1
	O	Square butt	60 − 90	1/16	25	3/32	1
1/8	F	Square butt	125 − 160	3/32	20	1/8	1
	H, V	Square butt	115 − 150	3/32	20	1/8	1
	O	Square butt	115 − 150	3/32	25	1/8	1
1/4	F	60° single bevel	225 − 275	5/32	30	3/16	2
	H, V	60° single bevel	200 − 240	5/32	30	3/16	2
	O	100° single bevel	210 − 260	5/32	35	3/16	2
3/8	F	60° single bevel	325 − 400	1/4	35	1/4	2
	H, V	60° single bevel	250 − 320	3/16	35	1/4	3
	O	100° single bevel	275 − 350	3/16	40	1/4	3
1/2	F	60° single bevel	375 − 450	1/4	35	1/4	3
	H, V	60° single bevel	250 − 320	3/16	35	1/4	3
	O	100° single bevel	275 − 340	3/16	40	1/4	4
1	F	60° single bevel	500 − 600	5/16 − 3/8	35 − 45	1/4 − 3/8	8 − 10

a   F = flat; H = horizontal; V = vertical; O = overhead.

b   Diameters are for standard pure or zirconium tungsten electrodes. Thoriated tungsten electrodes not generally used for AC TIG.

c   Helium is not generally used in AC TIG welding aluminum. When helium is used, however, flow rates are about twice those used for argon.

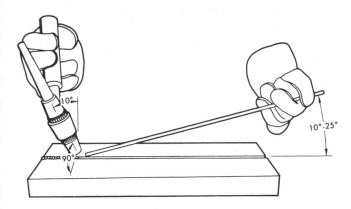

Fig. 17-14. Proper positions of torch and filler rod for manual TIG welding.

ried to the workpiece. A carbon starting block should not be used. This method was used in the past, but is no longer recommended, because tungsten carbide is formed when carbon impinges on tungsten. The carbide has a lower melting point than pure tungsten and forms a molten ball on the end of the electrode, causing poor current distribution.

Arc Initiation Difficulties: When high-frequency current is used to start the AC welding arc, a gap of 1/8 to 1/16 in. in an inert-gas atmosphere is sufficient. The high-frequency arc should not jump a gap of more than 3/16 in. Inability to jump a 1/16-in. gap may be caused by a poor electrical connection in the high-frequency circuit, improper arc gap in the high-frequency oscillator, or excessive oxide film on the base material. Standard procedure should include checking the ground-cable-to-work connection, the high-frequency-unit spark-gap adjustment, and cleanliness of base material. A gap of 0.004 to 0.008 in. in each of the series gaps of the high-frequency oscillator is usually satisfactory, provided that the high-frequency leads to the torch are not excessively long. However, the manufacturer's gap-setting recommendations should be followed.

Before the main weld bead is started, the joint should be tack-welded unless hold-down fixtures are used to secure the work.

Feeding Filler Metal: Filler rod is added manually to the leading edge of the weld pool as needed. Most operators develop a technique of moving the torch and filler rod intermittently. This consists of holding the torch at a point until the pool is formed, then adding filler metal. The filler rod is then withdrawn and the torch moved forward. This sequence of feeding, moving the torch, and holding until a new pool forms, is repeated until the weld is completed. Practice with this technique produces a smooth weld bead.

It is important to feed the filler rod into the arc at as low an angle as possible, as illustrated in Fig. 17-14. This assures good gas coverage of the molten filler metal and also reduces the possibility of touching the tungsten electrode with the filler rod.

In automatic TIG welding, the torch moves steadily forward, and the filler metal, when used, is fed as spooled wire to the leading edge of the pool.

Completing the Weld: The manner in which the arc is broken at the end of a weld is important. One method is to withdraw quickly or twist the torch tip up from the work. This rapid breaking of the TIG arc is not recommended, because it leaves a shrink crater. It also promotes porosity, especially when subsequent cover or overlap passes are made over the craters. Craters also may be objectionable in appearance, and reduced weld strength or leakage may result.

One method for eliminating craters is to finish welding with a decreasing current. This technique is frequently called "decaying arc" and is usually done by means of a foot or hand-actuated control switch. Backtracking (or overlapping, where applicable) for about 1-1/2 in. on the bead before removing the torch or cutting off the current is also good practice. Still another method is to use runoff tabs made from scrap material.

Preheating: Preheating the work for AC TIG welding of aluminum is necessary for heavier sections, where the heat is conducted away from the joint so fast that the welding arc cannot produce fusion. Preheating can be done with a gas torch or any other suitable means. Unless the ambient temperature is below 40°F, no preheating is used on plate up to 3/8 in. thick and is optional between 3/8 and 1/2 in. thick. Plates 3/4 in. and thicker may require preheating, but the preheat temperature should not exceed 350°F. Maximum temperatures of heat-treatable alloys are particularly critical because of the narrow temperature range that must be maintained to avoid adverse effects of the heat of welding on mechanical properties of the joint.

Rough and Dirty Weld Beads: Various factors can affect the surface appearance of a weld; principal appearance characteristics are described in Table 17-19. As discussed previously, cleanliness is extremely important. Contaminated shielding gas, base material, or filler rod can cause porosity and dross in welds. Insufficient shielding gas can do the same. Poor arc-cleaning action in AC TIG welding can be the result of an insufficient amount of the reverse-polarity portion of the current. Reduction of the half cycle of the current that does the cleaning (DCRP) can be due to poor re-ignition of the arc as the current cycle passes zero. It can also be due to partial rectification, so that the DCRP portion of the AC wave is reduced. The first is caused by the high-frequency unit, and can be corrected by adjusting it. The second, partial rectification, can be alleviated by installing capacitors or a battery "balance" in the welding circuit.

Rough and dirty weld beads can also be caused by poor welding technique. Examples of this are welding with too little current for the travel speed, sloppy torch manipulation, erratic arc due to letting the electrode touch the aluminum, welding in a drafty area, or leaks in the shielding-gas system.

Welding Speed: Within the practical limits of the welding conditions on a given job, the faster the welding speed, the greater the savings in time and the less extensive the heat-affected area in the work. The best speed can be achieved with the highest-practical welding current and use of a downhand position. Often, the increase in efficiency obtainable warrants repositioning of the work.

Shielding Gas: Although any inert gas could be used for shielding the arc in the TIG process, argon and helium are used because of their availability, economy, and efficiency. A higher gas flow is required with helium than with argon, but helium permits faster welding speeds and greater penetration. Differentials in rates of gas flow are often about equalized in welding thicker sections. Deeper penetration is obtained with helium, because the AC arc in a helium atmosphere is hotter than in argon.

Many operators prefer argon for manual AC TIG welding, because the arc has greater stability. Additives to argon shielding gas increase the arc temperature and gain some of the advantages of helium shielding gas. Generally, when 10% or more helium is added to argon, arc penetration increases significantly.

Purity of the inert gas is very important. Only welding-grade gases should be used. Furthermore, contamination of the gas must be prevented during its passage from the cylinder to the torch. Moisture, oil residues or fumes, and dust are the common contaminants to guard against. Hoses previously used for acetylene, compressed air, or water are not suitable for TIG welding.

Inert gas for TIG welding is available in pressurized cylinders. For consistent results, a pressure-reducing regulator-flowmeter of the proper type for the gas being used should be included in the system. Shutoff can be manual, effected by hanging the torch on a hook arm which actuates a shutoff valve, but automatic control is preferred. This can be accomplished by connecting a time-

delay solenoid valve (controlled by the welding circuit) in the gas line. Production TIG welding equipment has automatic gas and water-control valves built into the welding unit.

DIRECT-CURRENT, STRAIGHT POLARITY TIG WELDING

One of the most reliable and useful methods for welding aluminum is the DCSP TIG process. It can be used in the flat, horizontal, and vertical welding positions, and is supplanting MIG welding in many applications.

In DCSP TIG welding, the electrode is negative and the work positive; the electrons go from the electrode to the plate. This electron flow (Fig. 17-15) results in considerable heating of the base plate, while the electrode stays relatively cool.

DCSP TIG produces a narrow, deep weld. Because the best results on aluminum are obtained with very short arc lengths, this process is best suited for automatic welding. Arc lengths are about 1/16 in. for manual and as little as 1/64 in. for machine welding. This critical arc length is somewhat difficult to control in manual DCSP TIG welding.

Since a DCSP system provides no arc cleaning action to remove the oxide film on aluminum, thorough cleaning and oxide removal are necessary.

Equipment: A DC welding generator or rectifier is used for DCSP. (Some welding engineers feel that three-phase power supplies are superior for this process because they provide a smoother current flow.) In addition to the power supply, the same equipment used for AC TIG welding aluminum is employed.

Electrode Selection: Electrode requirements are different for DCSP than for AC TIG welding. For DCSP, most weldors prefer thoriated tungsten electrodes over pure tungsten. The thoriated tungsten electrode has a higher heat resistance than the pure tungsten and, therefore, lasts longer. In ad-

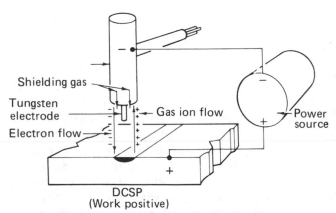

Shielding gas

Tungsten electrode

Gas ion flow

Electron flow

Power source

DCSP
(Work positive)

Fig. 17-15. Machine connections for a DCSP TIG welding system; the electrode is negative and the work positive.

dition, the thoriated tungsten appears to repel the "skin" on the weld pool and thus permits welding with the electrode in closer proximity to the molten aluminum. Other weldors prefer pure tungsten electrodes, expressing the opinion that thoriated electrodes tend to shatter or splinter.

Whether the preference is for thoriated or pure tungsten, there is general agreement to use oversized electrodes and to taper the point. Recommended electrode sizes for DCRP, DCSP, and AC TIG welding are shown in Table 17-21.

Shielding Gas: A helium-argon mixture (7 to 35% argon) or helium alone is preferred as the shielding gas in DCSP TIG welding aluminum. Although a helium-shielded arc is hotter than an argon-shielded arc, this does not entirely account for the apparent superiority of helium (or of a helium-argon mixture) over pure argon in DCSP TIG welding.

Argon shielding gas has been used for automatic DCSP TIG welding where the length of arc can be controlled closely. However, welding speed drops considerably. The welding voltage does not vary with the arc length as much in helium as it does in argon.

Joint Design: Use of the DCSP method of TIG welding to its best advantage requires careful joint design. Square butt joints in aluminum are readily welded by this process. When the plate thickness is

so great that V joints are required for DCSP welding, the land can be increased and the included angle of the V decreased. Both changes permit faster welding and require less filler metal.

Distortion is less with DCSP than with AC TIG because of the lower heat input per unit length of weld.

Welding Techniques: High-frequency current is not needed to maintain a stable DCSP arc as in AC TIG welding. It is desirable for initiating the arc, although the arc can be started without it. Thus, the arc can be initiated by touching the work with the electrode tip and then retracting to the proper arc length. The DCSP arc is quieter and smoother than the AC arc, and the weld pool is formed more rapidly. There is no need to play the arc on the base plate to form the pool if sufficient welding current is used.

Because the DCSP arc is so much hotter than the AC arc, manual welding techniques for the two processes differ. In DCSP TIG welding, many operators prefer to hold the filler rod in contact with the joint and to move the arc steadily forward. The rod is not intermittently fed into the weld pool.

Excessive weaving is not desirable in welding aluminum. Instead, multiple stringer beads are recommended for large welds. Interpass brushing is mandatory to remove the oxide from previously completed beads. Standard techniques for eliminat-

TABLE 17-23. Recommended Practices for DCSP Tig Welding Aluminum in the Flat Position

Material Thickness (in.)	Joint Design	Current[a] (amp)	Volts	Diameter of Electrode[b] (in.)	Helium Gas Flow[c] (cfh)	Travel (ipm)	Filler Rod or Wire Diameter (in.)	Number of Passes
0.010	Standing edge	10 — 15		0.020	20 — 50			1
0.020	Square butt	15 — 30		0.020	20 — 50		0.020	1
0.030	Square butt	20 — 50		0.020 or 0.040	20 — 50		0.020 or 0.047	1
0.032	Square butt	65 — 70	10	3/32	20 — 50	52	None	1
0.040	Square butt	25 — 65		3/64	20 — 50		3/64	1
0.050	Square butt	35 — 95		3/64	20 — 50		3/64	1
0.050	Square butt	70 — 80	10	3/32	20 — 50	36	None	1
0.060	Square butt	45 — 120		3/64 or 1/16	20 — 50		3/64 or 1/16	1
0.070	Square butt	55 — 145		1/16	20 — 50		1/16	1
0.080	Square butt	80 — 175		1/16	50 — 50		1/16	1
0.090	Square butt	90 — 185		1/16	20 — 50		1/16	1
1/8	Square butt	120 — 220		1/8	20 — 50		1/8	1
1/8	Square butt	180 — 200	12.5	1/8	20 — 50	24	None	1
1/4	Square butt	230 — 340		1/8	25 — 60		1/8 or 3/16	1
1/4	Square butt	220 — 240	12.5	1/8	25 — 60	22	None	1
1/2	60°V bevel, 1/4-in. root face	300 — 450		3/16	25 — 60		1/8 or 1/4	1
1/2	Square butt	260 — 300	13	5/32	25 — 60	20	None	2
3/4	60°V or double-V bevel, 3/16-in. root face	300 — 450		3/16	25 — 60		1/8 or 1/4	3 (single-V) 2 (double-V)
3/4	Square butt	450 — 470	9.5	3/16	40 — 60	6	None	2
1	60°V or double-V bevel, 3/16-in. root face	300 — 450		3/16	25 — 60		1/8 or 1/4	4 (single-V) 2 (double-V)
1	Square butt	550 — 570	9.5	1/4	40 — 60	5	None	2

a   Automatic welding is required for the higher amperages. Manual welding can be done at the lower amperages.

b   In lighter gages, it is common to use larger diameter electrodes than recommended and to taper the tip.

c   Helium-argon mixtures may be substituted. In automatic welding, the arc can be started in argon, and the helium added to the shielded gas when welding begins. The best ratio of He-A is usually determined by experimentation. Gas flow depends in part on welding speed.

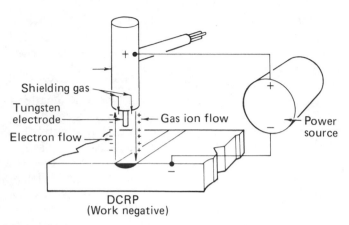

Fig. 17-16. Machine connections for a DCRP TIG welding system; the electrode is positive and the work negative.

ing or reducing craters at ends of welds are applicable to this welding method. Recommended joint designs and other details for DCSP TIG welding are given in Table 17-23.

Welds can be made with or without filler addition, depending upon the alloy, thickness, joint design, and whether force is exerted to push the two weld edges together during fusion. Edge undercutting sometimes occurs, due to the highly concentrated heat of the DCSP arc.

In high-speed welding, the DCSP torch is sometimes followed by an AC TIG torch to smooth the weld bead. Also, an AC torch can precede the DC torch, acting as a preheater and surface cleaner.

Weld Appearance: A dull oxide film always covers the DCSP bead at the edge and may cover the entire surface. This film is removed easily by wire brushing. A particularly shiny bead, with dark edges, is obtained in DCSP welding aluminum when helium is used.

Mechanical Properties: Because of the high welding speed possible with DCSP, the heat-affected zones adjacent to the weld are usually narrower than with the AC TIG process. This is more apparent in the heat-treatable alloys, such as 6061 or 6063, than in the nonheat-treatable alloys, such as 5086 or 5083.

DIRECT-CURRENT, REVERSE-POLARITY TIG WELDING

Equipment required for the DCRP TIG process is the same as that used for DCSP welding. The machine connections for torch and work cables, however, are reversed, as shown in Fig. 17-16.

In DCRP welding, the tungsten electrode is heated and the plate stays relatively cool. For this reason, electrodes used with DCRP welding must be considerably larger in diameter than those used with AC or DCSP TIG welding. For example, a 1/4-

in.-diameter electrode is required for 125 amp of DCRP welding current, whereas a 1/16-in. electrode will handle the same current in DCSP. If an electrode is too small, the tip will overheat and drop off, contaminating the weld.

The DCRP arc produces an excellent cleaning action on an aluminum surface, breaking up any oxide present. But the bead produced by this process is shallow (because the plate stays relatively cool), which limits DCRP welding of aluminum to thin sheet — to about 0.050 in. maximum.

The shielding gas usually used with DCRP TIG welding is argon. Recommended flow rates, along with suggested procedures for DCRP welding of aluminum, are listed in Table 17-24.

RESISTANCE WELDING OF ALUMINUM

Aluminum may be resistance-welded by any of the methods described in Chapter 22 for welding steel. Techniques are similar, although the actual procedures vary. Surface preparation with aluminum is more critical than with steel and is vital to the production of high quality welds.

Spot Welding: The main difference between the techniques used in spot welding aluminum and spot welding steel arises from aluminum's higher electrical conductivity; more electrical energy must be put into the aluminum weld. For this reason, aluminum spot-welding machines have greater electrical capacity than similar machines for welding steel.

All aluminum alloys can be spot welded. First, however, the surface must be prepared by cleaning, degreasing, and deoxidizing. Chemical processes are recommended, although mechanical abrasion may be used. For all production work, chemical cleaning and deoxidizing are essential for uniform weld quality. Passage of the material through a series of baths partially dissolves the oxide surface or whittles it down, so to speak, to a thin film that is easily penetrated by the welding current.

After proper surface preparation, the two parts to be joined are placed on the welding machine at the point (bottom electrode) where the weld is to be made. The upper electrode is then moved down to contact the work and apply correct pressure. A sudden pulse of electric current is passed through the work, breaking down the thin oxide film and melting the two parts being joined. The "nugget" of molten aluminum grows as the current continues. The duration of current is accurately timed and cut off when the desired nugget size is reached. Upon solidification, the two parts are bonded together. There is no arc. A sudden single pulse of electric current does the entire job in a split second.

Flash Welding: Aluminum may be flash-welded by methods similar to the flash-welding of steel. Flash welding — as described more fully in Chapter 22 — is a resistance butt-welding process in which two workpieces are clamped in suitable current-carrying fixtures that hold them end-to-end in light contact. An electrical potential is applied, causing current to flash an arc across the joint. Resistance heating, plus arcing, fuses the abutting ends of the workpieces together.

Flash welding is suitable not only for joining aluminum to aluminum, but also for joining aluminum to other metals. For example, a short length of aluminum tubing can be joined to a short piece of copper tubing by this method to make fittings for aluminum refrigerator evaporators. Another typical flash-welding job is the joining of extruded aluminum members to make window frames. It is easy to make accurate 90° joints to precise dimensions with this process. Flash welds develop 80-95 percent of the strength of the original material.

Stud Welding: Arc stud welding is a special type of flash welding in which an aluminum stud (it can be a bolt, screw, or similar item) is attached endwise to any flat aluminum surface. Most stud welds are made with a hand gun, which makes possible the placing of a stud at any point on a surface.

In practice, the stud is positioned in the welding gun. The three tripod-type legs of the gun are then pushed against the surface of the work, with the stud over the point of attachment. When the operator pulls the trigger of the gun, the stud moves down to contact the work. The end of the stud is cone-shaped. As its tip contacts the work surface, an electric circuit is completed, producing an electric arc. Point fusion occurs, the current is interrupted, and the stud is forced into the molten pool on the work. The gun is withdrawn, leaving the stud in the now solidified pool.

There are two basic types of stud welding — arc stud welding (as described) and capacitor-discharge stud welding. A shielding gas is required when either of these processes are used on aluminum.

Stud welding is ideal for attaching a bolt, rivet, or screw to any flat aluminum surface. It is widely used in the manufacture of aluminum products.

SOLID-STATE WELDING OF ALUMINUM AND ITS ALLOYS

Solid-state welding is a term that includes a group of welding processes wherein coalescence is produced at temperatures below the melting point of the base metals being joined. These processes are characterized by the absence of a discernible liquid phase. Thus, the parts joined are free from heat-affected zones and dilution by extraneous elements.

Cold Welding: External force supplies the pressure used in so-called cold welding. No heat is required. By proper arrangement of workpiece and dies, sufficient pressure is supplied to cause ductile metals to flow, bringing surfaces into the intimacy of contact that effects molecular bonding. Two pieces become one, not necessarily because of interface admixture, but because molecular proximity has been achieved.

Successful commercial uses of cold welding include the seam-welding of box configurations and

TABLE 17-24. Recommended Practices for DCRP Tig Welding of Aluminum in the Flat Position

Material Thickness t (in.)	Joint Design[a]	Electrode Diameter[b] (in.)	Welding Current[b] (amp)	Gas Flow (cfh)	Filler Diameter (in.)
0.010	2 — 4t	3/32	15 — 25	15 — 25	—
0.020	2 — 3t	1/8 — 5/32	40 — 55	15 — 25	—
	0 — 1/32″ 2t	1/8 — 5/32	40 — 55	15 — 20	0.020
0.030		3/16	50 — 65	15 — 25	—
	0 — 1/32″	3/16	50 — 65	15 — 20	0.020 or 3/64
0.040	1 — 2t	3/16	60 — 80	20 — 30	—
	0 — 1/32″	3/16	60 — 80	25 — 30	3/64
0.050	1 — 2t	3/16	70 — 90	20 — 30	—
	0 — 1/32″	3/16	70 — 90	25 — 30	3/64 or 1/16

a Use of a backup with a generous groove is recommended in all cases.
b High currents, with correspondingly larger electrodes, can be used for automatic welding.

the sealing of tube ends. The process especially has achieved utility in products built with aluminum tubing. It is most suitable for aluminum and aluminum alloys, but has also been employed successfully with cadmium, lead, copper, nickel, zinc, and silver. It can be applied only to metals sufficiently ductile to flow readily under pressure. Not more than 3% manganese or silicon can be tolerated in aluminum alloys to be cold-welded. Heat-treatable alloys, such as 2017 and 2024, can be joined in the soft condition and then allowed to harden (age at room temperature) in the usual way.

For successful cold welding, the shapes of the dies are the utmost importance. The dies must apply pressure over a comparatively narrow strip and in such a manner as to make the metal flow sidewise at the weld interface. Proper control of metal flow is the critical factor. The pressure required for aluminum is approximately 24,000-36,000 pounds per square inch.

Another solid-state welding process that can be applied to aluminum is explosion welding. This is discussed in Chapter 25.

BRAZING ALUMINUM AND ITS ALLOYS

Aluminum and aluminum alloys can also be joined by brazing. The three most common methods used are the torch, furnace, and dip brazing processes. In each, a flux is used to remove the aluminum oxide film and to keep it from reforming.

Torch Brazing: With this process, a liquid flux is applied to the surfaces to be joined. The work is heated, drying out the flux, which changes into a white powdery substance. As additional heat is supplied, the flux melts, indicating that the work has reached the correct temperature for brazing. The flux, thus, does three things — dissolves the oxide film at the joint area, forms a liquid cover preventing the film from reforming, and indicates correct brazing temperature by melting to give a "wet" appearance.

At this point, the brazing alloy is flowed into the joint, displacing the flux at the metal surface and bonding directly to the base metal. The brazing process differs from soldering by being done at a much higher temperature and by producing a much stronger joint.

Furnace Brazing: While torch brazing is seldom mechanized and is thus mostly a hand operation with limited production potential, furnace brazing is ideal for high-production work. Heat is applied to the assembled parts as they pass through a furnace on a chain conveyor belt. This means that temperatures can be controlled with precision, an absolute necessity in brazing since the temperature

of the work must be high enough to melt the brazing alloy but not so high that it melts the base metal of the parts. Usually a narrow temperature range (20°-50°F) must be maintained.

To prepare the work for furnace brazing, parts are first chemically cleaned. Then a paste flux is painted on the joint areas, and the brazing material in the form of strip or wire clips is placed between the parts to be joined. The brazing-material elements are so designed and positioned that they will melt and flow into all portions of the joint when the work reaches brazing temperature. Weights or clamps are usually added to hold the parts in correct position and to keep them in contact during brazing.

Sometimes the brazing alloy is supplied as a clad layer on the parts themselves. This greatly facilitates making joints that otherwise might be inaccessible. Heat exchangers, such as used in air conditioners and heater units, are examples of products using clad material to supply the brazing alloy at many joints simultaneously.

After going through the heating and cooling zones in the furnace, the work passes through a washer to remove all traces of flux. Thorough washing and rinsing is necessary to prevent any possibility of subsequent chemical reactions from traces of flux.

Furnace brazing is especially suitable for making long, continuous joints, such as those between tube and sheet in refrigerator evaporators. The brazed joints are characterized by smooth, fine-appearing fillets that require no grinding or finishing. Many joints can be made simultaneously in a single assembly, and inaccessible locations create no problem.

Dip Brazing: Like furnace brazing, dip brazing is a high-production process; hundreds of joints in an assembly can be made at one operation. Here, too, joints can be made at inaccessible locations just as easily as at outside corners. Before putting the parts together for the assembly, all dirt and oil are removed by running through a vapor degreaser. A molten salt is used as the heating medium. The salt also supplies the fluxing action, eliminating the need for a separate fluxing operation.

In most dip brazing, the brazing material is provided at the joint in the form of a clad layer on the surface of the aluminum parts themselves. This eliminates the necessity of inserting separate pieces of brazing alloy at each joint and greatly facilitates making internal or otherwise inaccessible joints. Proper jigs and fixtures ensure intimate contact at the joint areas.

Assemblies are preheated in an air furnace to 1000°F to remove moisture and to avoid freezing of the salt when the parts are submerged in the salt bath. This also reduces the heat load on the salt bath and makes holding precise brazing temperatures easier. Transfer from the furnace to the salt bath must be rapid because most assemblies will lose heat fast enough to drop their temperature 100° F per minute. As the molten salt penetrates the assembly, it fluxes all joint areas, assuring proper flow of the brazing alloy into all portions of the joints. The temperature of the molten salt is easy to control, so that it melts the brazing material but not the aluminum parts themselves.

SOLDERING ALUMINUM AND ITS ALLOYS

Aluminum and many aluminum-base alloys can be soldered with techniques similar to those used with other metals. High purity and commercial aluminum are the easiest to solder. Next easiest are the alloys containing not more than 1% magnesium, 5% silicon, and 1% manganese. Alloys containing high copper or zinc have poor soldering characteristics. Forgings and castings are seldom soldered due to alloy additions and surface conditions.

The AWS Handbook, Sixth Edtion, Section 3A, lists a solder suitable for aluminum composed of 95% zinc and 5% aluminum. There are various fluxes available for soldering aluminum, and they generally are of two types, so-called "chemical" and "reaction". Chemical fluxes are used mostly with the low-temperature solders and usually not above 525° F. Above that temperature they tend to decompose too rapidly to make their use practical. The reaction fluxes contain zinc chloride in combination with other halides. At reaction temperatures (550-725° F), they react with the aluminum oxide film, facilitating wetting by the solder. In general, fluxes promote corrosion, and after the soldering is completed the flux residue must be completely removed.

Friction Soldering: Friction soldering is considered by some as the most practical method for soldering aluminum. The method is characterized by the use of a glass-fiber brush for removing oxide film and to "tin" the surfaces to be joined.

To friction solder, the work is heated to the point where the solder will melt when applied to the aluminum surface. Enough solder is then applied to "tin" the surface. A glass-fiber brush is then used to scrub the surface through the overlying layer of molten solder. The sharp ends of the glass fibers scratch away the aluminum oxide film and allow the molten solder to bond directly to the base metal. The pool of molten solder prevents the reforming of oxide film. Glass fiber provides the metal-abrading ability without drawing heat from the molten pool. A brush built from metal fibers would absorb heat and freeze the molten solder.

Once the joint areas on aluminum parts have been tinned with the glass brush technique, it is easy to make a soldered joint by heating both parts and flowing additional solder into the joint if that provided by the tinning is inadequate.

Flow Soldering: A suitable flux is required when following the conventional technique of flow soldering. With aluminum, as with other metals, soldered joints should not be relied upon for mechanical strength — they are to seal or to assure good electrical or thermal connections only. Where mechanical strength is required, roll seaming, riveting, or other mechanical joining should be employed to provide mechanical strength at the soldered joint.

Ultrasonic Soldering: Ultrasonic energy can be used to facilitate wetting of work surfaces during the application of solder, eliminating either the need for friction (glass-fiber brushing) or flux. The high-frequency vibratory energy from an ultrasonic generator produces cavitation in the molten solder, which disrupts or removes the aluminum oxide film on the base metal. This allows the solder to wet and tin the aluminum surface — just as when using a glass-fiber brush. Tinned areas can then be joined by heating, with the addition of more solder if necessary.

Welding The Stainless Steels

The stainless steels are of major importance in high-quality manufactured products ranging from chemical vessels and jet engine parts to tableware and razor blades. The types are numerous and their metallurgy so involved as to be beyond the scope of this text. Similarly, the detailing of the many variables in welding these materials would be too comprehensive a work for a book of this nature. The intent in the following is merely to give the student an introduction to the stainless steels and the modes for fusion joining. For elaboration and greater detail on types of stainless steel and the procedures and problems in welding, the student should refer to the Lincoln *Procedure Handbook of Arc Welding.*

From one steel designed specifically for its anti-corrosion properties, stainless steels have evolved into a group consisting of more than 30 standard AISI (American Iron and Steel Institute) grades and perhaps twice that many variations. Each was designed to produce one or more desirable characteristics — in addition to its anti-corrosion properties. All are iron-base alloys. Stainless steels are cataloged into three major classifications:

1. **Ferritic Grades** — "Straight chrome — AISI type 400 series. See Table 18-1 and Fig. 18-1. When 11.5% or more chromium is added to iron, a thin, silvery, tightly adherent film of chromium-oxide forms spontaneously on the surfaces exposed to air. This film acts as a barrier to protect against

TABLE 18-1. Typical Compositions of Ferritic Stainless Steels

AISI Type	Composition* (%)			
	Carbon	Chromium	Manganese	Other†
405	0.08	11.5 — 14.5	1.0	0.1 — 0.3 Al
430	0.12	14.0 — 18.0	1.0	—
430F	0.12	14.0 — 18.0	1.25	0.060 P, 0.15 S (min), 0.60 Mo (opt)
430FSe	0.12	14.0 — 18.0	1.25	0.060 P, 0.060 S, 0.15 Se (min)
442	0.20	18.0 — 23.0	1.0	—
446	0.20	23.0 — 27.0	1.5	0.25 N

* Single values denote maximum percentage unless otherwise noted.

† Unless otherwise noted, other elements of all alloys listed include maximum contents of 1.0% Si, 0.060% P, and 0.030% S. Balance is Fe.

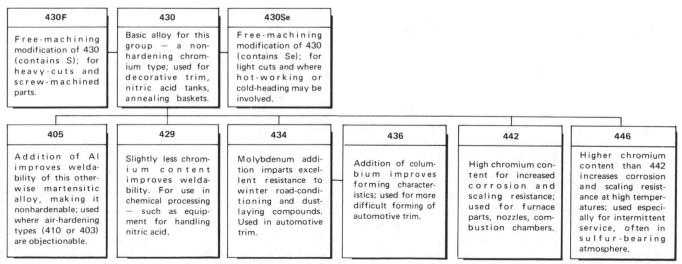

430F — Free-machining modification of 430 (contains S); for heavy-cuts and screw-machined parts.

430 — Basic alloy for this group — a non-hardening chromium type; used for decorative trim, nitric acid tanks, annealing baskets.

430Se — Free-machining modification of 430 (contains Se); for light cuts and where hot-working or cold-heading may be involved.

405 — Addition of Al improves weldability of this otherwise martensitic alloy, making it nonhardenable; used where air-hardening types (410 or 403) are objectionable.

429 — Slightly less chromium content improves weldability. For use in chemical processing — such as equipment for handling nitric acid.

434 — Molybdenum addition imparts excellent resistance to winter road-conditioning and dust-laying compounds. Used in automotive trim.

436 — Addition of columbium improves forming characteristics; used for more difficult forming of automotive trim.

442 — High chromium content for increased corrosion and scaling resistance; used for furnace parts, nozzles, combustion chambers.

446 — Higher chromium content than 442 increases corrosion and scaling resistance at high temperatures; used especially for intermittent service, often in sulfur-bearing atmosphere.

Fig. 18-1. Applications for the AISI ferritic stainless steels.

TABLE 18-2. Typical Properties* of Austenitic Stainless Steels

AISI Type	Room Temperature (annealed)				Max Service Temp (°F) in Air	
	Tensile Strength (1000 psi)	Yield Strength, 0.2% (1000 psi)	Elongation, 2 in. (%)	Hardness Rockwell B	Continuous	Intermittent
201	115	55	55	90	1550	1450
202	105	55	55	90	1550	1450
301	110	40	60	85	1650	1500
302	90	40	50	85	1650	1500
302B	95	40	55	85	1750	1600
304	84	42	55	80	1650	1550
304L	81	39	55	79	1650	1550
305	85	38	50	80	1650	. . . . .
308	85	35	50	80	1700	1550
309	90	45	45	85	1950	1850
310	95	45	45	85	2050	1900
314	100	50	40	85	. . . . .	. . . . .
316	84	42	50	79	1650	1550
316L	81	42	50	79	1650	1550
317	90	40	45	85	1700	1600
321	90	35	45	80	1650	1550
347	95	40	45	85	1650	1550

* Mechanical property values are for sheet and strip materials. Properties of bar and plate may vary from these values slightly.

more oxidation or corrosion. Three of the most widely used are types 405, 430, and 446 having a chromium content from 11.5% to 27%. The 400 series are highly magnetic. By keeping the carbon content low there is less chance of producing a hard martensitic structure. As the chromium content increases, the steel's resistance to corrosion and high-temperature oxidation also increases.

2. **Austenitic Grades** — Chrome-nickel steels — strong and ductile — AISI 200 and 300 series. See Table 18-2 and Fig. 18-2. These steels constitute the bulk of the stainless steels used in industry. Adding nickel to the straight "chrome" type results in increased corrosion resistance, impact strength, ductility, fatigue resistance, and electrical resistance, while reducing heat conductivity. Weldability also improves with the addition of nickel.

The 200 series steels are becoming more popular due to increasing nickel costs for the 300 series. The replacement of about one half the nickel with some manganese is the main metallurgical difference. These steels have equivalent or superior strengths compared to their 300 series counterparts as well as equivalent corrosion resistance and mechanical properties. They are welded with the same electrode as their 300 series counterparts.

3. **Martensitic Grades** — Hard and brittle — AISI 400 series. See Table 18-3 and Fig. 18-3. These steels represent the hardenable straight "chrome" types containing 11.5% to 18% chromium as the chief alloying element. They are used extensively for their ability to resist both wear and corrosion and for their tensile strength and resist-

ance to creep at elevated temperatures. Typical applications include turbine blades and valve-seat facings where high-velocity fluid flow is encountered. The 400-series steels are often air-hardenable, requiring both preheating and postheating when welded. Types 414, 416, and 420 are typical.

PROPERTIES THAT AFFECT WELDING

Heat conductivity of chrome-nickel steels is about 50% less than that of mild steel. This means the heat is concentrated in the weld pool rather than traveling rapidly throughout the plates. For this reason, less heat is required for a given job. As a general rule, about 10% less current is used with stainless electrodes as compared to mild-steel procedures.

Melt-off rates of stainless-steel electrodes are higher than the rates for mild-steel electrodes, which is another reason for slightly lower currents being used.

Thermal expansion of chrome-nickel steels is about 50% greater than for mild steel. This increases the tendency for warping and buckling, especially on thin sheets. Clamps and fixtures are widely used to cope with buckling.

Electrical resistance is 6 to 12 times that of mild steel. This may cause overheating in the electrodes. Shorter electrodes are often used to reduce electrode heating.

The austenitic (chrome-nickel) grades are considered more readily weldable than the ferritic (straight-chrome) types. The austenitic grades are

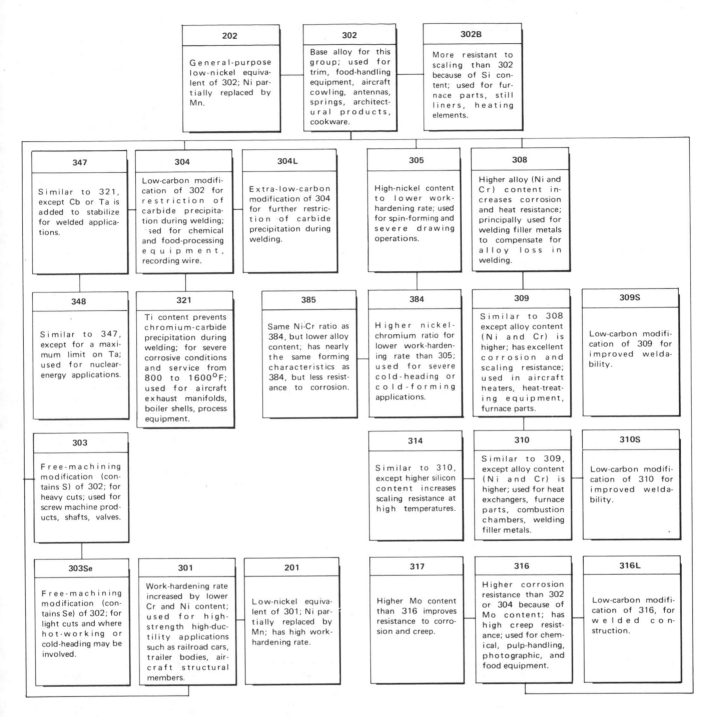

Fig. 18-2. Applications for the AISI austenitic stainless steels.

nonhardening, and welding usually does not adversely affect the strength or ductility of the deposit, fusion zone, or base metal. However, one detrimental effect of heating on the chrome-nickel steels is to cause carbide precipitation at the grain boundaries, resulting in reduced corrosion resistance. When heated in a range between 800-1600°F, a change takes place that is detrimental to corrosion resistance. This is caused by the precipitation at the grain boundaries of a very fine film of chromium-rich carbides, containing as much as 90% chromium, taken from the layer of metal next to the grain boundary. Under these conditions, the chromium content of the metal next to the grain boundaries may be so reduced that resistance to corrosion is seriously impaired. The corrosion that is likely to occur is known as intergranular corrosion.

Carbide precipitation can be controlled by:

1. **Using stabilized steels.** This is the most practical solution. Both columbium and titanium have a greater affinity for carbon

TABLE 18-3. Typical Properties* of Martensitic Stainless Steels

| AISI Type | Room Temperature (annealed) | | | | Max Service Temp (°F) in Air | |
	Tensile Strength (1000 psi)	Yield Strength, 0.2% (1000 psi)	Elongation 2 in. (%)	Hardness Rockwell B[†]	Continuous	Intermittent
403	75	40	35	82	1300	1450
410	75	40	35	82	1300	1450
414	115	90	20	97	1300	1450
416, 416Se	75	40	30	82	1250	1400
420	95	50	25	92	1200	1400
431	125	95	20	24 (Rc)	1500	1600
440A	105	60	20	95	1400	1500
440B	107	62	18	96	1400	1500
440C	110	65	14	97	1400	1500

* Mechanical property values are for bar materials. Properties of sheet, strip, or plate may vary from these values slightly.

† Rockwell B unless otherwise noted.

than does chromium, so when either of these elements is added to these stainless steels in proper amounts, the carbon combines with the columbium or titanium instead of with the chromium. Stainless steels with columbium or titanium additions are called stabilized steels. They can be held in the 800-1600°F range without seriously affecting the corrosion-resisting properties, and no heat treatment is required. Columbium is used almost exclusively for this purpose in welding electrodes, since titanium tends to be lost in transferring across the arc. Stabilized steels are normally welded with stabilized filler metal.

2. **Rapid Quenching.** Heating to 1850-2100°F and quenching through the range of 800-1600°F is another method to control carbide precipitation. However, this incurs considerable expense and some parts do not lend themselves well to quenching. By

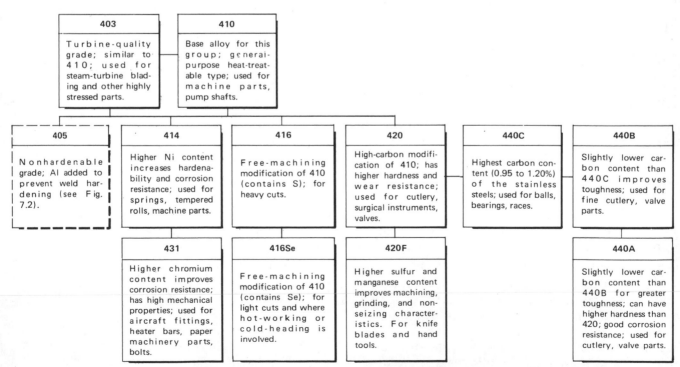

Fig. 18-3. Applications for the AISI martensitic stainless steels.

using small-diameter electrodes and single-pass welds, the time the work is within the 800-1600°F range is so short that very little carbide precipitation occurs.

3. **Limiting Carbon Content.** Stainless steels with 0.03% maximum carbon levels are referred to as ELC (extra low-carbon) or L (low-carbon) types.

WELDING PROCESSES FOR STAINLESS STEELS

The **shielded metal-arc process** is widely used in the welding of stainless steels. A wide variety of covered electrode types makes the process versatile. The AWS method of identifying stainless-steel electrodes uses E to indicate an electrode, the first three digits to indicate the composition of the electrode, and the last two after a dash to indicate the type of covering (see Chapter 5).

An example is E308-16. The number 308 indicates composition, and the number 16 tells the weldor the type of current to use by its specification of type of electrode covering. The number 16 means the electrode is titania-covered, for use with AC or DC reverse polarity. If the final number had been 15, it would indicate a lime covering and the need to use DC reverse polarity only. Lime-type coverings result in a globular transfer and a slightly rougher finish. Metal transfer with the titania-type (16) electrode covering is more of a spray type and results in a smoother deposit.

Covered electrodes for stainless steel are also available in which a granular alloy is contained inside an extra-low-carbon steel tube. The desired alloy is produced during the welding process. Fig. 18-4 illustrates this type of electrode and the mechanics of alloy formation.

In using stainless steel electrodes, the following considerations apply:

- Be sure all weld surfaces are clean and dry. Use stainless-steel wire brushes only to avoid contamination.

- Amperage settings should be about 10% less than with comparable mild-steel procedures

- In flat welding, hold an electrode angle of about 15 degrees in the direction of travel and weld with a short arc.

- In vertical welding, hold the electrode perpendicular to the work. Use slightly less amperage and oscillate the electrode a slight amount in the root area. EXXX-15 electrodes are preferred for vertical welding.

- In overhead welding, the deposits should be in stringer beads, using a short arc without oscil-

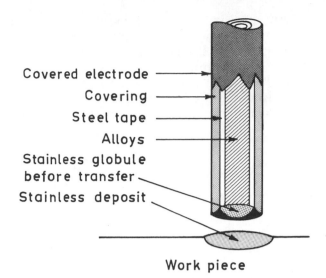

Work piece

Fig. 18-4. The granular alloys and extra-low-carbon steel tube dissolve at the electrode tip to produce the desired stainless chemistry before transfer to the workpiece. This alloying action is instantaneous with the arc strike, precluding any possibility of a weld deposit other than that originally engineered into the electrode.

lation. EXXX-15 electrodes are preferred. Stringer beads minimize heat input and reduce cracking tendencies. Weave beads should always be limited to 2-1/2 times the electrode diameter. Craters should always be filled before breaking the arc.

Suggested electrode diameters for varying plate thicknesses are as follows:

3/32''	18 ga. to 12 ga.
1/8''	12 ga. to 3/16''
5/32''	3/16'' to 1/2''
3/16''	3/8'' and heavier

For procedure details, see the first three procedure tables, entitled Shielded Metal-Arc (Manual), at the end of this chapter.

The **submerged-arc process** is often the choice method of welding stainless steel when the work is heavy and the pieces can be positioned for flat welding. Only fluxes intended for stainless steel welding should be used. See Chapters 5 and 11.

The **gas tungsten-arc (TIG)** process is excellent for stainless steels, especially with thin sections. Fillers metal may or may not be added. Welds are clean and strong. See Chapter 13 for information on TIG welding and the procedure table at the end of this chapter.

Gas metal-arc (MIG) welding is also used extensively in the welding of stainless steel. An inert gas shield is used in conjunction with a rod or bare-wire electrode. See Chapter 13 for information on the MIG process and the procedure table at the end of this chapter for typical semiautomatic procedures.

Resistance spot welding is ideally suited to the spot-joining of stainless steel pieces. The high electrical resistance of stainless steel is beneficial in this instance. See Chapter 22 for information on this process.

Torch and furnace brazing is also widely used in fabricating stainless-steel products. See Chapter 16 for information on brazing.

WELDING PROCEDURES

The following procedures are representative of those used for welding the stainless steels by shielded metal-arc, TIG, and MIG processes:

SHIELDED METAL-ARC (MANUAL)
AISI 300 Series Stainless Steels

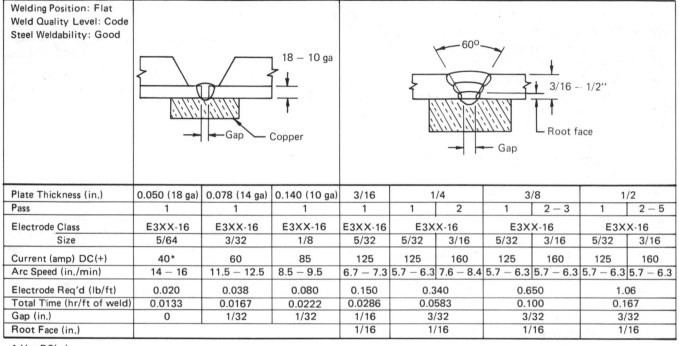

Welding Position: Flat
Weld Quality Level: Code
Steel Weldability: Good

Plate Thickness (in.)	0.050 (18 ga)	0.078 (14 ga)	0.140 (10 ga)	3/16	1/4		3/8		1/2	
Pass	1	1	1	1	1	2	1	2 – 3	1	2 – 5
Electrode Class	E3XX-16	E3XX-16	E3XX-16	E3XX-16	E3XX-16		E3XX-16		E3XX-16	
Size	5/64	3/32	1/8	5/32	5/32	3/16	5/32	3/16	5/32	3/16
Current (amp) DC(+)	40*	60	85	125	125	160	125	160	125	160
Arc Speed (in./min)	14 – 16	11.5 – 12.5	8.5 – 9.5	6.7 – 7.3	5.7 – 6.3	7.6 – 8.4	5.7 – 6.3	5.7 – 6.3	5.7 – 6.3	5.7 – 6.3
Electrode Req'd (lb/ft)	0.020	0.038	0.080	0.150	0.340		0.650		1.06	
Total Time (hr/ft of weld)	0.0133	0.0167	0.0222	0.0286	0.0583		0.100		0.167	
Gap (in.)	0	1/32	1/32	1/16	3/32		3/32		3/32	
Root Face (in.)				1/16	1/16		1/16		1/16	

* Use DC(−)

Note: AC can be used with a 10% increase in current. E3XX-15 electrode can be used with a 10% decrease in current.
See Procedure Notes in Section 6-2.

SHIELDED METAL-ARC (MANUAL)

AISI 300 Series Stainless Steels

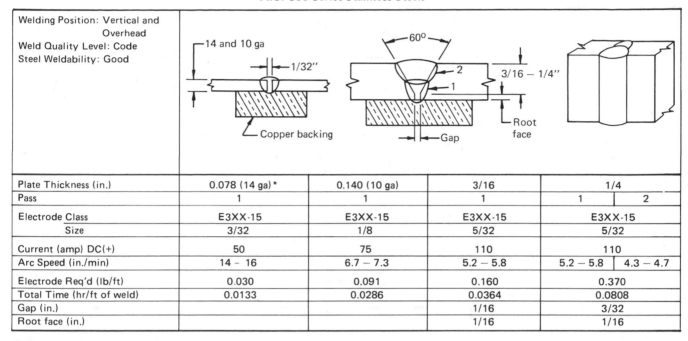

Plate Thickness (in.)	0.078 (14 ga)*	0.140 (10 ga)	3/16	1/4	
Pass	1	1	1	1	2
Electrode Class	E3XX-15	E3XX-15	E3XX-15	E3XX-15	
Size	3/32	1/8	5/32	5/32	
Current (amp) DC(+)	50	75	110	110	
Arc Speed (in./min)	14 – 16	6.7 – 7.3	5.2 – 5.8	5.2 – 5.8	4.3 – 4.7
Electrode Req'd (lb/ft)	0.030	0.091	0.160	0.370	
Total Time (hr/ft of weld)	0.0133	0.0286	0.0364	0.0808	
Gap (in.)			1/16	3/32	
Root face (in.)			1/16	1/16	

* Vertical down, all others vertical up.

See Procedure Notes in Section 6.2.

SHIELDED METAL-ARC (MANUAL)

AISI 300 Series Stainless Steels

Welding Position: Flat or Horizontal*						

Weld Size (in.)	3/32	1/8	3/16	1/4	5/16	
Plate Thickness (in.)	0.078 (14 ga)	0.140 (10 ga)	3/16	1/4	3/8	
Pass	1	1	1	1	1	2
Electrode Class	E3XX-16	E3XX-16	E3XX-16	E3XX-16	E3XX-16	
Size	3/32	1/8	5/32	3/16	3/16	
Current (amp) DC(+)	60	85	120	160	170	
Arc Speed (in./min)	12.5 – 13.5	12.5 – 13.5	8.6 – 9.4	6.2 – 6.8	6.2 – 6.8	6.7 – 7.3
Electrode Req'd (lb/ft)	0.036	0.056	0.120	0.220	0.430	
Total Time (hr/ft of weld)	0.0154	0.0154	0.0222	0.0308	0.0594	

* For vertical and overhead use same procedures as for vertical and overhead butt welds.

Note: AC can be used with a 10% increase in current. E3XX-15 can be used with a 10% decrease in current.
See Procedure Notes in Section 6.2.

**Typical Procedures for Welding Stainless Steels
with the Gas Tungsten-Arc Process**

Plate Thickness, T (in.)	1/16	3/32	1/8	3/16
Current, DCSP	80 – 100	100 – 120	120 – 140	200 – 250
Electrode Diameter (in.)	1/16	1/16	1/16	3/32
Gas Flow, Argon (cfh)	10	10	10	15
Filler-Rod Diameter (in.)	1/16	1/16	3/32	1/8
Arc Speed (ipm)	12	12	12	10
Total Time (hr/ft of weld)	0.0167	0.0167	0.0167	0.0200

Plate Thickness, T (in.)	1/16	3/32	1/8	3/16
Current, DCSP	90 – 110	110 – 130	130 – 150	225 – 275
Electrode Diameter (in.)	1/16	1/16	1/16	3/32
Gas Flow, Argon (cfh)	10	10	10	15
Filler-Rod Diameter (in.)	1/16	1/16	3/32	1/8
Arc Speed (ipm)	10	10	10	8
Total Time (hr/ft of weld)	0.0200	0.0200	0.0200	0.0250

For vertical-up and overhead, decrease the current 10 to 20%.

**Gas Metal-Arc Welding (Semiautomatic)
General Welding Conditions for Spray-Arc Transfer
AISI 200 and 300 Series Stainless Steels**

Gas-Argon + 1% Oxygen.
Gas flow 35 cfh.

Plate Thickness (in.)	1/8	1/4	3/8	1/2
Electrode Size	1/16	1/16	1/16	3/32
Passes	1	2	2	4
Current DCRP	225	275	300	325
Wire Feed Speed (ipm)	140	175	200	225
Arc Speed (ipm)	19 – 21	19 – 21	15 – 17	15 – 17
Electrode Required (lb/ft)	0.075	0.189	0.272	0.495
Total Time (hr/ft of weld)	0.010	0.020	0.025	0.050

Hardsurfacing By Welding

Often, the prime requirement of a metal part is that it have exceptionally good resistance to wear, corrosion, or high temperatures. Rather than make the entire part from some expensive wear-resistant, corrosion-resistant, or temperature-resistant alloy, it is more economical to make it from an ordinary steel and then cover the critical surfaces with a layer of weld metal capable of withstanding the service conditions. The application of a durable surface layer to a metal is called "hardsurfacing" — a term that is misleading when the surfacing material is for some service condition other than wear. A simple way to apply hardsurfacing materials is by welding, usually arc welding. Except as noted otherwise in the following text, the reference will be to the arc-welding method of applying hardsurfacing.

There are various materials that can be used for hardsurfacing, and selecting the one best suited to a particular application involves balancing cost against performance, as in the selection of any engineering material. Two AWS specifications that pertain to hardsurfacing are *Surfacing Rods and Electrodes, A5.13-70* and *Composite Surfacing Rods and Electrodes, A5.21-70.*

Although some materials are hardsurfaced to improve their resistance to corrosion or high temperatures, by far the most common reason for hardsurfacing is to improve wear resistance. Hardsurfacing for wear resistance will be the main consideration in the following text, with corrosion resistance and elevated-temperature resistance alluded to where they are also factors in the selection of welding materials. Wear is encountered primarily in two forms. An abrasive or galling type of wear occurs when two surfaces rub or slide over one another, and an impact or spalling type of wear occurs when a surface is subjected to repeated blows or impingement.

HARDSURFACING MATERIALS

The *ASM Metals Handbook, Eighth Edition, Volume Six,* lists 86 typical iron-base hardsurfacing compositions, ranging from 2.35% to 51.80% alloy content, and there are many more compositions available including cobalt-base, nickel-base, and copper-base alloys. In addition to the rods and electrodes included in the AWS specifications, there are many rods, electrodes, powders, and inserts marketed under trade designations. Often, the outstanding properties of the deposit from proprietary products are described without mention of the composition of the product. As a result, the suitability of a hardsurfacing material can not always be assessed with a strictly metallurgical approach.

Hardsurfacing materials for wear resistance tend to be suited to specific types of wear. For example, resistance to abrasive wear generally requires extremely hard materials that also happen to be somewhat brittle and thus not particularly resistant to impact or chipping. On the other hand, high resistance to impact is best provided by ductile or malleable materials that, in turn, are not particularly resistant to severe abrasive wear. There are, however, some hardsurfacing materials that provide a compromise between these two qualities.

The major hardsurfacing materials are discussed in the following text, and, except for copper alloys and the tool and die steels (which have specialized applications), are presented in order of decreasing hardness. This means that, in general, they are also presented in order of decreasing abrasion resistance and increasing impact resistance.

The relative hardness and abrasion resistance of most of these materials are plotted in Fig. 19-1. which provides a graphical indication of their primary application areas. Thus, materials in the upper right portion of the graph are most resistant to abrasive or frictional types of wear, while those in the lower left portion provide maximum resistance to impact or spalling.

Tungsten Carbide: Tungsten carbide is the hardest and generally the most abrasion-resistant of all hardsurfacing materials. It is, thus, best suited to applications requiring exceptional resistance to abrasion and is commonly used on the surfaces of tools for cutting earth or rock. It is particularly well suited to digging in sandy formations, where a coarse form of tungsten carbide is used so that as the hardsurfacing wears it leaves a rough, fast-cutting edge.

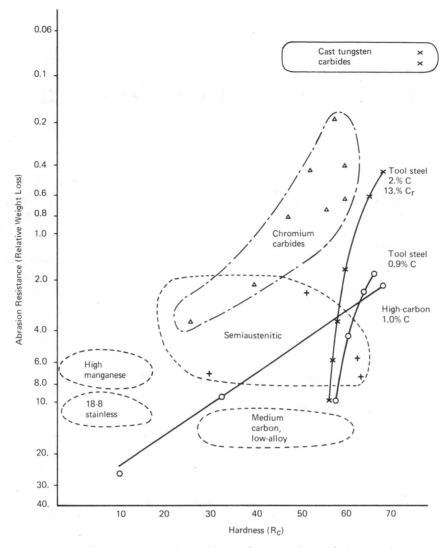

Fig. 19-1. Hardness and abrasion resistance of common hardsurfacing materials.

This material is also used to protect machine parts that come into contact with severely abrasive material. Screw conveyors, for example, are often hardsurfaced with tungsten carbide. This material is *not* recommended for protecting both surfaces in sliding contact, because the wear pattern is not smooth enough for bearing-type applications. The surface finish is similar to that of fine sandpaper.

For hardsurfacing, tungsten carbide consists of tungsten carbide crystals embedded in an iron-base alloy. This form of tungsten carbide is a cast material and is not to be confused with the sintered (or cemented) carbides used for metal-cutting tools. The sintered form cannot be fusion welded. Hardness of the deposit cannot be measured directly on the Rockwell C scale, because the bonding alloy has a relatively low hardness, and the tungsten carbide particles have a high hardness. Metallurgists use a different procedure in evalu-

ating the hardness of such materials, and hardness values when given are on the Rockwell A scale.

Hardsurfacing electrodes and rods are made by encasing the cast tungsten carbide and tungsten-carbon alloy in powder form within mild-steel tubes. Crushed tungsten carbide particles of controlled mesh size are metered into steel tubes, as illustrated in Fig. 19-2. Such tubes are produced as bare electrodes for DC arc application, as covered electrodes for AC-DC application, and as bare rods for oxyacetylene application. During deposition, the steel tube dissolves some carbon and tungsten from the tungsten carbide particles. As deposited, the tungsten carbide is thus embedded in a tungsten-iron or steel.

Chromium Carbides: Chromium-carbide hard-surfacing materials are surpassed in hardness and abrasion resistance only by the tungsten carbides. But the chromium carbides, being slightly softer,

Fig. 19-2. A hardsurfacing welding rod for oxyacetylene use made up of a steel tube filled with tungsten carbide particles.

are slightly superior to tungsten carbide for impact resistance. Chromium carbides are, nevertheless, still considered to be hard, brittle materials compared to other hardsurfacing materials. They are extremely resistant to wear and abrasion, but do not provide much resistance to chipping, spalling, or damage from impact.

The applications for chromium carbide are generally the same as those for tungsten carbide, except that chromium carbide may also be used where its good corrosion resistance is a desirable property. Typical applications are coatings for earth-cutting tools, for machine parts exposed to abrasive materials, and for chutes and slides that convey ores or other materials not likely to impose significant impact loads.

There are dozens of specific hardsurfacing alloys within the chromium carbide group. Some of these are ferrous-based, and some are based on cobalt or tungsten. The ferrous chromium carbide alloys (Table 19-1) are too hard to be machined

and provide excellent resistance to wear by abrasion. They also maintain high hardness at elevated temperatures. Tong tips for handling hot ingots are often faced with chromium carbide.

The nonferrous chromium carbides (Table 19-2) are often referred to by the term "Stellite," a proprietary trade name. Applications for the nonferrous types are similar to those of the ferrous, but the nonferrous chromium carbides are more resistant to some types of corrosion. However, they also are more expensive than the ferrous types and are not quite as abrasion-resistant. A newer form of nonferrous chromium carbide electrode, having a wrought-cobalt core wire, can be deposited much more easily than the conventional cast electrode.

Chromium carbides generally are nonmagnetic. The deposits are not affected by heat treatment, thus cooling rate has no effect on wear resistance. The materials develop a smooth surface with wear and can, thus, be used to protect surfaces in sliding

TABLE 19-1. Ferrous Chromium Carbide Hardsurfacing Deposits

	Typical Chemistry* (%)					Typical Hardness † (Rc)			
	C	Mn	Si	Cr	Mo	Single Layer Room Temperature	Multiple Layer Room Temperature	Multiple Layer 1000°F	Multiple Layer 1500°F
Manual Electrodes									
Max. abrasion	4.2	5.4	0.70	22.5	0.25	40 — 52	50 — 58	38	30
Abrasion with mild impact	4.5	1.0	1.0	18.5	6.0	45 — 55	55 — 64	49	38
Submerged-arc, alloy flux	3.8	0.9	0.5	29.0	1.2	53 — 58	58 — 61		

* Two layers in mild steel

† Deposits on mild steel

TABLE 19-2. Nonferrous Chromium Carbide Hardsurfacing Deposits

	Typical Chemistry* (%)					Typical Hot Hardness (Rc)			
	C	Si	Cr	W	Co	Room Temperature	650°F	1050°F	1400°F
Max. abrasion	3.2	0.8	26.0	13.5	53.0	43 — 58	36 — 46	30 — 37	51 — 54*
Abrasion with mild impact	1.1	1.5	29.0	5.5	62.0	23 — 47	26 — 40	19 — 32	15 — 50*

Note: Chemistry and hardness values are for multilayer deposits with manual electrodes

* Rockwell A

TABLE 19-3. Semiaustenitic Steel Hardfacing Deposits

	Typical Chemistry * (%)					Typical Hardness (Rc)	
	C	Mn	Si	Cr	Mo	Single Layer	Double Layer
Impact and abrasion Manual Electrode	2.1	1.1	0.75	6.5	0.4	24 — 53	28 — 53
Submerged-arc, alloy flux	0.95	2.5	1.8	7.0	0.75	36 — 60	32 — 60

* Double Layer

contact. Bearings for use at high temperatures or in corrosive environments are often faced with chromium carbide. Deposits typically range in hardness from 40 to 63 Rockwell C. For each material, there is a combination of carbon and alloy content that gives both good abrasion resistance and impact strength. An off-balance material, however, may have low resistance to abrasion and also may be brittle. Some electrodes are designed to produce good hardsurfacing deposits when diluted with steel, that is, they provide a one-layer deposit that is resistant to abrasion and to cracking. The best nonferrous chromium carbide electrodes deposit metal that features high hardness (54-63 Rockwell C) and very high abrasion resistance.

Admixture of base metal into the weld metal reduces abrasion resistance and increases impact resistance of the first layer. Thus, for maximum abrasion resistance, two layers should be used, with low current employed on the first layer to minimize admixture. Since the deposits are somewhat brittle, deposit thickness should be limited to no more than two layers to minimize the possibility of spalling. The workpiece surface should be prepared carefully, and underbead cracking should be avoided.

Semiaustenitic Steels: The semiaustenitic alloys can be thought of as intermediate between the hardest and the toughest hardsurfacing materials. They provide a balanced combination of good wear resistance and good impact resistance and probably are the most widely used of all hardsurfacing materials. The deposits are either hard as deposited or become hard with peening impact in service. They are also hardenable by heat treating.

These alloys are iron-based materials that contain up to 20% alloying elements. The varieties most commonly used have from 1 to 2% carbon and from 5 to 12% chromium (Table 19-3). The name for these materials comes from the fact that the alloy, principally austenitic as deposited, remains only semiaustenitic upon cooling. Various

metallurgical structures are possible, depending upon the specific composition of the deposit and its cooling rate.

If the deposit cools quickly (small electrode, short beads, and base metal cold before welding), the deposit will be predominantly austenitic and, thus, will be soft and tough. Slow cooling, however, does not impair wear resistance. Also, the surface will work-harden. For example, a material that is 30 Rockwell C as deposited will become more than 50 Rockwell C after moderate peening.

If the deposit cools slowly (large electrode, continuous welding, or preheated base metal), most of the austenite has time to transform to martensite, and the deposit will be less ductile. Both types of deposit work-harden to the same final value.

This group of alloys is machinable with tungsten carbide tools after a long anneal at high temperatures. Some of the alloys can be hot-forged. Although there is a wide range in hardness in this group, abrasion resistance does not vary greatly. Some of the alloys that are hard as deposited are not as resistant to grinding abrasion as some of those having a much lower hardness. The alloys that work-harden are superior for service involving a combination of impact and abrasion.

Two-layer deposits are generally recommended, except with certain submerged-arc processes that produce good wear resistance with one layer. If machining is required, the deposit must be annealed, machined, and then heat treated.

Some alloys of this group may tend to lift or peel away from the substrate upon cooling, particularly when the base metal has less than 0.15% carbon. This is caused by a highly brittle zone that forms between the base metal and weld metal. The transformation and shrinkage stresses then promote cracking and peeling. This effect can be minimized by slowing the cooling rate with a 300°F preheat, and by peening each bead while it is hot. Also, the first layer can be deposited with high current and fast travel as a series of stringer

TABLE 19-4. Austenitic Mn Steel Hardsurfacing Deposits

	Typical Chemistry * (%)					Typical Hardness* (Rc)	
	C	Mn	Si	Ni	Mo	As-Welded	Work Hardened
Severe impact Manual electrode	0.62	14.2	0.15		1.15	17 — 20	43 — 48
Self-shielded flux-cored electrode	0.65	13.5	0.5	2.6	0.5	10 — 15	35 — 45

* Multiple layers on Mn Steel

beads separated by small gaps. The high admixture that results avoids a brittle zone. The second layer is then applied conventionally.

Austenitic Manganese Steels: The austenitic manganese-steel hardsurfacing materials (Table 19-4) are tougher and slightly less abrasion-resistant than the semiaustenitic materials, and are considered to be extremely good alloys for resistance to impact. A typical application might be for coating an ore chute where large rocks may occasionally strike the chute with great force.

The deposit normally contains from 11 to 14% manganese and is work-hardenable. Worn manganese-steel parts often are built up nearly to size with austenitic manganese-steel electrodes, and then are coated with a thin layer of semiaustenitic steel to enhance the abrasion resistance. There is not much variation in the hardness or the abrasion resistance of austenitic manganese deposits. Most deposits contain about 1.0% carbon and some molybdenum or nickel. High-manganese deposits are not recommended for resistance to grinding abrasion but are superior for resistance to a combination of severe impact and abrasion.

The required alloy content of the overlay can be deposited easily without special precautions. Admixture of a manganese-steel base metal into the weld metal has no effect on wear resistance. Admixture of carbon steel into the weld metal can reduce wear resistance slightly. Two-layer deposits are recommended for best performance. Cooling rate has no effect on wear resistance, nor does heat treating have any effect on machinability or wear resistance. Prolonged heating above 500°F, however, may embrittle manganese steel base metal.

Spalling is rarely encountered with these de-posits, especially if the surface is prepared properly and if thick deposits are peened after each layer is applied. There is the possibility, however, that prolonged or repeated heating of manganese-steel base metal over 500°F may promote embrittlement and spalling. Thus, heat input should be limited by such techniques as keeping preheat to 70°F (except when a 100 to 200°F preheat may be needed to prevent cracking of a massive part), by using skip welding, or by employing low welding currents. Because weld metal has a lower carbon and silicon content than manganese-steel base metal, the deposit generally does not become embrittled.

Austenitic Stainless Steels: Though not "hard" materials in the generally accepted sense, austenitic stainless steels are grouped with hardsurfacing alloys because this type of stainless steel provides an extremely tough, ductile coating with exceptionally good resistance to chipping from repeated impact forces. These deposits also provide good corrosion resistance. Such coatings typically are used to protect water-turbine blades from corrosion and cavitation erosion. The E300 series stainless steels work-harden, but not to the extent of the manganese steels. Abrasion resistance is higher than that of high-carbon steel of the same hardness.

Stainless steel deposits are sometimes used as base layers for other hardsurfacing materials. For example, an initial layer of stainless avoids a brittle bond that otherwise would develop between a carbon-steel base and a manganese-steel coating. E308 and E312 electrodes are usually used for these base layers. E312, being a higher alloy than E308, is less affected by admixture of the base

TABLE 19-5. Martensitic Stainless Steel Hardsurfacing Deposits

	Typical Chemistry * (%)				Typical Hardness (Rc)		
	C	Mn	Si	Cr	Single Layer	Double Layer	Multiple Layer
Type 420	0.23	1.1	0.9	13.0	45 — 47	49 — 51	52 — 54
Type 410	0.08	1.1	1.0	12.5	38 — 40	37 — 40	30 — 32

* Three-layer deposit by submerged-arc.

TABLE 19-6. Heat-Treatable Hardsurfacing Deposits

	Typical Chemistry * (%)						Typical Hardness (Rc)		
	C	Mn	Si	Cr	V	Mo	Single Layer	Double Layer	Multiple Layer
Manual †	0.16	1.15	0.60	1.4			15 — 20	18 — 23	23 — 28
Submerged-arc†	0.24	1.20	0.70	1.8		0.30	25 — 32	30 — 43	34 — 45
Submerged-arc ¶	0.10	2.50	0.30	2.8	0.15	0.30	34 — 39	39 — 42	39 — 42
Manual ¶	0.37	2.20	0.15	3.3			40 — 45	48 — 52	50 — 55

* Three-layer deposit on mild steel

† Deposits can be machined with carbide tools without annealing if welded with proper procedures.

¶ Must be annealed before machining

metal.

Martensitic Stainless Steels: Types 410 and 420 stainless steels (Table 19-5) produce dense, homogeneous weld metal with good resistance to cracking. For best results the deposit should be at least two layers thick, and preferably should be three or more layers thick.

Type 420 must be finished by grinding if a machined finish is required. Type 410 can be machined with carbide tools at slow cutting speeds. The deposits usually are used in the as-welded condition.

These stainless steel deposits are widely used for metal-to-metal wear, such as that encountered with bearings operating at elevated temperatures and with rolls used in steel mills. A typical application is a deposit for a backup roll on a hot-rolling mill.

Heat-Treatable Steels: Several types of heat-treatable steels are used as hardsurfacing materials, (Table 19-6). These steels produce hard, abrasion-resistant surfaces if the deposit is cooled quickly, or they produce a softer, tougher deposit if allowed to cool slowly. Hard deposits can be softened by annealing. These materials are commonly used for surfacing or for building up parts prior to hardsurfacing by other alloys.

High-Carbon Steels: The cooling rate of high-carbon steel must be rapid to produce maximum abrasion resistance. At best, the high-carbon steels may rival some of the chromium carbides, but if cooled slowly the deposit is less abrasion-resistant.

The abrasion resistance of high-carbon weld deposits increases with hardness. The maximum ductility and impact resistance for a given hardness is obtained by quenching and tempering; however, heat-treated properties may be approached by welding alone. To achieve such results, use minimum preheat and deposit the weld metal in small stringer beads or thin layers. Before depositing the next bead or layer, allow sufficient time for the high-carbon weld metal to transform to martensite. Using this procedure, each bead tempers the martensite of the previous bead and the weld as a whole approaches the quenched and tempered condition.

Published hardness values are normally for multilayer deposits applied manually, but the hardness of single-layer welds, which are influenced more by admixture with the base metal, may be higher or lower than that of multilayer deposits. This effect depends on the hardenability of the weld metal. A low-carbon electrode deposited on high-carbon steel produces a medium-carbon weld metal.

It is possible to have a combination of analyses that produces an exceptionally hard deposit. For example, a low-carbon but high-alloy base metal, when surfaced with a high-carbon electrode, produces weld metal that is high in carbon and has absorbed enough alloying elements to produce higher hardenability than either a multilayer high-carbon deposit or the low-carbon high-alloy base metal.

Medium-Carbon Alloy Steels: These materials are most often used to provide protection against metal-to-metal wear, and for building up steels before they are surfaced with the carbide types of hardsurfacing alloys. Though these alloys have low abrasion resistance, some of them have exceptionally high tensile strength and ductility, and thus resist deformation and cracking from impact.

The chemical analyses of this group range from 0.15% carbon with a total of 2.0% chromium, manganese, molybdenum, silicon, and other elements, on up to 0.5% carbon with 5.0% alloying elements. Hardenability increases with alloy content; the as-welded hardness on preheated work is higher than can be obtained with high-carbon deposits. The lower limit on carbon restricts the maximum hardness obtainable, but also increases impact resistance. The metal-arc deposits are air-hardenable and, in the as-welded condition, have high toughness and good abrasion resistance.

A low-alloy content in the deposit reduces abrasion resistance, but increases impact strength. On some deposits, normal procedural variations do not change alloy content significantly, while with other deposits the alloy content can be varied easily by altering procedures.

Admixture has little effect on multiple layer deposits. However, admixture may raise the carbon or alloy content in the first layer on medium to high-carbon steel and on some low-alloy steels. High admixture also may lower the first-layer alloy content with substrates of low-carbon steel.

Slow cooling increases the impact strength of medium-carbon alloy steel deposits and also improves the machinability of some deposits. For best machinability, deposits should be annealed (and then heat treated after machining).

Tool and Die Steels: Hardsurfacing with these alloys is commonly used to repair worn edges or surfaces of tools and dies and for applying durable wearing surfaces to dies made up of low-cost alloys such as mild steel. Electrodes for these applications generally are of either the chromium-type or molybdenum-type, although some tungsten-types are also available (Table 19-7).

The chromium-type consists of general-purpose alloys that provide a balanced combination of properties. These alloys are generally used when die temperatures are not expected to exceed 600°F. For cutting tools and other high-temperature operations, the molybdenum types are used. These alloys, commonly referred to as high-speed tool steels, retain full hardness at temperatures to about 1000°F. The molybdenum high-speed steel is the type most commonly used as an electrode.

Copper Alloys: Copper alloy overlays are used primarily to provide bearing surfaces for sliding metal-to-metal contact, and for corrosion resistance. The copper-based materials used primarily are aluminum bronze, phosphor bronze, and silicon bronze. Pure copper is seldom used.

Aluminum bronze provides a good bearing surface against steel and has fairly good corrosion resistance. Phosphor bronze, although not as hard as aluminum bronze, also makes a good bearing surface and resists corrosion. Silicon bronze has poor bearing properties and is used only for corrosion resistance.

For best results, if applied to steel, the copper-based overlays should be applied in three layers to reduce admixture in the final deposit. Total thickness of the deposit should not be less than 1/4-in. after final machining. Deposits are readily machined, unless there is excessive admixture of iron base metal, which causes hard spots.

SELECTING HARDSURFACING ALLOYS

The choice of hardsurfacing alloy depends in part on the reason for applying the deposit. Nearly all applications can be categorized in one of three classes:

1. A cutting edge is to be maintained.
2. A single surface is to be protected without regard for maintaining a sharp edge.
3. Two surfaces in sliding contact are to be protected.

Selection of an alloy also depends on the nature of the service creating the need for hardsurfacing. Wear-producing conditions usually result from some combinations of:

1. Abrasion or erosion from sliding contact.
2. Impact or chipping forces.
3. Loss of hardness or strength from extreme heat.
4. Corrosion or other chemical effects.

Selecting to Maintain a Cutting Edge: Selection of an alloy to maintain a cutting edge depends upon whether the primary concern is to minimize over-all wear while maintaining the cutting edge, or whether the objective is merely to maintain a sharp edge without particular concern for tool wear. A metal-cutting tool, for example, must maintain shape and length as well as sharpness, while the efficiency of earth-cutting tools, on the other hand, is not particularly impaired by nominal dimensional wear so long as the edge stays sharp.

Hardfacings of tool steel and high-speed steel are recommended where dimensional features as well as sharpness are to be maintained. Typical applications are shear blades, punches, and metal-cutting tools where the cutting edge must not only stay sharp, but must maintain its initial size and shape to perform satisfactorily. Failure of these parts usually is by upsetting, chipping, spalling, or galling — caused by high compressive loads and by the flow of metal being cut. Impact and abrasion are seldom problems.

High-speed steel is applied where high temperatures are encountered, while the less expensive tool

TABLE 19-7. Typical Tool and Die Steels

	C	Cr	Mo	W	V
Cr-Type	0.35	5.0	1.5	1.5	0.4
W-Type	0.70	4.0	–	18.0	1.0
Mo-Type	0.85	4.0	5.0	6.2	2.0

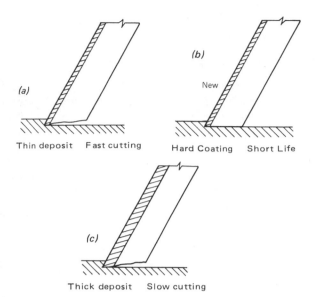

Fig. 19-3. Producing a self-sharpening surface by hardfacing. A thin, wear-resistant advancing surface (a) promotes a wear pattern that tends to maintain a sharp front edge. A thin, hard coating (b) provides fast cutting but short life, while a thick deposit (c) provides longer life but slower cutting.

steels are applied for service below 600°F. Deposits of either of these alloys are homogeneous and fine-grained. They can thus be ground to a sharp thin edge that resists upsetting or chipping.

Entirely different materials are recommended if dimensional wear is not of concern. Typical applications of this type are earth-scraping tools, earth-drilling bits, ensilage knives, and shredder blades.

An important aspect of this class of hardsurfacing is the principle of self sharpening. If a wear-resistant coating is placed only on the advancing edge of the tool, the back surface wears away at a greater rate and thus tends to promote a sharp cutting edge as shown in Fig. 19-3. Rate of wear and sharpness of the cutting edge are both inversely proportional to the thickness of the hardsurfacing. Thin deposit provides a sharp, fast-cutting tool that wears relatively fast, while a thicker deposit wears more slowly but provides a duller edge. If both front and back sides of the tool are hardsurfaced, the tool tends to dull rapidly and soon begins to slide over rather than cut into the earth or workpiece.

In this class of applications where sharpness rather than dimensional wear is of main concern, carbide materials are often selected. Coarse particles of tungsten carbide provide longest life for earth-cutting tools used in highly abrasive sandy formations. As the bonding material in the hardsurfacing wears away, coarse particles of tungsten carbide are exposed to produce a rough, fast-cutting edge. Fine carbide deposits are preferred where smoother wear patterns are required as with

various types of knives.

Chromium carbides are used on cutting edges where abrasive conditions are not particularly severe and where a lower-cost material is preferred. These materials readily self-sharpen and provide smoother, lower-friction edges than those of tungsten carbide.

Neither tungsten carbide nor chromium carbide is suited to applications where high impact loads occur. The semiaustenitic and austenitic manganese steels provide longest life for edges subjected to chipping and impact. Edges protected by these materials are not self-sharpening, but wear to a rounded contour that is tough and ductile. Tungsten carbide and chromium carbide tend to chip away from dipper teeth handling large rock. But austenitic manganese or semiaustenitic deposits work-harden and, thus, become resistant to abrasion, while impact forces are cushioned by the softer metal below the surface.

Selecting to Protect a Single Surface: The need to protect a single surface accounts for the largest number of hardsurfacing applications. The objective is to prevent wear of the surface without regard for a cutting edge or for wear on a contacting surface. It may be desirable to have a low-friction surface that polishes well (a plowshare or moldboard, for example), or a rough high-friction surface (dredge stud clamps) may be preferred.

Chutes for conveying bulk materials are commonly hardsurfaced. In general, hard materials such as chromium carbide are preferred if fine-grained ores or earth are being conveyed without large rocks or other objects that could cause impact. Semi-austenitic or manganese steels are preferred if heavy bulky pieces are being dumped onto a chute or if other service demands are likely to produce high impact forces.

Screw conveyors and earth-drilling tools are normally protected by hard materials such as the carbides. Stainless steels are used to provide corrosion resistance and protection against erosion in water pumps, and for applications requiring good impact resistance.

Selecting To Protect Contacting Surfaces: This type of application normally entails metal-to-metal wear under various combinations of abrasion, impact, friction, and corrosion. The surfacing material must wear smoothly, have a low coefficient of friction, and have little or no tendency to seize or gall. One type of hardsurfacing definitely not suitable for this class of application is tungsten carbide.

Often one surface requires more protection than the other. In such cases, one surface may be coated with bronze while the other surface is not coated. The bronze then wears sacrificially, thereby protecting the other surface.

High-carbon electrodes are used to build up shafts that are to operate with lubrication. The high-carbon deposit when machined or ground provides a smoother surface than is readily obtainable with a mild-steel electrode deposit. Bearings operated at elevated temperatures are surfaced with the chromium carbides, the stainless steels, and the high-chromium and nickel alloys.

Parts operating under corrosive conditions are protected by surfacing with chromium carbides and some of the stainless steels. Chromium carbide facings also give good service on parts operating in sand or mud. Rubber, though obviously not applied by welding, is quite wear-resistant and is a good wearing material for journals and bushings used underwater. Steel shafts give long service when they run in rubber bearings and are lubricated with water to keep out sand and mud.

Galling is the major problem in nonlubricated metal-to-metal contact. Two alloys of identical type are more prone to seize or gall than two different materials, probably because the materials are alike in chemical analysis or in surface condtion. Two alloys that provide good service underwater and fair service in sandy mud may soon chew each other up when they are run dry. Soft iron alloys are more likely to gall than harder ones, and rough surfaces gall more readily than smooth ones.

A running-in period with lubricant is recommended for freshly machined or ground surfaces because they often have irregularities that intermesh and produce tears that promote seizing.

PRACTICAL CONSIDERATIONS IN SELECTION

A tough, ductile hardsurfacing material may be specified for a new application where no prior experience exists. With a tough material, any failure that may occur is likely to be gradual rather than catastrophic. The semiaustenitic steels are recommended for such initial trials. If these materials hold up without chipping or impact fracture, one of the tougher chromium carbides might be used on the next trial. Progressively harder alloys could then be tried to improve abrasion resistance.

Examination of prior hardsurfacing failures provides valuable clues to selecting a superior material. However, meaningful information can be gained by examining a part that is only partially worn, since a totally worn part often tells very little about the way the wear progressed. For example, it may be impossible to determine whether hardsurfacing was worn away by abrasion or by impact if no hardsurfacing material remains on the part.

Also, it is often less costly to refinish a part

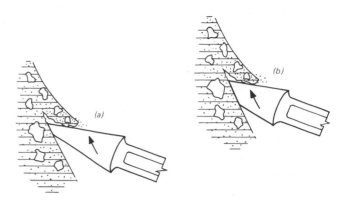

Fig. 19-4. Configuration where rate of wear increases as wear progresses. Minimal bulk material is abraded from slightly worn dipper tooth (a), but increasingly larger amounts of bulk material are removed (b) as advancing edges wears, because more wearing surface is exposed to the abrading action of earth flow.

while it is only partially worn instead of waiting until it is severely worn. The reason is that rate of wear often increases as wear progresses. A rock that scratches a dipper tooth, for example, will remove only a small amount of surface material if it abrades against hardsurfacing. But if the hardsurfacing is worn away, the same rock will likely create a large gouge in the tooth, thereby requiring expensive rebuilding of underlying metal prior to hardsurfacing. Self-sharpening blades in particular, where hardsurfacing is applied only to the advancing edge, should be hardsurfaced regularly (Fig. 19-4) to avoid excessive wear of the softer blade material.

The hardsurfacing job may have restrictions that narrow the field of possible surfacing materials. Examples are where:

- The deposit must be machinable as welded. This requirement eliminates all materials except the medium-carbon, low-alloy types. The machinability of a medium-carbon deposit depends on the rate of cooling; preheating must be used on large members to provide a deposit that is readily machinable. Deposits of austenitic manganese steel, chromium carbide, and stainless steel can be finished by grinding. The possibility of using an alloy that requires grinding should always be considered, for the increased life may more than offset the higher finishing costs.

- The deposit is to be machined, but may be annealed after welding and then hardened after finishing. This requirement increases the number of deposits that may be used. Possible surfacing materials are high-carbon tool steel and some of the low-carbon, low-alloy types. Materials that should not be used include stainless steel, chromium carbides, tungsten carbides, and high-manganese steel.

- The part and the deposit are to be hot-forged. This requirement eliminates the tungsten carbides and the chromium carbides. The high-carbon and medium-carbon deposits are forgeable at red heat and are also ductile enough to be straightened and forged to some extent after quenching for hardening. These steels form hard martensite when quenched, but the transformation does not take place until the work has cooled to 300 or 200°F. The part may be taken from the quenching bath at 400-500°F and then straightened or forged a small amount while it is still in the ductile austenitic state. If then cooled in air or in the quenching bath, it will be just as hard as if it had been given a complete quench. It may also be tougher, for the martensite is given more time to form.

- A cutting edge is required for cutting or turning steel. This specification necessitates the use of a material with high hardness, high red hardness, and a high edge strength. The field is limited to one of the high-speed tool steels or a tungsten carbide insert.

- The deposit must have maximum resistance to grinding abrasion. Tungsten carbides or chromium carbides are likely to be best for this requirement. Chromium carbides are preferred if low cost is important.

METHODS FOR DEPOSITING HARDSURFACING

Hardsurfacing may be deposited by various arc-welding processes and by the oxyacetylene torch. Arc welding processes are generally preferred for hardsurfacing for reasons of speed and low cost. However, some hardsurfacing is done best by the oxyacetylene process. The arc processes used are simply counterparts of the methods used to join metals, except that hardsurfacing electrodes are used in place of other welding electrodes or filler wires. In submerged-arc hardsurfacing, alloy elements can be added to the deposit by the flux. Carbon-arc processes are also used.

On steels that are sensitive to overheating, such as an austenitic manganese steel, the oxyacetylene and gas tungsten-arc processes should be avoided. Other steels and other surfacing materials may be hardsurfaced by the oxyacetylene or gas tungsten-arc processes as well as the metal-arc processes.

The oxyacetylene and the carbon-arc processes are used for small, delicate parts and where only a thin layer of surfacing is to be applied. Coal cutter bits, for example, often are hardsurfaced by oxyacetylene welding.

Either the oxyacetylene or the carbon-arc process is recommended to deposit nonferrous chromium carbide alloys in cases where the surfacing must be iron-free. By careful manipulation, the alloy may be sweated to the steel base metal and welded without penetration or alloying with the steel. Corrosion resistance and abrasion resistance are lowered when these alloys are diluted with iron.

A possible drawback of metal-arc processes for hardsurfacing is the deep penetration they produce. The more the base metal is melted, the greater the alloying of the deposit with the base metal. Deep penetration is usually a disadvantage since it increases the thickness of the hardsurfaced deposit. The total amount of hardsurfacing is the build-up from the surface plus the penetration below. If the amount of build-up is limited, then deep penetration may be desirable.

In most cases, the first layer of surfacing has lower abrasion resistance but more resistance to impact than the undiluted alloy. This gives a gradual change from the base metal to the hard-surface. But diluted surfacing may produce brittle alloys, as sometimes occurs when carbon steel is deposited on austenitic manganese steel.

Hardsurfacing alloys containing boron should be deposited with an oxyacetylene torch, and care must be taken to prevent the formation of the brittle iron-boride crystals.

Manual hardsurfacing for repair or renewal of worn surfaces is usually done by metal-arc welding and coated or bare electrodes. Semiautomatic and automatic hardsurfacing techniques are often used on large volume production or for protection of large contact areas, such as tread-type tractor idler rolls, or where composite hardsurfacings must be provided on new equipment.

CONTROL OF PROPERTIES

Once a specific hardsurfacing deposit is selected, the alloy content and cooling rate of the deposit must be carefully tailored to provide the desired abrasion resistance and impact properties. Alloy content is determined primarily by the material selected, the procedures employed to lay the deposit, and by the resulting admixture of deposit and base metal. Important procedural considerations are:

Surface Preparation: Remove grease and oil with a solvent, and remove rust and dirt by wire-brushing. If contaminants are not removed, they can cause porosity, cracking, and poor deposit quality. For a good bond between base metal and weld, use arc-gouging or grinding to remove cracks, the remains of old high-alloy hardsurfacing deposits, or badly work-hardened or distorted surfaces. Fill cracks, gouges and surface depressions by manual welding.

Preheating: Most hardsurfacing does not require preheating, except for bringing the part to a room temperature of 70-100°F. Medium to high-carbon and low-alloy steels may require higher preheat to prevent underbead cracking, weld cracking, spalling, or stress failure. Higher preheat is needed for massive or rigid parts and when cracking actually is encountered. Parts are normally preheated by gas or oil torches, ovens, or electrical heating devices. The particular method used depends upon the size of the part and the equipment available. Preheating is of no benefit if the part cools before welding.

Always be sure the area to be surfaced is at the specified preheat temperature before starting to weld. Sometimes it is advisable to check the temperature of the part during welding to be sure it has not cooled. More heating may be needed if welding is interrupted. Interpass temperature — the temperature of the surface when welding all layers except the first — is just as important as preheat temperature and should usually be as high as the preheat. (Special care should be taken to avoid overheating manganese steel.)

Build-up: Some hardsurfacing deposits are limited to two or three layers, therefore badly worn surfaces are normally rebuilt to within 3/16-3/8 in. of original size before hardsurfacing. The electrode for the preliminary build-up usually should have a strength similar to the base metal.

Pattern of Deposit: Pattern of deposition usually is not important. However, these guidelines can be applied:

- The best pattern is usually the one most economical to apply.

- The pattern affects shrinkage stresses and can thus be used to help control distortion and cracking tendencies.

- A pattern with openings between beads is acceptable if the openings fill with abrasive material in service.

- For roller applications, beads placed on the rolls across the flow of material help pull material through the rolls, for example, rock crusher rolls.

- Beads placed parallel to the flow of abrasive material smooth the flow and thereby reduce wear.

Admixture and Cooling Rate: Small beads made with small electrodes and low currents have fast cooling rates and low admixture. Using two layers reduces admixture in the final layer.

Although cooling rate affects wear resistance of some deposits, it has a much greater effect on the control of spalling, cracking, and distortion. Therefore, a slow cooling rate may be required to reduce these undesirable effects even if wear resistance is reduced as a result.

Methods of controlling cooling rate include:

- Providing adequate preheat.

- Utilizing heat input from the arc or flame during hardsurfacing.

- Insulating the hot part immediately after hardsurfacing with dry sand, lime, or an asbestos blanket. This method helps minimize residual cooling stresses, weld cracking, and distortion but does not affect wear resistance of most deposits. Large parts draw heat away from the weld more quickly than small parts and thus cool the weld faster.

AVOIDING SPALLING

Spalling is the breaking of weld metal particles away from the base metal or underlying hardsurfacing layers. The broken pieces may vary in size from small chips to large chunks that expose the base metal. To avoid spalling:

Prepare the Surface: As in production welding, hardsurfacing welds must have a sound crack-free bond with the base metal. Such bonds are obtained when the workpiece surface is clean and all cracks and surface damage are repaired.

Avoid Underbead Cracking: Rapid cooling from welding temperature can cause brittle, crack-sensitive heat-affected zones in some base metals. These zones tend to crack in service and thus lead to spalling. Proper preheating is the surest way to avoid this problem.

Limit Deposit Thickness: Applying hardsurfacing in thick deposits builds up shrinkage stresses that promote spalling. Do not use more hardsurfacing layers than specified for each type of deposit. If thicker welding is required, rebuild before hardsurfacing. Peen each layer of thick build-up to relieve stresses.

Other causes of spalling are presented in Fig.19-5.

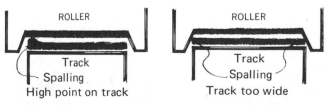

Fig. 19-5. Conditions that promotes spalling. High points on a rough deposit or a bead higher than the rest of the deposit (a) absorb a disproportionate amount of load and may thus tend to break away. Mismatched mating surfaces or improper alignment (b) produce load concentrations that promote wear or fracture in the coating.

AVOIDING UNDERBEAD CRACKING

Underbead cracks are small cracks that may occur in the heat-affected zone of the base metal under the weld. The cracks do not usually show on the surface but can promote spalling or cracking in the deposit.

The tendency for underbead cracking depends primarily upon the carbon and alloy content of the base metal. It is independent of the type of weld deposit when low-hydrogen processes or electrodes are used. Electrodes that are not the low-hydrogen type may require 100 to 300°F higher preheat than other build-up or hardsurfacing electrodes. However, welding with these electrodes on hot build-up layers usually avoids problems. All build-up and hardsurfacing should be completed without long delays to keep the part hot.

The easiest way to prevent underbead cracking is to slow the cooling rate by preheating. Always be sure the part is up to room temperature (70-100°F) before welding or use higher preheats if specified for the particular base metal.

RECOMMENDED PREHEATS

Low-Carbon Steel: Materials with carbon contents of approximately 0.10 to 0.30% are only slightly hardenable, thus preheating above room temperature is rarely needed. However, heavy, massive, or rigid parts containing more than 0.20% carbon should be preheated to 100 to 300°F.

Medium-Carbon Steel: Materials of 0.30 to 0.45% carbon are moderately hardenable, especially in large parts and heavy sections. Preheats to 300-500°F are recommended for higher carbon contents and for large, rigid, or complex parts.

High-Carbon Steel: Materials of approximately 0.45 to 0.80% carbon are highly hardenable and crack-sensitive in all sizes and shapes. Preheat to 500-800°F, using the higher temperatures for the higher carbon contents and for large, rigid, or complex shapes. When carbon content is near 0.80%, deposit a "buttering" layer with E7018 electrode (or with a mild-steel submerged-arc flux and electrode) prior to depositing build-up or hardsurfacing layers. The buttering layer minimizes the danger of

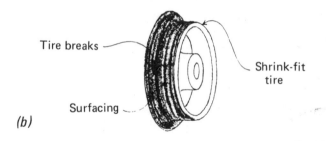

(a)

Spoked tractor idler — complex shape is inherently rigid. Preheat to prevent stress failure at any weak point.

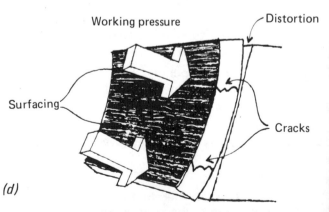

(b)

Mine locomotive wheel — shrink-fit tire is highly pre-stressed. Expand by preheating to prevent stress failure of the tire.

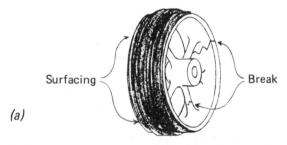

(c)

Crusher roller — massive size and jammed end pieces cause extreme rigidity. Loosen through bolts and expand the roll with preheat to loosen plugs.

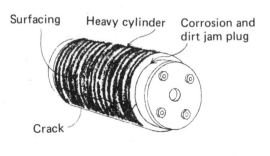

(d)

Jaw crusher — if distortion leaves crusher plate unsupported at the ends, working pressure causes bending stresses that can lead to failure.

Fig. 19-6. Typical part failures encountered with hardsurfacing. Complex shapes (a) frequently have weak sections easily fractured by thermal stresses. Special precautions are advised in shrink-fit parts, (b). Cracks can be avoided in crusher rolls (c) by loosening bolts and expanding the roll by preheat. Distortion may leave working surfaces unsupported (d) so that service stresses produce cracks.

underbead cracking and provides a good bond between base metal and hardsurfacing deposits.

Low-Alloy Steel: These steels vary from medium hardenable to highly hardenable, depending upon carbon and alloy content. Preheat to 100-500°F, using the higher temperatures for higher carbon and alloy contents and for large, rigid, or complex shapes. Preheat temperatures up to 800°F or a buttering layer may be required if the carbon content is over 0.35%.

Manganese Steel: Steels containing 12 to 14% manganese are not particularly hardenable or crack-sensitive. Preheat is not often required. But if parts are massive or highly rigid, preheat to 100-200°F. Prolonged heating over 500°F can cause embrittlement, so avoid high localized heating. On small parts, avoid high localized heating by using a skip welding technique.

Cast Iron: This material is extremely crack sensitive. The heat-affected zone may be full of cracks even with preheat temperatures of 1200-1400°F. Therefore, hardsurfacing cast iron is generally uneconomical. If it must be welded, follow standard cast-iron welding precautions.

AVOIDING STRESS FAILURE

Some parts contain high retained internal stresses. When welding stresses are added to these retained stresses, the part can fracture.

Several typical failures are shown in Fig. 19-6. Such failure can occur near the weld or at any weak point in the part, and is most commonly encountered when hardsurfacing:

- Highly rigid parts. (Massive parts and complex shapes are inherently rigid.)
- Shrink-fit parts.
- Some large castings, particularly when they are made of medium to high-carbon steel or medium-carbon low-alloy steels.
- Parts hardened by heat treatment.

The danger of stress failure can be minimized by:

- Preheating slowly to the high side of the temperature range specified for the particular type of base metal. This preheat should be as uniform as possible. Shrink-fit parts should be preheated until they are loose. (Manganese steel requires a lower temperature because it has a higher coefficient of expansion.)
- Controlled-atmosphere annealing and slow cooling to the specified preheat temperature parts that have been hardened by heat treatment.

- Arranging the welding schedule so it can be completed without long interruptions.
- Cooling the part slowly and uniformly. This can be done by covering the part with a blanket of asbestos, glass, or some other insulating material, or by cooling in a furnace.

AVOIDING WELD CRACKING

Transverse or Cross Cracking: Hardsurfacing deposits for resisting severe abrasion commonly cross-crack. This cracking is beneficial because it relieves stresses that could otherwise cause spalling or distortion. The cracking does not impair the wear resistance of the deposit, but it can be minimized by preheating to 1200°F. In other types of deposits, cross cracking can be detrimental. It generally occurs in parts that are massive, rigid, or of complex shape. The preheating used to prevent underbead or stress-failure cracking will also minimize cross cracking.

Longitudinal or Center-Line Cracking: This type of cracking is associated with poor bead shape and is caused by making the bead too flat. Several measures help avoid this problem:

- Use a stringer-bead or minimum weaving technique and low current.
- Be sure fillet welds are slightly convex.
- Use submerged-arc surfacing with the weave-bead technique. (Center-line cracking does not often occur with submerged-arc because the high heat input of the process assures sufficiently slow cooling.)
- With submerged-arc hardsurfacing, decrease the stepover (or increase the bead overlap) enough to remelt the center of the previous bead.
- When submerged-arc surfacing on roundabouts, set the correct electrode displacement from the center line.

AVOIDING DISTORTION

Distortion in welding is caused principally by the unbalanced stresses that result from expansion of the metal during heating and from contraction during cooling. These stresses and their effects are uneven both in strength and direction. They depend on many factors.

In many cases the amount of workpiece distortion resulting from hardsurfacing is negligible. Consequently, clamping the part in position for welding is the only precaution needed. In some cases the part is hardsurfaced oversize to allow for distortion. It is then machined or ground to size. This method is most often used on parts that must be machined or ground to finish after surfacing. Sometimes the part is allowed to distort and then straightened while still hot enough to bend without cracking.

Where distortion forces must be controlled, the following methods may be used:

- Preforming can be employed with flat pieces and with thin or simply shaped parts. Here the part is bent, formed, or clamped with the proper preset before welding. The distortion forces then pull the part back to its original shape.

- Stesses may be balanced in parts that cannot be straightened after welding (where the increased rigidity does not cause underbead cracking). In this method, two similar parts are welded or clamped back to back. Welding is then alternated back and forth from one part to the other. Or the parts may be welded or clamped to a strongback, fixture, or platen.

- Limit the temperature of the part, particularly when high rigidity could cause cracking. This can be done by a number of methods. One is to distribute the heat evenly by first welding one area, then welding a different area as the first cools. Another is to reduce the heat input by using a procedure with low current.

- Relieve stresses, especially with large parts, rigid shapes, shrink-fitted parts, and other highly stressed pieces. This can be done by peening each layer during cooling, a practice most effective with deposits designed for impact or abrasion and impact. Another way to relieve stress is to preheat the entire part slowly and uniformly.

- Use a cross-cracking deposit, namely those designed for resistance to severe abrasion. The cracks minimize distortion by relieving stresses.

HARDSURFACING WITH ALLOY FLUXES

As mentioned previously, alloy fluxes can be used with mild-steel or alloy electrodes when hardsurfacing with the submerged-arc process to give the desired alloy composition in the weld deposit. By combining various alloy fluxes with various types of electrodes and changing procedure variables to change the melt-off rates and penetration, a wide range of properties can be developed in the weld metal. The use of an alloy flux gives the most flexible and least expensive method of controlling weld chemistry. In many instances, a mild-steel electrode with an appropriate alloy flux will give the desired hardsurfacing properties at the minimal cost.

The alloy fluxes used are referred to as "agglomerated" alloy fluxes. Agglomeration is the process of mixing properly formulated, finely ground particles together with a binder and drying to give a homogeneous mass. The properly sized grains of flux produced from this mass have identical chemical constituency; the alloy particles cannot settle out or separate from the individual grains during shipping or use. Agglomerated alloy fluxes for hardsurfacing are produced in low-alloy, medium-alloy, medium-high alloy, and high-alloy types.

Since the alloy content in the weld deposit can be varied by changing the welding procedure, the latter can be critical in obtaining desired weld properties. Procedure guides are available from flux manufacturers. Once a satisfactory weld deposit has been obtained with a certain procedure, it is necessary to follow that procedure strictly in order to get consistent results. Accurate meters are necessary to measure voltage and current so the procedures can be reproduced consistently.

In general, when using these fluxes with mild-steel electrodes, carbon and alloy content of the deposit is increased as:

- The welding current is decreased.

- The arc voltage is increased.

- The carbon or alloying content of the base metal is increased.

- The electrode size is increased.

- Welding speed is decreased.

- The bead overlap is increased.

- The number of layers up to and including three is increased.

Low-Alloy Hardsurfacing Flux: With mild-steel electrode, a typical low-alloy type of hardsurfacing flux produces a machinable deposit of fair to good abrasion resistance and excellent impact resistance. The deposit, depending on the procedure, can be machined either with carbide or high-speed tools. It will produce a dense deposit less sensitive to cracking than a high-carbon deposit of the same abrasion resistance. A typical two-layer deposit made with this flux and 0.12%C mild-steel electrode will have 1.5-2.5 times the abrasion resistance of a machinable hot-rolled medium-carbon steel and up to twice the abrasion resistance of a deposit made with SAE 6150 wire and mild-steel flux.

The weld metal is typically an alloy of carbon, manganese, silicon, chromium, molybdenum and vanadium.

The flux and mild-steel wire may be used wherever a smooth, dense, crack-free, machinable deposit is required. Typical applications include rolls used in processing steel, kiln rollers, crane wheels, rams, and rollers and idlers on tread-type tractors.

Medium-Alloy Hardsurfacing Flux: The deposit made with mild-steel wire and medium-alloy flux is useful wherever smoothness and minimum porosity are the essential requirements in the particular alloy range. A minimum of two layers is recommended for good abrasion resistance. The deposit is a good selection for applications wherever metal-to-metal wear exists. A typical deposit is magnetic at room temperature, and, with recommended procedures, has a consistent hardness of 44-53 Rockwell C. It is heat-treatable with normal heat-treating practices.

For all practical purposes, the hardness, abrasion resistance, and deposit analysis change only very slightly after the third layer. A typical weld deposit is an alloy of carbon, manganese, silicon, chromium, molybdenum, and vanadium.

This flux and 0.12%C mild-steel electrode are recommended for:

1. Deposits to be forged, such as plow share blanks.
2. Metal-to-metal wear, such as tractor rollers, idlers, and extruder rams.
3. Smooth deposits without porosity and underbead cracking, such as steel-mill roughing rolls that do not require machining.

High-Alloy Hardsurfacing Flux: When used with a mild-steel electrode, a typical high-alloy flux produces a high-carbon, high-alloy weld deposit. It is recommended for fabrication and maintenance of wearing parts where the service involves severe abrasion under medium impact or high compression loads. It may be used for abrasive service at temperatures up to 1100°F.

The microstructure of the deposit is composed of complex chromium carbides and some secondary carbides in a chromium-iron matrix. The deposit will have a hardness of 53 to 61 Rockwell C, cannot be torch-cut or forged, and retains hardness and resistance to scaling at high temperatures. It will not respond to heat treatment; resists galling and seizing, but will cross-crack on cooling, thereby minimizing locked-up stresses and warpage. It will retain a high polished surface when subjected to metal friction or earth scouring. Hardness and abrasion resistance are unaffected by cooling rates normally encountered in welding.

High-alloy flux and mild-steel wire are used for hardsurfacing crusher rolls and rings of various types used in the coal, rock, cement, and clay industries; mixer parts used in the rubber industry; lining the inside of catalyst towers and piping; lining baffle plates in refinery equipment; lining the inside of ball mills; and in many similar applications in the extractive and processing industries.

TESTS FOR ABRASION AND IMPACT RESISTANCE

There are no standardized methods for testing abrasion or impact resistance because of the many different types of wear and service environments. There are, however, various tests that are commonly applied to give relative measures of these properties.

One type of test drags the specimen over a copper slab in a mixture of quartz sand and water; the abrasion factor is the loss of weight of the specimen compared to the loss of weight of a standard annealed SAE 1020 steel specimen. A material that loses the same weight as the SAE 1020 steel will have an abrasion factor of 1.00. The ideal material would not lose any weight and would have a factor of 0.00.

Another test presses the specimen against a notched rubber wheel, which is rotated in a slurry of sand and water; the loss of weight is taken as the abrasion value.

A preferred method is the use of a grinding wheel of aluminum oxide as the abradant. The amount of wheel that is ground away to remove a standard weight of the hardsurfacing material is taken as the abrasion index. This test is excellent for evaluating the cutting ability of hardsurfacing materials used to dig earth. The loss of weight of the specimen when run against the wheel at standard conditions is taken as the abrasion value for the material when it is to be used for wear-resistant purposes. It is important to have both values, because the material that shows the least loss of weight may not be the one that cuts the best on, for example, a rotary well-drilling bit.

The grinding wheel test is preferred to the wet-sand test because the wet-sand results do not show as much difference in hardsurfacing materials as is usually found in the field. The grinding wheel method gives a very large difference in weight loss: 0.02 gram loss for a hard grade of sintered tungsten carbide and about 10.0 grams loss for mild steel — a ratio of 1 to 500.

Abrasion values are not directly applicable to field service. Some of the variables that can change the order of abrasion resistance of hardsurfacing are temperature, size, properties of the abradant, and the amount of impact.

Impact tests are commonly made on commercial hardsurfacing materials by pounding weld deposits against each other and against standards. The materials are then arranged according to their resistance to cracking, chipping, or spalling.

Welding The High-Strength Steels; Preheating and Post Heating

The high-strength low-alloy and the quenched and tempered steels require special considerations when weld joining, often including preheating to prevent cracks and maintain desired mechanical properties, and postheating for stress relief. These steels, their weldability, and the special treatments required will be discussed in a generalized way in this chapter. Since many of the high-strength alloy steels are known and sold under trade names, the manufacturer's literature on their properties, treatment, and welding should be referred to for more specific and detailed information.

HIGH-STRENGTH LOW-ALLOY STRUCTURAL STEELS

Higher mechanical properties and, usually, better corrosion resistance than the structural carbon steels are characteristics of the high-strength low-alloy (HSLA) steels. These improved properties are achieved by additions of small amounts of alloying elements. Some of the HSLA types are carbon-manganese steels; other contain different alloy additions, governed by requirements for weldability, formability, toughness, or economy. Strength of these steels is between those of structural carbon steels and the high-strength quenched and tempered steels.

High-strength low-alloy steels are usually used in the as-rolled condition, although some are available that require heat treatment after fabrication. These steels are produced to specific mechanical-property requirements rather than to chemical compositions. Minimum mechanical properties available in the as-rolled condition vary among the grades and, within most grades, with thickness. Ranges of properties available in this group of steels are:

1. Minimum yield point from 42,000 to 70,000 psi.

2. Minimum tensile strength from 60,000 to 85,000 psi.

3. Resistance to corrosion, classed as: equal to that of carbon steels, twice that of carbon steels, or four to six times that of carbon steels.

The HSLA steels are available in most commercial wrought forms and are used extensively in products and structures that require higher strength-to-weight ratios than the carbon structural steels offer. Typical applications are supports and panels for truck bodies, railway cars, mobile homes, and other transportation equipment; components for tractors, threshers, fertilizer spreaders, and other agricultural machinery; materials-handling and storage equipment; and buildings, bridge decks, and similar structures.

The high-strength low-alloy steels should not be confused with the high-strength quenched and tempered alloy steels. Both groups are sold primarily on a trade name basis, and they frequently share the same trade name, with different letters or numbers being used to identify each. The quenched and tempered steels are full-alloy steels that are heat-treated at the mill to develop optimum properties. They are generally martensitic in structure, whereas the HSLA steels are mainly ferritic steels; this is the clue to the metallurgical and fabricating differences between the two types. In the as-rolled condition, ferritic steels are composed of relatively soft, ductile constituents; martensitic steels have hard, brittle constituents that require heat treatment to produce their high-strength properties.

Strength in the HSLA steels is achieved instead by relatively small amounts of alloying elements dissolved in a ferritic structure. Carbon content rarely exceeds 0.28% and is usually between 0.15 and 0.22%. Manganese content ranges from 0.85 to 1.60%, depending on grade, and other alloy additions — chromium, nickel, silicon, phosphorus, copper, vanadium, columbium, and nitrogen — are used in amounts less than one percent. Welding, forming, and machining characteristics of most grades do not differ markedly from those of the low-carbon steels.

To be weldable, the high-strength steels must have enough ductility to avoid cracking from the rapid cooling inherent in welding processes. Weldable HSLA steels must be sufficiently low in carbon, manganese, and all "deep-hardening" elements to ensure that appreciable amounts of martensite are not formed upon rapid cooling. Superior strength is provided by solution of the alloying elements in the ferrite of the as-rolled steel. Corrosion resistance is also increased in certain of the HSLA steels by the alloying additions.

Addition of a minimum of 0.20% copper usually produces steels with about twice the atmospheric corrosion resistance of structural carbon steels. Steels with four to six times the atmospheric corrosion resistance of structural carbon steels are obtained in many ways, but, typically, with additions of nickel and/or chromium, often with more than 0.10% phosphorus. These alloys are usually used in addition to the copper.

Standard specifications or recommended practices covering the major types of HSLA steels are available from the American Society for Testing Materials, the Society of Automotive Engineers, and the Department of Defense. These standards are summarized in Table 20-1.

Other standardizing organizations such as the American Institute of Steel Construction, The American Association of Railroads, and the Department of Transportation have established specifications or practices for the use of HSLA steels in certain industries and applications.

ASTM SPECIFICATIONS

ASTM's specifications are oriented principally to mill form and mechanical properties; SAE's recommended practices include, in addition, information on fabrication characteristics — toughness, weldability, and formability.

ASTM A242 covers HSLA structural steel shapes, plates, and bars for welded, riveted, or bolted construction. Maximum carbon content of these steels is 0.24%; typical content is from 0.09 to 0.17%. Materials produced to this specification are intended primarily for structural members where light weight and durability are important.

Some producers can supply copper-bearing steels (0.20% minimum copper) with about twice the atmospheric corrosion resistance of carbon steels. Steels meeting the general requirements of ASTM A242 but modified to give four times the atmospheric corrosion resistance of structural steels are also available. These latter grades — sometimes called "weathering steels" — are used for architectural and other structural purposes where it is desirable to avoid painting for either esthetic or economic reasons.

Welding characteristics vary according to the type of steel; producers can recommend the most

weldable material and offer welding advice if the conditions under which the welding will be done are known.

ASTM A440 covers high-strength intermediate-manganese copper-bearing HSLA steels used principally for riveted or bolted structures. These steels are not generally recommended for welding because of their relatively high carbon and manganese contents. ASTM A440 and its companion,

TABLE 20-1. Specifications for High-Strength Low-Alloy Steels

Specification or Practice	Coverage
ASTM	
A-242	42,000 to 50,000-psi yield-point steels with atmospheric corrosion resistance equal to twice (with copper) or four or more times that of structural carbon steels. The more corrosion-resistant grades are used as "weathering steels."
A-374	Cold-rolled sheets and strip with 45,000-psi yield point; similar in many respects to A-242.
A-375	Hot-rolled sheets and strip with 50,000-psi yield point; similar in many respects to A-242.
A-440	Intermediate-manganese steels with 42,000 to 50,000-psi yield points. Copper additions provide atmospheric corrosion resistance double that of carbon steel. Good abrasion resistance; only fair weldability. Used primarily for riveted or bolted products.
A-441	Manganese-vanadium steels with 40,000 to 50,000-psi yield points. Copper additions provide atmospheric corrosion resistance double that of carbon steel. Lower manganese and carbon; therefore, improved weldability over A-440 steels.
A-572	Columbium-vanadium-nitrogen grades with six yield points from 42,000 to 65,000 psi. Grades with copper additions for improved atmospheric corrosion resistance are available. Modifications high in columbium may have excellent low-temperature notch toughness when produced to fine-grain practice (by roller quenching or normalizing).
A-588	Similar in most respects to A-242 steels, except that a 50,000-psi yield-point minimum is provided up to 4 in. thick and material up to 8 in. thick and is covered in the specification. Has four times the atmospheric corrosion resistance of carbon steel.
SAE (Recommended Practice — not a specification)	
J410b	Covers all major HSLA types, with yield strengths from 42,000 to 70,000 psi. Unlike ASTM, SAE gives greater attention to formability, toughness, and weldability. However, ASTM specs give wider coverage of mill forms and larger section thicknesses.
DoD	
Mil-S-7809A (May 3, 1963)	Covers HSLA steels in bars, shapes, sheets, strip, and plates.
Mil-S-13281B (Oct. 10, 1966)	Covers carbon, alloy, and HSLA steels for welded structures.

Source: "High-Strength Low-Alloy Steels", *Machine Design*, Feb. 17, 1972.

A441, have the same minimum mechanical properties as A242.

ASTM A440 steels have about twice the atmospheric corrosion resistance of structural carbon steel and very good abrasion resistance. The high manganese content (typically, about 1.45%) tends to cause weld metal to air harden — a condition that may produce high stresses and cracks in the weld. If these steels must be welded, careful preheating (higher than for A441) is necessary.

ASTM A441 covers the intermediate-manganese HSLA steels that are readily weldable with proper procedures. The specification calls for additions of vanadium and a lower manganese content (1.25% maximum) than ASTM A440. Minimum mechanical properties are the same as A242 and A440 steels, except that plates and bars from 4 to 8-in. thick are covered in A441.

Atmospheric corrosion resistance of this steel is approximately twice that of structural carbon steel. Another property of ASTM A441 steel is its superior toughness at low temperatures. Only shapes, plates, and bars are covered by the specification, but weldable sheets and strip can be supplied by some producers with approximately the same minimum mechanical properties.

ASTM A572 includes six grades of high-strength low-alloy structural steels in shapes, plates, and bars. These steels offer a choice of strength levels ranging from 42,000 to 65,000-psi yields. Proprietary HSLA steels of this type with 70,000 and 75,000-psi yield points are also available. Increasing care is required for welding these steels as strength level increases.

A572 steels are distinguished from other HSLA steels by their columbium, vanadium, and nitrogen content. Copper additions above a minimum of 0.20% may be specified for atmospheric corrosion resistance about double that of structural carbon steels.

A supplementary requirement is included in the specification that permits designating the specific alloying elements required in the steel. Examples are the Type 1 designation, for columbium; Type 2, for vanadium; Type 3, for columbium and vanadium; and Type 4, for vanadium and nitrogen. Specific grade designations must accompany this type of requirement.

ASTM A588 provides for a steel similar in most respects to A242 weathering steel, except that the 50,000-psi yield point is available in thicknesses to at least 4 in.

SAE SPECIFICATIONS

High-strength low-alloy steels are also covered in the SAE Recommended Practice J410b. This is not a standard. Rather, it is a recommended practice — a guide or memorandum from SAE to its members to help standardize their engineering practices. SAE J410b was written long before most of the HSLA steels had ASTM specifications. Its content is more general than the ASTM documents, and its intent is to guide material selection in the light of fabrication requirements. Now that ASTM has defined almost all of the HSLA steels in standard specifications, SAE J410b is seldom used as a material specification. But the SAE document is still valuable as a general guide to using the HSLA steels.

The SAE document addresses itself primarily to the specific needs of fabricators of automobiles, trucks, trailers, agricultural equipment, and aircraft. This is why SAE J410b does not cover the thicker plates and heavier structural shapes. Minimum mechanical properties of commonly used steels covered by SAE J410b are listed in Table 20-2.

For mechanical-property data on materials thicker than those listed in the table, suppliers should be consulted. SAE J410b high-strength low-alloy steels may be specified as annealed, normalized, or otherwise specially prepared for forming. When this is done, mechanical properties are agreed upon between supplier and purchaser.

Grade 945A has excellent arc and resistance-welding characteristics and the best formability, weldability, and low-temperature notch toughness. It is available in sheets, strip, and light plate.

Grade 945C is a carbon-manganese steel with

TABLE 20-2. Minimum Mechanical Properties for SAE J410b HSLA Steels

Grade, Form, and Thickness	Tensile Strength (1000 psi)	Yield Strength 0.2% Offset (1000 psi)	Elongation (%)	
			2 in.	8 in.
945 A, C				
Sheet, strip	60	45	22	. . .
Plate, bar				
To 1/2 in.	65	45	22	18
1/2 to 1-1/2 in.	62	42	24	19
1-1/2 to 3 in.	62	40	24	19
950 A, B, C, D				
Sheet, strip	70	50	22	. . .
Plate, bar				
To 1/2 in.	70	50	22	18
1/2 to 1-1/2 in.	67	45	24	19
1-1/2 in. to 3 in.	63	42	24	19
945X*	60	45	22	18
950X*	65	50	22	18
955X*	70	55	20	17
960X*	75	60	18	16
965X+	80	65	16	15
970X+	85	70	14	12

* To 3/8 in. thick.   From Machine Design,
+ To 3/4 in. thick.   Feb. 17, 1972

satisfactory arc-welding properties if proper procedures are used to prevent hardening of the weld metal. Moderate preheat is usually required, especially for thick sections. It is similar to Grade 950C, but has lower carbon and manganese content to improve arc-welding characteristics, formability, and low-temperature notch toughness, at some sacrifice in strength.

Grade 945X is a columbium or vanadium-treated carbon-manganese steel similar to 945C except for improved toughness and weldability.

Grade 950A has good weldability, low-temperature notch toughness, and formability. It is normally available only in sheet, strip, and light plate.

Grade 950B has satisfactory arc-welding properties and fairly good low-temperature notch toughness and formability.

Grade 950C is a carbon-manganese steel that can be arc welded if the cooling rate is controlled, but is unsuitable for resistance welding. Formability and toughness are fair.

Grade 950D has good weldability and fairly good formability. Its phosphorus content reduces its low-temperature properties.

Grade 950X is a columbium or vanadium-treated carbon-manganese steel similar to 950C except for somewhat improved welding and forming properties.

Several other grades are also covered by SAE J410b — higher-strength steels that have reduced formability and weldability.

Modifications of standard SAE-grade designations are also available. For example, fully killed steels made to fine-grain practice are indicated by the suffix "K." Thus, 945AK is a fully killed, fine-grain, HSLA steel with maximum ladle analysis of 0.15% carbon and a yield strength of about 45,000 psi. All grades made to K practice may not be available from all suppliers. This fine-grain practice is usually specified when low-temperature notch toughness is important.

Steels designated by the suffix "X" contain strengthening elements, such as columbium or vanadium (with or without nitrogen) added singly or in combination. These are usually made semi-killed. However, killed steel may be specified by indicating both suffixes, such as SAE 950XK.

Available HSLA-steel grades often have characteristics in excess of the specification minimums. Literature from producer companies contains information on physical and mechanical property ranges and suggested fabricating and welding practices.

HIGH-YIELD-STRENGTH QUENCHED AND TEMPERED ALLOY STEELS

The high-yield-strength quenched and tempered construction steels are full-alloy steels that are treated at the steel mill to develop optimum properties. Unlike conventional alloy steels, these grades do not require additional heat treatment by the fabricator except, in some cases, for a stress relief.

These steels are generally low-carbon grades (upper carbon limit of about 0.20%) that have minimum yield strengths from 80,000 to 125,000 psi.

Some high-yield-strength grades are also available in abrasion-resistant modifications (AR steels), produced to a high hardness. Although these steels can have yield strengths to 173,000 psi, hardness (up to 400 Bhn) rather than strength is their key characteristic.

The high-yield-strength quenched and tempered alloy steels are used in such widely varying applications as hoist and crane components; end, side, and bottom plates for ore and waste-haulage cars, hopper cars, and gondolas; pressure hulls for submarines; and components for dust-collecting equipment. The AR (abrasion-resistant) modifications are used in applications requiring maximum resistance to abrasive materials — in chutes, hoppers, and dump-truck beds, for example. In such uses, strength properties are secondary and are not usually specified.

Good toughness can be combined with abrasion resistance in these steels, for use in buckets, cutter bars, scraper blades, and impact plates. However, the most abrasion-resistant grades sacrifice impact strength to gain maximum wear resistance.

HY Steels: An important group of high-yield-strength quenched and tempered steels is the HY steels. The most common and most available of these is HY80, which has a minimum yield strength of 80,000 psi. Higher-strength grades are HY100, HY130, HY150, and HY180. Availability of HY steels with yield strengths above 100,000 psi was limited at the time of publication, but considerable development work was being done on these materials and availability was increasing.

HY80 is commonly available in plate form. However, it can also be obtained in beams, channels, angles, and tubing. Strength and toughness of HY80 steel and its ability to be welded (under carefully controlled conditions) qualify it for use in critical applications such as pressure hulls for submarines and deep-submergence research and rescue vessels. The higher-strength HY steels will probably also qualify for the same types of applications after sufficient testing has been done to determine their reliability in welded structures.

Mechanical properties of these steels are influenced by section size. Carbon content is the principal factor that determines maximum attainable strength. Most alloying elements make a small contribution to strength, but their dominant effect is on hardenability — which determines the maximum thickness or depth of steel that can be fully hardened on quenching.

HY80 is normally supplied to the toughness requirements of MIL-S-16216. In plate 1/2 to 1-1/2-in. thick, 50 ft.-lb. of impact energy absorption is required at minus 120°F with a longitudinal Charpy V-notch specimen.

A typical value of the ductile-to-brittle transition temperature of a 100,000-psi steel in 1/2-in. plate is minus 180°F, as determined with both longitudinal and transverse Charpy V-notch specimens.

Many of the high-yield-strength steels are available in three or four strength or hardness levels. The different levels are achieved by variations in carbon and alloy content, tempering temperature, and tempering time.

In general, the 100,000-psi steels have fatigue strengths in the 50,000 to 70,000-psi range in rotating-beam tests. Higher-strength grades have higher endurance limits — about 60% of their tensile strength.

The compressive yield strength of 100,000-psi steels is usually about the same as tensile yield strength. Shear strength generally ranges from about 85 to 100% of the tensile yield strength.

ASTM Specifications: Two plate specifications, ASTM A-514 for welded structures and A517 for boilers and other pressure vessels, allow for the effect of section size on yield strength, tensile strength, and ductility. ASTM A514 requires a minimum yield strength of 100,000 psi for material up to 2-1/2-in. thick, and 90,000 psi for material from 2-1/2 to 4-in. thick. ASTM A517 requires uniform yield strengths of 100,000 psi for all material up to 3/4-in. thick. Representative trade names of the A514 and A517 steels are given in Table 20-3.

Weldability of the Q and T Steels: Most high-yield-strength quenched and tempered alloy steels can be welded without preheat or postheat. If suppliers' recommendations are followed for controlling welding procedures, 100% joint efficiency can be expected in the as-welded condition for the 90,000 and 100,000 psi yield-strength grades.

If the heat-affected zone cools too slowly, the beneficial effects of the original heat treatment (particularly notch toughness) are destroyed. This can be caused by excessive preheat temperature, interpass temperature, or heat input. On the other hand, if the heat-affected zone cools too rapidly, it can become hard and brittle and may crack. This is caused by insufficient preheat or interpass temperature or insufficient heat input during welding. Producers' recommendations should be followed closely.

The quenched and tempered steels can be welded by the shielded metal-arc, submerged-arc and gas-shielded-arc processes. Weld cooling rates for these processes are relatively rapid, and mechanical properties of the heat-affected zones approach those of the steel in the quenched condition. Reheat-treatment, such as quenching and tempering after welding, is not recommended.

Because of the desirability of relatively rapid cooling after welding, thin sections of these materials can usually be welded without preheating. When preheating is required, both maximum and minimum temperatures are important. If the sections to be welded are warm as a result of preheating and heat input from previous welding passes, it may be necessary to reduce current or increase arc travel speed for subsequent passes, or to wait until the metal cools somewhat. Interpass temperature is just as important as preheat temperature and should be controlled with the same care.

In the ASTM specifications A514 and A517 there are several grades of quenched and tempered constructional steels listed. Welding procedures for all of these steels are similar but no one procedure is right for all grades. Welding procedures are available from the steel manufacturers. When in doubt, consult the steel manufacturer.

The following is a general shielded metal-arc procedure for one of the popular grades of quenched and tempered constructional steels and can be used as a *guide* for all grades or other welding

TABLE 20-3. Representative ASTM A514/517 Steels

Producer	Trade Name
Armco Steel Corp.	SSS-100 SSS-100A SSS-100B
Bethlehem Steel Corp.	RQ-100A, RQ-100 RQ-100B
Great Lakes Steel Corp. and Phoenix Steel Corp.*	N-A-XTRA 100 N-A-XTRA 110
Jones & Laughlin Steel Corp.	Jalloy-S-100 Jalloy-S-110
United States Steel Corp. and Lukens Steel Corp.*	T-1 T-1 Type A T-1 Type B

* Licensee

processes:

Use only low-hydrogen-type electrodes, and usually the electrode specified for A514 and A517 steels is E11018. Under some conditions a lower tensile strength electrode may be used. Make sure electrodes are dry. Under normal conditions of humidity, electrodes should be returned to the drying ovens after an exposure of four hours maximum. If the humidity is high, reduce the exposure time. Electrodes are shipped in hermetically sealed containers and the contents of any damaged container should be redried before using.

Clean the joint thoroughly. Remove all rust and scale preferably by grinding. If the base metal has been exposed to moisture, preheat to drive off the moisture. On thin sections, allow the plate to cool, if necessary, before starting to weld.

The amount of preheat and the amount of welding heat put into the weld must be kept within definite boundaries during the actual welding. Usually preheating is not necessary or desirable on thin sections but in order to avoid cracks preheating is necessary if:

The joints are highly restrained.

The structure is very rigid.

The weld joint is on thick sections.

Whether or not the base metal is preheated, it is necessary to approximate the heat input before starting to weld. The heat input in watt-seconds (joules) per linear inch of weld is:

$$\text{Heat Input} = \frac{I \times E \times 60}{V}$$

where I is the arc amperes, E is the arc volts, and V is the welding speed in in./min. Calculation by this formula is only approximate because the heat losses can be large. Also, there are many variables that affect the heat distribution and the maximum temperature of the base metal at the joint but the formula is sufficiently accurate to predict the maximum allowable heat input for a given set of conditions.

In industry, the term "heat unit" is used and is equal to the watt-seconds per linear inch of weld divided by 1000.*

Maximum suggested heat units input for USS T-1 steel per linear inch of weld is shown in the table, right-hand column above. (See Preheating Recommendations later in this chapter.)

Before making a production weld it is recommended to set up a tentative procedure and make a test weld. The tentative procedure includes the pre-

* A calculator is available from the Unites States Steel Corporation for quickly determining heat units. Also available are tables for maximum heat units when welding T-1, T-1 Type A, and T-1 Type B.

Suggested Maximum Heat Units[†]

Preheat and Interpass Temperature	Plate Thickness							
	3/16"	1/4"	1/2"	3/4"	1"	1-1/4"	1-1/2"	2"
70°F	27	36	70	121	any	any	any	any
200°F	21	29	56	99	173	any	any	any
300°F	17	24	47	82	126	175	any	any
350°F	15	21.5	43.5	73.5	109.5	151	any	any
400°F	13	19	40	65	93	127	165	any

† From the "*Welding Heat Input Calculator*" by the United States Steel Corporation.

heat, if any, interpass temperature, welding current, voltage, and welding speed. It is important to keep the welding current, speed and interpass temperature under close control.

The following are some general rules to follow to promote good weld quality.

Always use stringer beads, never wide weave beads.

Clean thoroughly between passes.

Back-gouge with arc gouging and remove the scale by grinding. Do not use oxyacetylene to back-gouge.

Usually the electrodes used are the E11018 type but lower strength electrodes may be specified where the stress does not require the high yield strength of E11018. A good example is the lower stress in web-to-flange fillet welds. However, if lower strength electrodes are used the same limitations apply as to heat input and interpass temperature.

LOW-ALLOY STEELS

Small amounts of alloying elements such as nickel, chromium, and molybdenum can be added to steels to increase strength, hardness, or toughness, or to improve resistance to heat, corrosion, or other environmental factors. These improvements are sometimes gained with little effect on weldability or other fabricability characteristics. Generally, however, welding of low-alloy steels requires more careful control of procedures and selection of electrodes than welding of the carbon steels.

Nickel Steels

A low nickel addition (2 to 5%) greatly increases strength and hardenability and improves the corrosion resistance of a steel without a proportional reduction in ductility or a significant effect on weldability. The compositions of various thicknesses of nickel-steel plate (ASTM A-203), used principally for pressure vessels, are listed in Table 20-4.

Straight nickel steels are used mainly for low-

**TABLE 20-4. Composition of ASTM A-203-69
Nickel-Steel Plate for Pressure Vessels**

Element and Plate Thickness	Composition (%)			
	Grade			
	A*	B*	D†	E†
Carbon, max				
To 2 in.	0.17	0.21	0.17	0.20
2 to 4 in.	0.20	0.24	0.20	0.23
4 to 6 in.	0.23	0.25	. . .	. . .
Manganese, max				
To 2 in.	0.70	0.70	0.70	0.70
2 to 4 in.	0.80	0.80	0.80	0.80
4 to 6 in.	0.80	0.80	. . .	. . .
Phosphorus, max	0.035	0.035	0.035	0.035
Sulfur, max	0.04	0.04	0.04	0.04
Silicon (ladle analysis)	0.15-0.30	0.15-0.30	0.15-0.30	0.15-0.30
Nickel (ladle analysis)	2.10-2.50	2.10-2.50	3.25-3.75	3.25-3.75

*   Covers plate to 6-in. thick.
†   Covers plate to 4-in. thick.

temperature pressure vessels. The nickel content significantly improves toughness and impact strength at subzero temperatures. Nickel is also very effective in improving the hardenability of steels; heat treatment is easy because nickel lowers the critical cooling rate necessary to produce hardening on quenching.

A nickel steel containing 0.24% carbon and 2.7% nickel can have a tensile strength (normalized and drawn) of over 85,000 psi; an unalloyed steel would require a carbon content of over 0.45% to be that strong. Notch toughness of a 3-1/2% nickel steel, with a tinsile strength of 70,000 to 85,000 psi, would be 15 ft.-lb. at minus 150°F (Charpy keyhole test), whereas a carbon steel of that strength would have a notch toughness of 15 ft.-lb down to only minus 50°F.

Nickel increases hardenability for a given carbon content. For best weldability and minimum cracking tendency, carbon content should, of course, be low — no more than 0.18% if extensive welding is to be done without preheat.

Chromium Steels

In the low-alloy steels, chromium increases tensile strength, hardenability and, to some extent, atmospheric corrosion resistance. Chromium steels with less than 0.18% carbon are readily weldable, using proper precautions against cracking. The combination of chromium and higher carbon increases hardenability and requires preheating and sometimes postheating to prevent brittle weld deposits. Production welding is not recommended for chromium steels containing more than 0.30% carbon.

Nickel-Chromium Steels

The nickel-chromium steels of the AISI series are no longer standard alloys but occasionally there is a need to weld these alloys, especially in maintenance work.

The addition of chromium is intended to increase hardenability and response to heat treatment for a given carbon content over that of the straight nickel low-alloy steels. Also a small amount of several alloying elements judiciously chosen may give a greater range of hardenability plus toughness than a larger or more costly amount of a single alloying element.

Chromium is a potent hardening agent and it is necessary to keep the carbon content low for weldability. Thin sections of the lowest carbon-content type can usually be welded without preheat but the higher carbon grades require preheat and subsequent stress relief or annealing.

The lower carbon grades of the nickel-chromium steels can be welded with electrodes of the EXX15-16-18 classes and in the as-welded condition the weld properties will match the base metal. However, if the weldment must be heat treated after welding, special low-hydrogen electrodes are required. These electrodes must deposit weld metal that will respond to the same heat treatment as the base metal and match base-metal properties.

The higher carbon alloys (above .40%) are not readily welded but, if necessary, a weld can usually be made with stainless E309 (second choice E310) electrodes. The weld will usually be tough and ductile but the fusion zone may be brittle. The fact that the weld is ductile allows it to give a little without putting too much bending in the brittle zone. Preheat is advised.

Molybdenum Steels

Molybdenum increases the hardenability and high-temperature strength of low-alloy steels. The low-alloy molybdenum steels are of three general types: carbon-molybdenum (AISI 4000 series), chromium-molybdenum (4100 series), and nickel-molybdenum (4300, 4600, 4700, and 4800 series).

A common use of carbon-moly and chrome-moly steels is in high-pressure piping used at high temperatures. These steels are usually purchased to an ASTM specification. Another typical use of the chrome-moly alloys — usually in the form of tubing — is in highly stressed aircraft parts. Weldability of these thin-secion members is good because of the low carbon content. Low-carbon grades of these steels (below 0.18%) can usually be welded without preheat. The higher-carbon nickel and chromium grades of molybdenum steels are air-hardening.

The low-carbon grades (below .18%) of carbon-moly steel can be welded much the same as mild steel. E7010-A1, E7018, and E7027-A1 electrodes will give tensile strengths in the same range as plate strength in the as-welded condition. The above electrodes with .5% moly will come close to approximating plate properties and analysis where subsequent heat treatment is required.

When carbon content of the carbon-moly alloys is low (approximately .15%), these steels are readily weldable. In pressure vessels, this low-carbon content is usually used, but in piping the carbon may be somewhat higher. Where carbon is above .18% preheating is generally required.

Welding procedure is essentially the same as for mild steel. In the case of piping, a back-up ring is recommended generally to keep the inside of the pipe clean. The ring if of proper design causes only slight obstruction, which is not objectionable in most cases.

Where backing ring is not used, an experienced weldor can put in a first pass with a small reinforcement in the inside. It is important that this first pass completely penetrate the joint so that no notch is left at the root.

Stress relieving is generally specified when the thickness of the metal is greater than 3/8". Temperatures of 1200 — 1250°F are used, with usual procedure as to time of heating (one hour per inch of thickness) and length of pipe heated (6 times thickness on each side of weld).

The cooling rate is from 200 — 250°F per hour down to 150 — 200°F, in which case cooling may be done in still air.

For the welding of the steels mentioned herein, the use of E7010-A1 electrode is recommended for ease of welding in out-of-position work. The preheat and postheat treatment is also required when E7010-A1 electrodes are used. Where the work can be positioned for downhand welding or where large welds are required in any position, the low-hydrogen electrodes can be used to advantage, as they will reduce the preheat temperatures required.

In applications where tensile strength of weld need not be as high as the base metal but where other physical characteristics of the weld should be comparable to the base metal, the regular type of electrode, as used for welding mild steel, can be employed with very satisfactory results. For joining work of this type, E6010 electrodes are recommended.

On light chrome-moly tubing, E6013 electrodes designed especially for aircraft work are often used. These mild-steel electrodes usually pick up enough alloy from the base metal to give the required tensile strength in the as-welded condition. When welded on AISI 4130, their normal 70,000 to 80,000-psi tensile strength is increased by pick-up of alloy and carbon to a satisfactory approximation of the physical properties of AISI 4130. The additional thickness of weld due to the usual build-up on light-guage work makes the welded joint stronger than the base metal.

On the higher-carbon and alloy grades where heat-treated welds with properties similar to plate properties are necessary, special electrodes can be used that will deposit the proper analysis. A low-hydrogen-type electrode is used to reduce the tendency for cracking that is prevalent with these steels. Preheat and postheat treatment usually will be required.

On the grades over .40% carbon where production welding is not recommended, it is possible to make a weld with E309-type stainless electrode or E310 as a second choice. The weld will be fairly ductile if the proper low-penetrating procedure is used; however, the fusion zone may be very brittle depending upon the air-hardenability of the alloy. Preheating and slow cooling will tend to reduce this hardness in the fusion zone.

Where molybdenum is added to base metals to increase the resistance to creep at elevated temperatures, the electrode deposit must have a similar amount of molybdenum.

ALLOY STEEL ELECTRODES

Alloy content of the weld deposit is not critically important in welding the common grades of mild steel. As discussed earlier, electrode selection for these steels is based largely on whether maximum deposition rates or rapid-freeze characteristics are preferred. But for alloy steels — chosen specifically for their high mechanical properties, superior corrosion resistance, or ability to withstand high temperatures — the electrode must be carefully selected so that it provides the specific chemical composition needed to maintain the desired properties of the base metal in the weld deposit.

There are many types of electrodes available for welding low-alloy steels. These types are described completely in AWS A5.5, and a brief summary of typical electrode characteristics and applications is presented in the following paragraphs. The chemical requirements of deposited weld metal are given in Table 5-5. Typical mechanical properties of some of the weld deposits are given in Table 20-5. A guide to the selection of electrodes for welding steels of specific trade names is presented in Table 20-6.

Except for electrodes for welding high-strength line pipe, most electrodes for welding low-alloy steel have low-hydrogen, fill-freeze characteristics similar to those of E7018 and are suitable for all-position fabrication and repair welding. Even though these electrodes are suitable for all-position welding, their operating characteristics are quite different from those of fast-freeze electrodes for the common steels. Weld metal from alloy-steel electrodes freezes rapidly even though the slag remains relatively fluid. Deposition rate is high, partially because the coverings contain iron powder.

Beads are flat or slightly convex and have distinct ripples with little spatter. The moderately heavy slag is easy to remove.

Some of the commonly used low-alloy high-strength electrodes include:

E8018-B2: This electrode produces a 1.25%-chromium, 0.5%-molybdenum deposit, commonly required for high-temperature, high-pressure piping. It usually meets requirements of E9018-G for some high-strength (90,000-psi tensile) steels.

E8018-C3: The electrode conforms to MIL-8018-C3 and produces a weld having a tensile strength of 80,000 psi, suitable for general-purpose welding on many high-strength alloys. This type also provides a 1%-nickel deposit for welding alloys that are to be used at low temperatures and which require good notch toughness down to −60°F. The electrode is also used for fillet welds on high-strength (110,000-psi tensile) quenched and tempered steels, such as ASTM A514 and A517.

E8018-C1: The type produces a 2.25%-nickel deposit with notch toughness of 50 ft.-lb. at −75°F and is, thus, commonly required for welding low-temperature alloys. Such alloys are frequently used to fabricate storage, piping, and transportation equipment for liquid ammonia, propane, and other gases. This group of electrodes is also recommended for the best color match on unpainted corrosion-resistant ASTM A242 steels. (Cor-Ten, Mayari-R, and others).

E11018-M: The electrode conforms to MIL-11018-M and produces a 110,000-psi tensile strength needed for full-strength welds on quenched and tempered steels, ASTM A514 and A517 (T-1, SSS-100, HY-80, and others).

PREHEATING THE WELDMENT

In some welding operations, it is necessary to apply heat to the assembly before starting the welding. In others, a postheat — or application of heat after welding — is needed to relieve the internal stresses that have been developed. With certain weldments, heat may also be applied between welding passes to maintain a required temperature.

TABLE 20-5. Typical Mechanical Properties of AWS A5.5-69 Weld Metal

	E7010-A1	E8018-B2	E8018-C3	E8018-C1	E11018-M
As-Welded					
Tensile Strength (psi)	75,000	102,000	86,000	87,000	112,000
Yield Strength (psi)	68,000	90,000	78,000	74,000	102,000
Elongation (% in 2 in.)	24	21	25	22	21
Charpy V Notch (ft-lb)	68 at 70°F	65 at 70°F	48 at −20°F	61 at −75°F	35 at −60°F
Stress Relieved 1150°F					
Tensile Strength (psi)	72,000	93,000 83,000*	81,000	84,000	112,000+
Yield Strength (psi)	60,000	81,000 70,000*	70,000	71,000	96,000+
Elongation (% of 2 in.)	29	20 22*	26	24	22+
Charpy V Notch (ft-lb)	68 at 70°F	65 at 70°F 65 at 70°F*	88 at −20°F	40 at −75°F	35 at −60°F+

* Stress relieved at 1275°F
+ Stress relieved at 1025°F

**TABLE 20-6. Recommended Electrodes for Trade-Name Steels
(See Note 2.)**

Steel Producer	Steel Trade Name		Recommended Electrodes
Alan Wood Steel Company	AWX-42, 45	V45	Note 1
	V50, 55	AWX-50, 55	E7018 or E7028
	AW-Ten	AW Dynalloy 50	
	AW-441, 440	Cor-Ten A, B	
	V60, 65	Cor-Ten C	E8018-C3
Armco Steel Corporation	C-42, 45		Note 1
	C-50, 55	Armco LTM	E7018 or E7028
	High-Strength B, D		
	C-60, 65	High-Strength A	E8018-C3
	V-60, 65		
	Lo-Temp	Super Lo-Temp	E8018-C1
	Armco LTM, VNT		
	C-70		E8018-B2
	SSS-100, 100A, 100B		E11018-M
	HY80, HY100	QTC	
Bethlehem Steel Corporation	V42, 45, 50, 55		E7018 or E7028
	RQC-60N	Mn-V A441	
	Mayari R, R-50 Med. Mn		
	V60, 65	Mayari R-60	E8018-C3
	RQC-60 Q & T		E8010-C1
	RQC80, 90	RQ100, 100A, 100B	E11018-M
Inland Steel Company	INX-42, 45		Note 1
	INX-50, 55	Cor-Ten A, B	Note 7 E7018 or E7028
	Hi-Man,		
	Tri-Steel		
	INX-60, 65	Cor-Ten C	E8018-C3
	Hi-Steel		
	INX-70		E8018-B2
Jones & Laughlin Steel Corporation	JLX-42, 50		Note 1
	JLX-50, 55	50CC, 55CC	E7018 or E7028
	Jalten 1, 3R, 3S		
	Cor-TenA	Ni-Cu-Ti	
	JLX-60, 65, 60CC, 65CC		E8018-C3
	JLX-70, 70CC		E8018-B2
	Jalloy S-90, 100		E11018-M
	VAN-80		
Kaiser Steel Corporation	Kaisaloy 42-CV, 45-CV		Note 1
	Kaisaloy 50-CV, 55-CV,		E7018 or E7028
	Kaisaloy 45FG, 50CR, 50MM, 50MV		
	Kaisaloy 60Sg, 60CV		E8018-C3
	Kaisaloy 70MB		E8018-B2

Steel Producer	Steel Trade Name			Recommended Electrodes
Lukens Steel Company	Lukens 45, 50	LT-75N		E7018 or E7028
	Lukens A440, A441			
	Cor-Ten A			
	Lukens 55, 60			E8018-C3
	Lukens LT-75QT			E8018-B2
	Lukens T1, T1A, T1B, LT-75HS			E11018-M
National Steel Corporation	GLX-45W			Note 1
	GLX-50W, 55W	GLS-441		E7018 or E7028
	NAX-Fine Grain NAX-Hi Mang			
	NAX High Tensile			
	GLX-60W, 65W			E8018-C3
	GLX-70W			E8018-B2
	N-A-XTRA 80, 90, 100			E11018-M
Republic Steel Corporation	35, X42W, X45W			Note 1
	X50W, X55W, A441,	Cor-Ten A		E7018 or E7028
	NAX High Tensile			
	Republic 50, 60, M			E8018-C3
	X60W, X65W			
	Republic 70	X70W		E8018-B2
	Republic 80			E11018-M
United States Steel Corporation	EX-Ten 42, 45			Note 1
	EX-Ten 50, 55			E7018 or E7028
	Cor-Ten A, B	Par-Ten		
	Tri-Ten	Man-Ten (A440)		
	Cor-Ten C	Man-Ten		E8018-C3
	EX-Ten 60, 65			
	Cor-Ten	Char-Pac		E8018-C1
	EX-Ten 70			E8018-B2
	T-1, T-1A, T-1B			E11018-M
Youngstown Sheet & Tube Company	YSW-42, 45			Note 1
	YSW-50, 55	YB-Ten	YSW A441	E7018 or E7028
	YSW-60, 65	Yo Man		E8018-C3
	Yoloy HS, HSX			Note 7
	Yoloy S			E8018-C1
	YSW-70			E8018-B2

Note 1.
Unless restricted by specifications, any E60XX or E70XX electrode can be used.

Note 2.
These recommendations are based on matching the mechanical properties of the weld deposit to the plate, and also the chemical properties of the weld deposit to the plate where chemistry is important. Since it is impossible to foresee all conditions of every application, other electrodes than those recommended here may also be satisfactory and should be tested.

Each of these applications of heat has a bearing on the quality of weld or the integrity of the finished weldment, and, in code work, control of temperature before, during, and after welding may be rigidly specified.

When to Preheat: Preheating is used for one of the following reasons:

1. To reduce shrinkage stresses in the weld and adjacent base metal — especially important with highly restrained joints.

2. To provide a slower rate of cooling through the critical temperature range (about 1600°F to 1300°F), preventing excessive hardening and lowering ductility of both the weld and heat-affected area of the base plate.

3. To provide a slower rate of cooling through the 400°F range, allowing more time for any hydrogen that is present to diffuse away from the weld and adjacent plate to avoid underbead cracking.

As suggested by the foregoing, a main purpose of preheat is to slow down the cooling rate — to allow more "Time at Temperature," as illustrated in Fig. 20-1. Thus, the *amount* of heat in the weld area as well as the temperature is important. A

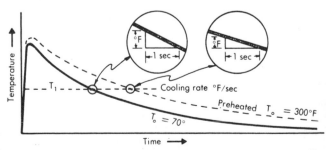

Fig. 20-1. A main purpose of preheat is to slow down the cooling rate. As the insets show, there is a greater temperature drop in one second at a given temperature (T_1) when the inital temperature of the plate is 70°F than when the initial temperature is 300°F. In other words, the cooling rate (°F/sec) is slower when preheat is used.

thick plate could be preheated to specified temperature in a localized area and the heating be ineffective because of rapid heat transfer, the reduction of heat in the welding area, and, thus, no marked effect on slowing the cooling rate. Having a thin surface area at a preheat temperature is not enough if there is a mass of cold metal beneath it into which the heat can rapidly transfer.

Because of the heat-absorption capacity of a thick plate, the heat-affected zone and the weld metal after cooling may be in highly quenched condition unless sufficient preheat is provided. What really matters is how long the weld metal and adjacent base metal is maintained in a certain temperature range during the cooling period. This, in turn, depends on the amount of heat in the assembly and the heat-transfer properties of the material and its configuration. Without adequate preheat, the cooling could be rapid and intolerably high hardness and brittleness could occur in the weld or adjacent area.

Welding at low ambient temperatures or on steel brought in from outside storage on cold winter days greatly increases the need for preheat. It is true that preheating rids the joint of moisture, but preheating is usually not specified for that purpose.

Amount of Preheat Required: The amount of preheat required for any application depends on such factors as base metal chemistry, plate thickness, restraint and rigidity of the members, and heat input of the process. Unfortunately, there is no method for metering the *amount* of heat put into an assembly by a preheat torch. The best shop approach for estimating the preheat input is a measure of the temperature at the welding area by temperature-indicating crayon marks or pellets. These give approximate measures of temperature at the spots where they are placed, which measurements are taken as indices to the heat input and are correlated with thickness of metal and chemistry of metal in tables specifying minimum preheat temperatures. Thus, temperature is the gage to preheat inputs, and preheating to specified temperatures is the practical method of obtaining the amount of preheat needed to control the cooling rate after welding.

TABLE 20-7. Minimum Preheat and Interpass Temperature,[1,2] (Deg. F)
From AWS D1.1 — Rev. 1-73

Thickness of Thickest Part at Point of Welding — Inches	Welding Process				
	Shielded Metal-Arc Welding with other than Low-Hydrogen Electrodes	Shield Metal-Arc Welding with Low-Hydrogen Electrodes Submerged-Arc Welding; Gas Metal-Arc Welding; or Flux-Cored Arc Welding		Shielded Metal-Arc Welding with Low-Hydrogen Electrodes; Submerged-Arc Welding with Carbon or Alloy Steel Wire, Neutral Flux; Gas Metal-Arc Welding or Flux-Cored Arc Welding	Submerged-Arc Welding with Carbon Steel Wire, Alloy Flux
	ASTM A36,[4] A53 Gr. B, A106, A131, A139, A375, A381 Gr. Y35 A500, A501, A516, A524, A529, A570 Gr. D and E, A573; API 5L Gr. B; ABS Gr. A, B, C, CS, D, E, R	ASTM A36, A106, A131 A139, A242 Weldable Grade A375, A381 Gr. Y35, A441, A516, A524, A529, A537 Gr. A and B, A570 Gr. D and E, A572, Gr. 42, 45, 50, A573, A588, A618, API 5L Gr. B and 5LX Gr. 42; ABS Gr. A, B, C, CS, D, E, R, AH, DH, EH	ASTM A572 Grades 55, 60 and 65	ASTM A514, A517	ASTM A514, A517
To 3/4, incl.	None[3]	None[3]	70	50	50
Over 3/4 to 1-1/2, incl.	150	70	150	125	200
Over 1-1/2 to 2-1/2, incl.	225	150	225	175	300
Over 2-1/2	300	225	300	225	400

[1] Welding shall not be done when the ambient temperature is lower than zero F. When the base metal is below the temperature listed for the welding procedure used and the thickness of material being welded, it shall be preheated (except as otherwise provided) in such manner that the surfaces of the parts on which weld metal is being deposited are at or above the specified minimum temperature for a distance equal to the thickness of the part being welded, but not less than 3 in., both laterally and in advance of the welding. Preheat and interpass temperatures must be sufficient to prevent crack formation. Temperature above the minimum shown may be required for highly restrained welds. For quenched-and-tempered steel the maximum preheat and interpass temperature shall not exceed 400°F for thicknesses up to 1-1/2 in., inclusive, and 450°F for greater thicknesses. Heat input when welding quenched-and-tempered steel shall not exceed the steel producer's recommendation.

[2] In joints involving combinations of base metals, preheat shall be as specified for the higher strength steel being welded.

[3] When the base-metal temperature is below 32°F, preheat the base metal to at least 70° F and maintain this minimum temperature during welding.

[4] Only low-hydrogen electrodes shall be used for welding A36 steel more than 1 inch thick for bridges.

TABLE 20-8. Approximate Preheat and Interpass Temperature for AISI Alloy Steel Bars*

AISI Steel	Preheat and Interpass Temperature °F		
	section thickness, in.		
	To 1/2	1/2 − 1	1 − 2
1330	350 − 450	400 − 500	450 − 550
1340	400 − 500	500 − 600	600 − 700
4023	100 min.	200 − 300	250 − 350
4028	200 − 300	250 − 350	400 − 500
4047	400 − 500	450 − 550	500 − 600
4118	200 − 300	350 − 450	400 − 500
4130	300 − 400	400 − 500	450 − 550
4140	400 − 500	600 − 700	600 − 700
4150	600 − 700	600 − 700	600 − 700
4320	200 − 300	350 − 450	400 − 500
4340	600 − 700	600 − 700	600 − 700
4620	100 min.	200 − 300	250 − 350
4640	350 − 450	400 − 500	450 − 550
5120	100 min	200 − 300	250 − 350
5145	400 − 500	450 − 550	500 − 600
8620	100 min	200 − 300	250 − 350
8630	200 − 300	250 − 350	400 − 500
8640	350 − 450	400 − 500	450 − 550

* From ASM Metal Handbook Volume 6, Eighth Edition.

There are various guides for use in estimating preheat temperatures, including the recommendation of the suppliers of special steels. No guide, however, can be completely and universally applicable because of the varying factors of rigidity and restraint in assemblies. Recommendations are, thus, presented as "minimum preheat recommendations," and they should be accepted as such. However, the quenched and tempered steels can be damaged if the preheat is too high, and the precautions necessary for these steels are discussed later.

The American Welding Society and the American Institute of Steel Construction have established minimum preheat and interpass temperature requirements for common weldable steels, as shown in Table 20-7. While material thickness, ranges of metal chemistry, and the welding process are taken into account in the minimum requirements, some adjustments may be needed for specific steel chemistry, welding heat input, joint geometry, and other factors.

Table 20-8 gives the approximate preheat and interpass temperatures for AISI alloy-steel bars when welded with low-hydrogen electrodes.

Generally, the higher the carbon content of a steel, the lower the critical cooling rate and the greater the necessity for preheating and using low-hydrogen electrodes. The Lincoln Preheat and Interpass Temperature Calculator (Fig. 20-2), available from The Lincoln Electric Company, is a convenient tool to use in estimating preheats or adjusting recommended temperatures to specific carbon contents and low alloy additions.

Carbon, however, is not the only element that influences the critical cooling rate. Other elements in the steel are responsible for the hardening and loss of ductility that occur with rapid cooling. Total hardenability is thus a factor to be considered when determining preheat requirements. Total hardenability can be expressed in terms of a "carbon equivalent," and this common measure of the effects of carbon and other alloying elements on hardening can be the basis for preheat and interpass temperature estimates.

Carbon equivalents (C_{eq}) are empirical values, determined by various carbon-equivalent formulas that represent the sum of the effects of various elements in steel on its hardenability. One of these is:

$$C_{eq} = \%C + \frac{\% Mn}{6} + \frac{\% Ni}{15} + \frac{\% Mo}{4} + \frac{\% Cr}{4} + \frac{\% Cu}{13}$$

This formula is valid only if the alloy contents are less than the following:

0.50% C	3.50% Ni	1.00% Cr
1.60% Mn	0.60% Mo	1.00% Cu

Approximate preheat and interpass temperatures, based on carbon-equivalent values for steels, are:

C_{eq} up to 0.45% . . . . . preheat is optional
C_{eq} = 0.45 to 0.60% . . . . 200 to 400°F
C_{eq} over 0.60% . . . . 400 to 700°F

These temperatures are only approximate and are expressed in broad ranges. The carbon-equivalent method of arriving at a preheat range has utility largely when working with steels of unusual chemistries, when the alloy contents fall within the

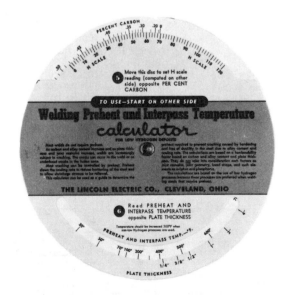

Fig. 20-2. The Lincoln Preheat and Interpass Temperature Calculator is a convenient tool for estimating preheats.

limits specified for the particular formula. Once the carbon-equivalent of such a steel has been determined, it can be correlated to a steel listed in Table 20-7 with a similar carbon-equivalent to judge the effects of plate thickness and the welding process in narrowing the preheat-temperature range.

Whatever the method used to estimate preheat temperature, the value obtained should be confirmed by welding tests on simulated or actual assemblies before it is committed to production welding. Only then can the effects of restraint and welding heat input be taken into account.

Theoretically, it is possible to reduce the preheat temperature requirement below the value listed in preheat tables when using welding currents in the high range of the procedures for semiautomatic and automatic processes. The justification for this is that the welding heat input is likely to be much higher than anticipated by the preheat recommendations. In such cases, heat losses from the assembly might more than be balanced by the welding heat input, bringing the affected metal up to or beyond the minimum preheat and interpass recommendations before it starts to cool.

The heat input during welding for a specific welding procedure is readily calculated by the formula:

$$J = \frac{I \times E \times 60}{V}$$

where:

J = Heat input in kilojoules/in. or kilowatt-sec./in.

E = Arc voltage in volts

I = Welding current in amperes

V = Arc speed in in./min.

Since all the welding heat input at the arc does not enter the plate, the following heat inefficiencies are suggested for use with the formula:

75 — 80% for manual welding

90 — 100% for submerged-arc welding

Only after thorough analysis and test of the heat input, transfer, and loss factors should one deviate from recommended practices. A bulletin, entitled "Why Preheat — An Approach to Estimating Correct Preheat Temperature," by Omer W. Blodgett, available from The Lincoln Electric Company, elaborates on the analysis of heat intput during welding and describes methods for determining cooling rates and for calculating preheat temperatures that will produce the required cooling rates for given heat inputs and plate thicknesses.

Methods of Preheating: The method of preheating depends on the thickness of the plate, the size of the weldment, and the heating equipment available. In the production welding of small assemblies, preheating in a furnace is the most satisfactory method. Another satisfactory method is torch heating, using natural gas premixed with compressed air. This produces a hot flame and burns clean. Torches can be connected to convenient gas and compressed-air outlets around the shop. Acetylene, propane, and oil torches can also be used. On large weldments, banks of heating torches may be used to bring the material up to temperature quickly and uniformly.

Electrical strip heaters are used on longitudinal and girth seams on plate up to 2 in. thick. The heaters are clamped to the plate parallel to the joint and about 6 in. from the seam. After the plate reaches the proper preheat temperature, the heaters may remain in place to add heat if necessary to maintain the proper interpass temperature.

Other means of preheating are induction heating — often used on piping — and radiant heating.

High accuracy is not required in preheating carbon steels. Although it is important that the work be heated to a minimum temperature, no harm is done if this temperature is exceeded by 100°F. This is not true, however, for quenched and tempered steels, since welding on an overheated plate may cause damage in the heat-affected zone. For this reason the temperature should be measured as accurately as possible with such steels.

Temperature-indicating crayons and pellets are available for a wide range of temperatures. A crayon mark for a given temperature on the work will melt suddenly when the work reaches that temperature. Two crayon marks, one for the lower limit and one for the upper limit of temperature, show clearly when the work is heated to the desired temperature range.

Several types of portable pyrometers are available for measuring surface temperature. Properly used, these instruments are sufficiently accurate, but must be periodically calibrated to insure reliability.

Thermocouples may be attached to the work and used to measure temperature. Thermocouples are the temperature-sensing devices used with ovens for preheating small assemblies.

INTERPASS TEMPERATURES

Usually a steel that requires preheating to a specified temperature also must be kept at this temperature between weld passes. With many weldments, the heat input during welding is adequate to maintain the interpass temperature. On a massive weldment, it is not likely that the heat input of the

TABLE 20-9. Comparison Chart of Suggested Preheat Temperatures When
Shielded Metal-Arc Welding Representative Quenched and Tempered Alloy Steels

Plate thickness, in.	Minimum preheat or interpass temperature for welding with low-hydrogen electrodes, °F						
	A533B Steel	A517 Steel	A542 Steel	A543 Steel	HY-130 Steel	Mod. A203D Steel	A553 Steel
To 1/2, incl.	50	50	150	100	75	50	50
Over 1/2 to 5/8, incl.	100	50	200	125	75	50	50
Over 5/8 to 3/4, incl.	100	50	200	125	125	50	50
Over 3/4 to 7/8, incl.	100	50	200	150	125	50	50
Over 7/8 to 1, Incl.	100	50	200	150	200	50	50
Over 1 to 1-3/8, incl.	200	150	250	200	200	150	150
Over 1-3/8 to 1-1/2, incl.	200	150	250	200	225	150	150
Over 1-1/2 to 2, incl.	200	150	250	200	225	150	150
Over 2 to 3, incl.	300	200	300	200	225	200	200
Over 3	300	200	300	200	225	200	200

Note: A preheat temperature above the minimum may be required for highly restrained welds. No welding should be done when ambient temperature is below 0°F. Welding of steel at an initial temperature below 100°F may require preheating to remove moisture from the surface of the steel. From ASM Metals Handbook, Volume 6, 8th Edition.

welding process will be sufficient to maintain the required interpass temperature. If this is the case, torch heating between passes may be required.

Once an assembly has been preheated and the welding begun, it is desirable to finish the welding as soon as possible so as to avoid the need for interpass heating.

Since the purpose of preheating is to reduce the quench rate, it logically follows that the same slow cooling should be accorded all passes. This can only be accomplished by maintaining an interpass temperature which is at least equal to the preheat temperature. If this is not done, each individual bead will be subjected to the same high quench rate as the first bead of a non-preheated assembly.

PREHEATS FOR QUENCHED AND TEMPERED STEELS

Since the low-alloy quenched and tempered steels are already in a heat-treated condition, any heating beyond a certain temperature will destroy

TABLE 20-10. Suggested Preheat Temperatures for
ASTM A517, Grade B, F, and H Steels

Plate thickness, in.	Minimum* preheat or interpass temperature, °F			
	Shielded metal-arc process	Gas metal-arc process	Submerged-arc Process	
			Alloy or carbon-steel wire, neutral flux	Carbon-steel wire, alloy flux
Up to 1/2, incl.	50†	50†	50†	50†
Over 1/2 to 1, incl.	50†	50†	50†	200
Over 1 to 2, incl.	150	150	150	300
Over 2	200	200	200	400

* A preheat temperature above the minimum shown may be required for highly restrained welds.
† Welding at any initial plate temperature below 100°F will require extreme care to minimize moisture on the steel being welded.

TABLE 20-11. Maximum Welding Heat Input in
Kilojoules/Inch for Butt Joints in ASTM
A533, Grade B Steel

Preheat and inter-pass tem-perature, °F	Plate thickness, in.				
	1/4	3/8	1/2	5/8	3/4
70	23.7	35.6	47.4	64.5	88.6
150	20.9	31.4	41.9	57.4	77.4
200	19.2	28.8	38.5	53.0	69.9
300	15.8	23.8	31.9	42.5	55.7
400	12.3	19.1	25.9	33.5	41.9

the properties developed in them by the manufacturing process. Some assemblies must be preheated before welding to prevent cracking or rapid cooling, but the preheat must be controlled so as not to destroy throughout the mass of material the high yield strength and toughness that characterize these steels and give them special applications, Yet, during welding the heat-affected zone will be heated far above the allowable preheat temperatures. This zone must then cool rapidly enough so as to re-establish the original properties and avoid a brittle structure. As a consequence, preheat temperatures and welding heat inputs must be closely controlled. Narrow limits are thus placed on the procedures.

Through research, welding procedures have been developed that assure high strength and good toughness, ductility, and impact properties in the welded joints. The recommended heat inputs and preheat temperatures are intended to allow sufficiently fast cooling rates to avoid brittle structure. In general, this means a cooling rate of 6°F or more per second through the 900°F temperature range. The chemistry of these steels is such that the carbon equivalent is low enough to minimize the

TABLE 20-12. Maximum Welding Heat Input in Kilojoules/Inch
for Butt Joints in ASTM A517, Grade B and H Steels

Preheat and inter-pass temperature, °F	Plate thickness, in.							1-1/4 and over
	3/16	1/4	3/8	1/2	5/8	3/4	1	
70	17.5	23.7	35.0	47.4	64.5	88.6	Any	Any
150	15.3	20.9	30.7	41.9	57.4	77.4	120.0	Any
200	14.0	19.2	28.0	35.5	53.0	69.9	110.3	154.0
300	11.5	15.8	23.5	31.9	42.5	55.7	86.0	120.0
400	9.0	12.3	18.5	25.9	33.5	41.9	65.6	94.0

TABLE 20-13. Maximum Welding Heat Input in Kilojoules/Inch
for Butt Joints in ASTM A517, Grade F Steel

Preheat and inter-pass temperature, °F	Plate thickness, in.							
	3/16	1/4	1/2	3/4	1	1-1/4	1-1/2	2
70	27.0	36.0	70.0	121.0	Any	Any	Any	Any
200	21.0	29.0	56.0	99.0	173.0	Any	Any	Any
300	17.0	24.0	47.0	82.0	126.0	175.0	Any	Any
400	13.0	19.0	40.0	65.0	93.0	127.0	165.0	Any

Note: Heat-input limits for temperatures and thicknesses included, but not shown, in this
table may be obtained by interpolation; 25% higher heat inputs are allowable for fillet welds.

preheat.

In welding quenched and tempered steels, the proper low-hydrogen welding process is selected. Next, the required preheat temperature is determined, based upon the chemistry of the weld metal and plate thickness. Knowing the preheat temperature and the plate thickness, the maximum permissible welding heat input per pass can be found. A welding procedure is then selected that will stay below this maximum value. Welding heat input may be reduced by decreasing the welding current or increasing the arc travel speed. Either change will decrease the amount of weld metal deposited per pass and will result in more passes being used for a given joint. For this reason, stringer beads are used extensively in welding quenched and tempered steels.

Tables 20-9 through 20-14 give recommended minimum preheat temperatures and maximum welding heat inputs for various quenched and tempered steels in various thicknesses. Kilo joules per inch of weld in the heat-input table are determined by Formula (1) in this chapter. Similar data on other steels of this type are available from the steel producers.

Sometimes, the procedures most desirable from the economic standpoint in welding these steels will lead to a total heat input — preheat plus welding heat — that exceeds the steel manufacturer's recommendations. In such cases, one might question whether the weldment needs maximum notch toughness as well as high yield strength. If it does, the procedures should be modified to reduce the total heat input — not the preheat. Reducing preheat would be too risky, since such action might lead to weld cracking, and maximum toughness in the heat-affected zone would then be of no value. If maximum notch toughness is not required, total heat input limits can be exceeded somewhat without materially reducing the yield strength.

POINTERS ON PREHEAT

- A cardinal rule when welding materials that require preheat is "keep it hot." It is costly to reheat to maintain assembly temperature.

- Preheat requirements can be reduced when running two automatic welding heads a few inches from each other — such as on each side of a web that is being fillet-welded to a flange. The heat input into the flange will be essentially double that resulting from a single head.

TABLE 20-14. Suggested Welding Heat Input
for Joints in HY-130 Steel

Plate thickness-in.	Heat input, Kilojoules	
	Shielded metal-arc process	Gas metal-arc process
3/8 to 5/8, incl.	40	35
Over 5/8 to 7/8, incl.	45	40
Over 7/8 to 1-3/8, incl.	45	45
Over 1-3/8 to 4, incl.	50	50

- Don't overlook the value of a preheat to prevent weld cracking in weldments with highly restrained joints — even though the chemistry of the steel does not call for a preheat.

- Heat flow from the joint is faster at a fillet weld than at a butt weld. Heat has three avenues for escape from a conventional fillet (tri-thermal heat flow); two, from a conventional butt weld (bi-thermal heat flow). This is made clear by Fig. 20-3.

- Even though adequately preheating a thick section increases the fabrication cost, one experience with field repairs usually teaches that preheating is well worth the cost.

- Consider the use of lower alloy metal — even for highly restrained joints — to minimize the need for preheating.

STRESS RELIEF

Stress relieving is defined as heating to a suitable temperature (for steel, below the critical); holding long enough to reduce residual stresses; and then cooling slowly enough to minimize the development of new residual stresses. Stress relieving should not be confused with normalizing or annealing, which are done at higher temperatures.

The ASME Code requires certain pressure vessels and power piping to be stress relieved. This is to reduce internal stress. Other weldments such as machine-tool bases are stress relieved to attain dimensional stability after machining.

Heating and cooling must be done slowly and uniformly; uneven cooling could nullify much of the value of the heat treatment or even cause additional stresses in the weldment. In general, the greater the difference between maximum and minimum thickness of the component parts, the slower should be the rate of temperature change. If the ratio of maximum to minimum thickness of the component parts is less than 4 to 1, heating and cooling rates should not exceed 400°F/hour divided by the thickness in inches of the thickest section. However, the heating and cooling rates

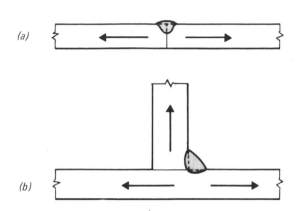

Fig. 20-3. Heat has two avenues of escape from a conventional butt weld (bi-thermal heat flow) and three avenues of escape from a conventional fillet weld (tri-thermal heat flow).

should not exceed 400°F/hour. If the ratios of the thicknesses of the components parts vary more, rates should be reduced accordingly. For example, with complex structures containing members of widely varying thicknesses, heating and cooling rates should be such that the maximum temperature difference of sections of the same weldment should not exceed 75°F. Temperatures of critical sections can be monitored using thermocouples mounted on the weldment.

The stress-relief range for most carbon steels is 1100 to 1200°F, and the soaking time is usually one hour per inch of thickness.* For the low-alloy chrome-molybdenum steels, with the chromium in the range of 1/2 to 2-1/4% and the molybdenum up to 1%, the stress-relief range is 1250 to 1300°F for one hour. Some of the higher alloy steels require more soaking time. For example, E410, E502, and E505 weld metal is stress relieved at 1550 to 1600°F for two hours, and E430 at 1400 1450°F for four hours.

Local stress relieving can be done on girth joints of pipe and pressure vessels when required by codes. The same precautions are necessary as for furnace heating: slow heating, time-at-temperature, and slow cooling.

---

* AWS proposes to say "per inch of weld thickness, when the specified stress-relief is for dimensional stability, the holding time shall be one hour per inch of thickness of the thicker part." However, sometimes ASME Sect. VIII refers also to the "thinner of two adjacent butt-welded plates."

Welding Steel Pipe

Although various welding processes are used in the manufacture of steel pipe, in industrial practice the term "pipe welding" almost always refers to the joining of pipes and fittings for transmission lines and in-plant piping systems. This type of pipe welding is a highly specialized art. The weld-joining of piping differs so much from plate welding that operators must pass separate tests on pipe techniques to qualify as pipe weldors. Much of the skill required in plate welding, however, is applicable to pipe techniques. This chapter covers techniques, electrodes, procedures, and qualifications for welding cross-country lines and in-plant systems.

PIPE STEELS AND ELECTRODES

The American Petroleum Institute (API) publishes a standard for welding pipe, which includes procedures, qualification of operators, joint design, testing, and inspection. The standard also includes specifications for the types of pipe steel used for cross-country lines.

The most common steels used for cross-country pipelines are the API 5LX series. The "5L" indicates line pipe, the "X" indicates high-test line pipe, and two additional numbers indicate minimum yield strength in thousands of pounds per square inch. For example, 5LX65 is high-test line pipe with a 65,000-psi minimum yield strength. Table 21-1 lists chemical requirements and Table 21-2 mechanical-property requirements of this series.

For complete specifications on pipe and pipe fittings, see *API Specification for Line Pipe* (API Standard 5L) and *API Specification for High-Test Line Pipe* (API Standard 5LX). Standards for procedure and operator qualification, joint preparation, and weld inspection are included in *Standard for Welding Pipe Lines and Related Facilities* (API Standard 1104). These standards are available from: American Petroleum Institute, 1271 Avenue of the Americas, New York, N.Y. 10020.

Weld cracking may occur in some of the pipe steels, particularly when the carbon and manganese contents are near the maximum allowable amounts and when the weather is cold. The X56, X60, and X65 steels may be treated with small amounts of

TABLE 21-2. Mechanical Property Requirements of 5LX Series High-Test Line Pipe

API Grade	Min. Yield Strength (1000 psi)	Min. Tensile Strength (1000 psi)
X42	42	60
X46	46	63
X52	52	66*
X56	56	71*
X60	60	75*
X65	65	77*

* Tensile-strength requirements for pipe of 20-in. OD and larger, with 0.375-in. or less wall, are 3000 to 6000 psi higher.

TABLE 21-1. Chemical Requirements (ladle analysis) For Welded 5LX Series High-Test Line Pipe

API Grade	Manufacturing Process	Composition, Max (%)			
		C	Mn	P	S
X42	Nonexpanded	0.28	1.25	0.04	0.05
X46, X52	Nonexpanded	0.30	1.35	0.04	0.05
X42, X46, X52	Cold-expanded	0.28	1.25	0.04	0.05
X56*, X60*	Nonexp. or cold-exp.	0.26	1.35	0.04	0.05
X65*	Nonexp. or cold-exp.	0.26	1.40	0.04	0.05

* These steels may also contain small amounts of columbium, vanadium, or titanium. Other analyses may be furnished by agreement between purchaser and producer. For good weldability, carbon and alloy content should be as low as practical.

**TABLE 21-3. Typical Mechanical Properties of Deposited Weld Metal
Pipe-Welding Electrodes of The EXX10 Classes**

	E6010 For Pipe	E7010-A1	E7010-G For Pipe	High-Yield Pipe Electrode
As-Welded				
Tensile Strength (psi)	68,000	75,000	75,000	85,000
Yield Strength (psi)	60,000	68,000	61,000	75,000
Elongation (% in 2 in)	29	26	25	22
Charpy V Notch (ft-lb @ 70°F)	55*	68	68	55
Stress-Relieved 1150°F				
Tensile Strength (psi)	65,000	75,000	72,000	85,000
Yield Strength (psi)	56,000	62,000	62,000	80,000
Elongation (% in 2 in)	32	33	24	26
Charpy V Notch (ft-lb @ 70°F)	71	64	68	68

* at −20°F

alloying elements to increase their yield strength. With no top limit on tensile strength, this property can, and sometimes does, exceed 100,000 psi. Special techniques are required to prevent cracking in these steels. Some pipe steels have a silicon content up to 0.35%, which tends to produce pinholes unless special pipe electrodes are used.

Pipe and tubing for power plants, boiler tubes, and refinery still tubes are usually specified to an ASTM standard. These specifications cover both mild steels and alloy steels for many types of service. Where specific codes apply, check the specification for electrode requirements or recommendations.

Since pipe welding is a specialized application, electrodes have been designed especially for vertical-down welding of pipe joints. These special electrodes are in the EXX10 class, but they may or may not have an AWS classification designation; the electrode supplier must be consulted for the proper product.

Pipe electrodes have several unique operating properties:

1. They produce a steady, concentrated arc, which forms a continuous bead on the inside of the pipe when the first pass is made.

2. They produce a thin covering of slag, which promotes good wetting to the sides of the groove but does not run into the crater and interfere with the arc.

3. They have a minimum tendency to produce pinholes.

The special pipe electrodes of the EXX10 class (Table 21-3) are used on pipe up to 5LX65; low-hydrogen electrodes are recommended for pipe with higher specified yield strength and for alloy pipe.

Generally, pipe with a wall thickness of 1/2-in. or less (which includes most cross-country lines) is welded vertical-down with special EXX10 electrodes. Pipe with heavier walls is welded with low-hydrogen electrodes.

VERTICAL-DOWN TECHNIQUES

Joint Preparation: Typical joint design and tolerances for a 30-in. 5LX pipe are shown in Fig. 21-1. Standard practice is to use internal line-up clamps on 16-in. and larger pipe. Often this does not produce a uniform spacing and, since hammering with a sledge is not recommended, the weldor must compensate for the poor fits that usually occur.

Stringer Bead: The first pass in the bottom of the groove — the stringer bead (Fig. 21-2) — is made by two weldors (more on large-diameter pipe) working on opposite sides of the pipe. The welds are started at the top, and the electrodes are dragged downhill to the bottom of the pipe. Too narrow a gap, too low a welding current, or too large a root face can cause insufficient penetration or lack of fusion. Too high a current, too wide a gap, or too little root face can cause burnthrough (called "windows"), globular metal deposits on the inside of the pipe, external undercut (called "wagon tracks"), or internal undercut that can be repaired only from the inside of the pipe. Repairs from the inside of the pipe are, of course, difficult and are impossible on small-diameter pipe.

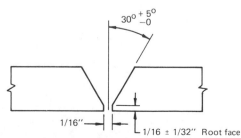

Fig. 21-1. Standard joint design for a 30-in.-diameter 5LX pipe.

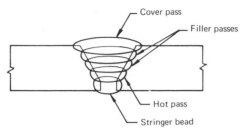

Fig. 21-2. Typical weld cross section on a 3/8-in. wall pipe.

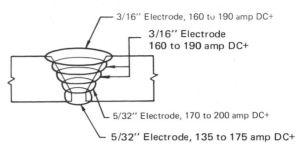

Fig. 21-4. Procedures for vertical-down pipe welding.

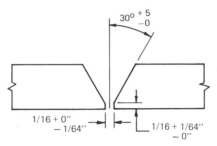

Fig. 21-3. Preferred joint design for X60 and X65 pipe.

Hot Pass: The stringer should be cleaned with a power brush. If special pipe-welding electrode is not used, the stringer pass may be very convex and require grinding to remove the slag and to prepare the surface for the hot pass (Fig. 21-2). The hot pass should be applied with sufficient current to melt out all "wagon tracks" and any remaining slag. It should be applied as soon as possible after the stringer is completed — within five minutes.

Filler Passes: A slight weave — only enough to obtain fusion at the sides of the groove — is used to apply the filler passes. Filler passes may fill the groove flush or almost flush at the top and bottom of the pipe, but more weld metal is usually required at the 2 to 5 o'clock positions. These lengths of groove are made flush with short filler passes called "stripper beads."

Cover Pass: The cover pass should be 1/32 to 1/16 inch higher than the pipe surface, and it should overlap the groove about 1/16 inch on each side, as illustrated in Fig. 21-2.

Preventing Cracks: Many factors contribute to weld cracking, but the primary causes are the chemistry, wall thickness, and the temperature of the pipe. Pipeline techniques recommended to prevent cracking are:

- Make the stringer as large as practical.
- Do not remove the line-up clamp until the stringer is completed.
- Make the hot pass as soon as possible after the stringer bead — within five minutes.
- Preheat if the pipe is less than 40°F. Proper

preheat temperature depends on the chemistry of the pipe and wall thickness.

For X60 and X65 pipe, additional precautions and more stringent preparation are required:

- Joint preparation and tolerances should be as shown in Fig. 21-3.
- Use only electrodes of the EXX10 class designed for X60 and X65 pipe.
- Preheat to 300°F if the pipe temperature is less than 70°F.
- Always weld the stringer pass and hot pass with two (or more) men working on opposite sides of the pipe.

Vertical-Down Procedures: The procedures illustrated by the accompanying figures and tables are for EXX10-type electrode, designed for welding circumferential pipe joints vertical-down. Joint preparation is shown in Fig. 21-1, and current and electrode size are given in Fig. 21-4.

Table 21-4 shows the number of passes required for various wall thicknesses. This may vary with different operators, especially on thicker walls. One or two stripper beads may be required at the 2 to 5 o'clock location.

Table 21-5 shows the amount of electrode required per joint. Amounts are based on 4-in. stub lengths — about normal for cross-country pipeline welding.

Thin-Wall Pipe Procedures: Electrodes and procedures for thin-wall pipe are much the same as for cross-country pipe. One variation is the occasional use of negative polarity. Where a wide gap

TABLE 21-4. Passes Required for Vertical-Down Welding of Pipe

Wall Thickness of Pipe (in.)	Number of Passes
1/4	3
5/16	4
3/8	5
1/2	7

TABLE 21-5. Type EXX10 Electrode Consumption for Vertical-Down Welding of Pipe

Pipe Diam. (in.)	Wall Thickness of Pipe (in.)											
	1/4			5/16			3/8			1/2		
	Electrode Required* (lb/joint)											
	5/32	3/16	Total	5/32	3/16	Total	5/32	3/16	Total	5/32	5/16	Total
6	0.47	0.24	0.71	0.47	0.47	0.94	0.47	0.75	1.2	....	....	.....
8	0.63	0.32	0.95	0.63	0.63	1.3	0.63	1.0	1.6	0.63	2.0	2.6
10	0.79	0.40	1.2	0.78	0.78	1.6	0.78	1.1	1.9	0.79	2.4	3.2
12	0.95	0.47	1.4	0.95	0.95	1.9	0.95	1.5	2.5	0.95	3.0	4.0
14	1.1	0.55	1.7	1.1	1.1	2.2	1.1	1.8	2.9	1.1	3.5	4.6
16	1.2	0.63	1.8	1.2	1.3	2.5	1.3	2.0	3.3	1.2	4.0	5.2
18	1.4	0.70	2.1	1.4	1.4	2.8	1.4	2.3	3.7	1.4	4.5	5.9
20	1.5	0.76	2.3	1.5	1.6	3.1	1.6	2.4	4.0	1.5	4.8	6.3
22	1.7	0.90	2.6	1.7	1.8	3.5	1.7	2.9	4.6	1.7	5.5	7.2
24	1.9	0.94	2.8	1.9	1.9	3.8	1.9	3.0	4.9	1.9	6.0	7.9
26	2.0	1.1	3.1	2.0	2.1	4.1	2.0	3.3	5.3	2.0	6.5	8.5
28	2.2	1.1	3.3	2.2	2.2	4.4	2.2	3.5	5.7	2.2	7.0	9.2
30	2.3	1.2	3.5	2.3	2.4	4.7	2.3	3.8	6.1	2.4	7.5	9.9
32	2.5	1.3	3.8	2.5	2.5	5.0	2.5	4.1	6.6	2.5	8.0	10.5
34	2.7	1.3	4.0	2.7	2.7	5.4	2.7	4.3	7.0	2.7	8.5	11.2
36	2.8	1.4	4.2	2.8	2.8	5.6	2.8	4.5	7.3	2.8	9.0	11.8

*Values given include 4-in. stubs.

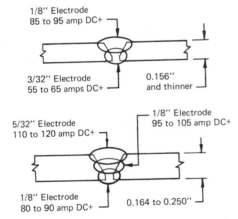

1/8″ Electrode
85 to 95 amp DC+

3/32″ Electrode
55 to 65 amps DC+

0.156″ and thinner

5/32″ Electrode
110 to 120 amp DC+

1/8″ Electrode
95 to 105 amp DC+

1/8″ Electrode
80 to 90 amp DC+

0.164 to 0.250″

Fig. 21-5. Procedures for vertical-down welding on thin-wall pipe.

causes excessive burnthrough, negative polarity is used on the first pass.

Welding procedures for butt joints in thin-wall pipe are shown in Fig. 21-5. Table 21-6 shows the amount of electrode required per joint. Values are based on 4-in. stub lengths, normal for this type of welding.

Another type of connection used on thin-wall pipe is the bell-and-spigot joint (Fig. 21-6). Procedures for this type of joint are given in Table 21-7, and the amount of electrode required per joint is given in Table 21-8.

VERTICAL-UP TECHNIQUES

Vertical-up welding requires fewer beads than vertical-down and therefore less cleaning. The time saved results in an advantage for vertical-up welding on wall thicknesses of 1/2 inch and thicker.

Vertical-up welding is usually used for in-plant welding of pipe, such as in power stations and refineries; vertical-down welding is used on cross-country pipelines.

Joint Preparation Without Backup Ring: Recommended joint design is shown in Fig. 21-7. The 1/8-in. gap must be maintained accurately all around the joint and tack welded in at least four places on 6-in.-diameter and larger pipe.

Welding: All passes are made starting at the bottom and moving upward. Usually an E6010 or E7010 electrode is used for the first pass, except on alloy pipe, where an alloy electrode must be used. If low-hydrogen electrodes are used, such welding (without backup ring) requires an especially high degree of skill.

After the first pass, the bead should be cleaned thoroughly, and any bumps or imperfections should be ground before additional passes are placed. The finish pass should be about 1/16 in.

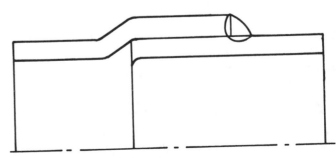

Fig. 21-6. Bell-and-spigot joint for thin-wall pipe.

TABLE 21-6. Type EXX10 Electrode Consumption for Butt Welds in Thin-Wall Pipe (Vertical-Down)

Pipe Diam. (in.)	Wall Thickness of Pipe (in.)								
	1/8			3/16			1/4		
	Electrode Required* (lb/joint)								
	3/32	1/8	Total	1/8	5/32	Total	1/8	5/32	Total
4	0.071	0.092	0.163	0.196	0.146	0.342	0.232	0.177	0.409
4-1/2	0.080	0.102	0.182	0.221	0.164	0.385	0.261	0.199	0.460
6	0.106	0.138	0.244	0.294	0.219	0.513	0.348	0.268	0.616
6-5/8	0.118	0.152	0.270	0.325	0.242	0.567	0.384	0.293	0.677
8	0.142	0.184	0.326	0.392	0.292	0.684	0.464	0.354	0.818
8-5/8	0.153	0.198	0.351	0.422	0.314	0.736	0.500	0.382	0.882
10	0.178	0.230	0.408	0.490	0.365	0.855	0.581	0.442	1.023
10-3/4	0.191	0.247	0.438	0.526	0.392	0.918	0.623	0.475	1.098
12-3/4	0.223	0.289	0.512	0.615	0.458	1.073	0.727	0.552	1.279
14	0.248	0.323	0.571	0.686	0.520	1.206	0.812	0.615	1.427
16	0.284	0.369	0.653	0.784	0.593	1.377	0.929	0.703	1.632
20	0.355	0.461	0.816	0.980	0.741	1.721	1.161	0.879	2.040
24	. . . . .	. . . . .	. . . . .	1.177	0.890	2.067	1.393	1.062	2.455
28	. . . . .	. . . . .	. . . . .	1.372	1.040	2.412	1.624	1.230	2.854
32	. . . . .	. . . . .	. . . . .	1.568	1.186	2.754	1.858	1.406	3.264
36	. . . . .	. . . . .	. . . . .	1.764	1.338	3.102	2.089	1.582	3.671

*Values given include 4-in. stubs.

TABLE 21-7. Type EXX10 Procedures for Bell-and-Spigot Joints in Thin-Wall Pipe

Wall Thickness of Pipe (in.)	Electrode Size (in.)	Current DC + (amp)
0.075	1/8	80 to 100
0.090	1/8	80 to 100
0.105	5/32	120 to 130
0.125	5/32	120 to 130
0.135	5/32	130 to 140

TABLE 21-8. Type EXX10 Electrode Consumption For Bell-and Spigot Joints in Thin-Wall Pipe

Pipe Diam. (in.)	Electrode Required (lb/joint)				
	Wall Thickness of Pipe (in.)				
	0.075	0.090	0.105	0.125	0.135
4	0.041	0.053	0.078	0.095	0.100
4-1/2	0.046	0.059	0.088	0.107	0.113
6	0.062	0.078	0.114	0.142	0.150
6-5/8	0.068	0.088	0.129	0.157	0.166
8	0.082	0.106	0.156	0.190	0.200
8-5/8	0.088	0.114	0.168	0.205	0.215
10	0.098	0.132	0.195	0.238	0.247
10-3/4	0.108	0.142	0.209	0.253	0.264
12-3/4	0.127	0.168	0.245	0.298	0.314
14	0.136	0.185	0.271	0.330	0.345
16	0.155	0.211	0.310	0.377	0.394
20	0.194	0.264	0.387	0.471	0.494

higher than the pipe and should overlap the original groove by 1/16 to 1/8 in.

Procedures: The procedures shown in Fig. 21-8 are for vertical-up welding of circumferential pipe joints. The first pass is an EXX10-type electrode and, for subsequent passes, procedures are given for either EXX10 or EXX18. Table 21-9 gives the approximate number of passes required for different wall thicknesses. This will vary with different operators.

Table 21-10 shows the electrode consumption per joint for vertical-up welding of pipe. Amounts are based on the use of EXX18 electrode and the joint design shown in Fig. 21-7. If the gap is changed, amounts must be revised accordingly.

Joint Preparation With a Backup Ring: Recommended joint design for vertical-up welding with backup ring is shown in Fig. 21-9. Gap distance

TABLE 21-9. Passes Required for Vertical-Up Welding of Pipe

Wall Thickness of Pipe (in.)	Number of Passes
1/4	2
5/16	2
3/8	3
1/2	3
5/8	4
3/4	6
1	7

TABLE 21-10. Type EXX18 Electrode Consumption for Vertical-Up Welding of Pipe

Pipe Diam. (in.)	Wall Thickness of Pipe (in.)														
	3/8			1/2			5/8			3/4			1		
	Electrode Required* (lb/joint)														
	3/32	1/8	Total	3/32	1/8	Total	3/32	1/8	Total	3/32	1/8 & 5/32	Total	3/32	1/8 & 5/32	Total
6	0.51	1.34	1.85	0.51	2.31	2.82	....	....	.....	....	....	.....	....	....	.....
8	0.7	1.8	2.5	0.7	3.1	3.8	0.7	4.7	5.4	....	....	.....	....	....	.....
12	1.0	2.7	3.7	1.0	4.7	5.7	1.0	7.1	8.1	1.0	9.9	10.9	1.0	16.7	17.7
16	1.4	3.6	5.0	1.4	6.1	7.5	1.4	9.8	11.2	1.4	13.1	14.5	1.4	22.1	23.5
20	1.7	4.5	6.2	1.7	7.7	9.4	1.7	11.7	13.4	1.7	16.4	18.1	1.7	27.6	29.3
24	2.0	5.4	7.4	2.0	9.3	11.3	2.0	14.2	16.2	2.0	19.8	21.8	2.0	33.4	35.4
28	2.4	6.2	8.6	2.4	10.8	13.2	2.4	16.5	18.9	2.4	23.0	25.4	2.4	38.8	41.2
32	2.7	7.2	9.9	2.7	12.4	15.1	2.7	19.0	21.7	2.7	26.5	29.2	2.7	44.5	47.2
36	3.1	8.0	11.1	3.1	13.9	17.0	3.1	21.6	24.7	3.1	29.6	32.7	3.1	49.9	53.0
40	3.4	8.9	12.3	3.4	15.4	18.8	3.4	23.5	26.9	3.4	32.8	36.2	3.4	55.3	58.7
48	4.1	14.7	18.8	4.1	18.5	22.6	4.1	28.3	32.4	4.1	39.5	43.6	4.1	66.6	70.7
60	....	....	....	5.1	23.2	28.3	5.1	45.4	50.5	5.1	49.4	54.5	5.1	83.2	88.3

*Values given include 4-in. stubs.

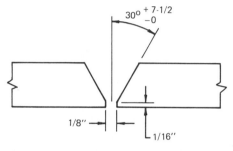

Fig. 21-7. Joint design for vertical-up welding on pipe without a backup ring.

should match the outside diameter of the electrode covering.

Welding: The first pass can be welded with either EXX10 or EXX18 electrode. The root pass must penetrate both lips of the pipe and the backup ring. Any unfused area at the bottom of the root pass is an objectionable defect. Since the gap is wider than that used for welding without a backup ring, the groove is also wider, and split layers are usually necessary after about the fifth layer.

Procedures: Procedures for welding with a backup ring are shown in Fig. 21-10. Approximate numbers of passes required are shown in Table 21-11.

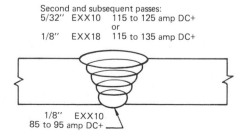

Second and subsequent passes:
5/32" EXX10   115 to 125 amp DC+
    or
1/8" EXX18   115 to 135 amp DC+

1/8" EXX10
85 to 95 amp DC+

Fig. 21-8. Procedures for vertical-up pipe welding without a backup ring.

HORIZONTAL TECHNIQUES

Piping in refineries and plants often requires joints with the axis of the pipe vertical. These horizontal joints required different techniques and procedures than vertical joints, but the designs of horizontal joints are the same as those for vertical-up welding — either with or without the backup ring.

Welding: Without a backup ring, the first pass is usually made with EXX10 electrode, and the weld is completed with either EXX10 or EXX18. With a backup ring, the entire weld can be made with EXX18 electrode.

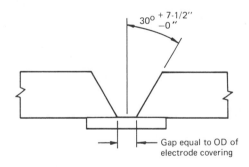

Gap equal to OD of electrode covering

Fig. 21-9. Joint design for vertical-up welding on pipe with backup ring.

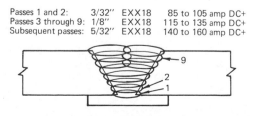

Passes 1 and 2:   3/32" EXX18   85 to 105 amp DC+
Passes 3 through 9: 1/8" EXX18   115 to 135 amp DC+
Subsequent passes: 5/32" EXX18   140 to 160 amp DC+

Fig. 21-10. Procedures for vertical-up pipe welding with backup ring.

TABLE 21-11. Passes Required for Vertical-Up Welding of Pipe Using Backup Ring

Wall Thickness of Pipe (in.)	Number of Passes
3/8	3
1/2	4
5/8	5
3/4	7
1	10

After the first pass, the next bead is placed on the lower side of the groove, penetrating both the root pass and the lower pipe member. The following bead is placed immediately above the second bead, so it penetrates both the second bead and the upper pipe member. Similarly, each layer is started at the lower side of the groove and built upward, as shown in Fig. 21-11.

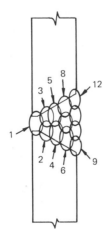

Fig. 21-11. Typical cross section of a horizontal butt weld on pipe, showing bead placement.

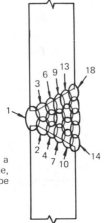

Fig. 21-12. Procedures for a horizontal butt weld on pipe, no-backup ring, EXX10-type electrode.

First pass: 1/8''   EXX10   80 to 110 amp DC+
Subsequent passes: 5/32''   EXX10   120 to 150 amp DC+
                                      or
                    1/8''   EXX18   115 to 135 amp DC+

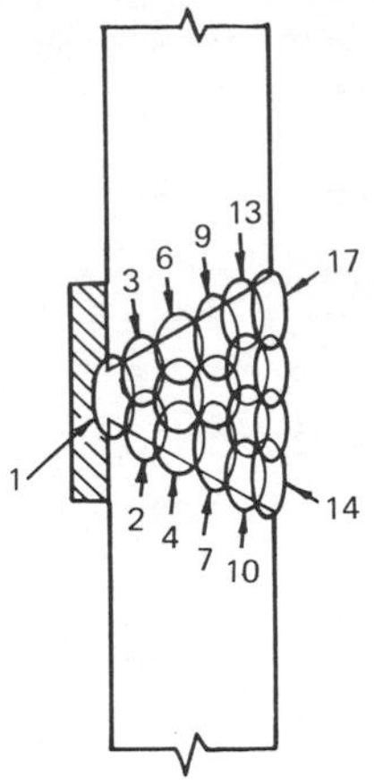

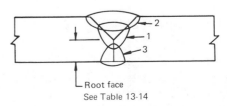

Fig. 21-13. Procedures for a horizontal butt weld on pipe, with backup ring, EXX18 electrode.

Passes 1 through 3: 3/32''   EXX18   85 to 105 amp DC+
Passes 4 through 9: 1/8''   EXX18   115 to 135 amp DC+
Subsequent passes: 5/32''   EXX18   140 to 160 amp DC+

Horizontal Procedures: Fig. 21-12 shows procedures, using EXX10 electrodes and a combination of EXX10 and EXX18. Fig. 21-13 shows procedures using EXX18 electrodes exclusively.

DOUBLE-ENDING

Double-ending is the welding of two or more lengths of pipe into one longer length. This is done frequently by submerged-arc automatic welding or a combination of submerged-arc and stick-electrode welding. It is practical and economical where the terrain permits hauling the double lengths of pipe to the field site.

One method of double-ending pipe is to assemble two lengths of pipe on a set of power-

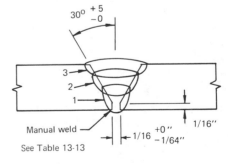

Fig. 21-14. Joint design and sequence for double-ending pipe with submerged-arc (stick-electrode stringer bead).

Fig. 21-15. Joint design and welding sequence for double-ending pipe with automatic submerged-arc welding.

TABLE 21-12. Procedures for Double-Ending Pipe (manual stringer bead, finish with submerged-arc)

Wall Thickness (in.)	All*	1/4		3/8		1/2	
Pass Number	1	2	3	2	3	2	3 - 5
Electrode Size	5/32	1/4		1/8		1/8	
Current (amp) DC+	160 - 180	350	400	450	600	475	600
Volts	. . . .	27	31	29	33	30	33
Arc Speed (in./min)	13 - 16	26	29	26	24	26	24
Electrode Req'd (lb/ft)	0.090	0.127		0.240		0.513	
Flux Req'd (lb/ft)	. . . .	0.10 - 0.14		0.19 - 0.25		0.40 - 0.54	
Total Time (hr/ft)	0.0138	0.0146		0.0160		0.0326	

*Manual stringer bead is used for all wall thicknesses. For manual electrode, see Fig. 13-5. Add manual time to submerged-arc time to get total time.

driven rolls. The joint is lined-up with an internal line-up clamp, and the first bead is made manually as described under vertical-down techniques. The second and third beads are made with submerged-arc while the pipe is rotated under an automatic welding head. The joint preparation shown in Fig. 21-14 and the submerged-arc procedures given in Table 21-12 are recommended.

Another method for double-ending pipe is to make all passes automatically. This method requires a joint preparation, as shown in Fig. 21-15. First, the two submerged-arc beads are made on the outside while the pipe is rotated under the automatic head. The third bead is made from the inside of the pipe. The automatic head is mounted at the end of a long boom that positions the head over the seam through the open end of the pipe. Procedures for the automatic welding are given in Table 21-13.

TABLE 21-13. Submerged-Arc Procedures for Double-Ending Pipe

Wall Thickness (in.)	1/4		3/8		1/2	
Root Face (in.)	5/32		1/4		1/4	
Electrode Size	1/8 or 5/32		1/8 or 5/32		1/8 or 5/32	
Pass Number	1,2	3	1 - 3	4	1 - 4	5
Current (amp) DC+	575	650	700	700	700	700
Volts	32	31	34	33	34	34
Arc Speed (in./min)	60	60	55	55	50	40
Electrode Req'd (lb/ft)	0.167		0.277		0.422	
Flux Req'd (lb/ft)	0.15 - 0.20		0.25 - 0.34		0.38 - 0.50	
Total Time (hr/ft)	0.0100		0.0145		0.0210	

API PROCEDURE AND QUALIFICATION TESTS

Procedures and operators for welding cross-country pipe lines are qualified by API Standard 1104. For complete details, the standard should be consulted. The following is a brief resume of the tests and requirements.

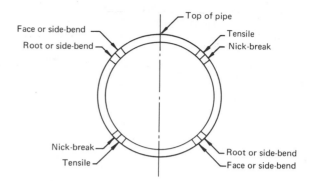

Fig. 21-16. Location of test specimens on pipe from 4-1/2 to 12-3/4-in. in diameter for API qualification tests.

Location of Specimens: Test specimens are cut from the pipe as shown in Fig. 21-16. In the field, the specimens are torch-cut and ground to size. In the shop, specimens are machined rather than ground; machining is the preferred method.

Tensile Requirements: Tensile strength of the weld and the fusion zone must be equal to or greater than the minimum specified tensile strength of the pipe. If the specimen breaks in the plate, the tensile strength must be at least 95% of the minimum specified for the plate.

It is not uncommon for a satisfactory test to break in the weld. This is because there are no maximum strengths specified for the plate, and the tensile strength of the plate may be considerably higher than that of the weld metal.

Nick-Break Test: This test is intended to expose any slag inclusions, gas pockets, or lack of fusion. The specimen is notched with a hack saw, and then broken to expose the interior of the weld. The exposed surfaces must show complete penetration and fusion. These must be no more than six gas pockets per square inch of surface area and no gas pocket larger than 1/16-in. Slag inclusions must not be more than 1/32-in. deep or 1/8-in. (or one-half the wall thickness) in length, and there shall be at least 1/2 in. of sound metal between inclusions.

Bend Tests: Specimens are prepared for bend tests by removing all weld reinforcement from both sides. Bending is done in a fixture as specified in API Standard 1104. The weld is unacceptable if the test produces a crack or defect with the largest dimension greater than 1/8-in. or one-half the wall thickness of the pipe, whichever is smaller. Cracks at the edges of the specimen that are less than 1/4-in in the greatest dimension can be disregarded.

CODES FOR IN-PLANT PIPING

For consistent high-quality work on in-plant piping, the welding procedure and the weldor should be qualified under some recognized national code. The ASME Boiler and Pressure Vessel Code, Section IX — *Welding Qualifications,* is the code most used to qualify weldors for power piping work. For a detailed review of operator's qualifica- tion tests for in-plant welding, see *Pipefitter Welder's Review of Metal-Arc Welding for Qualification Under ASME Code Rules.* This is published by The National Certified Pipe Welding Bureau, 5530 Wisconsin Ave., Washington, D.C. 20015.

Resistance Welding

Resistance welding is a high-production process for the joining of metals. It requires specialized machinery, and the student of welding will probably encounter the process only after he has been employed in a company engaged in the machine production of metal parts. Not withstanding the fact that the student will have little or no experience with resistance welding during his training, it is important that he have background knowledge on the process.

In resistance welding, the pieces to be joined are placed between two electrodes, which are the basic "tools" of the process. They furnish not only heat — via electric current — but also pressure. The resistance of the metal to the passage of a high-amperage, low-voltage electric current is the source of heat, and the power-actuated movement of the electrodes is the source of pressure. Sound welds are produced by accurate control and timing of current and pressure.

An important advantage of resistance welding is that there is no necessity for using consumable materials, such as electrodes, fluxes, inert gases, oxygen, or acetylene. The machinery operates without the need for replacement of consumable substances.

Most resistance welding machines operate on single-phase AC power. A step-down transformer converts the power-line voltage on the primary to a

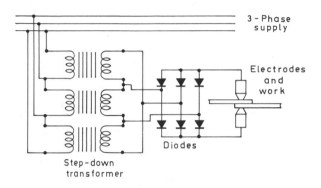

Fig. 22-2. Basic power circuit for a three-phase rectifier welder.

low voltage on the secondary, usually one to 25 volts, and the work to be welded forms a part of the secondary circuit (see Fig. 22-1). Even though the transformer is single-phase, it is usually connected to a three-phase power system; the high current required for resistance spot welding momentarily unbalances the three-phase system.

A three-phase resistance spot-welding machine consists of a three-phase step-down transformer with diodes connected to the secondary (see Fig. 22-2). The water-cooled silicon diodes are connected in parallel, the number depending on the capa-

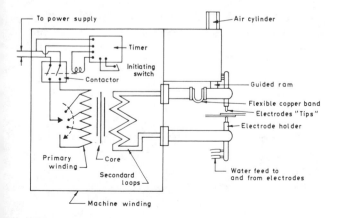

Fig. 22-1. Schematic of basic single-phase resistance spot-welding machine.

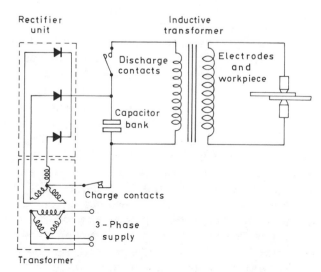

Fig. 22-3. Basic power circuit for a capacitor-discharge welder.

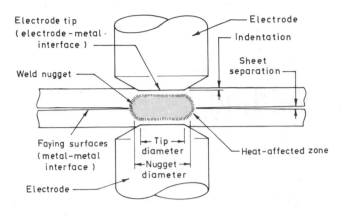

Fig. 22-4. Features of the resistance spot-weld process.

city of the machine. Another type of three-phase machine is the capacitor-discharge type (see Fig. 22-3). A bank of capacitors is charged from a three-phase rectifier and then discharged into an inductive transformer, the work being a part of the transformer secondary. Such machines are used for spot-welding dissimilar metals or delicate parts, as in the electronics industry.

All of these systems can be supplied with highly developed control units to regulate the electrode force, time, and welding energy. The pressure at the electrodes, which furnishes the "forging" action, is usually applied by air or hydraulic cylinders. In most cases, the upper electrode is movable. The electrode pressure may also be supplied by motor-driven rams, by foot and hand levers, or by other means.

METHODS OF RESISTANCE WELDING

There are five different methods of resistance welding — three for lap joints and two for butt joints. Lap joints are used in *spot, seam,* and *projection* welding, the parts to be welded being overlapped sufficiently to provide enough area for the weld. With the *flash* and *upset* butt methods, the parts to be welded are butted together end-to-end.

Spot welding is one of the most commonly used resistance welding methods. The weld is in the form of a spot averaging 1/4" to 3/8" in diameter. A lap joint is used, and the spot weld is made by two opposing electrodes, called "tips." When the tips are brought in pressure contact with the work on opposing sides of the lap, and current flow initiated (see Fig. 22-4), resistance to current is greatest at the interface between workpieces. Fusion takes place, moving from the interface outward, and a weld nugget is formed. As the electrodes withdraw, the nugget solidifies, effecting a spot bond.

Projection welding is a variation, differing from conventional spot welding in that projections or embossments at predetermined points are used to localize current flow and resistance heating (see Fig. 22-5). The projections — up to five or more — are usually made in only one of the lapped parts to be welded. Instead of tips, the electrodes have flat surfaces. The resistance heat is localized at the projections, which quickly rise to plastic temperatures, at which the projections are flattened and welded to the opposing metal by the pressure from the electrodes.

Projection has several advantages. Since the contacting area of the electrodes is relatively large, burning of electrodes — as with electrodes of small face diameter — is reduced and electrode life is prolonged. With electrodes of large face areas — often die-shaped — many individual spot welds can be made at one stroke of the machine. Production rates can thus, be increased — essentially to the extent that the electrode dies can give coverage of projection spots. Against this increase in welding rate must be balanced, of course, the cost of producing the projections in the part or parts.

Another advantage of projection welding is the control over heat balance. Materials of different thicknesses can be joined more easily by concentrating the heat in the part bearing the projections — usually the thicker piece. When dissimilar metals are to be joined, the projections are formed on the material of higher electrical and thermal conductivity. The rapid conduction of heat away from the projections allows designing the setup so contacting spots reach the proper temperature before the projections collapse.

Seam welding is a variation of spot welding in which "wheels" (see Fig. 22-6) are used in place of electrode tips. The opposing wheels carry the metal to be welded between them at a constant speed and pressure. If the weld is to be continuous, a series of spots so close together that they overlap is used. This joint is both liquid and gas-tight and is commonly used in the manufacture of tanks and containers. The seam welder can also be set to produce intermittent welds of any desired lengths

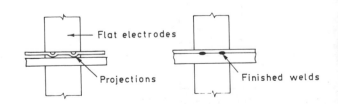

Fig. 22-5. Projection welding uses projections to localize resistance heating.

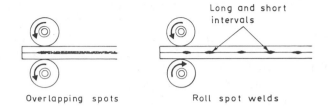

Fig. 22-6. The "wheel" electrodes used with seam welding can be fashioned to produce either continuous or intermittent resistance welds.

and intervals. Such welds are referred to as "roll spot welds."

With seam welding, individual pressure strokes of tips or electrode dies are eliminated — thus, a time savings in the opening and closing of electrodes results.

Flash butt welding requires a machine usually having one stationary and one movable platen on which are mounted the parts to be butt-welded (see Fig. 22-7). The clamps holding the parts are electrically energized, so that a flash arc occurs when the machine brings the parts, abutting each other together. The flash welder is usually a "table-top" machine with a movable platen and with dies and clamps sliding in rigid and accurate guides. A transformer is usually mounted in the base of the machine below the flash-welding area.

The principle of flash butt welding is illustrated in Fig. 22-7. Flashing occurs when initial contact produces an arc. The arc generates the heat needed to bring the parts to plastic temperature. While metal is being "burned off" by flashing, the parts are moved toward each other at a carefully controlled and accelerated rate. As the molten stage is reached, pressure is increased (the "upset force"), joining the two parts. The current is shut off as upset action occurs. The upset action expels the slag and molten metal, and the pressure forces the parts together in perfect fusion.

Following welding, the clamps are removed and the joined piece cleaned. Sometimes the joint is machined, in which case no visible evidence of a joint may be left.

Upset butt welding is very similar to flash butt welding, a difference being in the initial spacing of the parts. With upset butt welding, the parts are in

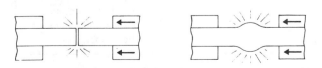

Fig. 22-7. Principle of the flash butt welder. An arc occurs at (A), melting the butt edges, and joining occurs at (B) when the parts meet under pressure.

contact and pressure applied before current is initiated. With application of current, heat of resistance causes the butt edges to become plastic, and the pressure forges them together.

This was the original method of resistance butt welding, but it has been replaced almost entirely by flash welding. The heat generated by the arc flash required less current, making flash welding more economical.

ELECTROBRAZING

Electrobrazing is another form of metal bonding made possible by taking advantage of electrical resistance heating. In electrobrazing, a brazing material is preplaced between the parts at the joint. A standard type of spot welder, set to give longer timing cycles, may be used to provide brazing heat. Longer timing cycles are usually needed because, when brazing, larger joint areas than weld spots are normally involved. Fig. 22-8 illustrates the basic principles of electrobrazing.

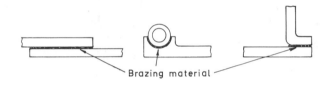

Fig. 22-8. With electrobrazing, a preplaced brazing material is placed in the joints before resistance heating is applied.

Electrobrazing is used extensively in the manufacture of electrical and electronic parts. Joints are quickly and uniformly made at much lower cost than mechanical or soldered joints. Electrobrazed joints have greater strength in shear than ordinary mechanical or soldered joints. Where equal strength is specified, joint lap size can be reduced, thus saving material. With silver brazing alloys, superior electrical conductivity can be produced in joints intended to carry electrical current.

FACTORS AFFECTING RESISTANCE WELD QUALITY

A resistance welder, whatever its type, is a complicated machine. Its settings, in respect to amount of current, the timing of current on-and-off cycles, the electrode pressure, and the shape and condition of the electrodes, affect weld quality. The requirements for each type of job are precise and must be worked out on the job and often in cooperation with the manufacturer of the welding equipment.

Certain generalizations can be made, however, about the machine factors affecting weld quality.

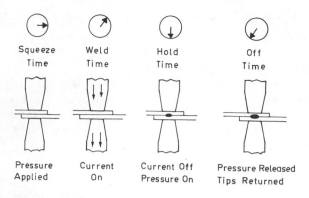

Fig. 22-9. The four basic timing steps that must be precisely controlled in resistance spot welding.

For instance, the current magnitude and timing can be said to be critial factors, and current magnitude and timing will depend on the materials being welded. When welding low-carbon steel, a successful weld may be produced by a wide range of current magnitude and timing, while aluminum requires a large amount of current in a short time. Current magnitude is controlled at the transformer by regulators at the primaries and usually also at the secondaries. Current timing is controlled by the timer and contactor mechanisms, which regulate the time the current is on and off during the welding cycle. Figure 22-9 illustrates the steps that must be precisely timed in spot resistance welding.

COMPARATIVE VALUES OF WELDING TIP AREAS
Adapted from *"Resistance Welding,"* by Wallace A. Stanley

400% TOO SMALL (A)	PROPER NEW TIPS (B)	56% TOO LARGE (C)	125% TOO LARGE (D)	300% TOO LARGE (E)
1/8" Diameter	1/4" Diameter	5/16" Diameter	3/8" Diameter	1/2" Diameter
2,000 amperes only would be required (T)	9,823 amperes would be required (T)	15,337 amperes would be required (T)	22,100 amperes would be required (T)	39,300 amperes would be required (T)
127,640 lbs. sq. in. pressure (*)	31,960 lbs. sq. in. pressure (*)	20,470 lbs. sq.in. pressure (*)	14,200 lbs. sq. in. pressure (*)	7,990 lbs. sq. in. pressure (*)
RESULT Four times too much pressure and current. Very severe indentation and spitting from high current density. CORRECTION Cut pressure to 1/4. Cut current to 1/4.	RESULT This is the correct tip size, current and pressure, for which adjustments are made.	RESULT This represents only 60% of the proper pressure. Produces a borderline weld unless current and pressure are adjusted.	RESULT Only 43% of the required pressure and current is present. Even with increased current and pressure a large weak weld would result.	RESULT This size produces only 25% of the required current and pressure. No weld would result. Before this condition is reached the tips should be dressed and brought back to the proper size.

(T) Current density required for this gage to be 200,000 amps. per sq. in. Setting is 9,900 amps for condition (B).
(*) 5"-diameter air cylinder at 80 lbs. air pressure — 1570 lbs. on ram.

Fig. 22-10. How electrode diameters affect welding parameters and weld quality.

Pressure is the least accurately controlled of the three machine factors affecting weld quality — current, time, and pressure. However, it can have significant effects on quality. Insufficient pressure will result in weak welds, surface burning, and other defects, while excessive pressure will result in indentation and insufficient welding heat because of lowered contact resistance. Resistance changes with pressure, since pressure affects the "degree of contact." Contact is increased with increased pressure — and thus resistance heating decreased — and vice versa. An optimum pressure gives optimum resistance and heating — and that is the objective in pressure regulation.

The condition of the electrodes has a decisive influence on weld quality. Alignment, surface area, and cleanliness are factors. Surface area is especially important. By necessity, the electrodes are made from copper-base alloys, which are relatively soft materials. The heat and pressure exerted on the electrodes tend to cause the face diameter to enlarge by mushrooming. Likewise, cleaning operations tend to enlarge the contact surface. As a result, it is necessary to occasionally dress the electrodes as closely as possible to their original size and shape. This is usually done by especially designed tools, but may be done by turning on a metal lathe.

Too much emphasis cannot be placed on the effect that an increase in face diameter has on the quality of the weld. Figure 22-10 illustrates the effects of varying tip diameters on welding parameters and weld quality.

WELDABILITY OF METALS BY RESISTANCE HEATING

Almost all metals that are weldable by any process are usually weldable by some form of resistance heating. Likewise, most metal combinations are weldable. Difficulties are encountered when there are differences in electrical resistances, melting temperatures and plastic temperature ranges (see Table 22-1).

Various metals differ greatly in their weldability, mainly because of their variable resistance to the electric current. Metals of high resistance require less current but more exacting control, while those that are better conductors require greater amounts of current. Pressure is also an important variable in adjusting the welder for a successful weld. Table 22-2 rates the comparative weldability of some metals commonly spot-welded.

The resistance of the parts to be welded is proportional to their thicknesses. As the thickness increases, so must the current magnitude and timing. The condition of the surface of the parts also affects welding.

Any dirt, grease, rust, or oxides between the surfaces to be welded result in increased resistance, which in turn will result in increased heat, metal spitting from between the parts, and overheated brittle welds. Galvanized, tin plating, and other coatings usually cause fouling of the electrodes in the form of "metal pickup." This, then, causes many of the same characteristics that result from dirt on the electrodes. The final result is usually a poor weld.

TABLE 22-1. Metals That Can Be Resistance Welded
(X Denotes combinations that can be welded)

Metals	Aluminum	Stainless Steel	Brass	Copper	Galv. Iron	Steel	Lead	Monel	Nickel	Nichrome	Tin Plate	Zinc	Phos. Bronze	Nickel-Silver	Terne Plate
Aluminum	X										X	X			
Stainless		X	X	X	X	X		X	X	X	X		X	X	X
Brass		X	X	X	X	X		X	X	X	X	X	X	X	X
Copper		X	X	X	X	X		X	X	X	X	X	X	X	X
Galv. Iron		X	X	X	X	X	X	X	X	X	X		X	X	X
Steel		X	X	X	X	X		X	X	X	X		X	X	X
Lead							X					X		X	X
Monel		X	X	X	X	X		X	X	X	X		X	X	X
Nickel		X	X	X	X	X	X	X	X	X	X		X	X	X
Nichrome		X	X	X	X	X	X	X	X	X	X		X	X	X
Tin Plate	X	X	X	X	X	X	X	X	X	X	X		X	X	X
Zinc	X		X	X			X					X			
Phos. Bronze		X	X	X	X	X		X	X	X	X		X	X	X
Nickel-Silver		X	X	X	X	X	X	X	X	X	X		X	X	X
Terne Plate		X	X	X	X	X	X	X	X	X	X		X	X	X

TABLE 22-2. Weldability Ratings of Various Metals*

Metal	Rating**
Low-Carbon Steel (SAE1010)	A-100
Stainless Steel (18-8)	B- 75
Aluminum 1100	C-250
Aluminum 5052	C-300
Magnesium (DOW "M")	B-290
Magnesium (Dow "J")	B-230
Nickel	B-130
Nickel Alloys (Monel, etc.)	B- 65
Nickel-Silver (30% Ni)	B-125
Nickel-Silver (10% Ni)	B-100
Copper	F-350
Silver	F-350
Red Brass (80% Cu)	E-150
Yellow Brass (65% Cu)	C-150
Phosphor Bronze (95% Cu)	C-120
Silicon Bronze (up to 3% Si)	B- 80
Aluminum Bronze (8% Al)	C- 80

* A — excellent, B — good, C — fair, D — poor, E — extremely poor, F — impractical.

** Relative weldability ratings of metals most commonly spot welded. The letter prefix indicates the general weldability, everything considered, in relation to low-carbon steel (rated A, or excellent). Stainless, for instance, required more pressure and more exacting control, hence its rating is B, or good. Stainless is readily weldable, but for best results carbon should be kept below 0.08%. The figure in the rating index indicates the amount of current required for a weld, hence stainless required only 75% as much as low-carbon steel.

When the fitup is poor and the parts have to be forced together by excessive pressure from the electrodes, resistance is increased. Overheating, "spit out" between the parts, and burning may occur.

DETERMINING RESISTANCE-WELD QUALITY

The quality of resistance welds can be determined by both nondestructive and destructive methods.

Nondestructive methods involve observation of what constitutes desirable characteristics and faults. Thus, a good spot weld should be nearly round and show only a slight area of discoloration around its perimeter. The weld diameter should be nearly equal to the face diameter of the electrodes. Indentation should be slight or absent. No undesirable characteristics should be present.

One undesirable characteristic in spot welds would be an asymmetrical spot, as illustrated in

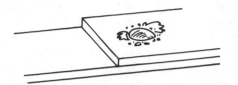

Fig. 22-12. Surface spitting and burrs are indicative of improper procedures.

Fig. 22-11. This indicates misalignment of the electrodes, metal pickup, or dirt on the electrodes. The weld spot would be something other than round in shape.

Another undesirable characteristic would be evidence of surface spitting and burns, as illustrated in Fig. 22-12. These are caused by such factors as too much heat, not enough pressure, excessive current, dirty electrodes or materials, too short a "squeeze" time, or too short a hold time after the weld has been made.

Still another undesirable characteristic is illustrated by Fig. 22-13 — severe discoloration around the spot. The usual causes are excessive current magnitude or duration and excessive pressure and/or heat.

If the weld diameter is too small in relation to the face diameter of the electrodes, poor weld quality is also suggested. Some causes of too-small weld diameters are insufficient current or duration of current, welds too close to each other, and inconsistent welding current.

X-ray tests are, of course, another way to be assured of weld quality without destroying the assembly. X-rays will detect small cracks, internal porosity, and other defects not visible to the eye.

Destructive tests — rather than nondestructive — are necessary to get assessments of the mechanical properties being produced by the procedures and machine settings. Destructive tests, however, do not necessarily have to be conducted with production parts; they can be made with simulated parts made from scrap material. The specimens developed for test purposes are tested to destruction to determine such properties as tensile strength, ductility, shear strength, and fatigue resistance. Certain standard destructive tests are used to evalu-

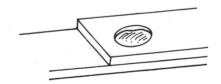

Fig. 22-11. An asymmetrical and unevenly indented spot weld suggests defects in procedures.

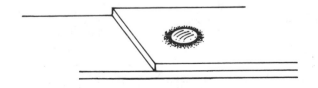

Fig. 22-13. Severe discoloration around a spot weld is an indication of faulty machine performance.

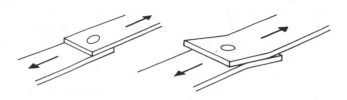

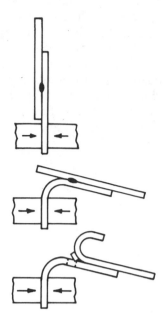

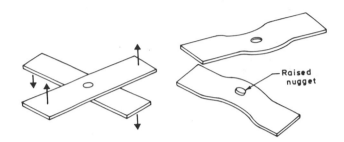

Fig. 22-16. The shear tension test gives a measure of the shear strength of the spot weld.

Fig. 22-14. The peel test for evaluating the quality of a spot weld. Here, the nugget torn out of the lower part is approximately the size of the electrode face, suggesting a high-quality weld.

Fig. 22-17. In the cross tension test, a spot-welded cross assembly is pulled apart. After pulling, the parts are likely to be deformed, as shown at the right.

ate spot welds. These are the peel, twist, drop-impact, and fatigue-resistance tests.

The **peel test** is the one most commonly used. One section of the spot-welded test specimen is secured in a vise and the upper piece is literally peeled from it by means of a grasping tool. A torn-out button or nugget will be produced on one piece. The quality of weld is evaluated by the following considerations:

Size of Nugget — The nearer the size of the torn-out nugget to the size of the face diameter of the electrode, the better the rating for the quality of the weld.

Nugget Shape — If the nugget is V-shaped and shows some of the metal from the opposing part attached, the weld can be assumed to be sound. A perfectly round nugget suggests brittle characteristics in the weld.

The peel test is illustrated by Fig. 22-14.

The **twist test**, illustrated by Fig. 22-15, is made by welding two pieces together with one spot and then twisting them radially, tearing apart and leaving a round button and a hole. This test can be done with the hands on thin material and gives a good indication of the size spot being produced by the machine. The button is subject to visual inspection, and the operator should look carefully for evidence of brittleness, cracking, or porosity.

Tension tests are of three types: shear, cross, and "U" tension. These tests give definite measures of weld strengths.

Shear tension implies pulling the specimens apart, as illustrated in Fig. 22-16. When done on a tensile-testing machine, an exact measure of shear strength is obtained.

Cross tension is one of the most revealing of the tension tests in that cracks, flaws, and blow-holes are revealed. It consists of fastening the ends of a crossed assembly to a rigid structure and

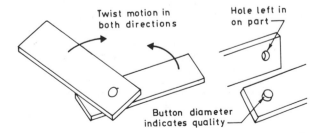

Fig. 22-15. The twist test is easy to perform on thin materials. The operator should look for evidence of brittleness, cracking, and porosity.

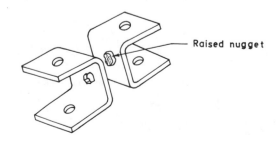

Fig. 22-18. The "U" tension test gives a measure of tensile strength.

pulling them apart. This leaves the parts arched in the middle and the nugget raised on the surface (Fig. 22-17), thus revealing the flaws, if any. A variation of the test is to drop a known weight on the bottom crossed part, while the top part is held stationary. This is called the drop-impact test.

The "U" tension test is illustrated by Fig. 22-18. Special clamps are used to maintain the "U" shape of the pieces while the spot-welded assembly is pulled apart. Tensile strength is thus measured.

Fatigue testing of spot-welded specimens is done with standard fatigue-testing machines. With the test machine set to simulate the type of repeated stress the weld will be subject to in service, the test is run to fatigue failure and the number of cycles of stress noted.

Weld Quality; Nondestructive Testing

The weldor is only partially responsible for the "quality" of a weld. The engineer who designed the joint, the supervisory personnel who selected the process and procedures, and the workers who prepared the joint and assembled the parts are also responsible. Likewise, the technicians who pretested mockups or simulated specimens and those who qualified procedures share in assuring the quality of the final weld. The inspector has nothing to do with the execution of the weld — merely passes judgement on it.

The term "weld quality" is relative in production welding. The application determines what is good or bad. Generally, any weld is a good weld if it meets appearance requirements and will continue indefinitely to do the job for which it is intended. But a weld can be "too good." This is the case when a high degree of quality has been obtained at excessive production cost and the buyer is getting no discernible value from the extra expenditure. Insisting on any method of inspection that serves no function is illogical as well as wasteful.

The first step, then, in assuring weld quality is to ascertain the degree required by the application. A standard should be established based on service needs. Engineering performance will be the main consideration in arriving at the standard, but appearance may also be important. A safety factor must, of necessity, be built into the standard, but it should be reasonable. Once the standard has been set, it is the responsibility of everyone concerned with the job to see that it is followed.

On the low side, the predetermined standard of quality should never be compromised. On the high side, there is no objection to extra quality, providing it has been obtained at no penalty in cost. If tests repeatedly show that the welds are exhibiting a degree of quality far greater than required by the standard, a cost reduction through modification of weldment design or procedures is possible.

Frequently, the standards are preset by prevailing specifications or engineering and legal codes. Sometimes such standards are ultraconservative, but when they apply they must be honored. The weldor can sometimes do his company or the customer a service by pointing out unrealistic specifications and the opportunities for cost savings, but the specifications must be adhered to rigidly until revised.

THE FIVE P'S THAT ASSURE QUALITY

After the quality standard has been established, the most important step toward its achievement is the selection of the best process and procedures. By giving attention to five "P's," weld quality will come about almost automatically, reducing subsequent inspection to a routine checking and policing activity. The five P's are:

1. **Process Selection** — the process must be right for the job.
2. **Preparation** — the joint configuration must be right and compatible with the welding process.
3. **Procedures** — to assure uniform results the procedures must be spelled out in detail and followed religiously during welding.
4. **Pretesting** — by full-scale mockups or simulated specimens the process and procedures are proved to give the desired standard of quality.
5. **Personnel** — qualified people must be assigned to the job.

In view of the various automatic and semiautomatic processes available, process selection imposes a challenging decision. Of all the processes, manual welding is the most versatile, but economic considerations necessitate its being ruled out in favor of a partially or fully mechanized process wherever such is applicable. Process selection is tied up integrally with the fill, follow, freeze, and penetration needs of the joint. Each process has its advantages and limitations, and each introduces problems affecting joint preparation, welding procedures, and operator training. The process that gives the correct balance between the needs of the joint in terms of fill, follow, freeze, and penetration is likely to be the one that gives optimum weld quality.

Manual and submerged-arc welded joints enjoy a "prequalified" status. Gas metal-arc and flux-cored arc-welded joints are also prequalified, but have strength and thickness limitations. (See AWS Structural Welding Code — D1.1-72.) Deviations from these prequalified joints may be accomplished by running prequalification tests, since practically all codes state that "other welding processes and procedures may be used, provided the contractor qualifies them in accordance with the prescribed requirements."

Joint preparations are standardized and specified by applicable codes. The decision as to joint preparation is made by the designer rather than the fabricator, with the latter usually given the choice of what process and procedures to use to make the weld with the prescribed preparation. The joint detail influences process selection, electrode size, and welding position. The joint preparation must be correct before welding is started, not only to meet specifications, but to give assurance of weld quality.

Reliable welding procedures are developed through firsthand experience. They should be completely detailed in advance of production work. A full-scale mockup of the joint, using the same type steel, sizes, and shapes that will be used on the job, should be made to test the procedures if such is possible. If a full-scale mockup is infeasible, a simulated setup should be used to produce specimens that can be destructively and nondestructively tested. By trial and error, all the procedure details for making an acceptable weld can be determined.

Pretesting production-size or simulated production specimens also test the process as well as the procedures. Once it has been ascertained that the procedures and the process give the desired quality, such test specimens can also be used as a final check on the qualifications of the operator.

The closer the conditions of test approach conditions of service, the more meaningful the results. The ideal would be service-life tests under slightly exaggerated conditions. Since this is usually impractical, simulated service tests are the next best choice. Specimen assemblies may be subjected to radiographic, ultrasonic, or other nondestructive inspection procedures to evaluate the weld quality. Or they may be prooftested or submitted to destructive tests to determine ultimate limits.

By proper use of process-procedure qualification — backed up by convincing test evidence — final inspection takes on the nature of a quality control activity. This is desirable; the intent should be to make the welding so deadly precise in giving the desired quality that all subsequent inspection is for the detection of the unexpected and unexplained, rather than the explainable defects.

Personnel qualification — the last of the five P's — can be evaluated in a preliminary way by the AWS Operator Qualification Test and the contractor's judgment. If a semiautomatic Process is to be used, some experience with it is desirable, or the weldor may require training. As mentioned previously, the welding of test specimens with the selected process and procedures will affirm the operator's capability.

QUALITY VERSUS ACCEPTABILITY

It is possible for a weld to be of "poor" quality by standards of inspection and judgement, yet perform its job admirably. If that weld is produced at a fraction of the cost of a weld that would be rated high-quality, there is no logical reason for increasing the manufacturing cost to obtain the high-quality weld. Acceptability is, thus, a consideration that must be balanced against the concept of quality in order to control fabrication costs and the cost of the product to the buyer. There is no point in welding a bracket to the undercarriage of a farm machine with a precisely laid, X-ray-quality weld if all the bracket supports is a lightweight dust shield and never in service will the weld be subject to view. If a weld of inferior appearance and strength can be made at a fraction of the cost that serves the function just as well, it is acceptable and just as good for the purpose.

The allowing of "acceptability" however, does not mean the toleration of sloppy or careless work. Rather, it means giving the joint what it needs by the most economical method at the best workmanship likely to prevail under the circumstances.

ABOUT WELD DEFECTS

Poor quality results from failure to follow instructions, poor workmanship, or from something being wrong with the process, procedures, equipment, preparation, or consumables. A defect such as an undercut is easily recognized, but a root crack or internal porosity is revealed only by the use of special inspection equipment. "Defect" is a relative term and can encompass any discontinuity in metal structure or any variation from the intended surface contour. If the defects in a weld are of a type specifically forbidden by the specifications, the weld is unacceptable. If the additive influence of singularly unimportant defects suggests that the weld will not meet quality standards, that weld is also unacceptable.

There is a tendency for inspectors to be too strict — and this can run up production costs. If the inspector demands X-rays free from porosity when the code allows a prescribed amount of porosity, he may be rejecting welds that would serve service purposes well and without the possibility of failure. It is an established fact that scatter-

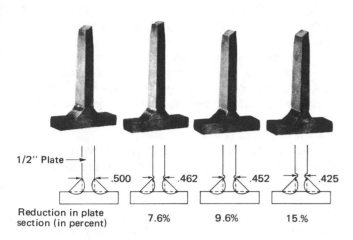

1/2" Plate

.500 .462 .452 .425

Reduction in plate
section (in percent)   7.6%   9.6%   15.%

Fig. 23-1. Samples were deliberately prepared to show the effect of undercut. All samples were pulled in tension under a static load. In all cases, failure occurred in the plate and not in the weld.

ed porosity much in excess of that permitted by some codes does not detract from the strength of the joint. In such instances, the defects are defects only to the extent that they deviate from the ideal.

Undercut is a defect on the vertical leg of fillet welds that also can be overrated in its significance. As Fig. 23-1 shows, an undercut reducing the vertical plate thickness in a T section as much as 15% has not impaired the strength of the joint in static loading. Unless there is concern about the performance of a weld under fatigue loading, there is no point for demanding repair of undercut on the average weldment.

Another defect controlled by standards and sometimes questionable, is the weld crater. Any arc-welding process or procedure produces a weld crater. The ability to fill this crater at the termination of a weld varies considerably with the welding current, weld size, and other factors. If these limitations are understood, and service requirements of the joint are considered, it should not be difficult to decide whether a crater must be filled.

Most codes make a general statement regarding crater filling. The AWS Structural Code D1.1-72 states in paragraphs 8.15.1.3 and 9.25.1.3: "All craters shall be filled to the full cross section of the weld."

These two statements appear harmless enough and, in fact, present no problem on long continuous welds. In this case, the start of each weld fills the crater left by the previous weld — a technique that any weldor can easily master. The only crater requiring special attention would be the final one at the end of the joint.

What happens on intermittent welds is entirely different. An example is the production of 5/16-in. fillet welds, each 3 inches long and spaced on 12-in. centers. A typical production welding pro-

cedure would specify the use of 1/4-in. electrode. But any procedure that will efficiently produce a sound weld of the required size will most certainly develop a pronounced crater that is very difficult to eliminate.

Strict adherence by the inspector to the code will require the weldor to change his procedure to one that is more conservative and calls for smaller-diameter electrodes, lower currents, slower travel speeds, or even changing to another electrode type having a slower deposition rate. An alternate approach would require the weldor to use a back-stepping method to fill the crater, which rarely produces a sound crater. In either case, the net result has a detrimental affect on weld speed and weld cost.

Where intermittent welds are acceptable, it would be more logical to require that the weld length be the total length exclusive of the crater. Thus, if 6-in. welds are required, they should measure 6 inches plus the crater. Then, the inspector's only concern with respect to craters would be to make sure they are free of cracks and undercut.

Weld cracks, wherever located or whatever their size, are a different matter from porosity, inclusions, undercut, or craters. A crack is a discontinuity that affects strength and one with a tendency to propagate. One of the most important jobs of the inspector is to detect cracks that will impair the serviceability of the weld.

THE ROLE OF INSPECTION

Whatever the standard of quality, all welds should be inspected, even if the inspection involves no more than the weldor glancing back over his work after running a bead. Testing may also be required, even in relatively rough weldments — such as leak-testing a container for liquids.

Inspection determines whether the prescribed standard of quality has been met. This function may be the responsiblity of the welding supervisor or foreman, a special employee of the company doing the welding, or a representative of the purchasing organization. The formal welding inspector may have a variety of duties. These may begin with interpretation of drawings and specifications and follow each step to the analysis of test results. His operations are both productive and nonproductive — depending on where they are applied.

Inspection after the job is finished is a policing action, rather than a productive function. Important as it is to assure quality, it is a burden added to the over-all production cost. No amount of after-the-job inspection will improve the weld; it merely tells what is acceptable and what must be reworked or rejected.

Inspection as the job progresses is a different matter. It detects errors in practice and defects while correction is feasible. It prevents minor defects from piling up into major defects and leading to ultimate rejection. Inspection while weld quality is in the making and can be controlled may justifiably be looked upon as a productive phase of cost, rather than an overburden.

Any program for assuring weld quality should, therefore, emphasize productive inspection and attempt to minimize the nonproductive type. This should be the guiding philosophy, even though its implementation may fall short. In most cases, such a philosophy means that visual inspection will be the main method of ascertaining quality, since it is the one method that can be applied routinely while the job is in progress.

VISUAL INSPECTION

In a sense, everyone connected with the job, as well as the formal inspector, participates in visual inspection. Visual inspection should begin before the first arc is struck. The materials should be examined to see if they meet specifications for quality, type, size, cleanliness, and freedom from defects. Foreign matter — grease, paint, oil, oxide film, heavy scale — that could be detrimental to the weld should be removed. The pieces to be joined should be checked for straightness, flatness, and dimensions. Warped, bent, improperly cut, or damaged pieces should be ordered for repair or rejected. Alignment and fitup of parts and the fixturing should be scrutinized. Joint preparation should be checked. Often, little more than a passing glance is required in this preliminary inspec-

tion, but, despite its almost casual nature, such inspection can be a significant factor in weld quality.

Inspection prior to welding also includes verification that the correct process and procedures are to be employed — that the electrode type and size and the equipment settings for voltage and amperage are as specified — and that provisions are made for the required preheat or postheat.

Assuming the preliminary requirements are in good order, the most productive inspection will take place while the weldment is being fabricated. Examination of a weld bead and the end crater may reveal quality deficiencies such as cracks, inadequate penetration, and gas and slag inclusions to a competent inspector. Figure 23-2 shows several types of defects that can be recognized visually.

On simple welds, inspection of a specimen at the beginning of the operation and periodically as the work progresses may be adequate. When more than one layer of filler metal is deposited, however, it may be desirable to inspect each layer before a subsequent layer is placed.

The root pass in a multi-pass weld is the most critical one from the standpoint of weld soundness. It is especially susceptible to cracking (Fig. 23-3), and, because it tends to solidify quickly, is prone to trap gas and slag. Subsequent passes are subject to a variety of weld defect-creating conditions that result from the shape of the weld bead or change in the configuration of the joint (Fig. 23-4). These can be visually detected by the weldor and repair cost minimized if the problem is corrected before welding progresses.

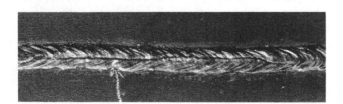

Cracking — can be detected visually unless the cracks are internal or are very fine. It is usually associated with excessively high current, insufficient preheat, insufficient bevel angle and/or highly restrained joints.

Surface Porosity — is often caused by excessive speed, rusty or dirty plate, wet electrode or flux, insufficient flux coverage, or critical arc-blow conditions.

Surface Slag Inclusions — are usually clues to faulty technique. Improper electrode manipulation, improper electrode size, or too steep a downhill angle are typical possibilities.

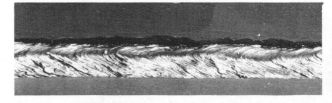

Undercut — results from poor procedural selections — may be due to too large an electrode or excessive current, voltage, or arc speed.

Fig. 23-2. Several types of defects that can be recognized visually.

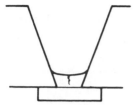

Fig. 23-3. The root pass in a multi-pass groove weld is especially susceptible to cracking because of the high shrinkage stresses.

Visual inspection at an early stage of the fabrication will also detect underwelding and overwelding. Underwelding (Fig. 23-5) is in violation of specifications and cannot be tolerated. Overwelding should be of as much concern to the purchaser's inspector as to those members of the shop responsible for monitoring costs, since it is a major cause of distortion. Usually the designer has specified a weld size approaching the limit possible in good practice. The weldor — perhaps wanting to make certain that the joint is strong enough, or having been criticized for making undersize welds — takes it upon himself to add 1/16 inch to a 1/4-in. fillet. Since the weld metal deposited increases as the square of the size, the 1/16-in. increase in leg size increases the amount of weld metal deposited 56%, and has the same effect on shrinkage stress and cost. Figure 23-5 illustrates how overwelding gives this exponential increase.

Visual inspection after the weldment has been completed is also useful in evaluating quality, even if ultrasonic, radiographic, or other methods are to be employed. Here , as with visual inspection as welding progresses, surface flaws such as cracks, porosity, and unfilled craters can be detected, and may be of such consequence that repairs are required or the work is rejected without use of subsequent inspection procedures. There is no point in

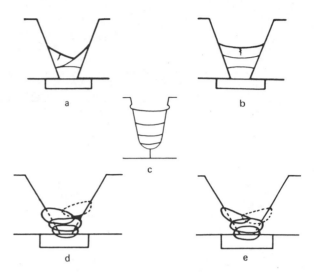

Fig. 23-4. The concave bead shape in (a) and (b) is partly responsible for the cracks. Groove welds are also prone to undercut along the edges, (c), which can trap slag when the next pass is made. Slag trapping can also be caused by a convex bead when there is too little space between the edges of the bead and the side of the joint (d). The correct bead shape is illustrated in (e). These defects should be corrected before welding progresses.

submitting an obviously bad weld to sophisticated inspection methods.

Dimensional variations from tolerances, warpage, and faults in appearance are detected visually at this stage. The extent and continuity of the weld, its size, and the length of segments in intermittent welds can be readily measured or noted.

Welds must be cleaned of slag to make inspection for surface flaws possible. A glass with a magnification of up to 10 diameters is helpful in detecting fine cracks and other defects. Shot-blasting should not be used in preparing the weld for examination, since the peening action may seal fine cracks and make them invisible.

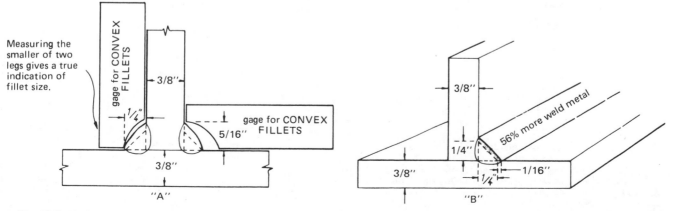

Fig. 23-5. Underwelding is a violation of specifications and cannot be tolerated, whereas overwelding is costly and serves no useful purpose. If 5/16-in. fillet welds were specified in "A," these welds would be undersize. If 1/4-in. fillet welds were specified, these welds would be overwelded. If 1/16-in. were added to both legs, as in "B," weld volume (and weld cost) would increase 56%.

**TABLE 23-1. Reference Guide to Major Methods for
the Nondestructive Testing of Welds**

INSPECTION METHOD	EQUIPMENT REQUIRED	ENABLES DETECTION OF	ADVANTAGES	LIMITATIONS	REMARKS
VISUAL	Magnifying Glass Weld-size gauge Pocket rule Straight edge Workmanship standards	Surface flaws — cracks, porosity, unfilled craters, slag inclusions. Warpage, under-welding, over-welding, poorly formed beads, misalignments, improper fitup.	Low cost Can be applied while work is in process, permitting correction of faults. Gives indication of incorrect procedures.	Applicable to surface defects only. Provides no permanent record.	Should always be the primary method of inspection, no matter what other techniques are required. Is the only "productive" type of inspection. Is the necessary function of everyone who in any way contributes to the making of the weld.
RADIO-GRAPHIC	Commercial X-ray or gamma units, made especially for inspecting welds, castings, and forgings. Film and processing facilities. Fluoroscopic viewing equipment.	Interior macroscopic flaws — cracks, porosity, blow holes, non-metallic inclusions, incomplete root penetration, undercutting, icicles, and burnthrough.	When the indications are recorded on film, gives a permanent record. When viewed on a fluoroscopic screen, a low-cost method of internal inspection.	Requires skill in choosing angles of exposure, operating equipment, and interpreting indications. Requires safety precautions. Not generally suitable for fillet-weld inspection.	X-ray inspection is required by many codes and specifications. Useful in qualification of weldors and welding processes. Because of cost, its use should be limited to those areas where other methods will not provide the assurance required.
MAGNETIC-PARTICLE	Special commercial equipment. Magnetic powders — dry or wet form; may be fluorescent for viewing under ultraviolet light.	Excellent for detecting surface discontinuities — especially surface cracks.	Simpler to use than radiographic inspection. Permits controlled sensitivity. Relatively low-cost method.	Applicable to ferromagnetic materials only. Requires skill in interpretation of indications and recognition of irrelevant patterns. Difficult to use on rough surfaces.	Elongated defects parallel to the magnetic field may not give pattern; for this reason the field should be applied from two directions at or near right angles to each other.
LIQUID-PENETRANT	Commercial kits, containing fluorescent or dye penetrants and developers. Application equipment for the developer. A source of ultraviolet light — if fluorescent method is used.	Surface cracks not readily visible to the unaided eye. Excellent for locating leaks in weldments.	Applicable to magnetic, nonmagnetic materials. Easy to use. Low cost.	Only surface defects are detectable. Cannot be used effectively on hot assemblies.	In thin-walled vessels, will reveal leaks not ordinarily located by usual air tests. Irrelevant surface conditions (smoke, slag) may give misleading indications.
ULTRASONIC	Special commercial equipment, either of the pulse-echo or transmission type. Standard reference patterns for interpretation of RF or video patterns.	Surface and sub-surface flaws, including those too small to be detected by other methods. Especially for detecting subsurface lamination-like defects.	Very sensitive. Permits probing of joints inaccessible to radiography.	Requires high degree of skill in interpreting pulse-echo patterns. Permanent record is not readily obtained.	Pulse-echo equipment is highly developed for weld inspection purposes. The transmission-type equipment simplifies pattern interpretation where it is applicable.

The objective of visual inspection at this stage is not only to seek defects not permissible under the quality standard, but also to give clues to what may be amiss in the entire fabrication process. If the inspector has a sound knowledge of the welding, he can read much from what he sees. Thus, the presence of excessive porosity and slag inclusions may be a tip-off to the fact that the current is not adequate, no matter what the dial readings may be. Subsequent tests will also give clues to faults in equipment or procedures, but the information acquired through visual examination permits corrections to be made before the results from complicated tests are available.

OTHER INSPECTION METHODS

Only the surface defects in welds are visible to the eye, and the specifications or applicable codes may require that the internal portion of the weld and the adjacent metal zones also be examined. Additionally, the application may require assurance that the chemical composition of the weld metal has not changed beyond specified limits. Thus, other inspection methods capable of gathering such information may be necessary.

These methods may be destructive or nondestructive. Destructive methods, obviously, cannot apply to production fabrication, other than for the testing-to-destruction of prototypes, "first units," or sparsely selected samples. In large weldments — building framing, for example — their use would be out of the question, but in an airframe component a periodic test-to-destruction may be regarded as essential to assurance of quality.

Nondestructive methods of testing welds include radiographic, ultrasonic, magnetic-particle, and penetrant techniques. Prooftesting is a mechanical method of determining whether the weld and other parts of the fabrication will withstand certain stresses encountered in service.

Chemical and metallographic methods of inspection may be completely nondestructive or destructive in a very minor way and to a reparable extent. If a sample for chemical or metallographic analysis is taken from a run-out portion of the weld bead, there is no damage; if a core drill is used to remove the sample from the weld proper, a hole results that must be repaired.

Table 23-1 is a condensed reference guide to the use of nondestructive inspection methods on steel weldments, and Table 23-2 shows a simplified scheme for determining the inspection method recommended for fillet and butt joints.

RADIOGRAPHIC INSPECTION

Because of its ability to reveal internal discontinuities in a variety of materials, radiography is one of the primary nondestructive test methods used in weld inspection. X-rays and gamma rays penetrate deeply into welds and show photographically such defects as porosity, nonmetallic inclusions, cracks, incomplete root penetration, and incomplete fusion.

Radiography makes use of the differential in penetration characteristics of radiation to examine materials for internal discontinuities. X-rays and gamma rays can penetrate materials that are opaque to light. In passing through dense materials, some of the radiation is absorbed. The amount of absorption at any point is dependent on the thickness and density of the material at that point. Therefore, the intensity of radiation emerging from the material and striking a sensitized photographic plate varies with any internal change in density, which change may result from voids or the presence of foreign substances. Detection of such variations, usually on film, amounts to "seeing" inside the material. Where the specimen has spots of less density (a void, crack, or nonmetallic inclusion) more rays pass through and "expose" the film more. When developed, darker areas, corresponding to the discontinuity, show up on the film. The resultant radiograph is similar to a black-and-white photographic negative. Examination of the radiograph is always from this negative, since too much detail is lost when making a positive. Typical weld defects as detected by radiography are shown in Table 23-3.

The operation of radiographic equipment and the interpretation of films are tasks requiring specialized training. Factors other than internal defects affect the "picture." Thus, surface defects,

TABLE 23-2. Inspection Methods for Fillet and Butt Joints

RECOMMENDED INSPECTION FOR:		
TYPE OF DEFECT	FILLET JOINTS	BUTT JOINTS
Undersize Weld	Visual (1)	Visual
Surface Porosity	Visual	Visual
Internal Porosity	Destructive	Radiographic
Undercut	Visual	Visual
Cracks	Magnetic-Particle Dye-Penetrant Visual Destructive (2)	Magnetic-Particle Dye-Penetrant Visual Ultrasonic Radiographic (3)
Lack of Penetration	Destructive Ultrasonic	Radiographic Ultrasonic
Slag Inclusions	Destructive Ultrasonic	Radiographic Ultrasonic

(1) Use fillet gages.
(2) Destructive test will reveal subsurface cracks.
(3) Radiographic inspection has its limitations in revealing crack-type defects.

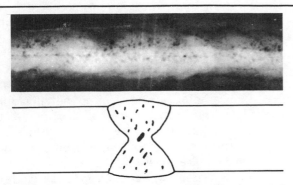

Porosity is shown as rounded shadows of varying size and density, occurring singly, in clusters, or randomly scattered.

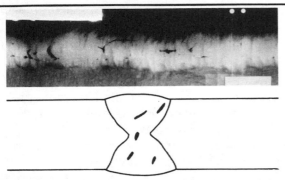

Nonmetallic Inclusions are usually indicated by elongated shadows of irregular shape, occurring singly, in a linear distribution, or scattered randomly.

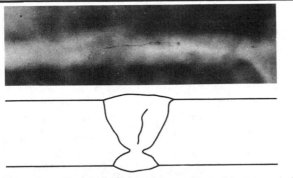

Cracks appear as fine, dark lines, which may be straight or wandering.

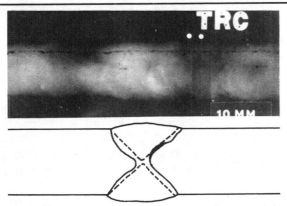

Incomplete Fusion gives dark shadows, usually of elongated shape.

TABLE 23-3. Radiographs of Weld Defects

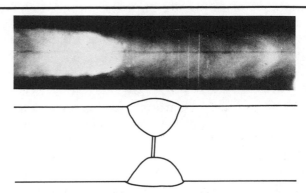

Incomplete Root Penetration is usually indicated as a straight, dark, continuous or intermittent line, often at the center of the weld.

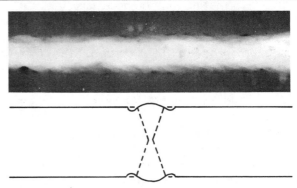

Undercutting shows up as a dark, linear shadow of wavy contour, occurring adjacent to the edge of the weld. This defect is usually detected visually, but its correct identification on the radiograph is needed to prevent misinterpretation as another type of defect.

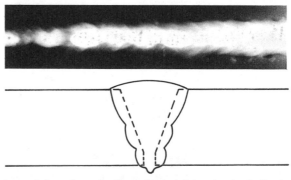

Icicles and Burnthrough give individual light circular indications or darkened areas of elongated or rounded contour that may be surrounded by light rings.

the angle of exposure, the geometry of the weld, and the accumulation of variations in one place will affect the interpretation. The making of radiographs and their interpretation are outside the province of the weldor — but the results of radiographs can determine whether a weldor has acceptable skill for an X-ray-quality job.

Radiography tests are used in the qualification of weldors for work on such projects as pipeline welding, structural steel erection, and pressure-vessel fabrication. The individual's ability to produce welds conforming to X-ray specifications is readily determined by the examination of welds produced on test plates. (See Chapter 24).

MAGNETIC-PARTICLE INSPECTION

Magnetic-particle inspection is a method of locating and defining discontinuities in magnetic materials. It is excellent for detecting surface defects in welds, revealing discontinuities that are too fine to be seen with the naked eye. With special equipment, it can also be used to detect defects

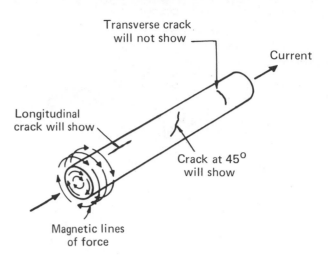

Fig. 23-7. When a current is passed through the workpiece, the magnetic lines of force are at right angles to the current, and discontinuities that are angled against the lines of force will create the diversion needed to produce magnetic poles on the surface. Under the illustrated arrangement, a transverse crack would not give an indication, but by changing the position of the probes 90 degrees it would be at right angle to the lines of force and would show.

that are close to the surface. Figure 23-6 gives a simple explanation of the principles of magnetic-particle testing. Circular magnetization results from longitudinal current transmission.

When using this method for weld inspection, probes are usually placed on each side of the area to be inspected and a high amperage passed through the workpiece. A magnetic flux is produced at right angles to the flow or current, which may be represented, as in Fig. 23-7, by circular lines of force within the workpiece. When these lines of force encounter a discontinuity, such as a longitudinal crack, they are diverted and leak through the surface out into the air, creating magnetic poles or points of attraction. A magnetic powder dusted onto the surface will thus cling to the leakage area more tenaciously than elsewhere, forming an indication of the discontinuity.

A workpiece can also be magnetized by putting it inside a solenoid. In this case, the magnetic lines of force are longitudinal and parallel with the workpiece. Transverse cracks show up under this arrangement. Figure 23-8 makes clear why the discontinuity must be angled against the magnetic lines of force for an indication to be developed. If the discontinuity is parallel to the lines of force, the diversion needed to break through the surface and create poles will not occur.

The magnetic-particle inspection method is much simpler to use than radiographic inspection, but has its limitations. It is applicable to ferromagnetic materials only. It cannot be used with austenitic steels. A joint between a base metal and a weld metal of different magnetic characteristics will create magnetic discontinuities, which may

CIRCULAR MAGNETIZATION

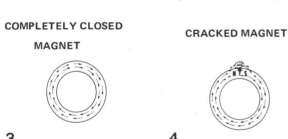

OPEN MAGNET

1.

An open magnet has two poles: North and South. The magnetic field between the two poles will attract and hold a nail.

PARTIALLY CLOSED MAGNET

2.

Bend the ends of the open magnet until they almost touch and the magnetic field between the poles will hold iron powder.

COMPLETELY CLOSED MAGNET

3.

Bend the magnet until its completely closed and fuse the ends. Now the magnet will not attract or hold iron powder because there is no polarity and the magnetic field is in a circle inside the ring. **THIS IS CIRCULAR MAGNETIZATION.**

CRACKED MAGNET

4.

A crack part way through the magnet will cause polarity and a magnetic field at the crack, which will hold iron powder and build up an indication of the crack. **THIS IS THE PRINCIPLE OF MAGNAFLUX INDICATIONS BY MEANS OF CIRCULAR MAGNETIZATION.**

Courtesy of Magnaflux Corporation

Fig. 23-6. A discontinuity, such as a crack, in a completely closed magnet causes polarity and the development of a magnetic field, which will hold iron powder and give an indication of the discontinuity.

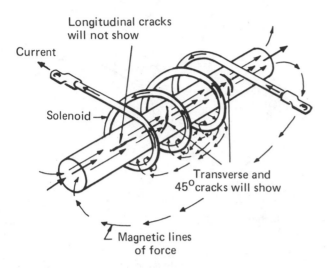

Fig. 23-8. When the magnetic flux is produced with a solenoid coil, the lines of force are parallel and longitudinal. A longitudinal crack will not show, but a transverse crack or one angled against the lines of force will produce an indication.

produce indications interpretable as unsoundness even though the joint is entirely sound. On the other hand, a true defect can be obscured by the powder clinging over the harmless magnetic discontinuity. The sensitivity of the method lessens with decrease in size of the defect. Sensitivity is less with round forms, such as gas pockets, and best with elongated forms, such as cracks.

To have external leakage, the magnetic field must be distorted sufficiently. Fine, elongated discontinuities, such as hairline cracks, seams, or inclusions, that are "strung" parallel with the magnetic field will not distort it sufficiently to develop leakage. Thus, no indication will result. By changing the direction of the field, however, the indications can be developed. To be certain that discon-

tinuities are detected, it is advisable to apply the field from two directions, preferably at right angles to each other.

Pieces to be inspected must be clean and dry. Wire-brushing or sand-blasting are satisfactory methods for cleaning welds. Surface roughness decreases the sensitivitiy, tends to distort the magnetic field, and interferes mechanically with formation of the powder pattern.

The shape, sharpness of outline, and width and height to which the particles have built up are features used for identifying discontinuities. When unusual patterns are produced, other test methods may be required to establish identity. Once a pattern has been interpreted by correlating it with the identification established by other methods, the interpretation can be applied to similar indications on other parts. Representative indications are shown in Fig. 23-9.

Since a powder pattern results from various types of discontinuities in the magnetic field, it is easy to mistake an irrelevant indication for a defect. As noted previously, a change in the magnetic characteristics of materials can create an irrelevant indication in the area of the interface. A change in section or a hole drilled in the part will tend to produce indications that have no significance in respect to weld soundness. These patterns are usually readily recognized for what they represent by their shapes and locations in the part. Abrupt changes in magnetic properties may occur at the edge of the heat-affected zone. The pattern will be fuzzy and diffused, running along the base metal close to the edge of the weld. It resembles the pattern caused by undercutting, a difference being that the particles are much less adherent. If a part is heat-treated or stress-relieved before subject-

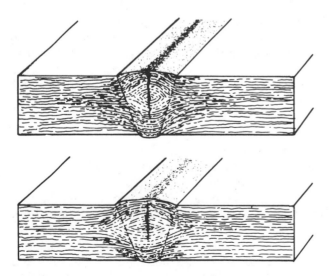

Surface Cracks give powder patterns that are sharply defined, tightly held, and usually built up heavily. The deeper the crack, the heavier the buildup of powder.

Subsurface Cracks produce a less sharply defined, fuzzy pattern, The powder is also less tightly adherent.

Crater Cracks may give a single line, running in almost any direction, or a pattern of lines. The pattern is small and occurs near the end of the weld.

Subsurface Porosity gives weak, poorly defined patterns, as do **Slag Inclusions**.

Fig. 23-9. Typical powder patterns and their interpretation in terms of weld defects.

ing to inspection, the magnetic characteristics of the heat-affected zone are restored and no indications will appear.

In the shop use of magnetic-particle inspection, judgment as to the significance of patterns can be guided by rules or standards based on experience or laboratory tests. Assuming that the inspector has ruled out the possibility of a false indication and has properly identified the indicated defect, he must then decide whether to pass or reject the part or require its repair. All defects do not affect the integrity of the part in service. Thus, slag inclusions and porosity may have no bearing on the serviceability of the weld. Surface cracks revealed by magnetic-particle inspection, however, should be considered potential stress raisers or focal points for fatigue and corrosion.

The equipment for magnetic-particle inspection is relatively simple. Commercial units, portable and stationary, provide for nearly every situation where the method is applicable.

Magnetic powders may be applied either by the dry or wet methods. Dry powder is dusted uniformly over the work with a spray gun, dusting bag, or atomizer. The finely divided magnetic particles are coated to give them greater mobility and are available in gray, black, and red colors. It is desirable that the particles impinge on the surface at low velocity and with just enough residual force after impact to move them to possible sites of leakage. Excess powder is removed with a light stream of air.

In the wet method, very fine red or black particles are suspended in water or light petroleum distillate. Powders for liquid suspension come from the manufacturer in either paste or dry form, prepared for use in water or oil baths. After the suspension has been made — in accordance with the manufacturer's instructions — it is flowed or sprayed onto the surface to be inspected, or the piece may be dipped into the liquid. The wet method is more sensitive than the dry method since extremely fine particles may be used; this enables detection of exceedingly fine defects. Red particles improve visibility on dark surfaces. When the particle coating is a dye that fluoresces under ultraviolet light, sensitivity is further increased. Fluorescent powders are excellent for locating discontinuities in corners, keyways, splines, deep holes, and similar locations.

Magnetic-particle inspection is applied to many types of weldments in production practice. The dry-powder method is especially popular for heavy weldments. Many steel weldments in aircraft manufacture are inspected by the wet method. Airframe parts are subjected to fatigue conditions, which

means that surface cracks cannot be tolerated. Since these weldments are relatively thin, magnetic-particle inspection will usually detect subsurface defects as well as show-up the finest surface cracks.

LIQUID-PENETRANT INSPECTION

Liquid-penetrant inspection is a nondestructive method for locating surface cracks and pinholes that are not visible to the naked eye. It is a favored technique for locating leaks in welds, and it can be applied where magnetic-particle inspection is useless, such as with austenitic steels or nonferrous metals. Two types of penetrant inspection are used — fluorescent and dye — which define the penetrating substance.

With fluorescent-penetrant inspection, a highly fluorescent liquid with good penetrating qualities is applied to the surface of the part to be examined. Capillary action draws the liquid into the surface openings. The excess liquid is then removed from the part, a so-called "developer" is used to draw the penetrant to the surface, and the resulting indication is viewed by ultraviolet (black) light. The high contrast between the fluorescent material and the background makes possible the detection of minute traces of penetrant.

Since penetration of minute openings is involved, the part to be inspected must be thoroughly clean and dry. Any foreign matter could close the openings leading to false conclusions. The penetrant is applied by dipping, spraying, or brushing. Time must be allowed for absorption of the material into the discontinuities — up to an hour or more in very exacting work.

When penetration is complete — or assumed to be adequate in accordance with testing specifications — the excess material is removed from the surface. If the penetrant is designed for water wash, a low-pressure water spray is used. Some commercial penetrant systems, however, require a solvent wash or what is called a "post emulsifier." With the latter, an emulsifier is applied to the part and allowed to remain on it for one to four minutes before the water spray. The instructions for use of emulsifiers and for the washing operation must be followed closely, since it is necessary that only excess penetrant be removed.

After the wash, the parts are dried if a dry developer is to be used. Hot air may be used to accelerate drying. A dry developer is applied with a powder gun, spray bulb, or by dipping the part into the powder. The developer draws the penetrant from the defects, making it accessible for viewing by ultraviolet light. If only large discontinuities are sought, a developer may not be required to make the indications visible. If a wet developer is to be used, drying of the part after removal of excess penetrant is not required. Wet developer is applied in the form of a colloidal water suspension by dipping or spraying, after which the part is dried by hot air.

Under ultraviolet light, the indications fluoresce brilliantly. The extent and depth of the discontinuity can be gaged by the width and length of the indication and the amount of penetrant bleeding to the surface. The darker the room in which viewing is done, the more brilliant the fluorescence and more easily very small indications are observed.

Dye-penetrant inspection is similar to fluorescent-penetrant inspection except that dyes visible under ordinary light are used. By eliminating the need for ultraviolet light, greater portability in equipment is achieved.

Liquid-penetrant inspection is widely used for leak detection. A common procedure is to apply fluorescent material to one side of a joint by brushing or spraying, allow adequate time for capillary action, and then view the other side of the joint with ultraviolet light. Dry developer may be used on the side being inspected to intensify the indications. In thin-walled vessels, this technique will show up leaks that are not ordinarily located by the usual air test with pressures of 5 to 20 psi. The sensitivity of the leak test decreases, however, when the wall thickness is over 1/4-in.

Penetrant inspection is also widely used in the inspection of large and small weldments for cracks and porosity when the materials are nonmagnetic. It must be remembered that only surface defects are revealed by this method. Fig. 23-10 shows a typical defect indication using dye penetrant.

ULTRASONIC INSPECTION

Ultrasonic inspection is a supersensitive method of detecting, locating, and measuring both surface and subsurface defects in metals. Flaws that cannot be discovered by other methods, and

Fig. 23-10. This hair-line intermittent crack typifies the type of weld defect for which dye-penetrant inspection techniques are particularly suited.

even cracks small enough to be termed microseparations, may be detected. In the practical inspection of welds, the sensitivity of the process is often curbed by designing or setting the equipment to give a response equivalent to a sensitivity of 2% of the metal thickness, thus giving results comparable with those obtained in radiographic inspection.

Ultrasonic inspection is based on the fact that a discontinuity or density change will act as a reflector for high frequency vibrations propagated through the metal. The searching unit of the pulse-echo type ultrasonic equipment contains a crystal of quartz (or other piezoelectric material). When a voltage is applied, the crystal vibrates rapidly, and imparts mechanical vibrations of the same frequency into materials it contacts.

When an ultrasonic probe is held against metal, the vibrational waves are propagated through the material until a discontinuity or change of density is reached. At these points, some of the vibrational energy is reflected back. If, in the meantime, the current that caused the vibration has been shut off, the quartz crystal can now act as a receiver to pick up the reflected energy. The reflected vibration causes pressure on the quartz crystal, which results in the generation of an electric current. Fed to a cathode-ray tube, this current produces vertical deflections in the horizontal base line. The pattern on the face of the tube is thus a representation of the reflected signal — and of the defect. The cycle of transmitting and receiving is repeated at a rate of 60 to 1,000 times per second.

Two types of cathode-ray-tube presentation are available — radio frequency (RF) and video. Most commercial units present the video pattern, although many inspectors believe RF provides more useful information on flaw identification. Figure 23-11 shows the video patterns produced on the cathode ray tube by different types of defects. It can be readily seen that expertness in interpretation of the deviations from the horizontal oscilloscope line is required, and a similar degree of expertness is needed for operation of the equipment. Interpretations are based on standard patterns made from reference plates, which are prepared in accordance with procedures approved by the ASTM, ASME, and AWS (D1.1-73, Section 6, Part III).

Pulse-echo ultrasonic equipment is available in compact form for field use. In addition to the greater sensitivity over radiographic equipment, ultrasonic inspection enables the probing of joints that are inaccessible to radiographic methods and is more dependable in locating all flaws. Operational costs are also less.

Another type of ultrasonic inspection equipment gives what is similar to a "television picture"

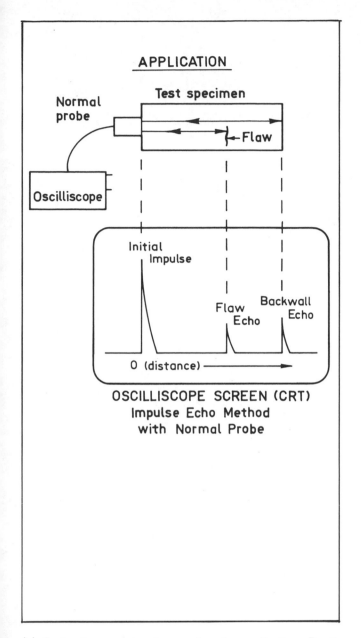

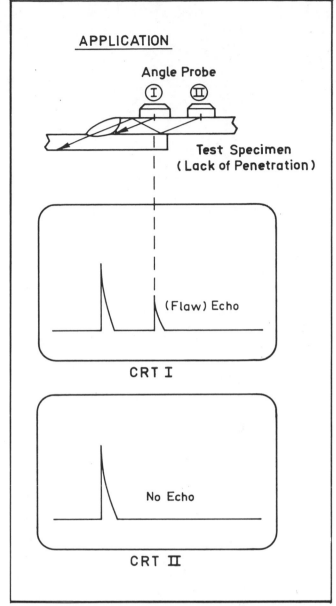

(a) A simple example of normal probe application. Depth of flaw can be easily determined.

(b) Angle probe detection of lack of penetration in a lap weld. This technique can be modified successfully for fillet and butt welds.

Fig. 23-11. Video patterns produced on the cathode-ray tube by different types of defects.

of the defect. Although not as popular as pulse-echo equipment, it is believed to have the potential for simplifying pattern interpretation where applicable, since the pattern is essentially a plane image. With this type of equipment, the ultrasonic energy from a generator is transmitted through the specimen, much as X-rays are transmitted in radiographic inspection. The transmitted energy impinges on a piezoelectric target, producing varying potentials on its face that are characteristics of the flaws in the specimen. The target is scanned with an electron beam, which is modulated by the varying surface potentials. This enables the development of a picture — a representation of the flaw — on a monitoring screen.

Welding Qualification Tests

Various codes and specifications require the welding procedures for a job be proved to give satisfactory welds by prescribed tests. In addition, the governing code or specifications may demand that the weldors and welding-machine operators be proved by tests as qualified for the job. All such tests are referred to as welding qualification tests.

The supervision of qualification tests has become a commercial enterprise, carried on by a number of reputable organizations including testing laboratories, consulting engineering firms, the American Bureau of Shipping, and some insurance companies. In some cases this supervision is exercised as part of the shop inspection of boilers, pressure vessels, pipelines, and other assemblies fabricated under code regulations. The clients of these organizations are design engineering firms, architects, or owners of the structure being built. The organizations act as inspectors or supervisors to insure the material and work meet the requirements of a code.

The fact that a "qualified" or "certified" weldor has been employed is not of itself absolute assurance that a given job has been satisfactorily welded. Passing a qualification test proves the weldor's ability to produce sound and acceptable welds under a given condition, but it is necessary to know in addition that a qualified procedure has been used and that the welded joints have been properly inspected before, during, and after completion.

When the testing laboratory is called upon to certify that a weldor has qualified under a certain code, the inspector witnesses the welding of the specimens (often at the contractor's plant or on the job site in the case of field work), marks them for identification, and witnesses the testing of the specimens. Cost is roughly between 50 to 100 dollars per test (plate test), and this cost is borne by the contractor. All authoritative codes require the manufacturer or contractor to be responsible for any welding done, and some codes, such as the ASME Code for Unfired Pressure Vessels, speci-

fically state that tests conducted by one employer do not qualify a weldor to weld for any other employer without requalifying.

It has been contended that codes have been too strict — often unrealistic. The latest edition of the AWS Building Code, D1.1-Rev. 1-73, however, is less restrictive — more realistic and imposes less costly tests on the employer. It now allows radiographic inspection of test plates, which eliminates considerable time and expense for bend-test specimens. Test-plate thickness has been reduced from 1-1/2" to 1". A weldor can now get complete qualification by performing satisfactorily with just two test plates — two groove welds with the prescribed bevel angle and root opening, joining 1"-thick material, using a low-hydrogen electrode. One weld is made vertical and the other overhead.

The qualification welds may be tested for soundness with guided bend tests if radiographic inspection is not used. Three different plunger diameters have been set for the guided bend test, using the largest diameter for the higher strength steels, due to their slightly lower ductility. Perhaps of even greater importance for the designer is the recognition of weld strength by the higher loads allowed, and recognition of deep penetration with reduction in weld size.

It should be understood that much welding is being performed that does not come under the provisions of any code. In recognition of this, some companies now "classify" all their weldors according to varying degrees of skill. Some are classified as "general" weldors and others as "code" weldors. Many weldors who fail to pass the code qualification tests successfully pass the general qualification tests. This provides opportunities for work for less skilled weldors while they are perfecting their skills, and at the same time prevents the unskilled worker from posing as a skilled weldor.

Codes governing the design, building, installation, and testing of pressure piping, pressure vessels (both fired and unfired), buildings, bridges, and nuclear applications serve to guide the designers as well as the fabricator and the inspector. In addition, industrial insurance companies require compliance with an approved code before issuing an insurance policy. Codes have grown from original rather simple documents to the detailed documents of today. Higher pressures, temperatures, stress levels, new and exotic metals and alloys, and new welding processes have required continuous updating by the code-writing bodies. Codes are written by special committees within recognized professional societies.

Although any code-writing body may prescribe its own welding qualification tests, most codes and specifications concerned with welded steel structures in the United States incorporate the welding qualification tests of the American Welding Society, the American Society of Mechanical Engineers, or the American Petroleum Institute in their specifications. Thus, the American Association of State Highway Officials in its specifications for highway bridges incorporates the AWS welding qualification tests for procedures and personnel, as those qualification tests are given in the AWS Structural Welding Code. Many other code-writing organizations, including private companies, industrial groups, or governmental agencies, also refer to AWS, ASME, or API specifications for welding qualification tests.

AWS tests are most widely recognized, but are not universally applicable. In certain types of work, other qualification tests may be required.

The contractor doing the welding must make certain that the qualifications of procedures and personnel he uses meet the requirements of the governing code.

There are three different qualification tests:

1. A test to qualify the welding procedure to be used for a specific welding project.
2. A test of the welding proficiency of the operator with hand-held welding equipment (the stick-electrode holder or the semiautomatic welding gun). This is referred to as weldor qualification.
3. A test of the proficiency of the operator with fully automatic welding equipment — referred to as welding operator qualification.

The student who is about to complete his studies and enter the market as a weldor is, of course, most interested in qualification tests for personnel. However, he may wish to know something about procedure tests as well as welding operator tests. In the following text, both procedure and operator tests are described in a condensed form. Before tests are undertaken, it would be desirable to obtain a copy of the applicable code or specification and study the detailed provisions.

AWS QUALIFICATION TESTS FOR BUILDINGS AND BRIDGES

The AWS Structural Welding Code is a source

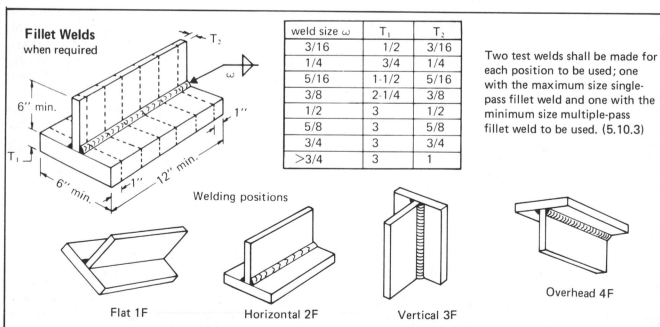

Fillet Welds when required

weld size ω	T_1	T_2
3/16	1/2	3/16
1/4	3/4	1/4
5/16	1-1/2	5/16
3/8	2-1/4	3/8
1/2	3	1/2
5/8	3	5/8
3/4	3	3/4
>3/4	3	1

Two test welds shall be made for each position to be used; one with the maximum size single-pass fillet weld and one with the minimum size multiple-pass fillet weld to be used. (5.10.3)

Welding positions

Flat 1F   Horizontal 2F   Vertical 3F   Overhead 4F

Macroetch Test — The fillet weld shall conform to the quality requirements of 8.15, 9.25, 10.17, whichever is applicable. They shall show fusion to the root, but not necessarily beyond the root, and shall be free from cracks. Convexity and concavity shall not exceed the limits of 3.6.1. Both legs of weld shall be equal to within 1/8" (5.12.1.3)

Fig. 24-1. Details of the AWS procedure qualification tests, continued in Fig. 24-2.

Groove Welds — Plate

Qualifies for material up to and including 3/4" thick.

Qualifies for material over 3/4" in thickness.

Discard
Reduced section tensile
Root bend
Face bend
Root bend
Face bend
Reduced section tensile
Discard

Discard
Side bend
Reduced section tensile
Side bend
Side bend
Reduced section tensile
Side bend
Discard

Joint details and welding procedures are specified by the procedures being qualified. (5.7)

Make 3/8" test plate for each position

For material over 3/4" thick a test weld shall be made in material of the maximum thickness, but need not exceed 1".

Welding positions

Flat 1G   Horizontal 2G   Vertical 3G   Overhead 4G

Reduced Section Tensile

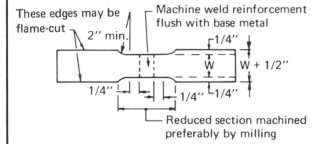

These edges may be flame-cut

2" min.

Machine weld reinforcement flush with base metal

1/4"
W
W + 1/2"

1/4"   1/4"   1/4"

Reduced section machined preferably by milling

Tensile strength shall not be less than the minimum specified tensile strength of the base metal used.
(may break in the weld)

$w = 1\text{-}1/2''$ if $t \leq 1''$
$w = 1''$ if $t > 1''$

Face and Root Bend

These edges may be flame-cut and may or may not be machined

1 - 1/2"

Remove weld reinforcement and backing strip, if any, flush with surface

6" min.   3/8"

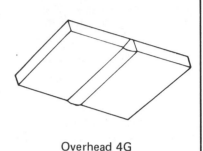

A

1/16" max radius on corners

Side Bend

If flame-cut, machine at least 1/8" from edge

3/8"

$W = t \leq 1\text{-}1/2''$

6" min.

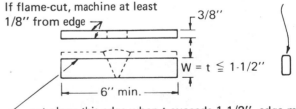

cut along this edge when t exceeds 1-1/2", edge may be flame-cut and may or may not be machined.

YP	A
50 ksi & under	1-1/2"
55 to 90 ksi	2"
over 90 ksi	2-1/2"

NOTE: For plates over 1-1/2" thick, cut specimens into a minimum number of approximately equal strips not exceeding 1-1/2" in width.

Bend specimen passes if crack or other opening does not exceed 1/8" after bending through an angle of 180^0. Cracks at corners are not considered. (5.12.1.2)

Fig. 24-2. Details of the AWS procedure qualification tests (continued from Fig. 24-1).

of information on qualifying procedures, weldors, and welding operators for the welding associated with building and bridge construction. Copies may be obtained from the American Welding Society, Inc., 2501 N.W. 7th Street, Miami, Florida, 33125.

PROCEDURE QUALIFICATION

The welding procedures for work done in accordance with the AWS Structural Welding Code must be "qualified" before fabrication can begin, except when the procedures are prequalified. Prequalified procedures are those that conform to Section 2 — Design, Section 3 — Workmanship, and Section 4 — Technique, of the Code. In many instances, the contractor will find that procedures he intends to use with the specified joints are already prequalified — in which case no procedure qualification tests will be needed.

The procedure qualification tests with fillet and groove welds are illustrated and described in Figs. 24-1 and 24-2.

For steels having a specified yield point of 50,000 psi or less, qualification on any one also qualifies for all, or for any combination of the others (5.5.1.1)* having a minimum specified yield point equal to or less than that of the base metal used in the test. If the steel has a specified yield point in excess of 50,000 psi, the procedure qualification test on this steel will only qualify this particular steel, grade, or type, and the same specified yield point. A reduction in yield point because of

an increase in thickness of the particular steel is permitted. For example, a procedure qualified with 1-in.-thick 100,000-psi yield steel also qualifies for 3-in.-thick 90,000-psi yield steel of the same ASTM specification. (5.5.1.3)

Qualification on either A242, A441, A534 Gr. A, A572 Gr. 50, A588, API 5LX Gr. 42, or ABS Gr. AH, DH, or EH will also qualify for any of these combinations of them or with other approved steels having lower specified yield points. (5.5.1.2)

If a steel having a specified yield point in excess of 50,000 psi is qualified to be welded to a steel having a specified yield point of 50,000 psi or less, it is qualified to be welded to any other of the steels having a specified yield point of 50,000 psi or less. (5.5.1.4)

The procedure qualification for groove welds joining material over 3/4-in. thick states that the test plate shall be the same thickness as the material but need not exceed 1 inch. Should the application in question involve 7/8-in.-thick material, the logical recommendation for procedure qualification would still call for 1-in.-thick plate, since the test is no more difficult than 7/8-in., and passing it would give "unlimited" qualification. Should 1-in. test places not be available, however, the qualification test can be performed on any thickness greater than 1-in. and still give unlimited qualification.

A test joint for partial-penetration groove welds shall be made for each type of joint and weld

* Parenthetical references are to paragraphs in the AWS Structural Welding Code.

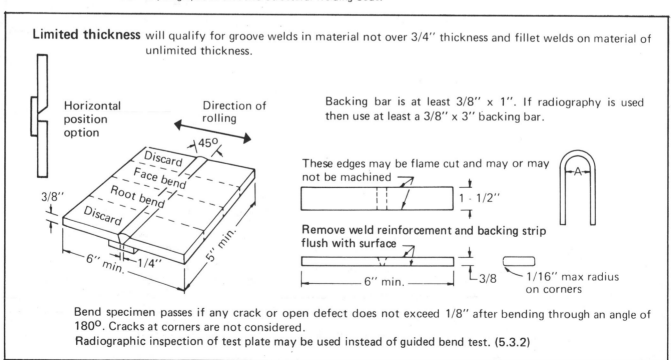

Limited thickness will qualify for groove welds in material not over 3/4" thickness and fillet welds on material of unlimited thickness.

Horizontal position option

Direction of rolling

45°

Discard
Face bend
Root bend
Discard

3/8"

6" min.   1/4"   5" min.

Backing bar is at least 3/8" x 1". If radiography is used then use at least a 3/8" x 3" backing bar.

These edges may be flame cut and may or may not be machined

1 - 1/2"

A

Remove weld reinforcement and backing strip flush with surface

6" min.   3/8

1/16" max radius on corners

Bend specimen passes if any crack or open defect does not exceed 1/8" after bending through an angle of 180°. Cracks at corners are not considered.
Radiographic inspection of test plate may be used instead of guided bend test. (5.3.2)

Fig. 24-3. Details of the AWS weldor qualification tests (continued in Fig. 24-4).

position, except that the depth of groove does not have to exceed 1 inch. A macroetched cross section of the completed joint shall be made to show that the designated effective throat thickness is obtained and shall conform to the requirements of the Procedure Specification. (5.10.2) The test plates for groove welds with gas metal-arc, flux-cored arc, electroslag, and electrogas welding shall be radiographically or ultrasonically tested. (5.10.1.1) (5.12.1.5)

WELDOR QUALIFICATION TESTS

Manual-electrode and semiautomatic weldors must be qualified for work covered by the AWS Structural Welding Code. The requirements are also sometimes used by individual companies or specific agencies to prove the skill of welding operators.

A weldor is qualified for any of the approved steels if he qualified on any one of them. For manual shielded metal-arc welding the proper electrode classification must be used. (5.17.1.3)

With manual shielded metal-arc welding, qualification with any of the following electrodes will qualify for any electrode having the same or lower group designation, where XX represents the strength level of the electrode — 60, 70, 80, 90, 100, 110, and 120. (5.17.1.3)

Group	AWS Electrode Classification			
F4	EXX15	EXX16	EXX18	
F3	EXX10	EXX11		
F2	EXX12	EXX13	EXX14	
F1	EXX20	EXX24	EXX27	EXX28

A weldor qualified with an approved combination of electrode and shielding medium is also qualified for any other approved combination of electrode and shielding medium for the same semiautomatic process as used in the qualification test (5.17.1.4).

The types of joints and welding positions qualified with each test are indicated in the following table:

POSITION AND TYPE OF WELD QUALIFIED

Test Position	Unlimited* & Limited** Thickness Test		Fillet Weld Tests***
Overhead OH	F & OH groove	F, H & OH fillet	F, H & OH fillet
Vertical V	F, H & V groove	F, H & V fillet	F, H & V fillet
Horizontal H	F & H groove	F & H fillet	F & H fillet
Flat F	F groove	F & H fillet	F fillet

* Qualifies for groove and fillet welds on material of unlimited thickness.
** Qualifies for groove welds in material not over 3/4-in. thick and fillet welds on material of unlimited thickness.
*** Qualifies for fillet welds on material of unlimited thickness.

Figures 24-3 and 24-4 detail the qualification tests. The weldor making and passing a procedure qualification test is also qualified for that process and test position for plates of thicknesses equal to or less than the thickness of the test plate welded. In the case of 1-in. or over in thickness, he will be qualified for all thicknesses.

A weldor could, thus, achieve unlimited qualification — would be qualified for making any type weld, in any welding position, on any thickness of plate, on any of the approved weldable steels — by performing satisfactorily with just two test plates. Involved would be two groove welds having the prescribed bevel angle and root opening and joining 1-in.-thick material of any of the twelve weldable types, using an EXX15, 16, or 18 electrode. One weld would be made vertical and the other overhead. Radiographic inspection would eliminate any machining and bending. If no overhead welding will be required on the job, just one test plate in the vertical position could be made.

Weldor qualification tests remain in effect indefinitely (5.30), unless:

1. The weldor does not work with the welding process for which he is qualified for a period exceeding six months. In this case a requalification test is required on 3/8-in.-thick plate.

2. There is specific reason to question his ability.

If a weldor fails his test, he may retest (5.29) as follows:

1. An immediate retest shall consist of two test welds of each type he failed, and all test specimens must pass.

2. A retest can be made if the weldor has had further training or practice. In this case, a complete retest shall be made.

WELDING OPERATOR QUALIFICATION

Qualification of the man who operates automatic welding equipment is covered in Part IV of Section 5. Here, also, the operator is qualified to weld any of the approved steels if he qualified on any one of them. (5.33.1.1) An operator qualified for any approved combination of electrode and shielding medium is also approved for any other approved combination of electrode and shielding medium for the same process as used in the qualification test. (5.33.1.2) Qualification with multiple electrodes also covers single electrodes. (5.33.1.3)

Figure 24-5 describes the test. The welding procedure shall be the same as that specified by the Procedure Specification. (5.36) The welding operator making and passing a procedure qualification test is also qualified for that process and test posi-

Unlimited thickness will qualify for groove or fillet welds in unlimited thickness

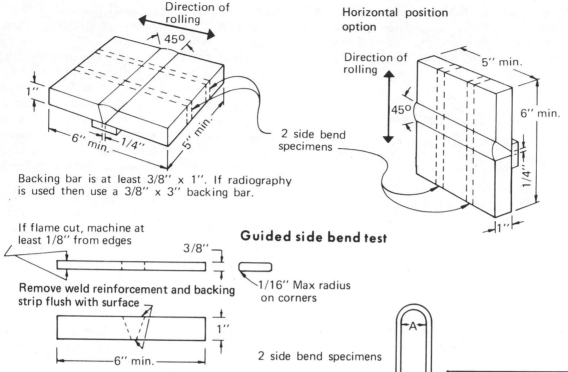

Backing bar is at least 3/8" x 1". If radiography is used then use a 3/8" x 3" backing bar.

If flame cut, machine at least 1/8" from edges

Remove weld reinforcement and backing strip flush with surface

Guided side bend test

1/16" Max radius on corners

2 side bend specimens

Bend specimen passes if any crack or other open defect does not exceed 1/8" after bending through an angle at 180°. Cracks at corners are not considered.

Radiographic inspection of test plate may be used instead of guided bend test. (5.3.2)

YP	A
50 ksi & under	1-1/2"
55 to 90 ksi	2"
over 90 ksi	2-1/2"

Fillet Welds will qualify for unlimited thickness of material.

Option 1

5/16" fillet weld

Fillet weld break specimen

Discard

Cut line

Stop and restart welding near center

Etch interior face

Macroetch specimen

Visual inspection — a reasonably uniform appearance; free of overlap, cracks, and excessive undercut; no surface porosity.

Next the 6" section is broken with the root of the weld in tension. The broken section of the weld shall show complete penetration into the root of the joint and fusion into the plate. No inclusion or porosity larger than 3/32". Sum of greatest dimension of all inclusions and porosity shall not exceed 3/8" in the 6" length. If plates are bent upon themselves without weld breaking, will pass.

Macroetch test — shall show fusion to the root but not necessarily beyond root and no cracks. Convexity and concavity shall not exceed 1/16". Legs are equal to within 1/8".

(Continued on next page.)

Fig. 24-4. Details of the AWS weldor qualification tests (continued from Fig. 24-3).

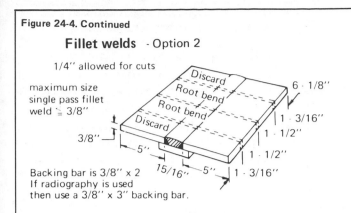

Figure 24-4. Continued

Fillet welds - Option 2

1/4" allowed for cuts

maximum size single pass fillet weld ≅ 3/8"

Backing bar is 3/8" x 2. If radiography is used then use a 3/8" x 3" backing bar.

Radiographic inspection of test plate may be used instead of guided bend test. (5.3.2)

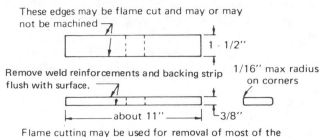

These edges may be flame cut and may or may not be machined

Remove weld reinforcements and backing strip flush with surface.

1/16" max radius on corners

Flame cutting may be used for removal of most of the backing provided the last 1/8" thickness is removed by machining or grinding.

Bend specimen passes if any crack or other opening does not exceed 1/8" after bending through an angle of 180°. Cracks at corners are not considered.

---

tion for plates of thicknesses equal to or less than the thickness of the test plate welded. In the case of 1 inch or over in thickness, he will be qualified for all thicknesses. (5.34.3)

RADIOGRAPHIC EXAMINATION OF WELDS

Radiographic examination of test plates for weldor and welding operator qualification may be used in place of the guided bend test. Radiographic examination, in addition to being more fair (in that it gives a more positive appraisal of the weld), could easily reduce the cost of qualification tests to but 10% of what they were before revision of the specifications in 1969 by eliminating the machining of test specimens. Furthermore, this option permits a weldor to be tested in the morning and put to work in the afternoon, avoiding the time delays that have frustrated employers and employees alike.

The AWS Structural Code standards for radiographic weld inspection are applicable to the examination of qualification welds by radiography. Sec-

tion 8 — Building (8.15) specifies that porosity or fusion-type defects less than 3/32 inch in their greatest dimension are acceptable if the sum of the greatest dimension, when scattered, does not exceed 3/8 inch in any linear inch of weld. Larger porosity or fusion defects are acceptable when:

1. The greatest dimension of the defect does not exceed 2/3t (t = joint or weld throat in inches) or 3/4 inch, and:

2. The sum of the greatest dimension of defects in line does not exceed (t) in a length of (6t), or the space between each pair of adjacent defects exceeds three times the greatest dimension of the larger defects. When the length of weld being examined is less than (6t), the permissible sum of the greatest dimension of all such defects shall be proportionately less than (t), and:

3. The defect does not lie closer than three times its greatest dimension to the end of a groove-welded joint carrying primary tensile stress.

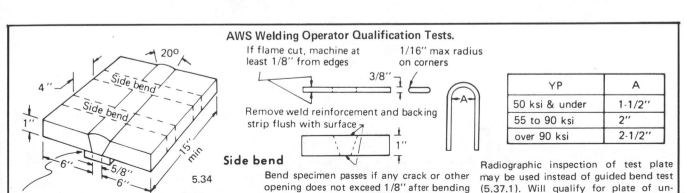

AWS Welding Operator Qualification Tests.

If flame cut, machine at least 1/8" from edges

1/16" max radius on corners

Remove weld reinforcement and backing strip flush with surface

Side bend

Bend specimen passes if any crack or other opening does not exceed 1/8" after bending through an angle of 180°. Cracks at corners are (5.39.1) not considered.

YP	A
50 ksi & under	1-1/2"
55 to 90 ksi	2"
over 90 ksi	2-1/2"

Radiographic inspection of test plate may be used instead of guided bend test (5.37.1). Will qualify for plate of unlimited thickness with groove and fillet welds.

3/8" x 1-1/2" backing bar — if radiography is used, use at least a 3/8" x 3" backing bar.

Fig. 24-5. Details of the AWS welding operator qualification tests.

Piping porosity is acceptable if the sum of the diameters does not exceed 3/8 inch in any linear inch of weld nor 3/4 inch in any 12-in. length of weld.

Figure 24-6 illustrates graphically these limitations in a groove-welded joint carrying primary tensile stress.

Figure 24-7 (a) and (b) illustrate acceptable defects in a 1-in.-thick joint, according to the AWS Section 8 — Building. In (a) are shown defect sizes and minimum spacings that would be acceptable on a 1″ plate. Since the minimum spacings are not violated, it is possible for the sum of the defects to exceed 1-in. (t) in any 6-in. (6t) length. In (b), the sum of the defects is less than 1-in. (t) in a 6-in. (6t) length; hence the minimum spacings may be violated.

Section 9 — Bridge would be applicable to the examination of qualification welds when the job pertains to a highway or railway bridge. It (9.25) specifies that regardless of the method of inspection welds shall have no cracks, and, shall have no other defects exceeding the following limits in size or frequency of occurrence:

1. The greatest dimension of any porosity or fusion-type defect that is 1/16-in. or larger in greatest dimension shall not exceed the size of defect (B) in Fig. 24-8 for the effective throat thickness or weld size involved. The distance from any porosity or fusion-type defect described above to another such defect, to an edge, or to any intersecting weld shall not be less than the minimum clearance allowed (C) in Fig. 24-8 for the size of defect under examination. The limitations given by Fig. 24-8 for a 1-1/2-in. joint or weld-throat thickness shall apply to all joints or weld throats of greater thickness.

2. Independent of the above requirements, the sum of the greatest dimensions of porosity and fusion-type defects less than 1/16 inch in greatest dimension shall not exceed 3/8 inch in any linear inch of weld.

3. The frequency of piping porosity in fillet welds shall not exceed one in each four inches of length, and the maximum diameter shall not exceed 3/32 inch. For fillet welds on web stiffeners the sum of diameters of piping porosity shall not exceed 3/8 inch per linear inch of weld, nor 3/4 inch per foot of weld.

HOW TO PASS QUALIFICATION TESTS

While the AWS tests are designed to separate capable weldors from amateurs, many professional weldors have failed for reasons not related to their welding ability. The 1972 Code minimizes such possibilities by making the test a more positive demonstration of weld quality and welding skill. However, it is still possible to fail the test because of poor plate quality, improperly prepared samples, or incorrect interpretation of the results.

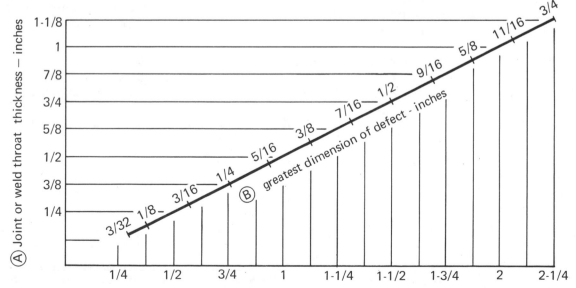

Ⓒ Minimum clearance allowed between edges of porosity or fusion type defects — inches, or between the defect and the end of groove welded joint carrying primary tensile stress. (Larger of adjacent defects governs.)

Fig. 24-6. Graphic representation of the defect limitations allowed by the AWS Building in a groove weld carrying primary tensile stress.

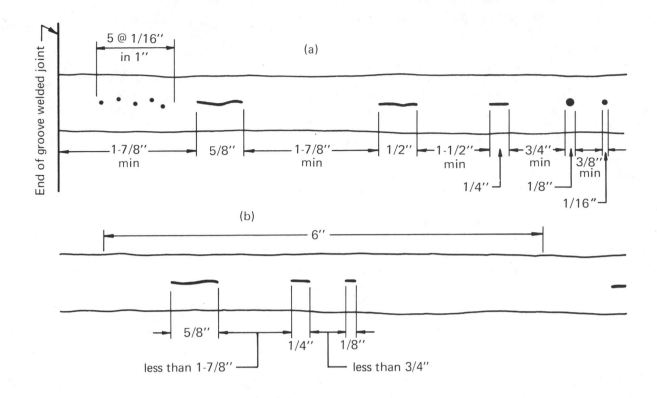

Fig. 24-7. Acceptable defects allowed by the AWS Building Code in a 1-in.-thick joint.

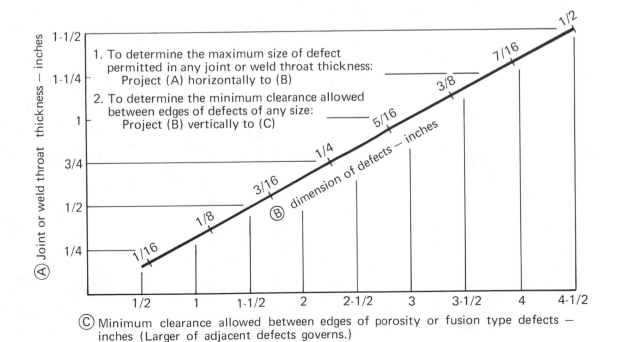

Fig. 24-8. Weld defect limitations of the AWS Bridge Specifications.

This is exasperating to the weldor and expensive to his employer. It is to everyone's advantage to see that the tests are run properly so the results are an accurate measure of welding ability.

Before taking a test, one should make certain that he has selected the test details that will qualify for the type steel, plate thickness, joint, and welding position to be used. (See Figs. 24-1 through 24-5.) Then, the strength of the plate should be checked. Face and root bend tests are designed so both plate and weld stretch during the test. If the plate has strength substantially higher than the weld metal (and this is possible with steel purchased as mild steel), the plate will not stretch sufficiently, thereby forcing the weld metal to stretch beyond its yield and crack.

As indicated previously, one vertical and one overhead test plate can qualify a manual-electrode or semiautomatic weldor for unlimited welding under the AWS Code. Since it permits using the weldor throughout the shop without restrictions, most testing is done in these two positions.

For unlimited manual-electrode qualification, low-hydrogen electrode (usually E7018) is required. EXX10 or EXX11 electrodes are also frequently used, but do not qualify the weldor to weld with low-hydrogen electrodes. Low-hydrogen electrodes require different techniques than EXX10 or EXX11, and weldors should be trained with low-hydrogen techniques before testing, even if they are expert EXX10 weldors.

Critical to passing any of the tests is getting good penetration and sound weld metal in the root passes. To get good penetration, generally it is best to use the highest current one can handle within the recommended range for the electrode. Electrode data tables should be consulted for current ranges for electrodes.

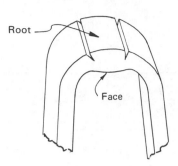

Fig. 24-10. If weld reinforcement is not removed, stretching is concentrated in two places and failure results.

Many operators worry too much about appearance on the first beads. Appearance means nothing to the testing machine. But poor penetration and unsound weld metal cause most failures.

When manual electrode welding, vertical welds should be made with the vertical-up technique. For gas metal-arc or flux-cored arc welding, vertical welds can be made either in the vertical-up or vertical-down direction. However, the weldor must use the same direction on the job as he used on the qualification test.

No preheat or postheat treatment is necessary or permissible to pass the test. It is, however, helpful to keep the plates hot during welding, and allow them to cool slowly after completion. Interpass temperatures of 300-400°F are ideal and can usually be maintained by operating at a normal pace. Never quench the plates in cold water or accelerate the cooling rate in any other way.

Poor specimen preparation can cause sound weld metal to fail. Specimen size, location, and preparation are specified for each test. Even a slight nick across the sample may open up under the severe bending stress of the test, causing failure. Therefore, always grind or machine lengthwise on the specimen, as indicated in Fig. 24-9. Always grind or machine both faces of the specimen until the entire bend area is even, leaving no indentations or irregular spots.

Remove all reinforcement. This is part of the test requirement and, more important to the weldor, failure to do so can cause failure of a good weld (see Fig. 24-10). Be sure the edges are rounded to a smooth 1/16-in. radius. This can quickly be done with a file and is good insurance against failure caused by cracks starting at the sharp corner.

When grinding specimens, do not water-quench them when they are hot. Quenching may create tiny surface cracks that become larger during the bend test.

The jig for testing weld specimens is shown in Fig. 24-11(a). Note that three plunger diameters

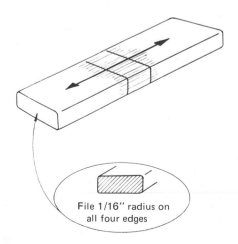

File 1/16" radius on all four edges

Fig. 24-9. Grinding marks must parallel specimen edges. Otherwise, they may have a notch effect that could cause failure.

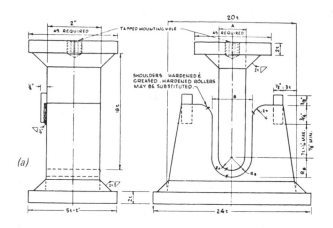

NOTE: "t" refers to specimen thickness
"t" for AWS test is 3/8"
"t" for API Std. 1104 is tabulated wall thickness of pipe

Jig Dimensions	AWS TEST For Mild Steel Min. Yield Strength-psi			API Std. 1104 For All Pipe Grades
	50,000 & under	55-90,000	90,000 & over	
Radius of plunger R_A	3/4	1	1-1/4	1-3/4
Radius of die R_B	1-3/16	1-7/16	1-11/16	2-5/16

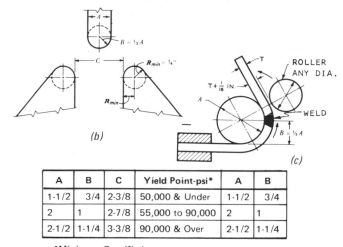

A	B	C	Yield Point-psi*	A	B
1-1/2	3/4	2-3/8	50,000 & Under	1-1/2	3/4
2	1	2-7/8	55,000 to 90,000	2	1
2-1/2	1-1/4	3-3/8	90,000 & Over	2-1/2	1-1/4

*Minimum Specified

Fig. 24-11. (a) Jig for guided bend test used to qualify operators for work done under AWS and API specifications. (b) Alternate roller-equipped test jig for bottom ejection. (c) Alternate wrap-around test jig.

are required, with the larger diameter used for the higher strength steels in recognition of their lower ductility. Alternate test jigs are shown in Fig. 24-11(b) and (c).

AWS QUALIFICATION TESTS FOR PIPING AND TUBING

American Welding Society Standard D10.9 covers the qualification of procedures and personnel for the welding of pipe, tubing, and associated components. The standard provides three levels of qualification, termed Acceptance Requirements 1,

2, and 3 — abbreviated AR-1, AR-2 and AR-3, respectively. AR-1 is the highest level of qualification, followed by AR-2 and AR-3. The differences lie in the type of tests and the acceptance requirements for the sample welds.

Each of the three levels of welding procedure qualification has a corresponding level of weldor qualification. Qualification to a given level automatically qualifies for all lower levels. For example, qualification to AR-1 also qualifies AR-2 and AR-3.

Typical applications for the three levels are as follows:

AR-1 — This level applies to systems where the highest degree of weld quality is required. Use of the AR-1 level of quality is intended to provide the confidence required for pipelines that may be found in nuclear-energy, space, high-pressure, high-temperature, chemical, or gas systems.

Some contract specifications may have requirements even more stringent than those required by AR-1. In such cases the qualification must comply with AR-1, plus the additional tests, inspection methods, and acceptance standards required by the contract specifications.

AR-2 — This level applies to systems where a high degree of weld quality is required. Use of the AR-2 level of quality is intended to provide the confidence necessary for some lines that may be found in nuclear-energy, steam, water, petroleum, gas, or chemical systems.

AR-3 — This level applies to systems where a nominal degree of weld quality is required. Use of the AR-3 level of quality is intended to provide the confidence adequate for lines such as low-pressure heating, air-conditioning, and sanitary water.

The standard provides for qualification with groove and fillet welds. Procedure and weldor qualification with groove welds automatically qualifies for fillet welds. However, if fillet welds alone are required for the specific job, the welding procedure and weldor can be qualified for fillet welds only.

AR-1 WELDING PROCEDURE QUALIFICATION

Table 24-1 shows the welds and tests required for AR-1 procedure qualification. The test positions are shown in Fig. 24-12.

The notes (a) through (k) for Table 24-1 are important to use of the table. They are too voluminous for inclusion in the table, itself and in lieu of this customary arrangement, are presented here in the text. The applicable notes to the table state that:

a. The pipe sizes in the table may not be appropriate for the job-size pipe to be welded. In

TABLE 24-1. AR-1 Level of Welding Procedure Qualification

SAMPLE WELDS					TESTS REQUIRED (d)(e)						
Wall Thickness 3/4" and Under											
Pipe Size (a) of Sample Weld	Pipe or Tube Size Qualified	Pipe or (b)(c) Tube Wall Thickness Qualified		Number of Sample Welds per Position	Visual (f) Inspection	Penetrant (g) Inspection Optional	Radiography (h)	Tensile (i) Test	Bend Tests (j)(k) Number of Specimens		
		Min.	Max.					Number of Specimens	Face	Root	Side
1/2" Sch. 40	Through 1-1/2"	.063"	.400"	2	Yes	Yes	Yes	2	0	0	0
2" Sch. 80	1" Through 4"	.063"	.674"	2	Yes	Yes	Yes	2	2	2	0
5" Sch. 80	Over 4"	.187"	.750"	1	Yes	Yes	Yes	2	2	2	0
Wall Thickness Over 3/4"											
8" Sch. 120	5" and Over	.187"	Any	1	Yes	Yes	Yes	2	0	0	4

Notes: See Text ("AR-1 Welding Procedure Qualification") for explanation of (a) through (k).

such instances, actual job-size pipe may be substituted.

b. For pipe having a wall thickness less than 0.063 in., individual qualification is required for each thickness by visual, penetrant, X-ray and tensile tests.

c. The maximum thickness qualified using the oxyacetylene process is the thickness of the base metal of the sample weld.

d. Procedures qualified prior to issuance of AWS D10.9 may be updated by performing any additional tests required by the standard.

e. For pipe used at low temperature, impact tests may be required. The purchaser and fabricator should agree in advance on the type and number of test specimens, areas from which the specimens are to be taken, testing temperature and the acceptance requirements.

f. Visual inspection before welding shall determine that the proper base metal is used and the fitup is proper.

Visual inspection during welding shall include determining that the proper filler metal is used and inspection for cracks, undercut, porosity, incomplete fusion and proper cleaning between passes.

Visual inspection after welding and heat treatment, if any, shall determine that the weld is free from cracks, surface porosity and unfilled craters and that the weld face is at least flush with the outside surface of the pipe. The weld reinforcement shall not exceed the following:

Pipe Wall Thickness, in.	Reinforcement max., in.
3/8 and less	3/32
Over 3/8 to 3/4 incl.	1/8
Over 3/4	3/16

The root of the weld shall show no evidence of cracks or incomplete fusion. A concave root surface is permitted providing the weld throat is equal to or greater than the base metal and the concavity or convexity of the root surface does not exceed the following:

Sample Weld Pipe Size	Maximum Root-Surface Concavity, in.	Maximum Root-Surface Convexity, in.
1/2" Sch. 40	1/32	1/16
2" Sch. 80	1/16	1/16
5" Sch. 80	1/16	3/32
8" Sch. 120	1/16	3/32

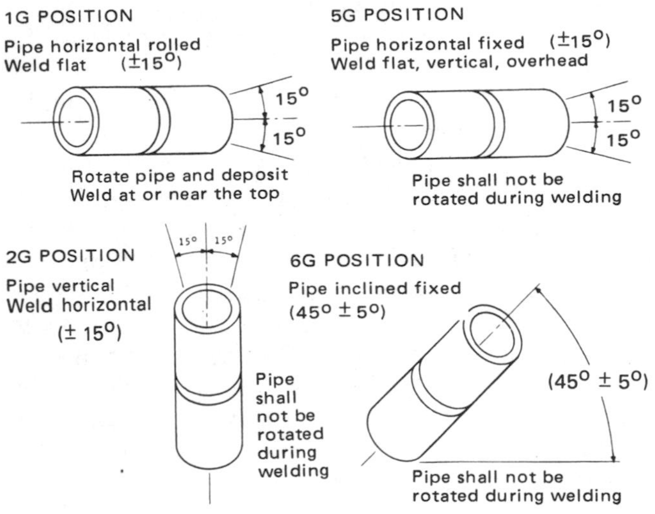

1G POSITION
Pipe horizontal rolled
Weld flat (±15°)

Rotate pipe and deposit
Weld at or near the top

5G POSITION
Pipe horizontal fixed (±15°)
Weld flat, vertical, overhead

Pipe shall not be
rotated during welding

2G POSITION
Pipe vertical
Weld horizontal
(±15°)

Pipe shall not be rotated during welding

6G POSITION
Pipe inclined fixed
(45° ±5°)

(45° ±5°)

Pipe shall not be rotated during welding

The limits of qualification in a given position are shown below:

1. Qualification in the 1G position qualifies only for this position.
2. Qualification in the 2G position qualifies for welding in the 1G and 2G positions only.
3. Qualification in the 5G position qualifies for welding in the 1G and 5G positions only.
4. Qualification in both the 2G and 5G positions qualifies for welding in all positions.
5. Qualification in the 6G position qualifies for welding in all positions, because it includes elements of those positions.
6. Qualification in a position other than the four standard positions described above is valid only for that position (plus or minus 15 degrees).

Fig. 24-12. Test positions used in qualifying procedures for welding pipe and tubing under AWS D10.9.

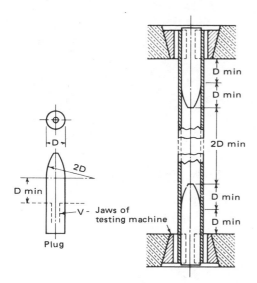

Fig. 24-13. Fixture used for the tensile testing of small-diameter and thin-wall pipe.

g. Penetrant inspection is required only if this type of examination is used in production. Each sample weld shall be examined by liquid penetrant in accordance with A-2 or B-3 of ASTM E165. The weld shall be inspected at the completion of welding, including any postheating. Dry-powder magnetic-particle inspection in accordance with ASTM E109 may be used in lieu of liquid-penetrant inspection.

h. Radiographic inspection is required for all welds of the AR-1 level. For specific techniques and acceptance requirements, see AWS D10.9.

i. For 1/2-in. pipe and all thin-wall pipe, the entire joint is tested in tension. Remove the weld reinforcement until it is flush with the base metal. Measure the outside diameter and the wall thickness before testing, and calculate the pipe cross section. Test the pipe in tension using a fixture as shown in Fig. 24-13.

From the 2-in. sample welds, two tensile specimens are cut from one sample weld and prepared as in Fig. 24-14.

From the 5 and 8-in. sample welds, tensile specimens are prepared as in Fig. 24-15.

The tensile test specimens may fail in the base metal, heat-affected zone, or in the weld metal and are acceptable if the tensile strength is equal to or greater than the minimum specified for the plate.

j. From 2-in. sample welds, four bend specimens are cut from one sample weld and are prepared

as in Fig. 24-16. From 5 and 8-in. sample welds, bend specimens are cut and prepared as in Fig. 24-15. Side bends may be used for wall thicknesses over 3/8 in.

Bend specimens are tested in a guided-bend jig or a wrap-around jig, as shown in Fig. 24-17.

When using the guided-bend jig, the specimen shall be placed on the die with the weld at mid-span. Face-bend specimens shall be placed with the face of the weld directed toward the gap; root-bend specimens shall be placed with the root of the weld directed toward the gap and side-bend specimens with the surface having the greatest defects, if any, toward the gap.

The plunger shall force the specimen into the die until the specimen becomes U-shaped and a 1/8-in.-diameter wire cannot be inserted between the die and the specimen. The weld and heat-affected zones shall be centered and completely within the bent portion of the specimen after testing.

When using the wrap-around jig, the specimen shall be firmly clamped on one end so that there is no sliding of the specimen during the bending operation. The weld and heat-affected zones shall be completely in the bent portion of the specimen after testing. Test specimens shall be removed from the jig when the outer roll has been moved 180° from the starting point.

In order to pass the test, the bent specimens shall have no cracks or other open defects exceeding 1/8-in. measured in any direction on the convex surface of the specimen, except that cracks occurring at the corners shall not be considered unless there is definite evidence that

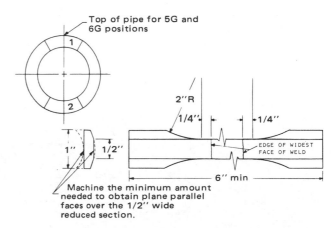

Fig. 24-14. Method of preparing tensile specimens from 2-in. pipe for procedure qualification tests.

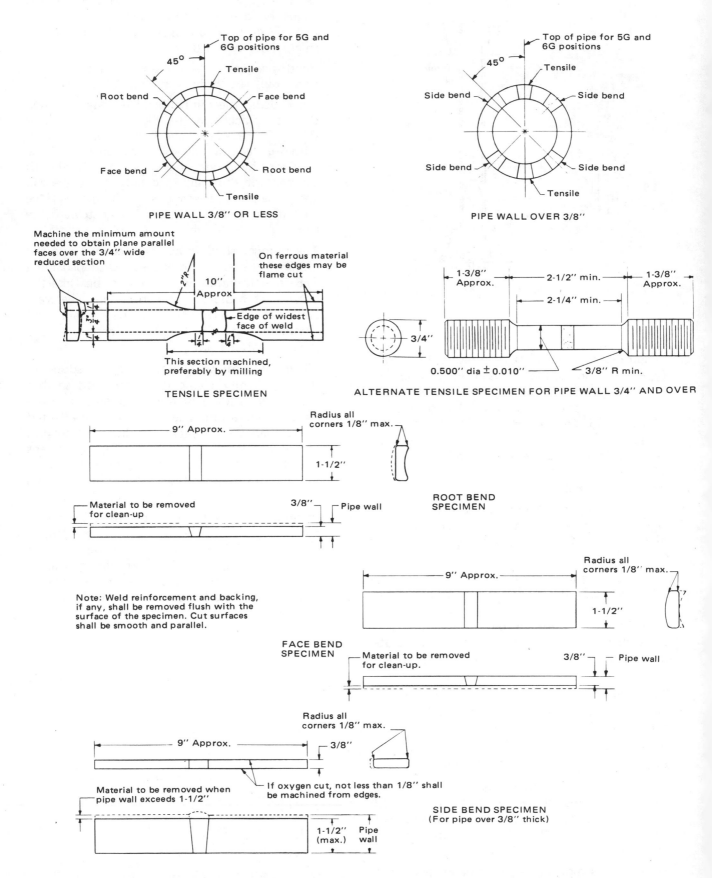

Fig. 24-15. Method of preparing test specimens from 5 and 8-in pipe for procedure qualification tests.

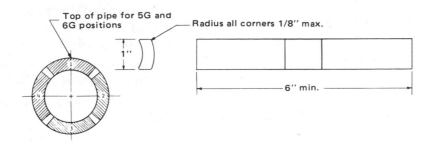

Fig. 24-16. Method of preparing bend specimens from 2-in. pipe for procedure qualification tests.

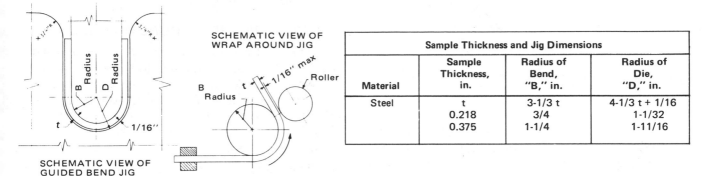

	Sample Thickness and Jig Dimensions		
Material	Sample Thickness, in.	Radius of Bend, "B," in.	Radius of Die, "D," in.
Steel	t	3-1/3 t	4-1/3 t + 1/16
	0.218	3/4	1-1/32
	0.375	1-1/4	1-11/16

Fig. 24-17. Jigs for the bend tests in procedure qualification. For metals other than steel, see AWS D10.9, Table 4.

they result from slag inclusions or other internal defects.

k. For more ductile materials, a higher sensitivity to bending may be required. Any changes in the bend test should be agreed upon in advance between the purchaser and the fabricator.

AR-1 WELDOR QUALIFICATION

The welding positions for weldor qualification are the same as for procedure qualification (Fig. 24-12).

The sample welds and the tests required are shown in Table 24-2. The notes to this table are as follows:

a. The same as Note A under AR-1 procedure qualification.

b. The same as Note C under AR-1 procedure qualification.

c. Weldors qualified prior to the issuance of Standard AWS D10.9 may be updated by performing any additional tests required by the standard.

d. The same as Note F under AR-1 procedure qualification, with the exception that —

Burring or grinding may be used on stops and starts and to remove local defects from bead to bead, but dressing of the completed sample weld is limited to removing local defects appearing on the outer surface of the weld reinforcement. Repair of any root defect is prohibited.

The weldor qualification test may be terminated at any stage of the testing whenever it

TABLE 24-2. AR-1 Level of Weldor Qualification

SAMPLE WELDS					TESTS REQUIRED ON SAMPLE WELDS (c)							
							Bend Tests (f) Number of Specimens					
Pipe Size (a) of Sample Weld	Pipe or Tube Size Qualified	Pipe or Tube (b) Wall Thickness Qualified, In.		Number of Sample Welds per Position	Visual (d) Inspection	Radiography (e)	All Positions except 5G & 6G			5G & 6G Positions Only		
		Min.	Max.				Face	Root	Side	Face	Root	Side
2" Sch. 80	Through 4"	.063	.674	1	Yes	Yes	1	1	0	2	2	0
5" Sch. 80	Over 4"	.187	.750	1	Yes	Yes	1	1	0	2	2	0
8" Sch. 120	5" and Over	.187	Any	1	Yes	Yes	0	0	2	0	0	4

Notes: See Text ("AR-1 Weldor Qualification") for explanation of (a) through (f).

SPECIMENS FOR 1G AND 2G POSITIONS

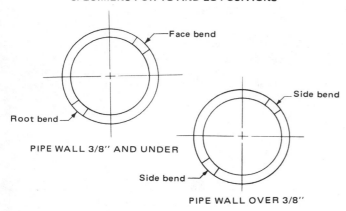

Fig. 24-18. Location of bend specimens for the 1G and 2G positions in weldor qualification tests.

becomes apparent to the supervisor conducting the test that the weldor is not following the welding procedure or does not have the skill required to produce satisfactory results.

e. Radiographic inspection is required by all weldor qualification tests for AR-1 level. For specific techniques and acceptance requirements, see AWS D10.9. Radiographic inspection shall not be used to locate sound or defective areas and thereafter make destructive tests to qualify or disqualify a weldor.

SPECIMENS FOR 5G and 6G POSITIONS

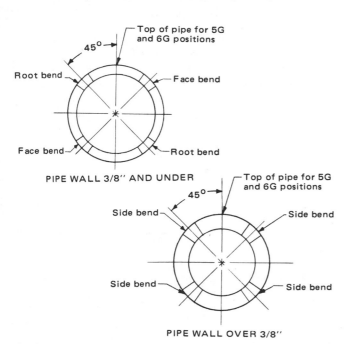

Fig. 24-19. Location of bend specimens for the 5G and 6G positions in weldor qualification tests.

f. For 1G and 2G positions, remove two specimens at random approximately 180° apart, as shown in Fig. 24-18.

For the 5G and 6G positions, remove four specimens as shown in Fig. 24-19.

Machine all bend specimens as shown in Fig. 24-20.

The bend jigs (Fig. 24-17), methods of testing and the acceptance requirements are the same as Note J to Table 24-1, in reference to procedure qualification.

AR-2 WELDING PROCEDURE QUALIFICATION

The qualifying welding positions for the AR-2 level of procedure qualification are the same as shown in Fig. 24-12. The sample welds and tests required are given in Table 24-3. Note that a major difference from the tests for AR-1 procedure qualification is that radiography tests are optional. The applicable notes are:

a. The same as Note A under AR-1 procedure qualification.

b. The same as Note C under AR-1 procedure qualification.

c. The same as Note D under AR-1 procedure qualification.

d. The same as Note F under AR-1 procedure qualification, except that an undercut not exceeding 1/32-in. is permissible on visual inspection and that a maximum root surface convexity 1/16-in. greater than with AR-1 procedures is permitted with 2-in., 5-in. and 8-in. pipe.

The applicable restrictions are as follows:

Sample Weld Pipe Size	Maximum Root-Surface Concavity, In.	Maximum Root-Surface Convexity, in.
1/2'' Sch. 40	1/32	1/16
2'' Sch. 80	1/16	1/8
5'' Sch. 80	1/16	1/8
8'' Sch. 120	1/16	1/8

e. Required only if production welds are to be radiographically inspected.

f. The same as Note I under AR-1 procedure qualification.

g. The same as Note J under AR-1 procedure qualification.

AR-2 WELDOR QUALIFICATION

The qualifying positions are those in Fig. 24-12 and the samples and tests required are shown in Table 24-4.

For the 2" sample welds, machine the specimens as shown below:

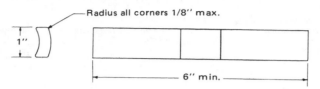

For the 5" and 8" sample welds, machine the specimens as shown below:

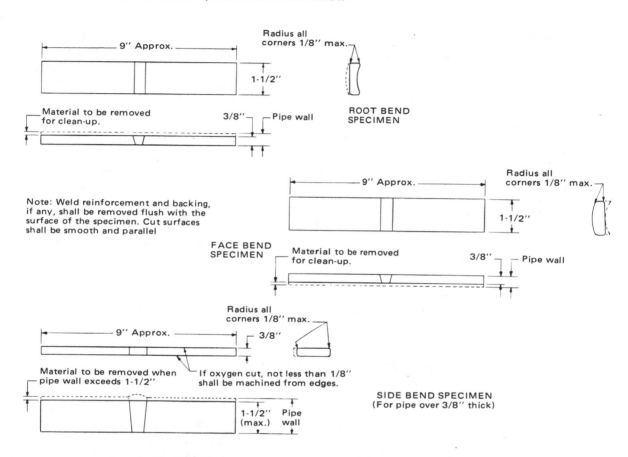

Fig. 24-20. Bend specimens for weldor qualification.

TABLE 24-3. AR-2 Level of Welding Procedure Qualification

SAMPLE WELDS				TESTS REQUIRED (c)					
Wall Thickness 3/4 inch and Under									
Pipe Size of (a) Sample Weld	Pipe or Tube Size Qualified	Pipe or Tube (b) Wall Thickness Qualified		Number of Sample Welds per Position	Visual (d) Inspection	Radiography (e) Optional	Tensile (f) Test	Bend Tests (g) Number of Specimens	
		Min.	Max.				Number of Specimens	Face	Root	Side
1/2" Sch. 40	Through 1-1/2"	.063"	.400"	2	Yes	Yes	2	0	0	0
2" Sch. 80	1" Through 4"	.063"	.674"	2	Yes	Yes	2	2	2	0
5" Sch. 80	Over 4"	.187"	.750"	1	Yes	Yes	2	2	2	0
Wall Thickness Over 3/4"									
8" Sch. 120	5" and Over	.187"	Any	1	Yes	Yes	2	0	0	4

Notes: See Text ("AR-2 Welding Procedure Qualification") for explanation of (a) through (g).

TABLE 24-4. AR-2 Level of Weldor Qualification

SAMPLE WELDS					TESTS REQUIRED ON SAMPLE WELDS (c)							
							Bend Tests (f) Number of Specimens					
Pipe Size (a) of Sample Weld	Pipe or Tube Size Qualified	Pipe or Tube (b) Wall Thickness Qualified, In.		Number of Sample Welds per Position	Visual (d) Inspection	Radiography (e)	All Positions except 5G & 6G			5G & 6G Positions Only		
		Min.	Max.				Face	Root	Side	Face	Root	Side
2″ Sch. 80	Through 4″	.063	.674	1	Yes	Optional (g)	1	1	0	2	2	0
5″ Sch. 80	Over 4″	.187	.750	1	Yes	Optional (g)	1	1	0	2	2	0
8″ Sch. 120	5″ and Over	.187	Any	1	Yes	Optional (g)	0	0	2	0	0	4

Notes: See Text ("AR-2 Weldor Qualification") for explanation of (a) through (g).

The notes to this table are as follows:

a. The same as Note A under AR-1 procedure qualification.

b. The same as Note C under AR-1 procedure qualification.

c. The same as Note C under AR-1 weldor qualification.

d. The same as Note D under the AR-1 weldor qualification.

e. Radiography tests are optional and are made in accordance with the techniques and acceptance requirements described in AWS D10.9.

f. The same as Note J under AR-1 procedure qualification.

g. Radiographic inspection may be used in place of the bend tests if the production welds require radiography.

AR-3 WELDING PROCEDURE QUALIFICATION

The qualifying positions are as shown in Fig. 24-12. The sample welds and tests required are given in Table 24-5.

The applicable notes are:

a. The same as Note A under AR-1 procedure qualification.

b. The same as Note C under AR-1 procedure qualification.

c. The same as Note F under AR-1 procedure qualification, except that an undercut not exceeding 1/32-in. is permissible and the concavity or convexity of the root surface may not exceed the following:

Sample Weld Pipe Size	Maximum Root-Surface Concavity, in.	Maximum Root-Surface Convexity, in.
1/2″ Sch. 40	1/32	1/16
2″ Sch. 40	1/16	1/8
5″ Sch. 40	1/16	1/8

d. Prepare one sample weld for each position to be qualified for the 1/2-in. Schedule 40 and 2-in. Schedule 40 pipe as shown in Fig. 24-21. Fill with water at city pressure (25 psig minimum) and close the valve. Bend around a 12-in.-diameter mandrel as shown. The weld is acceptable if there are no leaks after a 30° bend.

e. Section, polish and etch the 5-in. Schedule 40 specimen as shown in Fig. 24-22. The etched sections shall show no cracks, inadequate penetration, or incomplete fusion. Concavity shall not exceed 1/16-in. and the accumulated slag and porosity shall not exceed 1/8-in. from root to face of the weld.

In lieu of this test, the 5-in. weld sample may be tested by preparing four bend samples as shown

TABLE 24-5. AR-3 Level of Welding Procedure Qualification

LIMITED TO PIPE UP TO AND INCLUDING 10″ DIAMETER AND 3/8″ WALL THICKNESS

SAMPLE WELDS					TESTS REQUIRED		
Wall Thickness 3/8″ and Under							
Pipe Size of Sample Weld	Pipe or Tube Size Qualified	Pipe or Tube (b) Wall Thickness, (t) Qualified		Number of Sample Welds per Position	Visual (c) Inspection	Pressure (d) Bend	Macrostructure (e) No. of Specimens
		Min.	Max.			No. of Tests	
1/2″ Sch. 40	1-1/2″ and Under	1/16″	2 t	1	Yes	1	0
2″ Sch. 40	1″ Through 4″	1/2 t	2 t	1	Yes	1	0
5″ Sch. 40 (a)	4-1/2″ Through 10″	1/2 t	3/8″	1	Yes	0	4

Notes: See Text ("AR-3 Welding Procedure Qualification") for explanation of (a) through (e).

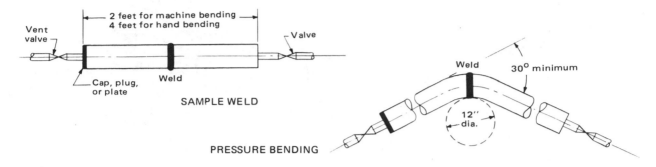

Fig. 24-21. The pressure bend test used in AR-3 procedure qualification.

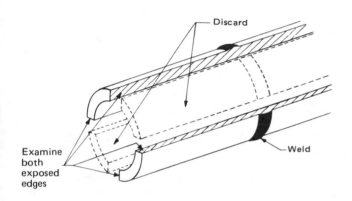

Fig. 24-22. Specimen for macrostructure examination as permitted in AR-3 procedure qualification.

in Fig. 24-16, except the sample width shall be 1-1/2 in. wide. Bend two face and two root specimens with a fixture shown in Fig. 24-17, with "t" equal to 0.375-in. The weld is acceptable if none of the specimens undergoes complete failure.

AR-3 WELDOR QUALIFICATION

The qualifying welding positions are as shown in Fig. 24-12. The sample welds and tests are shown in Table 24-6.

The notes are:

a. The same as Note A under AR-1 procedure qualification.

b. The same as Note C under AR-1 procedure qualification.

c. The same as Note C under AR-1 weldor qualification.

d. The same as Note D under AR-1 weldor qualification.

e. The same as Note D under AR-3 procedure qualification, except that the 1/2-in. Schedule 40 sample is omitted.

f. The same as Note E under AR-3 procedure qualification.

PROCEDURE AND WELDOR QUALIFICATION FOR FILLET WELDS

As mentioned earlier, welding procedure qualification and weldor qualification using groove welds automatically qualifies the procedure or the weldor for fillet welds. However, if only fillet welds are required in production, the welding procedure and the weldor can be qualified for fillet welds only. The sample welds, tests and acceptance requirements are the same for both procedure and weldor qualification.

A pipe assembly is prepared as shown in Fig. 24-23. Test welds are made as shown in Fig. 24-24 to qualify for all positions. Weld No. 1 is completed with the axis of the assembly in the horizontal position and without rotation. Weld No. 2 is

TABLE 24-6. AR-3 Level of Weldor Qualification

	SAMPLE WELDS				TESTS REQUIRED ON SAMPLE WELDS (c)		
Pipe Size (a) of Sample Weld	Pipe or Tube Size Qualified	Pipe or Tube (b) Wall Thickness Qualified, In.		Number of Sample Welds per Position	Visual (d) Inspection	Pressure (e) Bend, Number of Sample Welds Tested	Macrostructure (f) Examination, No. of Etched Specimens
		Min.	Max.				
2" Sch. 40	Through 4"	.063	.375	1	Yes	1	0
5" Sch. 40	4-1/2 Through 10"	.187	.375	1	Yes	0	4

Notes: See Text ("AR-3 Weldor Qualification") for explanation of (a) through (f).

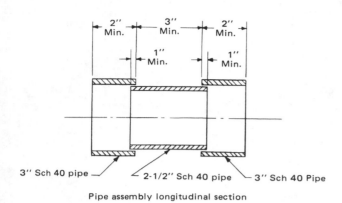

Fig. 24-23. The pipe assembly used for qualifying procedures and weldors for fillet welds.

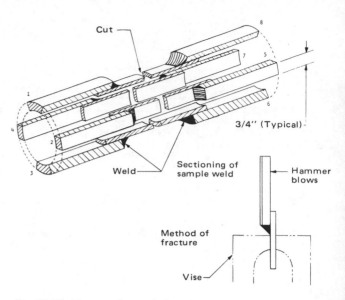

Fig. 24-25. The sampling technique and vise-fracturing method for examining fillet welds.

completed with axis of the assembly in the vertical position and without rotation.

Each sample joint must be inspected prior to welding to assure the material is correct, the parts are clean and the end preparation and fitup are correct. During welding, inspection is made to assure the proper filler metal is used and for cracks, lack of fusion, surface roughness and poor crater conditions. After welding and heat treating if any, the weld is inspected for surface defects.

This test may be terminated at any stage of the testing whenever it becomes apparent to the supervisor conducting the test that (1) the weldor is not following the welding procedure or (2) the weldor does not have the necessary skill to produce satisfactory results.

The test assembly is then cut into eight 3/4-in.-wide specimens, as shown in Fig. 24-25. Each specimen must have an acceptable or desirable profile, as illustrated in Fig. 24-26.

Each specimen is fractured in a vise, as shown in Fig. 24-25. The fractured surface must show no

evidence of cracks, incomplete fusion, or inadequate penetration at the root of the weld.

ASME BOILER AND PRESSURE VESSEL CODE QUALIFICATIONS

Section IX of the Boiler and Pressure Vessel Code of the American Society of Mechanical Engineers provides for qualification tests of procedures and personnel for welding under that code. The following is a condensed and incomplete description of these qualifications. The condensation does not cover qualification tests for steels of 85,000 psi or more and for quenched and tempered steels. Before making tests, a copy of the

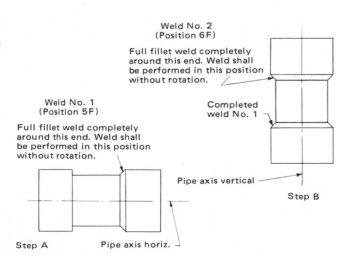

Fig. 24-24. Positions for the fillet-weld qualification tests.

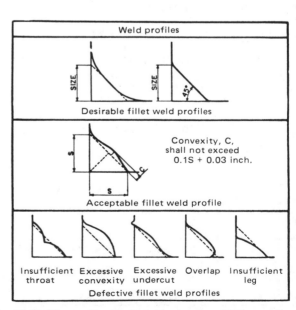

Fig. 24-26. The profile standards that sectioned fillet welds must meet in qualification testing.

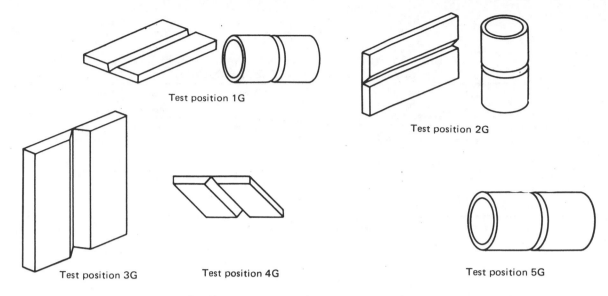

Fig. 24-27. Qualifying test positions for groove welds in pipe and plate.

complete code should be obtained from the American Society of Mechanical Engineers, Order Department, United Engineering Center, 345 East 47th Street, New York, N.Y. 10017.

PROCEDURE QUALIFICATION, ASME CODE

Tests for procedure qualification are prescribed for welds in pipe and plate. Procedure qualification for groove welds in pipe requires one test assembly be welded for each position shown in Fig. 25-27.

In position 1G, the pipe axis is horizontal and the pipe is rotated during welding. Weld metal is deposited from above (flat welding).

In position 2G, the pipe axis is vertical and the pipe is not rotated (horizontal welding).

In position 5G, the pipe axis is horizontal and the pipe is not rotated (a combination of flat, vertical and overhead welding).

Qualification in the horizontal, vertical, or overhead position also qualifies for the flat position. Qualification in the horizontal fixed position, 5G, qualifies for flat, vertical and overhead positions. Qualification in the horizontal, vertical and overhead positions qualifies for all positions.

Procedure qualification on pipe also qualifies for plate, but not vice versa.

Procedure qualification for groove welds in plate requires one test assembly to be welded for each position. Qualifying positions are shown in Fig. 24-27.

In position 1G, the plate is in the horizontal plane and weld metal is deposited from above (flat welding).

In position 2G, the plate is in the vertical plane with the axis of the weld horizontal (horizontal welding).

In position 3G, the plate is in the vertical plane and the axis of the weld is vertical (vertical welding).

In position 4G, the plate is in the horizontal plane and weld metal is deposited from underneath (overhead welding).

Groove weld tests qualify the welding procedure for use with both groove and fillet welds.

Procedure qualification for fillet welds requires one test assembly in each of the positions shown in Fig. 24-28.

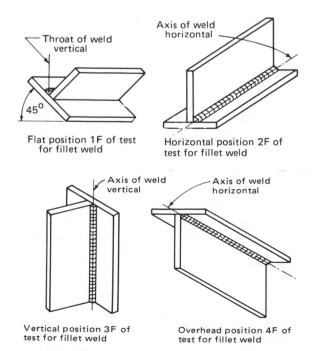

Fig. 24-28. Test positions for fillet welds in plate.

TABLE 24-7. Procedure Qualification. Type, Number of Test Specimens, and Range of Thickness Qualified

Thickness t of Test Plate or Pipe Wall (in.)	Range of Thickness Qualified (in.)		Type and Number of Tests Required			
	Min. (6)	Max. (1,3,6)	Tension	Transverse Bend Tests (5)		
				Side Bend	Face Bend	Root Bend
1/16 to 3/8 inclusive	1/16	2 t (2)	2		2	2
Over 3/8 to 3/4	3/16	2 t	2		2	2
3/4 and over	3/16	2 t	2	4 (4)		

Notes: See Text (''Welding Procedure Qualification, ASME Code'') for explanation of (1) through (6).

TABLE 24-8. Procedure Qualification. Type, Number of Tests Specimens, and Range of Thickness Qualified

Thickness t of Test Plate (in.)	Range of Thickness Qualified (in.)		Type and Number of Tests Required		
	Min.(6)	Max. (1,3,6)	Tension	Longitudinal Bend Tests (5)	
				Face Bend	Root Bend
1/16 to 3/8	1/16	2 t	2	2	2
Over 3/8	3/16	2 t	2	2	2

Notes: See Text (''Welding Procedure Qualification, ASME Code'') for explanation of (1) through (6)

Discard		this piece
Reduced section		tensile specimen
Root bend		specimen
Face bend		specimen
Root bend		specimen
Face bend		specimen
Reduced section		tensile specimen
Discard		this piece

Discard		this piece
Side bend		specimen
Reduced section		tensile specimen
Side bend		specimen
Side bend		specimen
Reduced section		tensile specimen
Side bend		specimen
Discard		this piece

For plate 1/16 to 3/4 in. thick.

For plate over 3/4 in. thick. May be used also for thicknesses from 3/8 to 3/4 in.

Fig. 24-29. Method of taking test specimens from plate for procedure qualification.

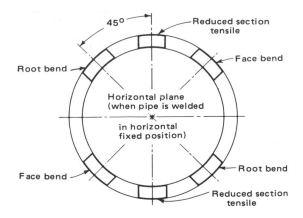

For pipe 1/16 to 3/4 in. in wall thickness.

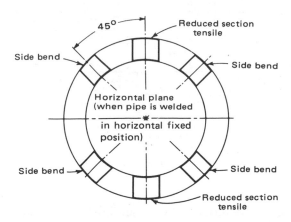

For pipe over 3/4 in. in wall thickness. May be used also for thicknesses from 3/8 to 3/4 in.

Fig. 24-30. Method of taking test specimens from pipe for procedure qualification.

Qualification in the horizontal, vertical, or overhead position qualifies also for the flat position. Qualification in the horizontal, vertical and overhead positions qualifies for all positions.

Preparation of the Test Joint. The base material, filler metal and the welding procedure for the test joint must comply with the job specification. The base material may be either plate or pipe (see Table 24-7). The recommended pipe size is 5 in. in diameter and 3/8 in. in the wall thickness, although larger pipe may be used. Smaller pipe size (job size) may be used, but in such cases the procedure must be qualified for thicknesses between 1/2 and two times the wall thickness of the test pipe, but not over 3/4 in.

The type and number of test specimens for procedure qualification are shown in Table 24-7 and Table 24-8. Also shown is the range of thickness that is qualified for use in construction by a given thickness of test plate or pipe used in making the qualification. Test specimens are to be removed as shown in Fig. 24-29 or Fig. 24-44 for plate and Fig. 24-30 for pipe.

The notes to Tables 24-7 and 24-8 are essential to the use of the tables. The applicable notes are:

1. The maximum thickness qualified in gas welding is the thickness of the test plate or pipe.

2. The maximum thickness qualified for pipe smaller than 5 in. is two times the thickness of the pipe but not more than 3/4-in.

3. For submerged-arc welding and gas metal-arc welding, the thickness limitation for production welding, based on plate thickness t, shall be as follows:

   a. For single-pass welding with no backing strip or against a metal or ceramic (flux) backing, the maximum thickness welded in production shall not exceed the thickness of the test plate or pipe.

   b. If the test plate is welded by a procedure involving one pass from each side, the maximum thickness that may be welded in production shall be 2t, where 2t shall not exceed 2 in. If sections heavier than 2 in. are to be welded in production, a separate test plate shall be prepared with the thickness not less than the thickness to be used in production.

   c. For multiple-pass welding, the thickness limitations in Table 24-7 and 24-8 apply.

4. Either face and root bends or side bends may be used for thicknesses from 3/8 to 3/4 in.

5. Longitudinal bend tests may be used in lieu of transverse bend tests in Table 24-7 only for testing material combinations differing markedly in physical bending properties between (a) the two base materials or (b) the weld metal

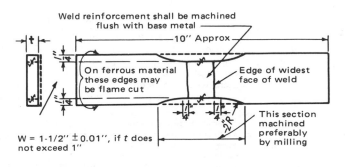

Fig. 24-31. Reduced-section tensile specimen from plate.

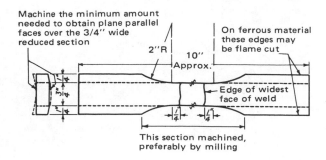

Machine the minimum amount needed to obtain plane parallel faces over the 3/4'' wide reduced section

On ferrous material these edges may be flame cut

2''R

10'' Approx.

Edge of widest face of weld

This section machined, preferably by milling

Fig. 24-32. Reduced-section tensile specimen from pipe.

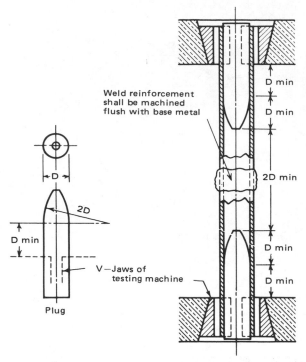

Weld reinforcement shall be machined flush with base metal

V—Jaws of testing machine

Plug

D min

D min

2D min

D min

D min

Fig. 24-34. Full-section tensile specimen for small-diameter pipe.

and base materials. (See Fig. 24-44 for weld test plate.)

6. For quenched and tempered steels (tensile strength 95,000 psi or higher) of thicknesses less than 5/8 in., the thickness of the test plate or pipe is the minimum thickness qualified. For test plates or pipe receiving a postweld heat treatment in which the lower critical temperature is exceeded, the maximum thickness qualified is the thickness of the test plate or pipe.

Tension Tests: Reduced-section tension-test specimens shall conform to Fig. 24-31 for plate and Fig. 24-32 for pipe of all wall thicknesses having an outside diameter greater than 3 in. Tension test specimens conforming to Fig. 24-33 may be used for thicknesses to and including 1-1/4 in. Over 1-1/4 in. multiple specimens shall be cut

through the full thickness of the weld with the centers parallel to the material surface and not over 1 in. apart.

Tensile specimens conforming to Fig. 24-34 may be used for testing pipe or tube with an outside diameter 3 in. or less.

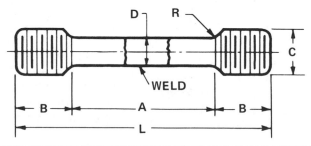

D   R

C

WELD

B   A   B

L

	Standard Dimensions, In.			
	(a) 0.505 Specimen	**(b)** 0.353 Specimen	**(c)** 0.252 Specimen	**(d)** 0.188 Specimen
A-Length reduced section	See Note 4	See Note 4	See Note 4	See Note 4
D-Diameter	0.500 ± 0.010	0.350 ± 0.007	0.250 ± 0.005	0.188 ± 0.003
R-Radius of fillet	3/8, min	1/4, min	3/16, min	1/8, min
B-Length of end section	1-3/8, approx	1-1/8, approx	7/8, approx	1/2, approx
C-Diameter of end section	3/4	1/2	3/8	1/4

NOTES:
2. Use maximum diameter specimen (a), (b), (c), or (d) that can be cut from the section.
2. Weld should be in center of reduced section.
3. Where only a single specimen is required the center of the specimen should be midway between the surfaces.
4. Reduced section "A" should not be less than width of weld plus two "D."
5. The ends may be of any shape to fit the holders of the testing machine in such a way that the load is applied axially.

Fig. 24-33. Alternate reduced-section tensile specimen.

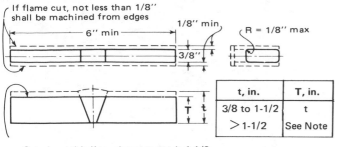

t, in.	T, in.
3/8 to 1-1/2	t
>1-1/2	See Note

Cut along this line when *t* exceeds 1-1/2;
Edge may be flame-cut and may or may
not be machined.

Note: For plates over 1-1/2-in. thick, cut specimen
into approximately equal strips between 3/4-in. and
1-1/2-in. wide and test each strip.

Fig. 24-35. Transverse side bend specimens, pipe and plate.

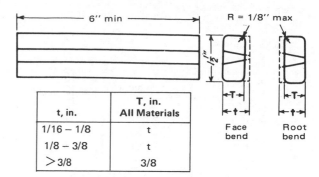

t, in.	T, in. All Materials
1/16 — 1/8	t
1/8 — 3/8	t
>3/8	3/8

Note: Weld reinforcement and backing strip, if any, shall be
removed flush with the surface of the specimen. If a recessed
strip is used this surface of the specimen may be machined to
a depth not exceeding the depth of the recess to remove the
strip, except that in such cases the thickness of the finished
specimen shall be that specified above.

Fig. 24-37. Longitudinal root and face bend specimens.

Tensile Strength Requirements: The tensile
strength must not be less than:

1. The minimum specified for the base material,
   or

2. The minimum specified for the weaker of the
   two, if materials of different specified minimum tensile strengths are used, or

3. The minimum specified for the weld metal
   where the weld metal has lower room-temperature strength than the base metal.

If the specimen breaks in the base metal, the
test shall be accepted if the tensile strength is not
more than 5% below the minimum specified for
the base metal.

Guided Bend Tests: Transverse side bend specimens shall conform to the dimensions shown in
Fig. 24-35.

Transverse root and face bend specimens shall
conform to the dimensions shown in Fig. 24-36.

Longitudinal root and face bend specimens
shall conform to the dimensions shown in Fig.
24-37. This type of specimen is used only for testing material combinations differing markedly in
physical bending properties.

The guided-bend specimens shall be bent in test
jigs that are substantially in accordance with Figs.
24-38, 24-39 and 24-40.

When using jigs in accordance with Figs. 24-38
or 24-39, the side of the specimen turned toward
the gap shall be the face for face bends, root for
root bends and the side with greater defects, if any,
for side bends. The specimen shall be forced into
the die until the curvature of the specimen is such
that a 1/8-in.-diameter wire cannot be inserted
between the die and the specimen.

When using the roller-type jig, Fig. 24-39, the
specimen shall be bottom-ejected. When using the
wrap-around jig, Fig. 24-40, the side of the speci-

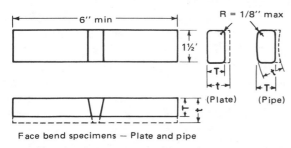

Face bend specimens — Plate and pipe

t, in.	T, in. All Ferrous Materials
1/16 — 1/8	t
1/8 — 3/8	t
>3/8	3/8

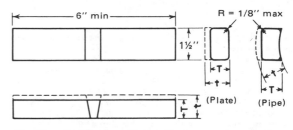

Root bend specimens — Plate and pipe

Note: Weld reinforcement and backing strip or backing ring, if
any, shall be removed flush with the surface of the specimen. If a
recessed ring is used, this surface of the specimen may be
machined to a depth not exceeding the depth of the recess to
remove the ring, except that in such cases the thickness of the
finished specimen shall be that specified above.

Fig. 24-36. Transverse root and face bend specimens, pipe and plate.

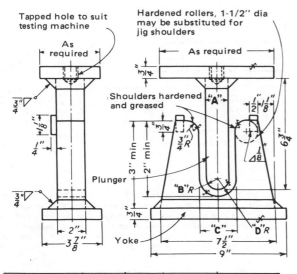

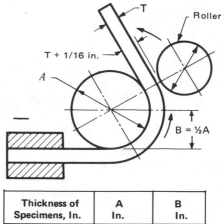

Thickness of Specimens, In.	A In.	B In.	C In.	D In.
3/8	1-1/2	3/4	2-3/8	1-3/16
t	4t	2t	6t + 1/8	3t + 1/16

Fig. 24-38. Guided-bend test jig.

Thickness of Specimens, In.	A In.	B In.
3/8	1-1/2	3/4
t	4t	2t

NOTES:
1. Dimensions not shown are the option of the designer. The essential consideration is to have adequate rigidity so that the jig parts will not spring.
2. The specimen shall be firmly clamped on one end so that there is no sliding of the specimen during the bending operation. The weld and heat-affected zone in the case of transverse weld bend specimens shall be completely within the bent portion of the specimen after testing.
3. Test specimens shall be removed from the jig when the outer roll has been removed 180 degrees from the starting point.

Fig. 24-40. Wrap-around guided-bend jig.

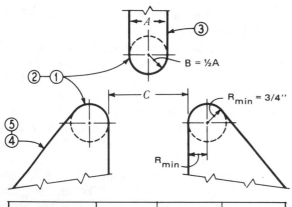

Thickness of Specimens, In.	A In.	B In.	D In.
3/8	1-1/2	3/4	2-3/8
t	4t	2t	6t + 1/8

NOTES:
1. Either hardened and greased shoulders or hardened rollers free to rotate shall be used.
2. The shoulders or rollers shall have a minimum bearing surface of 2 in. for placement of the specimen. The rollers shall be high enough above the bottom of the jig so that the specimens will clear the rollers when the ram is in the low position.
3. The ram shall be fitted with an appropriate base and provision made for attachment to the testing machine, and shall be designed to minimize deflection and misalignment. The ram to be used with the roller jig shall be of identical dimensions to the ram shown in Fig. 24-38.
4. If desired, either the rollers or the roller supports may be made adjustable in the horizontal direction so that specimens of t thickness may be tested on the same jig.
5. The roller supports shall be fitted with an appropriate base designed to safeguard against deflection or misalignment and equipped with means for maintaining the rollers centered, midpoint and aligned with respect to the ram.

Fig. 24-39. Roller-equipped guided-bend jig for bottom ejection of test specimen.

men toward the roller shall be face for face bends, root for root bends and the side with the greater defects, if any, for the side bends.

Bend Test Requirements: After bending, the specimen shall have no cracks or other open defects exceeding 1/8 in. measured in any direction on the convex surface. Cracks on the corners of the specimen shall not be considered unless there is evidence of slag inclusions or other internal defects.

If the wall thickness of the tube or pipe is less than 3/8 in., or the diameter-to-thickness ratio does not permit the preparation of a full-size rectangular guided-bend specimen, the 1-1/2-in.-wide standard bend specimen shown in Fig. 24-36 may be replaced by three subsize specimens having a width of 3/8 in. or 4t, whichever is less. The weld reinforcement and backing ring shall be removed flush with the pipe or tube surface and the corners may be provided with a radius not to exceed 1/3t.

Fillet Weld Tests: Fillet-weld test specimens for procedure qualification shall conform to Fig. 24-41. The weld shall not contain any visible cracks. The specimen shall be cut transversely in five sections approximately 2 in. long and one face of each section shall be smoothed and etched with a suitable etchant to give a clear definition of the structure. Visual examination shall show:

1. Complete fusion at the root and no cracks.

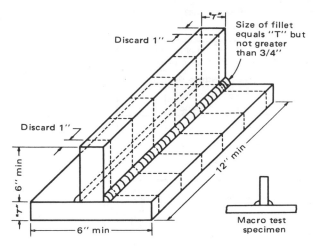

"T" maximum thickness of base material in the vessel at point of welding or 1", whichever is smaller.

Macro test: The fillet shall show fusion at the root of the weld but not necessarily beyond the root. The weld metal and heat-affected zone shall be free of cracks. Both legs of the fillet shall be equal to within 1/8 inch.

Fig. 24-41. Fillet-weld soundness test for procedure qualification.

2. Not more than 1/8 in. difference in the length of the legs of the fillet.

WELDOR QUALIFICATION, ASME CODE

Weldor qualification (called "performance qualification" in the ASME code) is to demonstrate that a weldor can make sound welds when using a previously qualified procedure. The code provides that the weldor who prepares the welding procedure qualification test specimens meeting the requirements of the code is thereby qualified without further testing.

Weldor qualification tests are made on groove welds or on fillet welds. Weldors qualified on groove welds are automatically qualified for fillet welds in all thicknesses. Weldors qualified on fillet welds only are qualified to make fillet welds only.

All the requirements for welding positions for procedure qualification also apply to weldor qualification.

The type, number of test specimens and the ranges of thickness qualified are given in Tables 24-9 and 24-10. The notes to these tables are as follows:

1. A total of four specimens are required to qualify for position 5G.

2. The maximum thickness qualified in gas welding is the thickness of the test plate or pipe.

3. The base material may consist of either plate or pipe. The minimum nominal diameter of 5 in. is recommended for pipe used as base material.

4. Either face and root bends or side bends may be used for thicknesses from 3/8 to 3/4 in.

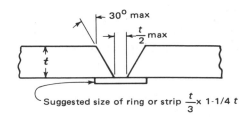

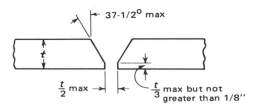

Fig. 24-42. Butt joints for weldor qualification tests, with and wirhout backing strip.

TABLE 24-9. Weldor Qualification. Type, Number of Test Specimens, and Ranges of Thickness Qualified

| Type of Joint | Thickness t of Test Plate or Pipe As Welded in. (3) | Range of Thickness of Material Qualified by Test Plate, in. | | Type and Number of Tests Required (1) | | | |
| | | | | Transverse Bend Tests (5) | | | |
		Min.	Max. (2,3)	Side Bend	Face Bend	Root Bend	T Joint
Groove	1/16 to 3/8 inclusive	1/16	2 t		1	1	
Groove (4)	Over 3/8 but less than 3/4	3/16	2 t		1	1	
Groove (4)	Over 3/8 but less than 3/4	3/16	2 t	2			
Groove	3/4 and over	3/16	Max to be welded	2 (4)			
Fillet	See Fig. 11-72	All thicknesses					1

Notes: See Text ("Weldor Qualification, ASME Code") for explanation of (1) through (4).

TABLE 24-10. Weldor Qualification. Type, Number of Test Specimens, and Ranges of Thickness Qualified(5)

Type of Joint	Thickness t of Test Plate or Pipe As Welded in.	Range of Thickness of Material Qualified by Test Plate, in.		Type and Number of Tests Required		
				Longitudinal Bend Tests		
		Min.	Max. (2)	Face Bend	Root Bend	T Joint
Groove	1/16 to 3/8 inclusive	1/16	2 t	1	1	
Groove	Over 3/8	3/16	2 t	1	1	
Fillet	See Fig. 11-72	All thicknesses				1

Notes: See Text ("Weldor Qualifications, ASME Code") for explanation of (2) through (5).

5. Longitudinal bend tests may be used in lieu of the transverse bend tests in Table 24-9 only for testing material combinations differing markedly in physical bending properties between (a) the two base materials or (b) the weld metal and base materials. See Fig. 24-44 for the weld test plate.

The dimensions of the welding groove for the test joint used in making weldor qualification tests, on double-welded butt joints and single-welded butt joints with backing strip, shall be the same as those for procedure qualification, or shall be as shown in Fig. 24-42.

Qualification on a single-welded plate with a backing strip shall also qualify for pipe with a backing strip and vice versa in positions 1G and 2G only (Fig. 24-27).

Qualification on a single-welded plate without a backing strip shall also qualify for single-welded pipe without a backing strip and vice versa in positions 1G and 2G only.

Qualification on double-welded plate shall also qualify for double-welded pipe and vice versa in positions 1G and 2G only.

For all other positions qualification on pipe shall qualify for plate but not vice versa.

Test Specimens: Test welds made in plate — the type and number of bend test specimens specified in Tables 24-9 and 24-10 — may be removed

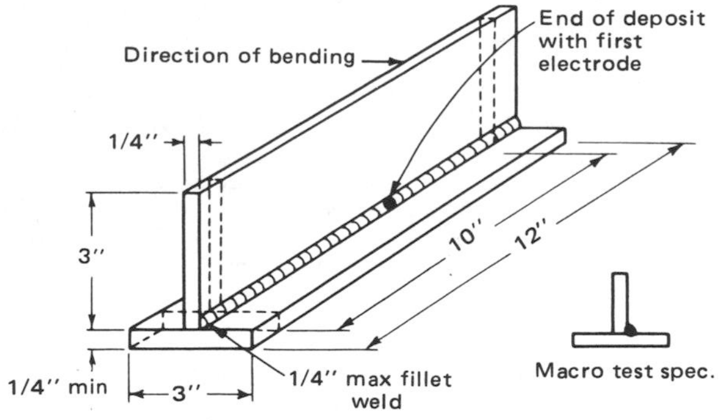

FILLET WELD SOUNDNESS TEST
FOR WELDOR QUALIFICATION

FRACTURE TEST: Maximum permissible defects such as slag, non-fusion, etc. — 20% or 2 in. Evidence of cracking of fillet shall constitute grounds for rejection.

MACRO TEST: The fillet shall show fusion to the root of the weld but not necessarily beyond the root. Convexity and/or concavity of the fillet shall not exceed 1/16 in. Both legs of the fillet shall be equal to within 1/16 in.

Fig. 24-43. Fillet-weld specimen for weldor qualification test.

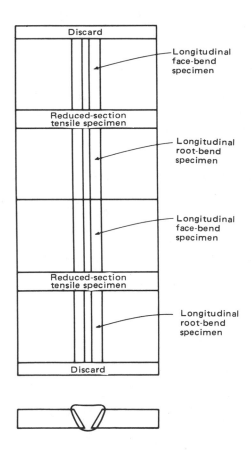

Fig. 24-44. Order of removal of test specimens from welded test plate for longitudinal bend tests.

**TABLE 24-11. Type and Number of Butt-Weld Test
Specimens for Procedure Qualification Test**

Pipe Size, Outside Diameter — In.	Number of Specimens					
	Tensile	Nick Break	Root Bend	Face Bend	Side Bend	Total
	Wall Thickness — 1/2 In. and Under					
Under 2-3/8	0	2	2	0	0	4*
2-3/8 to 4-1/2 inclusive	0	2	2	0	0	4
Over 4-1/2 to 12-3/4 inclusive	2	2	2	2	0	8
Over 12-3/4	4	4	4	4	0	16
	Wall Thickness — Over 1/2 In.					
4-1/2 and smaller	0	2	0	0	2	4
Over 4-1/2 to 12-3/4 inclusive	2	2	0	0	4	8
Over 12-3/4	4	4	0	0	8	16

* One nick-break and one root bend specimen from each of two test welds, or for pipe 1-5/16 in. and smaller, one full pipe section tensile specimen.

from the test plate in any order, but in a manner similar to that shown in Figs. 24-29, 24-30 and 24-44.

For test welds made in pipe in positions 1G or 2G, specimens shall be removed as shown for bend specimens in Fig. 24-30, at approximately 90° apart, omitting the tension specimens. For test welds made on a pipe in position 5G, specimens shall be removed in accordance with Fig. 24-30 and all four specimens shall pass the test.

All bend specimens shall be machined, tested and meet the same test requirements as the procedure qualification tests.

Fillet-Weld Tests: Dimensions and preparation of the fillet-weld test specimens shall conform to the requirements of Fig. 24-43. The test specimen shall contain no visible cracks. The specimen shall be cut transversely to provide a center section 10 in. long and two end sections each approximately 1 in. long.

The stem of the 10-in. center section shall be located laterally in such a way that the root of the weld is in tension. The load shall be applied until the specimen fractures or bends flat upon itself. In order to pass the test —

1. The specimen shall not fracture; or

2. If it fractures, the fractured surface shall show no evidence of cracks or incomplete fusion and the sum of the lengths of the inclusions and gas pockets shall not exceed 2 in.

One of the end sections shall be smoothed and etched with a suitable etchant to give a clear definition of the structure of the weld metal. In order to pass the test —

1. The section shall show complete fusion at the root and no cracks;

2. The weld shall not have a concavity or convexity greater than 1/16 in.; and

3. There shall be not more than 1/16 in. difference in the lengths of the legs of the fillet.

API QUALIFICATION TESTS FOR PIPELINE WELDING

The American Petroleum Institute (API) sets specifications for welding procedures and personnel employed on pipeline welding in its *"Standard for Welding Pipelines and Related Facilities"* (API Standard 1104). The standard is available from the American Petroleum Institute, 1271 Avenue of the Americas, New York, N.Y. 10020. The following is a highly condensed resume of the portions of the standard pertaining to procedure and weldor qualification.

API QUALIFICATION OF WELDING PROCEDURES

Prior to the start of production welding, a procedure specification must be established and qualified to demonstrate that welds having suitable mechanical properties and that soundness will result from the procedure. The quality of the weld is determined by destructive testing.

Table 24-11 shows the type and number of butt-weld test specimens required for procedure qualification and Figs. 24-45, 24-46 and 24-47 show how specimens are taken and prepared for testing. Fig. 24-48 shows the jig used for guided bend tests.

In the tensile test, the tensile strength of the weld, including the fusion zone, shall be equal to or greater than the minimum specified tensile strength of the pipe material.

In the nick-break test, the exposed surfaces of each specimen shall show complete penetration and fusion and no more than six gas pockets per sq. in. of surface area, with the greatest dimension

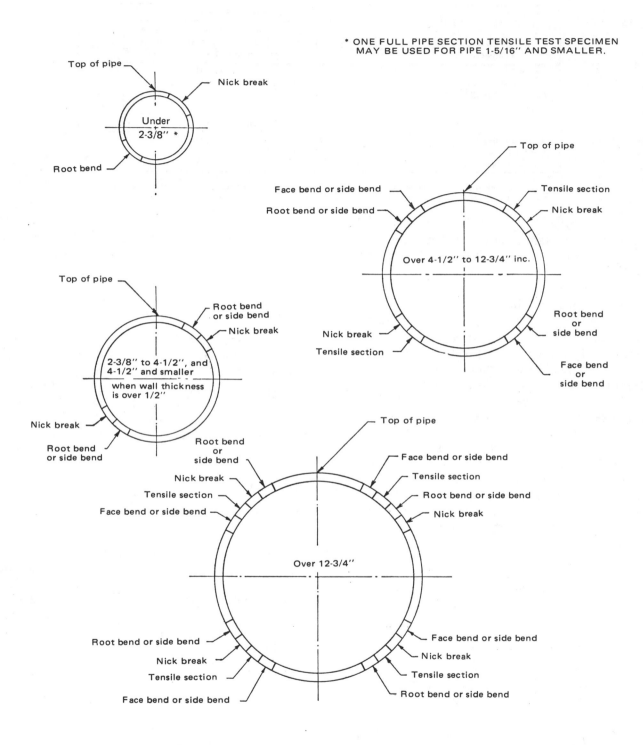

* ONE FULL PIPE SECTION TENSILE TEST SPECIMEN MAY BE USED FOR PIPE 1-5/16" AND SMALLER.

At the company's option, the locations may be rotated 45 degrees counterclockwise or they may be equally spaced around the pipe except specimens shall not include the longitudinal weld. Also, at the company's option, additional specimens may be taken.

Fig. 24-45. Location of butt-weld test specimens for API procedure qualification tests.

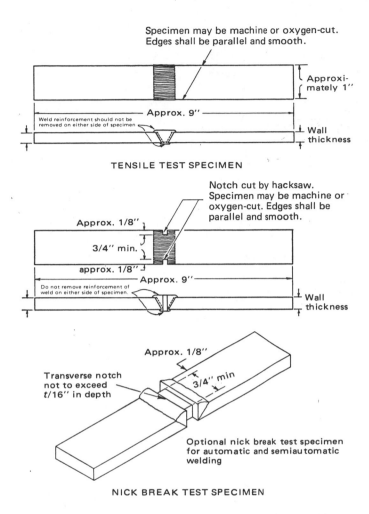

Specimen may be machine or oxygen-cut.
Edges shall be parallel and smooth.

Approximately 1''

Approx. 9''

Weld reinforcement should not be
removed on either side of specimen

Wall
thickness

TENSILE TEST SPECIMEN

Notch cut by hacksaw.
Specimen may be machine or
oxygen-cut. Edges shall be
parallel and smooth.

Approx. 1/8''

3/4'' min.

approx. 1/8''

Approx. 9''

Do not remove reinforcement of
weld on either side of specimen.

Wall
thickness

Approx. 1/8''

3/4'' min

Transverse notch
not to exceed
$t/16''$ in depth

Optional nick break test specimen
for automatic and semiautomatic
welding

NICK BREAK TEST SPECIMEN

Fig. 24-46. How tensile and nick-break specimens of butt welds are prepared for API procedure qualification tests.

not to exceed 1/16-in. Slag inclusions shall not be more than 1/32-in. in depth nor 1/8-in. or one-half the nominal wall thickness in length, whichever is shorter, and there shall be at least 1/2-in. of sound weld metal between adjacent inclusions.

The bend tests shall be considered acceptable if no crack or other defect exceeding 1/8 in. or one-half the nominal wall thickness, whichever is smaller, in any direction is present in the weld or between the weld and the fusion zone after bending. Cracks which originate along the edges of the specimen during testing and which are less than 1/4 in. measured in any direction, shall not be considered unless defects are observed.

The type and number of fillet-weld test specimens for procedure qualification are as follows:

Pipe Size, OD In.	Number of Specimens
Under 2-3/8	4 (Obtain from 2 welds)
2-3/8 to 12-3/4 inclusive . .	4
Over 12-3/4	6

The methods of taking and preparing fillet-weld specimens are illustrated in Figs. 24-49 and 24-50. The test requirements are similar to those for butt welds.

API QUALIFICATION OF WELDORS

The purpose of the weldor qualification tests is to determine the ability of weldors to make sound welds using a previously qualified procedure. Fillet welds are evaluated by destructive tests. Butt welds may be tested by destructice tests or by radiography. API Standard 1104 prescribes the radiographic standards of acceptability.

Table 24-12 gives the type and number of butt-weld specimens for weldor qualification testing and Fig. 24-51 shows how specimens are to be taken.

Tensile test requirements are the same as for procedure qualification, except that if the specimen should break in the weld, it must meet the nick-break test requirements. The nick-break test

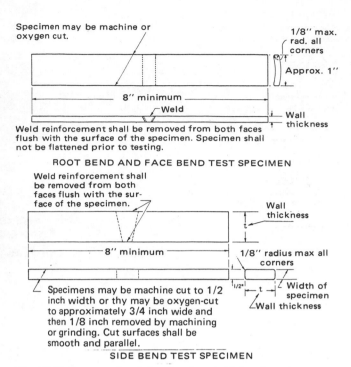

Specimen may be machine or
oxygen cut.

1/8'' max.
rad. all
corners

Approx. 1''

8'' minimum

Weld

Wall
thickness

Weld reinforcement shall be removed from both faces
flush with the surface of the specimen. Specimen shall
not be flattened prior to testing.

ROOT BEND AND FACE BEND TEST SPECIMEN

Weld reinforcement shall
be removed from both
faces flush with the sur-
face of the specimen.

Wall
thickness

t

8'' minimum

1/8'' radius max all
corners

1/2''   t

Width of
specimen

Wall thickness

Specimens may be machine cut to 1/2
inch width or thy may be oxygen-cut
to approximately 3/4 inch wide and
then 1/8 inch removed by machining
or grinding. Cut surfaces shall be
smooth and parallel.

SIDE BEND TEST SPECIMEN

Fig. 24-47. How root-bend, face-bend, and side-bend specimens are prepared.

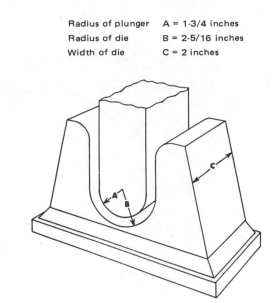

Radius of plunger   A = 1-3/4 inches
Radius of die   B = 2-5/16 inches
Width of die   C = 2 inches

Fig. 24-48. Jig for the API guided bend tests.

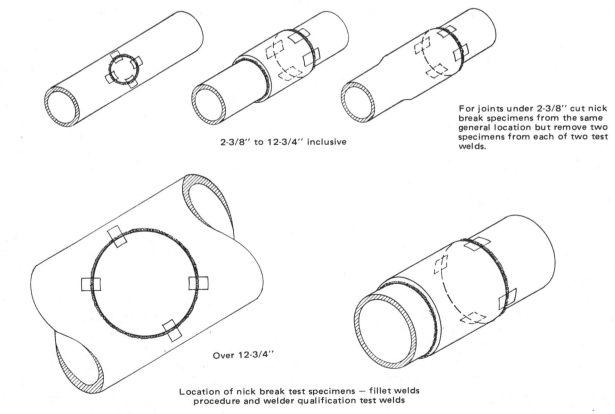

2-3/8'' to 12-3/4'' inclusive

For joints under 2-3/8'' cut nick
break specimens from the same
general location but remove two
specimens from each of two test
welds.

Over 12-3/4''

Location of nick break test specimens — fillet welds
procedure and welder qualification test welds

Note: At the option of the Company additional specimens may be taken.

Fig. 24-49. Method of taking nick-break fillet-weld test specimens for API procedure and weldor qualifications.

**TABLE 24-12. Type and Number of Butt-Weld Test
Specimens for Weldor Qualification Test
and for Destructive Testing of Production Welds**

Pipe Size, Outside Diameter — In.	Number of Specimens					
	Tensile**	Nick Break	Root Bend	Face Bend	Side Bend	Total
	Wall Thickness — 1/2 In. and Under					
Under 2-3/8	0	2	2	0	0	4*
2-3/8 to 4-1/2 inclusive	0	2	2	0	0	4
Over 4-1/2 to 12-3/4 inclusive	2	2	2	0	0	6
Over 12-3/4	4	4	2	2	0	12
	Wall Thickness — Over 1/2 In.					
4-1/2 and smaller	0	2	0	0	2	4
Over 4-1/2 to 12-3/4 inclusive	2	2	0	0	2	6
Over 12-3/4	4	4	0	0	4	12

* Obtain from two welds, or one full pipe section tensile specimen for pipe 1-5/16 in. and smaller.

** The tensile test may be omitted, in which case the specimens designated for this test shall be subjected to the nick-break test.

requirements are the same as for procedure qualification.

The bend test requirements are also the same as for procedure qualification. Welds on high-test pipe (API Std. 5LX) may not bend the full U shape. These shall be considered acceptable if the specimens that crack are broken apart and the exposed surfaces meet the nick-break test requirements.

Fillet-weld specimens are cut from each test weld. If the test weld is a complete circumferential weld, the locations from which the specimens are to be removed are as shown in Fig. 24-49. If the test weld consists of segments of pipe nipples, an approximately equal number of specimens must be removed from each segment. The specimens should be air-cooled to ambient temperature before testing.

The preparation of the fillet-weld test specimens, the testing procedures and the test requirements are the same as for procedure qualification.

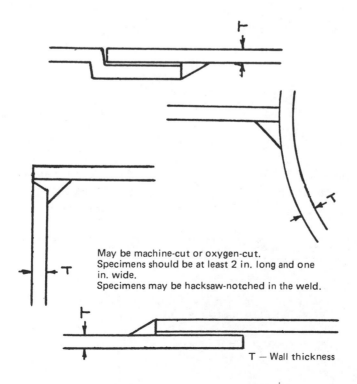

May be machine-cut or oxygen-cut.
Specimens should be at least 2 in. long and one in. wide.
Specimens may be hacksaw-notched in the weld.

T — Wall thickness

Fig. 24-50. Preparation of fillet-weld specimens.

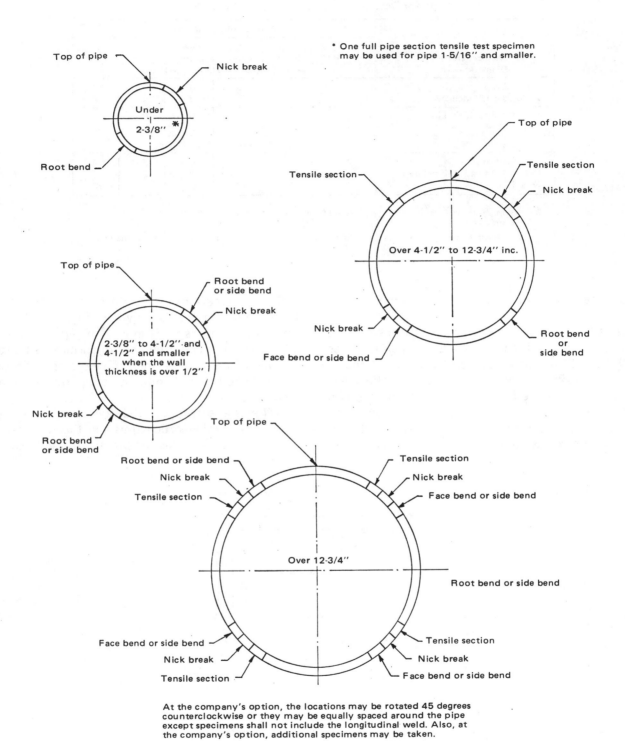

* One full pipe section tensile test specimen may be used for pipe 1-5/16″ and smaller.

At the company's option, the locations may be rotated 45 degrees counterclockwise or they may be equally spaced around the pipe except specimens shall not include the longitudinal weld. Also, at the company's option, additional specimens may be taken.

LOCATION OF TEST SPECIMENS — BUTT WELD
WELDOR QUALIFICATION TEST

Fig. 24-51. How butt-weld test specimens are to be taken for API weldor qualification tests.

Special Welding Processes

In industry, the student will find that various welding processes other than those previously described are used. Some of these are essentially innovative ways of applying the basic principles of the conventional processes; others are what might be termed exotic. In the following text, several of the most commonly used special welding processes will be described.

ELECTROSLAG WELDING

Electroslag welding is an adaptation of the submerged-arc process for joining thick materials in the vertical position in one pass. Figure 25-1 is a diagrammatic sketch of the electroslag process. Whereas some of the principles of the submerged-arc process apply, in other respects the process resembles a casting operation — casting filler metal between two vertical parts. Although a square butt joint is illustrated in Fig. 25-1, the electroslag process — with modifications and technique — is also applicable to T joints, corner joints, girth seams in heavy-wall cylinders and other joints. The process is best suited for joining materials one inch or more in thickness.

As illustrated by the open, square butt joint in Fig. 25-1, the assembly is positioned for the vertical deposition of weld metal. A starting pad at the bottom of the joint prevents the fall-out of the initially deposited weld metal and since it is penetrated, assures a full weld at this point. Welding is started at the bottom and progresses upward. Water-cooled dams, which may be looked upon as molds, are placed on each side of the joint. These dams are moved upward as the weld-metal deposition progresses. The joint is filled in one "pass" — a single upward progression — of one or more consumable electrodes. The electrode or electrodes may be oscillated across the joint if the width of the joint makes this desirable.

At the start of the operation, a layer of flux is placed in the bottom of the joint and an arc is struck between the electrode (or electrodes) and the work. The arc melts the slag, forming a molten layer, which subsequently acts as an electrolytic heating medium. The arc is then quenched or shorted-out by this molten conductive layer. Heat for melting the electrode and the base metal subsequently results from the electrical resistance heating of the electrode section extending from the contact tube and from the resistance heating within the molten slag layer. As the electrode (or electrodes) is consumed, the welding head (or heads) and the cooling dams move upward.

In conventional practice, the weld deposit usually contains about 1/3 melted base metal and 2/3 electrode metal — which means that the base metal substantially contributes to the chemical composition of the weld metal. Flux consumption is low, since the molten flux and the unmelted flux above it "ride" above the progressing weld.

The flux used has a degree of electrical conductivity and low viscosity in the molten condition and a high vaporization temperature. The consumable electrodes may be either solid wire or tubular wire filled with metal powders. Alloying elements

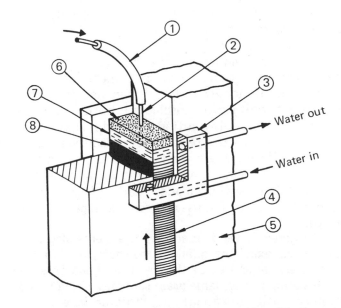

Fig. 25-1. Schematic sketch of electroslag welding. (1) electrode guide tube, (2) electrode, (3) water-cooled copper shoes, (4) finished weld, (5) base metal, (6) molten slag, (7) molten weld metal, (8) solidified weld metal.

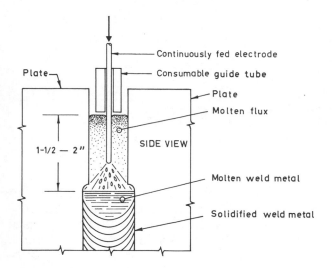

Fig. 25-2. Schematic of the electroslag process using a consumable electrode guide. *Courtesy Hobart Brothers Company.*

may be incorporated into the weld by each of these electrodes.

Some systems use a large-diameter (1/2" to 5/8") steel tube as a consumable electrode guide (see Fig. 25-2). The guide remains stationary and as the weld progresses, the bottom of the guide melts and adds to the filler metal. Some consumable guides are available with flux coverings; others are bare. If the consumable guide is bare, granulated flux is poured in manually or metered into the joint to maintain the necessary depth of slag over the molten weld metal.

The current is usually DC, supplied from large rectifiers or heavy-duty generators. AC can be used, but DC is preferred by most operators. A typical current for 1/8" electrodes is 550 to 650 amperes at 40 to 50 volts. One electrode is recommended for welding material up to 5 inches in thickness, two electrodes up to 9 inches and three electrodes up to 20 inches. When necessary, the electrodes are slowly oscillated horizontally to insure good heat distribution and maintain uniform penetration into the base metal. Electrode metal-transfer efficiency is almost 100 percent, with flux consumption being very low. One form of electroslag welding uses electrodes made of steel plate rather than wires and uses currents as high as 2,000 amps.

In general, welds made by the electroslag process have excellent quality. However, due to the extremely large area of the weld pool and possible slow cooling rates, large grain size may develop and require heat treatment in structures requiring optimum notch toughness. Sometimes the copper dams are provided with orifices just above the slag layer, through which a protective gas — argon or

carbon dioxide — is introduced to flush out the air above the weld and, thus, give additional assurance against oxidation. Such provisions are often considered worthwhile when welding highly alloyed steels or steels that contain easily oxidizing elements.

The electroslag process has various advantages, including no need for special edge preparations, a desirable sequence of cooling that places the outside surfaces of weld metal under compressive rather than tensile stresses and a relative freedom from porosity problems. Special equipment, however, is required and few users of welding have enough volume of welding subject to application of the process to warrant the cost of such equipment.

The applications for electroslag welding are growing in such areas as heavy structural steel sections, heavy machinery sections and nuclear reactor vessels. Low unit cost, high deposition rates and practically no distortion makes the process desirable on many heavy-steel welding jobs. Figure 25-3 shows a typical application.

ELECTROGAS WELDING

Electrogas welding is similar to electroslag welding in that the equipment is similar and the joint is in the vertical position. As the name implies, the shielding is by carbon dioxide or an inert gas. A thin layer of slag, supplied by the flux-cored electrode, covers the molten metal and the heat is supplied by an arc rather than by resistance heating as in the electroslag process.

A disadvantage of the process is that it requires

Fig. 25-3. Two eight-inch-thick steel plates are being welded together in one pass, using the electroslag process. Only four hours and 12 minutes are required to make the weld. *Courtesy Hobart Brothers Company.*

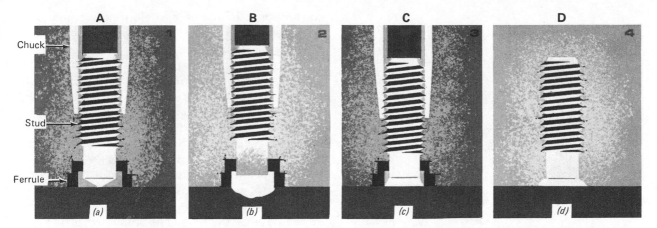

Fig. 25-4. Principles of stud welding, using a ceramic ferrule to shield the pool. (a) The stud with ceramic ferrule is grasped by the chuck of the gun and positioned for welding. (b) The trigger is pressed, the stud is lifted and the arc is created. (c) With the brief arcing period completed, the stud is plunged into the molten pool on the base plate. (d) The gun is withdrawn from the welded-on stud and the ferrule removed.

an external source of shielding gas. However, one advantage is that if the welding is stopped the electrogas process can be started again with less difficulty than the electroslag process.

A variation of electrogas welding uses a self-shielded flux-cored electrode. With this variation, the materials in the electrode core generate the vapors required for arc shielding and provide the needed fluxing substances. No external shielding gas or addition of flux are required. This vertical-up welding process is an offshoot of the automatic self-shielded flux-cored welding process.

STUD WELDING

Stud welding is a variation of the shielded metal-arc process that is widely used for attaching studs, screws, pins and similar fasteners to a larger workpiece. The stud (or small part), itself — often plus a ceramic ferrule at its tip — is the arc-welding electrode during the brief period of time required for studding.

In operation, the stud is held in a portable pistol-shaped tool called a stud gun and positioned by the operator over the spot where it is to be

Fig. 25-5. Some of the commonly used fastening devices attached to metal parts and assemblies by stud welding.

weld-attached. At a press of the trigger, current flows through the stud, which is lifted slightly, creating an arc. After a very short arcing period, the stud is then plunged down into the molten pool created on the base plate, the gun withdrawn

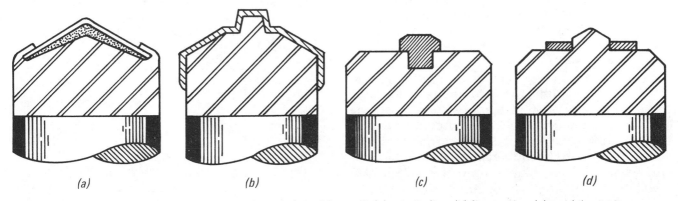

Fig. 25-6. Three methods of containing flux on the end of a welding stud: (a) granular flux; (b) flux coating; (c) and (d) solid flux.

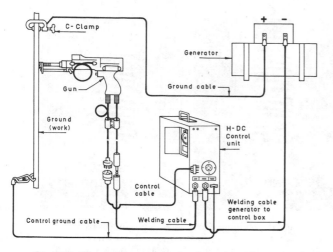

Fig. 25-7. Circuit diagram of a simple stud-welding setup.

from it and the ceramic ferrule — if one has been used — removed. The timing is controlled automatically and the stud is welded onto the workpiece in less than a second. The fundamentals of the process are illustrated in Fig. 25-4.

Studs are of many shapes, as illustrated in Fig. 25-5. All may be weld-attached with portable equipment. The stud may be used with a ceramic arc-shielding ferrule, as shown in Fig. 25-4, which prevents air infiltration and also acts as a dam to retain the molten metal, or may have a granular flux, flux coating, or solid flux affixed to the welding end, as illustrated in Fig. 25-6. The flux may include any of the agents found in a regular electrode covering; most important to stud welding is a deoxidizer to guard against porosity.

Two general methods of stud welding are used in industry — the "open-drawn-arc" method and the "capacitor-discharge" method. The drawn-arc method is most widely used for fastening heavy threaded parts, such as heavy steel bolts. The capacitor-discharge method is used for joining small threaded studs and pins.

In the drawn-arc method, a closely timed high current DC arc is held between the grounded base metal and the stud, melting both the base metal and the end of the stud. The necessary DC power is supplied by heavy-duty motor generators or rectifier units. Special timing devices in the control system stop the current and cause a spring plunger in the gun to push the two molten interfaces together, making a weld that is stronger than the stud itself. Ceramic ferrules placed over the end of the stud in the chuck act both as a centering device and to help keep the molten metal within the weld area when the stud plunges into the molten base metal. When desired, studs are available with a special flux cap, thus assuring a metallurgically

sound bond. In the case of aluminum studs, it may be necessary to supply a flow of inert gas, such as argon, as a shield against oxidation.

Operator skill is reduced to a minimum in stud welding as the result of the simplicity of operation and precise automatic controls. A circuit diagram for a stud-welding setup is shown in Fig. 25-7.

In the capacitor-discharge method, power is supplied by a rapid discharge of stored electrical energy. Pressure is applied during or immediately following the electrical discharge. The stored energy from the low-voltage, high-capacitance power source is released through a small projection at the base of the stud. The small projection offers high resistance to the stored energy but rapidly melts, leading to the formation of an arc that heats the surfaces to be joined.

There are several variations of the capacitor-discharge method, depending upon whether or not the stud is initially positioned in contact with the work and how the arc is formed. The AWS *Welding Handbook,* Sixth Edition, is a recommended reference for detailed information on the application of stud welding with the carbon and alloy steels, stainless steels, aluminum and other nonferrous metals.

ELECTRON-BEAM WELDING

Electron-beam welding uses the kinetic energy of high-velocity electrons to create heat and weld

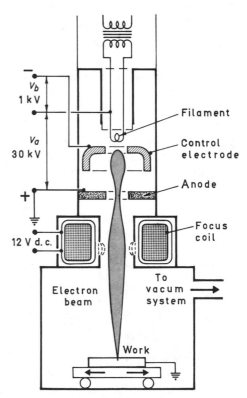

Fig. 25-8. Basic elements of the electron beam welding process.

together closely fitted parts. With this process, the parts to be joined are machined for accurate fit, assembled and placed in an electron-beam welder at the focal point of a dense electron-beam. Figure 25-8 is a schematic of a conventional electron-beam welder.

The electron beam is produced in a high vacuum by an electron gun. Electrons are emitted from the cathode of the gun, accelerated, focused by a magnetic focusing coil and directed against the joint. The electron-beam can be focused to a diameter as small as .010 inch, resulting in a very narrow heating zone. When the beam strikes the joint, it first creates a hole to the desired depth of penetration. As it is moved along the joint, molten metal on the leading edge of the beam flows to the trailing edge and solidifies. A very precise weld is thus produced.

With the electron beam, all the commercial metals that are conventionally arc welded, plus the refractory metals such as tungsten, molybdenum and zirconium, can be readily joined. The welds are of excellent quality, free from any impurities other than those in the material itself. Electron-beam welds have the largest depth-to-width ratios of any fusion welding process — as much as 20-to-1 — and are subjected to much lower total heat input for the same thickness of material.

Most electron-beam welding is done under high vacuum, which prevents the focused beam from being deflected by air molecules. High voltage and extremely low amperage characterize the process — in contrast to the low voltage and high amperage required for conventional arc welding. Electron-beam guns are rated at 30 to 175 kilovolts, but only 50 to 1,000 milliamperes.

Some electron-beam welding is being done using a low vacuum or even no vacuum. Welds made out-of-vacuum can be produced at very high production rates, but quality, penetration depth and versatility are reduced. Nonvacuum welds in production are seldom more than 1/2-inch deep, whereas in the high-vacuum chamber parts have been joined as thick as 6 inches and as thin as foil.

Advantages of electron-beam welding include:

- Extremely sound high-purity welds can be made on almost any metal and with a wide variety of dissimilar metals in sizes ranging from foil to heavy plate.

- No filler metal or flux of any kind is required for most welding. Where required, thin shim material can be placed in the joint — or additional filler metal can be added, but this is seldom required.

- Heat input is very low compared to other fusion welding processes, resulting in freedom from distortion and reduced heat-affected zones. This makes the process ideal for precision work with electronic systems, aircraft components, machined gears and numerous other assemblies.

The main disadvantages are:

- High initial cost of equipment. Complete electron beam machines range from about $30,000 to $100,000, with some even going over a million dollars.

- Because most welding is done inside a vacuum chamber, large structures are difficult if not impossible to weld.

- The process requires highly trained technical operators.

- When welding in a vacuum, the setup time is high.

EXPLOSION WELDING

This welding process is finding increased usage for cladding surfaces with special alloys. Basically, the process involves the placing of an explosive in plastic, liquid, or granular form over the top piece of the assembly to be welded. The base metal or "target" must rest on a suitable support, such as thick sand, a slab of steel, or concrete (Fig. 25-9). An air gap is provided, either by supports between the two surfaces or the use of inserts at the edges. The explosive is fired causing a detonation wave to progress across the surface of the parts. Upon impact, a weld bond results.

The two most important variables in this process are the collision velocity and the collision angle. Clads of over 300 square feet have been produced. Microscopic examinations of the typical bond shows that a plastic flow of metal takes place. A high bond strength results, verifiable by mechanical testing.

Combinations, such as aluminum to steel and titanium to steel, ordinarily impossible by other welding methods, are joined by this method. The only metals that cannot be welded are those too brittle to stand the explosive impact.

Typical applications include the cladding of vessels for the chemical industries, the joining of

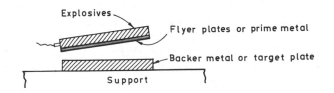

Fig. 25-9. Elements of the explosion welding process.

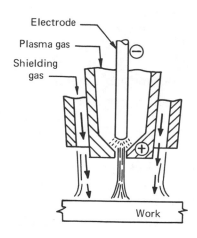

Fig. 25-10. Diagrammatic sketch of the plasma torch.

aluminum superstructures to steel decks for ships, and the making of leak-free tubular transition joints between stainless steel piping and aluminum vessel walls.

For obvious reasons, explosives must be handled only by qualified people.

FRICTION AND INERTIA WELDING

Both friction and inertia welding use the heat developed by friction when two parts are slid together under pressure.

In **friction welding,** a rotating rod or tube is pressed against a stationary part until forging heat is developed. At this point, rotation stops and axial thrust is increased. A hot pressure bond is produced, resulting in a very narrow heat-affected zone. Some metal squeezes from the interface to form an outer layer at the joint. This method is limited to an energy input of about 10 hp per square inch of weld. Large areas with relatively long heat cycles, 10 to 60 seconds, promote grain growth.

Inertia Welding overcomes most friction welding limitations. In inertia welding, kinetic energy from a flywheel is converted to heat by friction to make the weld. A rod or tube is held in a chuck attached to a free spinning flywheel rotated at a preset speed. It is then forced against a fixed part. As the flywheel slows, the energy discharges to the interface. After a preset time, a clutch disengages the spindle from the flywheel. Rotation stops, but a constant axial force continues to be applied. Energy from 20 to 150 hp per square inch of weld area combines with axial thrust and forging action to produce a weld free of oxide or voids. Higher energy input allows inertia welding to be used on metals that produce too little heat to be

welded with the friction method. After the initial testing and setup have been completed, either friction or inertia welds have the advantages of lowering costs through high-speed production. Welds are reliable, repeatable, fast and at a low unit cost.

In either process, no welding rods, flux, electrodes, or gases are required. Joint preparation is held to a minimum and operators are quickly trained. Production rates will vary according to the size and complexity. Solid steel bars up to 4 inches in diameter are being joined, as well as tubes 10-in. O.D. with 0.10-in. wall thickness. One fast machine welds the stem to a valve head at 1,200 pieces per hour.

PLASMA-ARC WELDING

Plasma-arc (or plasma-torch) welding is one of the new welding processes, which is used industrially, frequently as a substitute for the gas tungsten-arc process. In some applications, it offers greater welding speeds, better weld quality and less sensitivity to process variables than the conventional processes it replaces. With the plasma torch, temperatures as high as 60,000°F are developed and, theoretically, temperatures as high as 200,000°F are possible.

The heat in plasma-arc welding originates in an arc, but this arc is not diffused as is an ordinary welding arc. Instead, it is constricted by being forced through a relatively small orifice. The "orifice" or plasma gas (see Fig. 25-10) may be supplemented by an auxiliary source of shielding gas.

"Orifice" gas refers to the gas that is directed into the torch to surround the electrode. It becomes ionized in the arc to form the plasma and emerges from the orifice in the torch nozzle as a plasma jet. If a shielding gas is used, it is directed onto the workpiece from an outer shielding ring.

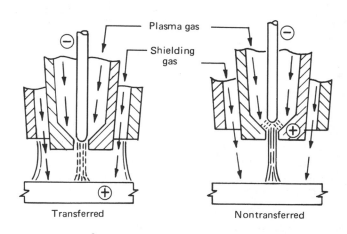

Fig. 25-11. Transferred and nontransferred arcs.

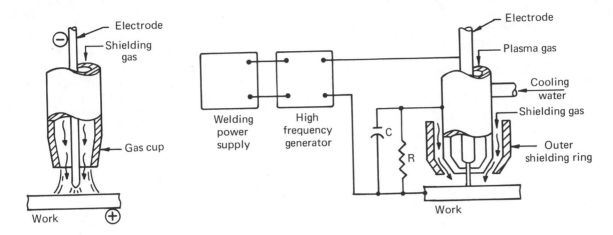

Fig. 25-12. Schematic comparison of gas tungsten-arc and plasma-arc welding torches.

The workpiece may or may not be part of the electrical circuit. In the "transferred-arc" system, the workpiece is a part of the circuit, as in other arc-welding processes. The arc "transfers" from the electrode through the orifice to the work. In the "nontransferred" system, the constricting nozzle surrounding the electrode acts as an electrical terminal and the arc is struck between it and the electrode tip; the plasma gas then carries the heat to the workpiece. Figure 25-11 illustrates transferred and nontransferred arcs.

The advantages gained by using a constricted-arc process over the gas tungsten-arc process include greater energy concentration, improved arc stability, higher welding speeds and lower width-to-depth ratio for a given penetration. "Keyhole" welding — or penetrating completely through the workpiece — is possible. Figure 25-12 compares gas tungsten-arc with transferred plasma-arc and schematically illustrates the concentration of energy with the latter and its superior penetration.

Manual and mechanized plasma-arc welding are described in detail in the *AWS Welding Handbook,* Sixth Edition, Section 3B. That volume also lists an extensive bibliography of literature on the subject, with emphasis on applications for the process.